HEINEMANN GNVQ

AND CARE

ONIE

KATE MAKEPEACE
JILL PATEL
BERYL STRETCH

Heinemann

Heinemann Educational,
a division of Heinemann Educational Books Ltd,
Halley Court, Jordan Hill, Oxford OX2 8EJ

OXFORD LONDON EDINBURGH
MADRID ATHENS BOLOGNA PARIS
MELBOURNE ATHENS BOLOGNA PARIS
MELBOURNE SYDNEY AUCKLAND SINGAPORE TOKYO
IBADAN NAIROBI HARARE GABARONE
PORTSMOUTH NH (USA)

© Beryl Stretch, Jill Patel, Kate Makepeace, Karen Hucker, Margaret Hilton,
Kip Chan Pensley, Richard Chaloner, Neil Moonie 1994

First published 1994
97 96 95 94
10 9 8 7 6 5 4 3 2

A catalogue record for this book is available from the British Library on
request

ISBN 0 435 452428

Typeset and illustrated by TecSet Ltd, Wallington, Surrey
Printed by Bath Press Ltd, Bath

Front cover
Designed by: Tad Kasa
Photograph by: Sally and Richard Greenhill

CONTENTS

Preface   v

Acknowledgements   vi

Introduction: Understanding GNVQs in Caring   1

1   Access, Equal Opportunities and Client
    Rights   35

    Human needs (PICES)   35
    Socialisation   43
    Discrimination   48
    Use of language   52
    Equal opportunities   59
    Fast Facts   71

2   Interpersonal Interaction   75

    Supportive skills   80
    Conveying warmth, understanding and
        sincerity   81
    Maslow's Hierarchy of Needs   85
    Types of behaviour   87
    Transactional Analysis   90
    Working in groups   96
    Client's rights in interpersonal situations   106
    Meeting individual needs   110
    Confidentiality   112
    Fast Facts   114

3   Physical Aspects of Health   117

    Cardio-vascular system   117
    Respiratory system   123
    Cell, tissue or internal respiration   125

Coronary heart disease   127
Classification of disease   131
Gonorrhoea   134
Food poisoning   136
Influenza   138
Diet   140
Balanced diets   147
Special diets   148
Factors influencing choice of food   156
Fast Facts   161

4   Psychological and Social Aspects of Health
    and Social Care   164

    Caring isn't always easy   164
    What is identity?   165
    The development of individual identity   170
    The construction of identity   176
    Interaction of social and psychological
        factors in personal experience   181
    Threats to the maintenance of identity   184
    Protecting and supporting threatened
        individuals   194
    Stress   195
    Coping with life-event threats   200
    Fast Facts   209

5   Health Promotion   213

    What is health?   213
    What is health promotion?   215
    Sexual practices   216
    Substance abuse   222
    Alcohol   222
    Risks to personal safety   228

Hazardous substances 231
Health promotion programmes 233
Planning a health promotion programme 234
Fast Facts 241

6 *Structure and Practices in Health and Social Care* 244

The structure of the NHS 244
Market for care 247
Mixed economy of care 251
Structure of social care provision 252
The legal context of care 253
The roles of health and care workers 260
Social care service provision 265
Access to health and social care 268
Priorities and strategies 269
Health care services: strategies for
   intervention 270
Fast Facts 271
Appendix – '*Health of the Nation*' targets 274

7 *Care Plans* 275

What is a care plan? 275
Assessment and care management 276
How assessment works 277
Development of a care plan 283
Implementing the macro care plan 286
Clients' rights 290
Monitoring 292
Reviewing 294
Maintaining clients' rights 297
Fast Facts 300

8 *Research in Health and Social Care* 302

Introducing research 302
Secondary research 304
Primary research 306
Techniques of data collection 307
Sampling methods 315
Doing research 319
Questionnaires 322
Structures interviews 329
Dealing with data 332
Presenting data 336
Fast Facts 341

9 *Communication* 344

Understanding and checking information 345
Using an appropriate tone and manner 346
Using the telephone 347
Writing correctly 349
Writing letters and memos 352
Filling in forms 353
Using images 362
Using photographs 364
Using maps and timetables 365
Developing written skills 366
Fast Facts 368

10 *Application of Number* 370

Estimation 370
Conversion tables 370
Collecting data 372
Calculating data 375
Grouped data 376
Presentation of data 377
Area, volume and perimeter 380
Symbolic notation 381
Probability 384
Fast Facts

11 *Information Technology* 389

Information technology – a core skill 389
What is Information Technology 390
Safety 393
Saving work 394
Files and directories 396
Using Information Technology 398
Word-processing 399
Using a database 405
Sharing information between applications 408
Using a spreadsheet 411
Creating a chart or graph 418
Compiling a report 419
Fast Facts 421

Answers 423

Icons for Photocopying 430

Index 432

What the book covers

This book is designed to provide a guide to the GNVQ at Advanced Level in Health and Social Care. Advanced GNVQs, or Vocational A-levels as they are also known, are new qualifications based on nationally defined standards. The assessment standards are defined but a learner's pathway to achieving them is not laid down. Learners and staff concerned with learning support must design their own approaches to meeting standards. GNVQs require candidates to develop skills of self-assessment, and use of theory if they are to achieve Merit or Distinction grades.

This book aims to support learners by offering:

- An introduction to GNVQs.
- An explanation of the structure of standards.
- An overview of assessment and evidence collection.
- An interpretation of the grading criteria and guidance on presenting evidence to achieve Merit and Distinction grades.
- Guidance on portfolio design and test preparation.
- The knowledge, skills and values associated with each of the eight mandatory units:
  1 **Access, equal opportunities and client rights**
  2 **Interpersonal interaction**
  3 **Physical aspects of health**
  4 **Psychological and social aspects of Health and Social Care**
  5 **Health promotion**
  6 **Structure and practices in Health and Social Care**
  7 **Care plans**

  8 **Research in Health and Social Care**.
- The knowledge and skill associated with the core skills of Information Technology, Communication and Application of Number, integrated with Health and Social Care theory at Advanced level.

Special features of the book

- Self-assessment tasks to test understanding (with suggested answers) are included in each chapter.
- Fast Facts – each chapter contains a quick reference section for key concepts.
- **Icons** are used throughout the book to identify sections. They are also used to indicate:

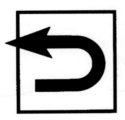

areas for **reflection**;

ideas for **evidence collection** to meet the requirement of national standards;

opportunities to evaluate the use of theory in relation to practice issues.

Icons are also suggested as a way of labelling your assignment or portfolio sections.

How to use this book

The book is designed to be used as a source of knowledge. It *can* be read from the beginning to the end, but it is also designed to be used whenever you need information. Fast Facts are listed alphabetically so that concepts can be checked quickly.

Following an introduction to GNVQs there are eight chapters on the mandatory units. You may not, however, want to use the chapters in this order and you could start at the beginning of any chapter.

Three further chapters cover the core skills of: Communication; Application of Number; and Information Technology. You may want to study these areas before finishing your work on the mandatory units. Core skills interlink with the mandatory units and evidence for them should be gathered with evidence for the mandatory units. You will probably wish to dip in and out of these chapters as you study the units.

Each reader will have his or her own needs and purposes for using this book. Therefore it has been designed with easy reference headings and icons, so that it can be used flexibly – in keeping with the ideas behind the GNVQs.

· ACKNOWLEDGEMENTS ·

The authors and publishers would like to thank the following: NCVQ – Health and Social Care Advanced 2.1 Standards 1994; Her Majesty's Stationery Office for permission to reproduce the tables – pages 141, 1434, 144 and 158, extract from 'Health of the Nation' – page 147, 'Health of the Nation' Targets – page 274 and the extracts from 'NHS Made Easy' Department of Health – chapter six.

They would also like to thank the following individuals and organisations for permission to reproduce photographs: Chris Coggins; Format/Jacky Chapman; Format/Mo Wilson; Format/Ulrike Preuss; Richard and Sally Greenhill; Impact Photos; Network/Mike Abrahams; Network/Steve Murez; Philip Parkhouse; Science Photo Library; Winged Fellowship Trust 'Images of Caring' Competition.

In addition they would like to thank Linda Claris-Mellor for her help in preparing the manuscript for publication.

The authors and publishers have endeavored to contact holders of copyright for the poems on pages 40 and 53, without success. Indeed, every effort has been made to contact copyright holders of material published in this book. We would be glad to hear from unacknowledged sources at the first opportunity.

UNDERSTANDING GNVQS IN CARING

What this section offers:

- The meaning of GNVQ
- Levels and pathways of qualification
- What does a GNVQ caring qualification lead to?
- The structure of Advanced GNVQ in Health and Social Care
- Links between the eight mandatory units
- Understanding standards – the technical explanation
- An example: how to interpret one element
- Understanding standards – how they might feel in the end
- GNVQ assessment
- Things that count as evidence
- Collecting evidence

- Reflection
- Using concepts and theory
- Assignments
- Action plans
- Grading criteria for Advanced GNVQs
- Differences between Merit and Distinction grades
- The portfolio
- What the portfolio might look like
- Tests
- Preparing for tests
- What does it take to achieve an Advanced GNVQ?
- Self-assessment of knowledge about GNVQ
- Fast Facts

GNVQs are a new system of qualifications designed to fit into a national pattern of 'levels'. GNVQs are designed so that they can be 'controlled' to some extent by the people taking them. This introduction explains how the national system works and how *you* can control or manage your own learning whilst working on a GNVQ programme. GNVQs are not intended to be simple, but this section will provide the knowledge needed to understand and manage your own study of the GNVQ at Advanced Level in Caring.

This introduction contains a range of *theory* and *advice*. Before starting, it may be worth checking what you need to know. Use the contents list above as a guide to what is on offer. If you know very little about GNVQs then start right at the beginning.

Getting a GNVQ qualification may be a bit like learning to drive a car or learning to ride a bicycle. It takes time and, most importantly, it takes *practice*. This introduction provides ideas for designing action plans and portfolios. What is said here will make most sense when you are actually working to get the GNVQ award. Like learning to drive, there is a limit to how much *theory* you might want to learn in one go. It may be best just to read parts of this section as you need them.

When you have finished the introduction you might like to test your understanding with the questions at the end. Alternatively, you could look at the questions to begin with and decide whether you need to know about these things. If so, then it is worth exploring to get more knowledge. If you just need to understand a technical word, look up Fast Facts.

You are in charge of your own learning, so please see this section as something to explore. Different people will use it in different ways at different stages of the GNVQ programme.

A note on change and development in GNVQs

Learners develop their skills by constantly building on their experience. Good learners are open to change – they drop things that don't work well in practice, and fine-tune behaviours that do seem to work, in order to get the best outcomes.

General National Vocational Qualifications are still very new. While their purpose and philosophy are unlikely to alter, the fine detail of how to achieve a GNVQ will almost certainly continue to build on experience over the next few years. The advice and guidance in this introduction is based on the GNVQ system as it was in the spring of 1994. Fine detail on issues like grading, revising for test questions and portfolio design will continue to develop.

Anyone reading this book is therefore recommended to check whether new details or new regulations have come about. In particular, the nature of test questions and grading criteria are quite likely to change. It is worth checking the latest information with a tutor or learning manager if you are enrolled on a GNVQ programme.

GNVQs involve exploring ideas and developing skills to manage information and knowledge. This introduction is designed to help you get started on your programme, but you should use your skills to check that the information has not become dated!

The meaning of GNVQ

GNVQ stands for General National Vocational Qualification:

- **General** means that the qualification is not just for a particular job. General qualifications are broad; they are designed to enable people to move on to higher qualifications or to get jobs in a wide range of employment.

- **National** means that the qualification is valuable nationally. The qualification has the same value everywhere in the 'nation'.

- **Vocational** means that the qualification focuses on areas of employment. A vocational qualification in Health and Social Care provides the knowledge and understanding that a person needs to go on to work in many different caring jobs. People with an Advanced GNVQ may go on to take up careers in caring or progress to Degree level study as the next step.

- **Qualification** means that an individual has passed at a definite standard. Advanced GNVQs are also known as Vocational A-levels. They are A-level qualifications. So 12 units (eight mandatory and four optionals) of GNVQ are 'worth' two academic A-levels; 18 units (eight mandatory, four optional and six additional units) of GNVQ are 'worth' three academic A-levels.

Levels and pathways of qualification

There is now a national system of qualifications at five levels, as shown in the diagram opposite. *Level 1* is the starting point for foundational qualifications. *Level 2* (Intermediate) covers jobs that are more complex, and academically is worth GCSE at good grades. *Level 3* covers jobs that involve high responsibility and complexity, perhaps including supervising others. This level also covers vocational A-levels. *Levels 4* and *5* cover professional and management jobs and are designed to be degree and post-graduate equivalents.

As well as the five levels, there are three *pathways* to qualifications. The first pathway – the 'academic' one – has been around for many years and has

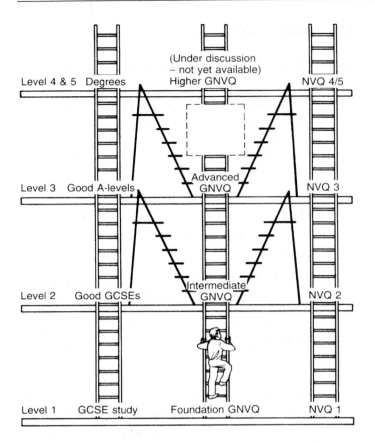

How the ladders work

a 'middle way' between academic and work-based qualifications. GNVQs are based on standards in just the same way that NVQs are. However, GNVQs cover a much wider range of knowledge and understanding than NVQs.

What does a GNVQ Health and Social Care qualification lead to?

The diagram (see left) shows the general 'ladder of opportunity' options available to a person with an Advanced GNVQ award. The two main options are: to continue with study and go into higher education; or to go into employment.

The first option – higher education – might include teacher training, nursing and social science qualifications. Anyone wishing to explore these routes should seek professional careers guidance, which might include advice on the best combinations of additional units or academic A-level combinations with GNVQ.

Candidates going straight into employment might subsequently be offered the chance to collect an NVQ at Level 3. An Advanced GNVQ qualification will provide much of the 'knowledge base' requirements for NVQ at Level 3. GNVQs also provide much of the 'know-how' when it comes to coping with NVQ assessment arrangements.

Many people may undertake an Advanced GNVQ out of personal interest. Some people may take GNVQ while they are in employment. Like other academic or vocational A-levels, Advanced GNVQ Health and Social Care should open up a wide range of learning and career opportunities.

The structure of Advanced GNVQ in Health and Social Care

All GNVQs are made up of **units**. Each unit can be 'passed' and then awarded to the person who has achieved it. So GNVQs can be 'passed' bit by bit, unit by unit. If a person doesn't complete a GNVQ programme, they still keep the units that they have

worked well for some people. But in 1986 the government decided to set up the National Council for Vocational Qualifications (NCVQ) so that there would be new ways to get qualifications. To begin with, the NCVQ designed qualifications called National Vocational Qualifications (or NVQs).

NVQs are designed to provide qualifications for particular jobs or professions. Sometimes NVQs can be studied at college, but many of these qualifications are easier for people to get if they already have a job. For many individuals, NVQs opened up the possibility of getting a recognised qualification for the skills and 'know-how' they had already learned at work. NVQs meant that people could become qualified at work without necessarily having to start at the beginning with their studies again.

The third pathway or ladder is a GNVQ. GNVQs first began in 1992 and their purpose was to provide

Mandatory Units

Optional Units

Core Skills Units

The mandatory units provide a study area which covers a range of knowledge, skills and values central to Health and Social Care work. Most mandatory units are tested. In 1994, Unit 2 (Interpersonal Interaction) was not tested.

Core skills units are different from mandatory units or optional units. This is because they are meant to be studied *with* the other units. The evidence needed to 'pass' core skills is meant to be collected with the evidence to pass the mandatory and optional units. Core skills and optional units are not tested.

The idea of core skills is that communication, number and information technology skills are needed in *all* work situations. GNVQs will probably cover 14 areas of work in the future, and Health and Social Care will be just one area. Core skills *standards* will be the same across all the areas, but the *evidence presented* will be different because it will be linked to practical assignment work for each qualification. In Health and Social Care, evidence opportunities for core skills like information technology will link with assignment work in Caring.

Only core skills units in communication, number and information technology have to be assessed and awarded for the award of a GNVQ qualification. However, there are three other areas of core skills: 'Problem Solving', 'Working With Others' and 'Improving Own Learning and Performance'. These core skills are worth including in a portfolio of evidence for two reasons: first, they can be recorded in your National Record of Achievement; and, secondly, they help towards getting evidence for Merit and Distinction grades (see pages 18–23).

passed. This means that they could start again without having to go right back to the beginning.

Advanced GNVQs can be taken as a two A-level programme or as a three A-level programme. The standard two A-level programme consists of eight mandatory units, four optional units and three core skills units. The three core skill units are integrated into the evidence collection work for the other 12 units. Because of this, the standard programme is often referred to as a 12 vocational unit route. This standard GNVQ programme can be linked with the study of academic A-levels or A/S-levels. The standard programme can also be extended to include an extra six additional units. This programme is worth three A-levels, and is sometimes referred to as an 18 vocational unit route.

Links between the eight mandatory units

Units can be studied and awarded in any order. The knowledge, skills and values studied in some early units are needed again in later units. So it might be appropriate to study for particular units before going on to study for others if you are taking GNVQ unit by unit. It is possible to study the underpinning themes of the advanced units. This knowledge can then be brought together in order to be assessed for the units. Whatever approach to learning you or your centre adopts, it may still be worth examining ways in which the units may link.

The value base for Health and Social Care

Most professions have ethical codes or *value bases* which guide the behaviour of members of that profession. Care work is an area where values are particularly important. People often receive health or social care services because they are vulnerable. Clients may often be afraid, in pain, unhappy or just simply young and easy to influence. A value base is considered to be at the heart of NVQ qualifications in Care. Care workers are required to use 'caring values' in all of their work with clients. In the NVQ awards the value base is referred to as the 'O' Unit of Competence. The 'O' Unit is not assessed for GNVQ, but its content is covered in Units 1, 2 and 4 of the Advanced GNVQ.

Elements of the NVQ value base or 'O' Unit

'O'a 'Promote anti-discriminatory practice'.
'O'b 'Maintain the confidentiality of information'.
'O'c 'Promote and support individual rights and choice'.
'O'd 'Acknowledge individuals' personal beliefs and identity'.
'O'e 'Support individuals through effective communication'.

GNVQ Unit 1 (Access, equal opportunities and client rights) covers 'O'a, 'Promote anti-discriminatory practice'. Unit 2 (Interpersonal interaction) covers the knowledge and skill needed for 'O'e, 'Support individuals through effective communication'. Unit 2 also covers the knowledge needed for 'O'b and 'O'c. Both confidentiality and client rights and choice are covered in Element 2.3, 'Analyse clients' rights in interpersonal situations'. Unit 4 (Psychological and social aspects of Health and Social Care) explores the issue of identity and threats to identity. Unit 4 provides for a detailed investigation into the knowledge which might underpin 'O'd.

Advanced GNVQ Units 1, 2 and 4 might be seen as a starting point to learn the knowledge, skills and values required for professional behaviour with clients.

Unit 3 (Physical aspects of health) introduces health care concepts which may be usefully linked with the health content of Unit 4.3 and Unit 5, 'Health Promotion'. The value base for care work might be seen as running through all subsequent units.

Unit 8, 'Research', provides a special skills focus for the collection of evidence. Evidence toward Unit 8 might be gathered whilst studying for other units. Units 5 and 6 might be possible areas for evidence collection toward Unit 8. Therefore the Research unit might be worth studying alongside or prior to Units 5 and 6.

Unit 7, 'Care Planning', requires the service structure knowledge contained in Unit 6 (Structure and Practices in Health and Social Care). The value base and legislative content of Units 1 and 2 will also be useful or necessary for the study of Units 6 and 7.

Generally, the Advanced GNVQ units should not be seen as existing in isolation. The content of units should be linked in project work. Core skills may also be integrated into study for the mandatory units.

A way of visualising just some of the links that are possible between units is set out in the diagram on page 6.

Understanding standards – the technical explanation

To collect GNVQ units and qualifications, candidates have to demonstrate that they have achieved a defined **standard of work**. GNVQ standards are definitions of what is required in order to 'pass' and be awarded the qualification. Because standards are definitions, they are not always easy to understand. This part of the chapter explains the technical detail of units, elements, performance criteria, range statements and evidence indicators. Some readers may prefer to go straight to the part

Units 1, 2, and 4
cover value base

Unit
1

Unit
2

Core skills are
studied and
evidenced
in relation
to all units

Unit
4

IT

N°

C

Unit
3

Unit 8 (research) may
link with any units –
but may have particular
links with units 5 and 6

Unit
8

Unit
5

Unit
6

Unit
7

Care
value
base

Care value base
should influence
additional units

How the Units might link together

on 'how standards may feel in the end'. A glance at that section might help to make sense of the detail here, but some people prefer the facts first!

The whole set of standards for a qualification runs to many pages. Most people who sit down and read standards will say that they are boring. Many people will say they cannot really understand them!

Why are standards so complicated?

Standards are difficult for three reasons:

1 Standards are a system for defining outcomes.

Because standards define things to be understood or done, they become a bit like legal statements. Standards try to give exact details of what is required rather than discuss ideas about what would be useful. Standards end up being technical rather than interesting, simply because they are definitions. Definitions are necessary because they have to be applied nationally in the same way. Standards are a guide to assessment: they explain what has to be done in order to pass the GNVQ. Standards don't really explain what has to be studied; rather, they define what has to be achieved in order to get the

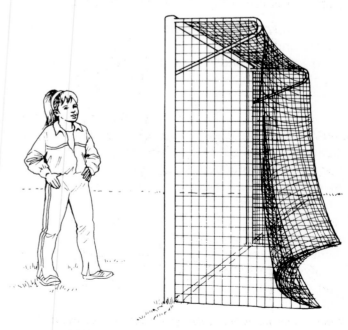

*It's boring just standing looking at the goal...
it's much more fun if you're doing something with it!*

qualification. So standards are like goal-posts in sport – they define the goal that has to be reached. Standards don't explain how to get there!

2 The value of a qualification will depend on the definition of standards.

There are two kinds of qualifications. One kind is based on what people can do or understand, and the other kind is based on who comes first in a competition. Many qualifications have exams, which are like a competition or a race. The people who run the fastest get to the end first – these people pass. In a running race, the people who come in last are not so good; in the exam, the people with the lowest marks fail. Not all exams are marked in terms of top and bottom, but they all have some degree of competition about them. Standards allow a different way of qualifying – instead of doing better than others in an exam, the candidate has to show that he or she definitely knows the details needed for the qualification.

Exams give people qualifications because they have come in the top group. Standards give people qualifications because those individuals have proved that they can do what is needed. The problem with the standards type of qualification is that the

Climbing to the top is like achieving a standard – you can do it in your own way at your own pace. Running a race is different – you have to beat the others!

qualification is only as good as the standards. If standards are not well defined, or if they don't cover much, then the qualification is not worth a lot. Standards need to define complicated details carefully if the qualification is going to be worthwhile in the end! The standards must show how much someone knows and can do when they get their qualification.

3 Standards are impossible to understand without the knowledge of the area they are about.

Because standards define areas of skill, values and knowledge, they are impossible to understand without the necessary knowledge. At the beginning of a course of study, the standards will be difficult because people will not know all the terms and detail involved. As a person learns about the issues, so the

It looks a long way up fom the bottom!

standards should become easier to understand. When a candidate's work is ready for assessment, the standards should be clear.

The way standards are written

Standards are written for guiding the assessment of GNVQs. They start with units.

- **Units**. GNVQ qualifications are split into units. Units cover particular areas of knowledge, values and skill. For instance, Unit 2 covers the knowledge, values and skill needed to engage in caring – interpersonal interaction with other people. This is an important part of care work. Units can be awarded and recorded in your National Record of Achievement. A person who is awarded Unit 2 has demonstrated that he or she has the skills and knowledge and can work within the values defined in the standards for that unit. Unit 2 is not a whole qualification, but it is part of an Advanced GNVQ in Health and Social Care.

- **Elements**. Each GNVQ unit is split into elements. Unit 2: 'Interpersonal interaction' is split into three elements. Each element defines an area of values, skill or knowledge. Elements are the smallest areas to be assessed, and *evidence* has to be presented for each element. When there is enough evidence, an element can be 'passed'; but a person has to provide evidence for all the elements in a unit before the unit is awarded. Elements are not awarded – they are not recorded in your NRA. Elements have titles such as, 'Communicate with individuals'. This may be a good definition, but it is not easy to see exactly what it means or how it should be assessed. To explain this definition, elements have *performance critieria*.

- **Performance criteria**. Performance criteria define what is required to pass the element. In a sense, they help to explain what the element title is all about. Performance criteria are *not* extra things to assess, they are there to help to explain what is needed to pass the element. When evidence is gathered to 'pass' an element, that evidence has to meet the requirements defined by the performance criteria.

  The element title therefore gives the focus of what has to be done, and the performance criteria help to explain this focus and provide rules for assessment. However, *range* is also needed to explain what the evidence has to cover.

- **Range**. This covers what is in range for evidence or out of range for evidence. The word 'range' comes from archery or from shooting ranges. In this context, to be in range means something has to be covered by evidence. If something is not in the range, then it is not required to have evidence

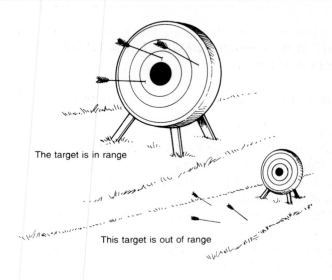

The target is in range

This target is out of range

when achievements are assessed. So standards are defined by units and elements: elements have titles, performance criteria and range statements which explain what has to be done or known in order to pass. Finally, each element has *evidence indicators*.

- **Evidence indicators**. Evidence indicators give a brief guide as to what type of evidence would be desirable in order to achieve the standards defined in an element. A project would be one way of providing evidence or 'indicating evidence' to meet requirements.

An example: how to interpret one element

The example on page 9 is taken from Unit 2, Interpersonal Interaction, of the Advanced GNVQ in Health and Social Care.

Performance criteria

These explain how communication with individuals should be performed – that's where the name 'performance criteria' comes from. Four areas have to be covered. First, verbal and non-verbal behaviour (methods) have to be suitable to other people's needs. Secondly, communication techniques have to convey or express effective, supportive skills. Thirdly, communication has to convey or express positive value for others. Fourthly, things which get

**UNIT 2: INTERPERSONAL INTERACTION
(1994 standards)**

Element 2.1: Communicate with individuals

Performance criteria:
1 the method of communication is suitable to the individual needs of others;
2 communication techniques are used to convey effective supportive skills;
3 the form of communication conveys positive value for others;
4 factors which inhibit interpersonal interaction are explained and avoided.

Range:
Method of communication: verbal; non-verbal
Communication techniques: face-to-face; tone of voice, body language, oral signals (e.g. 'ums', 'ahs'); reflection of own and others' behaviour; active listening and responding
Supportive skills: conveying warmth, conveying understanding, conveying sincerity
Individual needs: physical; cognitive; social; emotional; behavioural
Positive value of others: respect for others; personal preference; choice; independence
Factors: distractions; dominating the conversation; manipulating; blocking others' contributions; culturally-dependent behaviour

Evidence indicators:
Explanation and analysis of communication with two individuals with contrasting needs, to include an individual with a communication disability. Evidence should demonstrate an understanding of the implications of the range dimensions in relation to the element.

in the way of effective conversation are avoided – and could be explained!

The performance criteria explain what 'communication with individuals' involves as far as assessment is concerned. If there were no performance criteria then any communication issue might be explored. For assessment purposes it is very important that we know what we have to cover.

It is vital to remember that standards and, therefore, performance criteria define *what* is to be assessed. They do not define everything that would be useful to know. Performance criteria only define what should be covered in your evidence – they don't explain how to study! The four areas of Element 2.1 can be linked and may be demonstrated in practical work. Linking these performance criteria will require a range of theoretical knowledge which is put into practice.

Range

Range provides the definition of what should be assessed in relation to the technical terms used in the performance criteria. For example, 'method of communication' covers verbal and non-verbal behaviour – both areas have to be demonstrated. 'Communication techniques' is explained in relation to a list of non-verbal and verbal skills areas. 'Supportive skills' cover warmth, understanding and sincerity. In Element 2.1, range provides greater definition of the content of the performance criteria.

In order to make sense of all this definition, you have to understand the knowledge involved. Element 2.1 may not become clear until you have used the theory from Chapter 2 in personal, practical work with other people.

Evidence indicators

Evidence indicators suggest ways in which the standards for this element might be met. Here, the idea is that candidates might analyse their own communication skills in relation to two people with different needs. This provides an opportunity for putting theory into practice. If possible, it might be useful to explore how communication skills might be adapted if an individual had a communication disability. It might be possible to design different kinds of projects to collect evidence for Element 2.1. The evidence indicators suggest ways of collecting evidence to cover performance criteria and range.

In practice, communication skills might be videoed or tape-recorded. Some detail might be watched by an assessor. Perhaps some detail will be written about. Anyone who can provide evidence for Element 2.1 has achieved an Advanced level of skill. The standards define just how much has been learned and what can be done by a person who is awarded this element. This is a real qualification!

Understanding standards – how they might feel in the end

Imagine that you are having lunch with three other people that you know. After a while one of them says, 'I keep getting a headache and my eyes go funny so I can't see things for a while. Do you think I'm all right? What would you do – should I take something for it?' One of the others says, 'Don't worry, it's the tube lights. They affect me sometimes, it soon goes.' The third person says, 'Yes, I hate these lights – they should do something about them. It's not right!'

If you have studied the knowledge involved in Element 2.1, certain thoughts might immediately come to you: 'Um, that's interesting – the person with the headache hasn't been listened to. The other two people haven't been warm or understanding. They haven't really valued what the first person was saying and they have diverted the conversation to an issue about lights. 'The knowledge involved in Element 2.1 enables you to think about the conversation and notice things which other people might miss.

You watch the first person with the headache, who looks disappointed. Let's assume this person is male. You can tell from his eyes and face that he doesn't feel that he has been taken seriously. Once again, you are using your knowledge of 2.1. This time your knowledge and experience of non-verbal communication is helping you to understand the social and emotional needs of another person.

So you say something like, 'Tell me about this headache – when do you get it?' He looks more interested and answers you. Perhaps you repeat a few words that he said in a warm and understanding way. He tells you more. You ask questions about his eyesight, nodding and showing interest as he keeps talking.

You know what you are doing – you are using the skills and values identified in Element 2.1 to communicate in a supportive and caring way. You have chosen to be supportive.

The other two people at the table now become interested and start to join in. But the first person continues to centre his attention on you. Again you are aware of your own skill with conversations. You are now the person who is keeping the conversation going. You have gained the first person's trust.

This may be how the skills of Element 2.1 can be used in real life. As you gain the knowledge, skills and values involved in each element, you can use them in practical situations with other people. The skills in Element 2.1 not only cover ways in which you influence others, they can also influence the way in which others see you. A person with caring communication skills, as in the above example, may become the temporary leader of the group.

There is something even more valuable though. A person who really understands Element 2.1 can probably understand why the people who talked about tube lights were not very helpful. These two people were not performing to GNVQ standards – they were thinking about themselves and just letting the conversation drift. Perhaps they didn't really know much about conversation skills. Some people go through life without understanding how to make conversations interesting, or how to support others, or how to enable others to trust and like them. People who study Element 2.1 don't have to be like this; they will understand what behaviours make a person interesting and caring in a conversation.

Some Advanced GNVQ knowledge and skill cannot be used in social settings. But the knowledge, skills and values covered in the mandatory units should all lead to greater confidence when working with people.

GNVQ assessment

Each element of each unit has to be assessed before the unit is awarded. Assessment takes place when there is enough evidence to be assessed. In order to know what counts as enough evidence, candidates need to have their own assessment skills. Self-assessment of evidence is necessary in order to achieve good grades in GNVQs.

The individual working for a GNVQ qualification will go through a process of action planning, assignment work, checking and submitting the work for assessment. But this is not the whole story. When work is submitted or 'given in' for assessment, a whole system comes into operation.

The assessment

In the past, work was given to teachers or tutors who marked it. This approach was often much simpler than in GNVQ. Now, when work is given in, it is more than just 'work'. Assignments are now designed to provide evidence. Evidence has to be judged to decide if there is enough, and if it is the right quality, to show that a standard has been reached. The person who decides whether there is enough quality evidence is called an **assessor**. Often the people who act as assessors will be teachers or tutors; but when they collect the work in, they become assessors.

Assessors must have qualifications and knowledge in the field in which they work. They also have to understand fully the standards that they are checking evidence against. In time, assessors will also need to have gained an NVQ award which will guarantee that they understand the GNVQ assessment process. All these checks are required to try to ensure that the quality of GNVQ assessment is fair and works properly. But it is more complicated still. The assessments themselves have to be checked.

Assessments have to be checked by an **internal verifier**. 'Internal' means internal to or inside the centre (inside the college or school, etc.). 'Verifier' means they check the correctness of assessment. Internal verifiers will look at samples of assessment and check that evidence is being correctly and fairly measured in relation to standards. If candidates don't think their work is being fairly assessed, then they can appeal to the internal verifier to look at their work and re-check it. All the assessor's decisions can be checked by the internal verifier.

There is also an **external verifier**. 'External' means outside, from outside the centre (a school or college, etc.). External verifiers are appointed by the awarding body. An awarding body is BTEC, City & Guilds, or RSA. The awarding body checks the overall quality of the centre's assessment. The external verifier checks the quality of decisions made by both the assessor and the internal verifier. The idea of all this checking is to ensure that standards *really work* – what is accepted as evidence must not become too simple or too complicated. A qualification gained at one college or school should require the same amount and quality of evidence as elsewhere.

The system means that candidates can appeal to the internal verifier, or after that to the external verifier, if they feel that their assessment is not fair or reasonable.

Evidence, then, is the main issue in understanding assessment. Because standards are a bit like legal documents, evidence is needed before it is fair to give out an award. Evidence is information that proves that a person has achieved the outcomes the standards require.

Things that count as evidence

The following list provides examples of evidence:

Practical demonstration of skills can be watched by an assessor or they can be videoed or tape-recorded (with everyone's permission).

Assignments can provide evidence of knowledge achievement, records of practical work and projects. Most units will require some assignment work.

Past records of achievement and qualifications can count as evidence towards GNVQ units. For instance, GCSE work might count toward core skills assessment.

References from other people such as placement supervisors or employers can provide evidence of practical caring skills, and core skills.

Notes: not all written work needs to be put together into assignments – notes will often be enough to provide evidence for knowledge, or perhaps evidence of planning skills.

Log books or record books are a way of providing evidence to meet grading criteria standards. Log books may be easier to use than loose notes.

Photographs of placement work, perhaps of events organised by a candidate, can sometimes count as evidence towards achieving standards. Photos can often make assignments more interesting.

Things that are made, such as computer printouts, can provide evidence of skills and knowledge. Computer printouts will sometimes need to be 'certified' by an appropriate person to prove that they were done by the candidate.

Portfolio: usually, many different types of evidence will be put together into a collection. This collection is called a portfolio. When the collection is looked at, there should be enough information and evidence to judge that the candidate has performed to the level set by the standards.

Collecting evidence

Each element suggests a way of getting the necessary evidence in the 'Evidence indicators' section. Usually, tutors will provide more information and ideas on practical ways the evidence can be gathered. There are some practical points to watch:

- **Permission**. It is *always* necessary to have other people's permission before written details about them can be used. For instance, written details of a conversation can give evidence of conversation skills, but things other people have said must not be written down without their persmission and knowledge of what is written. Where someone is unable to understand, perhaps because they are too young, then their parents or guardians have to give permission.

- **Confidentiality**. When using written or taped evidence which involves clients it is also important that confidentiality is respected. This means that as well as having permission for work with individuals, you must also make sure that research details are anonymous. Names must be changed or deleted, personal details which could identify a client (for example, age, address, physical descriptions) should also be deleted or disguised.

- **Videos, photos and tapes**. Records of conversations and events also need the permission of the people who appear in them. This might be easy to get if the photograph or video is of a student group. Permission might be hard to get if the tape or video is about clients in a care setting.

- **Group work**. Working with other people is often the best way to plan to collect evidence. Sometimes a group project can meet the evidence requirements for an element. The only problem is that each individual's own work has to be separately recorded or noted, so that they have individual evidence of planning and achievement for their portfolio. Naturally, the general outcome can be recorded as well.

- **Evidence from others**. Evidence of skills used on placements is really valuable, but it will need to be confirmed by a manager or supervisor in the work setting. Usually the supervisor will also have to explain that he or she has watched practical work, and give reasons for agreeing with claims for evidence. Sometimes a report or reference will be needed.

Quality of evidence

Being assessed involves convincing an assessor that your evidence is good enough. Usually, candidates will get a lot of help and guidance to make sure the evidence is all right.

The process of assessment will probably start something like this:

1 Tutors suggest a project, assignment or demonstration to provide evidence for particular units. Written guidelines are given out.
2 Candidates discuss the guidelines, probably with a tutor, and think of ways of planning practical work.
3 Each individual designs an 'action plan' (see pages 15–18) for the assignment/project/demonstration.
4 Each individual discusses the action plan with a tutor.
5 The individual 'monitors' the implementation of the action plan, that is, they check and revise their ideas as the assignment gets going.
6 Candidates do the practical work and write about it.
7 The written work is checked by an assessor. If it is all right then it counts as evidence. If not, then

further work can be done until the evidence is right.
8 When there is enough evidence for an element, it is credited as complete.

At the start of a GNVQ programme, tutors and teachers will probably help with action plans and other practical work. As the programme progresses, candidates will have to do this work without help in order to get Merit and Distinction grades.

Reflection

Planning to collect evidence can be interesting. It involves a special skill called **reflection**. Think of a mirror. When a person looks in a mirror, their image is being bounced back from the reflective mirror. Reflection is the bouncing back of the original image. In social care, 'reflection' means the same sort of thing; except here we are thinking about thoughts and ideas rather than images. Thoughts

and ideas get bounced backwards and forwards between people.

Reflection can be very useful. When someone looks in a mirror, they can see what they look like, they can change their hairstyle or appearance until it looks right. The same idea goes for thoughts. If a person can have their thoughts mirrored or reflected by another person, then they have a chance to

change or alter their thoughts. Like changing hairstyle, reflection allows a person to experiment until their ideas are good.

Providing reflective listening is a special skill that is needed in Element 2.1. People who can help others to reflect are giving a care service with this skill. When people get very good at reflecting with others, they can sometimes reflect in their own mind – alone. This becomes a powerful learning skill as people can adapt their own thoughts using an internal mirror, rather than using another person. Reflection is also needed in order to plan the collection of evidence.

Using concepts and theory

As well as using reflective thinking, advanced candidates will need to be able to use care concepts and theory. *Using* concepts or ideas is very different from just being able to state what they are. A famous psychologist, Kurt Lewin, is reported to have once said, 'There is nothing as practical as a good theory.' Our concepts and theories about care help us to recognise situations. Concepts help us to make sense of what we hear and see. We organise our lives around our own personal theories of people and social behaviour. Most importantly, concepts – and theories which are made up of concepts – help us to guess what will happen next. Understanding and using the knowledge involved in the advanced mandatory units is about being able to recognise,

understand and predict what clients and colleagues are doing. Advanced skill in caring requires advanced understanding.

One theory of learning – the Kolb learning cycle – suggests that learning needs to involve practical experience. This experience is not enough on its own. For experience to be remembered and used it may need to be recalled in imagination. Experience may need to be reflected on. But reflection alone may not be enough to enable individuals to understand and predict what best to do. A stage of conceptualising or theorising may be needed. Concepts and theories don't always have to come from books. People can develop their own personal ideas without formal study. The idea of using book knowledge is to improve on personal concepts and ideas. Knowledge of other people's theories may give us a starting point for the development of our own ideas. Other people's ideas may help us to question false assumptions we have made. We may be able to build a better interpretation of other people, and their lives, if we link new theory to our own personal viewpoints.

The point of theory is that it should be useful in helping us to understand and work in Health and Social Care. Kolb saw this as the fourth stage in learning. We have to use theories if we are really learning, as opposed to just remembering! Using

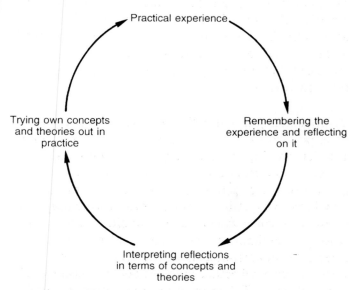

A learning sequence or learning cycle – adapted from D. Kolb (1979)

theory might mean checking whether we can explain something, or guessing what we think is the right thing to do, and checking this with tutors or supervisors. Using theory is about checking it out for its practical value. This stage is sometimes called 'experimenting', but here this might best be interpreted as 'trying out in practice'.

The concepts contained in this book may become part of a practical tool kit for work in Health and Social Care. Concepts and theories can become 'tools of analysis' – practical ideas which help us interpret our life experience.

Writing assignments or project reports

Evidence for mandatory and optional units will mostly be found in assignment work. There may be one or more assignments for each unit. Assignments will probably contain most of the evidence for the core skills units, spread across the mandatory and optional units.

Before getting started, it is important to think through what concepts and theories will be involved in an assignment. Candidates may need notes on the key concepts involved in an assignment. Most people will need to discuss how they plan to write assignments or do practical work. The act of talking a project through often helps to inspire and clarify ideas. Usually, ideas on assignment writing will need to be reflected on with a tutor. Ideas can be 'bounced' between people until the ideas get more practical and useful.

Before starting any practical or written work it will be important to construct an **action plan** for finding and determining the necessary information and evidence opportunities. Action plans can be monitored for progress. Keeping notes on progress may help to organise a project. Monitoring may also boost confidence when it comes to sitting down and writing an assignment. Planning involves self-awareness and self-assessment. Monitoring progress with evidence collection involves being in control of personal work. Taken together, self-awareness, self-assessment and control of work should provide a

very useful starting point for getting a GNVQ qualification.

Action plans

Action plans are records of the ideas that go into getting ready for assignments and evidence collection. They record ideas for the following:

Finding information

- looking up books for information and ideas
- asking people for their opinions
- asking tutors, learning advisors, librarians for advice on how to find information.

Reflecting on ideas

- discussing with tutors, with other candidates
- discussing with placement supervisors
- working out what information is needed in order to do assignments, etc.

Preparing to gather evidence – plans

- for practical activities
- to get evidence during placement
- for doing assignments
- for what to include in notes and written work.

Self-assessment and monitoring

- Self-assessment of evidence before it is formally assessed
- self-checking of own progress
- checking of ideas against assignment guidelines
- checking own study patterns and use of time.

Many people like to use a form to help record their ideas.

An **action plan form** might look like the one on page 16. People often invent their own forms and this is just one possible example. People also fill in their own ideas in different ways, but it is a good idea to aim to be consistent in how you go about it and to do it neatly.

Forms are useful because they can focus attention on what needs to be done. They also keep a record of planning activities which can fit neatly into a

GNVQ ACTION PLAN

Candidate's name ....

Planning dates ....

Unit title ....

Time period ....

Elements	Type of evidence	Knowledge needs	Sources of information	Placement activities which provide evidence	Opportunities for reflection	Self-assessment and progress checks	Dates for completion
Element 1	Demonstration. taped conversation with friend (name) Permission given, date:	Check communication techniques, supportive-skills, individual needs (cognitive?)	Second chapter, lectures, tutor, look up books on interviewing and psychology. Share ideas with group. (Check this week)	Talking to clients, asking carers how they run their conversation, talk to supervisor.	Tutorials, with placement supervisor, with friends. Dates completed:	Tape record a practice session with a friend – discuss it (next week). Write notes as extra evidence (2 weeks time)	Complete first conversation work in 4 weeks' time. Second conversation planned for (date)

Complete Element 1 first before going on to Element 2

portfolio. Records of planning are needed in order to get Merit and Distinction grades.

Forms are just one way of organising and recording a 'plan for action'. Some people prefer to write everything down in notes or to use notes to go with their forms. Others like to make 'pattern notes' to help display things visually.

Suppose someone wants to collect information to help with practical work on 'Communication with individuals' (2.1). Using sources is a criteria for grading, so some planning should be recorded before asking other people for ideas. What do you need to know about if you are doing an assignment on communication? One possibility is to identify areas of information with **pattern notes**. Pattern notes might be more useful than forms when planning for reflective or self-assessment work.

You can see opposite one person's pattern notes on information she needed for her assignment. She collected the words from the standards. The pattern has five long legs with branches coming out from the legs. The five legs list the main topics that the person

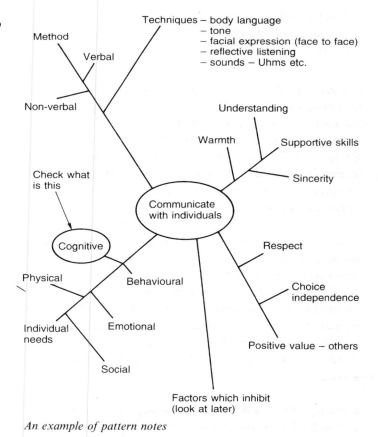

An example of pattern notes

wants to find out about. Other smaller areas of knowledge are linked with the five legs. Because of all the legs, some people call this kind of note-keeping a 'spider-graph'. But whatever you call it, it provides a record of planning and this will help towards a good grade.

Finding information and planning

Once someone has worked out what needs to be known they are ready for the next stage, which involves looking for the answers – finding out more about the topics noted.

The best place to find out more is probably the second chapter in this book. There are other sources of information which can be used as well. For instance, a candidate could go to a library and look for useful books. So, to start with, the plan of action might read:

Action plan

1 Knowledge needs – pattern notes
2 Read second chapter
3 Look in library

Looking in the library may sound all right, but it's not that straightforward. A person could just look along the shelves to see what books could be found with titles like 'Conversation Skills', 'Supportive Skills', etc. This idea probably won't work. One problem is that the books may be out on loan! So the person could look in the library catalogue. But this probably won't work either, because there may not be any single books with these titles! So what next? The person could ask the librarian for help, using the pattern notes as a guide. This might get a helpful response, but the librarian won't have read all the books and won't know everything about where all this knowledge could be found. The person could ask a tutor. This again should get a helpful answer, but the candidate can't get a Distinction grade if he or she always has to ask other people for advice.

Finding information and knowledge is always a problem. When there is a problem, it is important to try to use problem-solving skills! People should not just give up, there will be a way around the difficulty – to experiment and get a better answer.

The problem with finding the information identified in the pattern notes is that this information is hidden. It is hidden inside chapters of books with quite different titles. In order to find out what you need to know, you might have to look at books on helping skills, caring, interviewing, social skills, psychology and sociology. To find out where to start, you could look at the chapters and contents section at the beginning of a book. Another idea is to look up the index or the glossary at the back.

If you start to look through books, you will probably find something useful; but each answer often creates new problems. Even if what you have found is difficult to understand – don't give up! Think about why it is difficult. It may be because the book is really about something different from supportive conversational skills. If this is the case, then look for another book. Perhaps another book is still too difficult? One idea might be to get an interpretation of the difficult sections using tutorials? Perhaps it is worth taking a few photocopies of pages and discussing them with others?

The hunt for information usually shouldn't be too difficult. There are often booklists, articles and notes which get people started. Sometimes, information won't be in books anyway. You might do assignments where the information-finding involves talking to people who work in health or care settings. There may also be projects which involve searching newspapers for information. The important thing is to plan a strategy for collecting the information and to keep well-written notes which explain *how* information sources have been identified.

So the full action plan which started with the pattern notes might look like the example below (continued overleaf):

Sheet 2 – Unit 2

Information action plan
1 Information needs for assignment (project) work to be done with pattern notes.

---

2 Read second chapter.

3 Undertake information search in library by (a) looking up catalogue to identify headings and shelf areas, (b) looking at contents and indexes of books to see if they might be useful.

4 Talk to staff whilst on placement, or at work. Ask them for advice on how the theory might work in practice.

5 Practise and discuss issues connected with evidence requirements.

6 Get advice where necessary from tutors, supervisors, learning resource staff.

Following on from this planning stage it is important to **monitor** the planning. Monitoring means keeping a record of how the action plan worked. One idea might be to use the action plan form to help monitor how things went. Another way is just to keep notes. A third idea might be to keep a record or log book where notes are recorded. The notes might look like this:

Sheet 3 – Unit 2

Notes on monitoring
Used chapter in this book, made notes (enclosed). Searched in library: nothing useful in sociology, psychology, but found book on helping skills – photocopied two pages for discussion (enclosed – date). Made notes from book on interviewing (enclosed – date).

Talked to placement supervisor about 'Communication' pattern notes: points recorded in notes (enclosed – date).

Still haven't got information on 'cognitive' and how it is supposed to link with work. Action plan: ask for advice on (date) . . .

continued . . .

There are three reasons for keeping all these notes and records:

1 They will contribute to meeting the grading criteria for the GNVQ. They will help to provide the evidence needed to get Merits and Distinctions.

2 All this planning and note-taking will create records which can be reflected on. Reflection on your own notes will help to develop skills of problem-solving.

3 When people can reflect on and are confident about their own learning skills, they are more likely to feel 'in control' and 'on top of' their work. Work can feel interesting, rather than difficult or boring.

Grading criteria for Advanced GNVQs

Once all the evidence for a unit has been assessed as satisfactory and the test (where appropriate) has been passed, the unit is awarded. At this stage, units are not graded as a Pass, Merit or Distinction. Only the final qualification is graded. If all the appropriate units have been awarded then a GNVQ Pass grade can be automatically achieved. Merit and Distinction grades depend on extra evidence showing how the grading criteria have been met.

You should refer to your awarding body or course guidance notes for the fine detail of the advanced grading criteria. In outline the criteria are as follows:

To get Merit and Distinction grades candidates must:

 Independently draw up action plans for tasks that 'prioritise' or explain the order of activities to meet deadlines. At Distinction grade, this has to cover complex activities rather than just discrete tasks.

 Independently work out where monitoring skills need to be used. This might involve monitoring action planning, revising and changing action plans where necessary. Revisions may be made with guidance from a tutor. At Distinction grade, candidates have to demonstrate that they can make revisions independently.

Independently identify, access and collect information for tasks. The candidate will identify sources such as libraries and newspapers, but some help with finding material may be given by tutors. At Distinction grade, this skill has to cover complex activities rather than just discrete tasks. Candidates have to use a range of sources and justify why they were used.

Independently work out what information needs checking for validity. Validity may be checked using methods supplied or given by tutors. At Distinction grade, the selection of appropriate methods must be done independently by candidates.

Judge outcomes against criteria; identify alternative criteria that could be used to judge the success of activities. At Distinction grade, candidates have to apply a range of alternative criteria in order to judge the success of activities.

Justify approaches used; indicate that alternatives were (identified and) considered. At Distinction grade, justification must be based on a detailed consideration of relevant advantages and disadvantages. Alternatives and improvements must be identified.

The quality and content of assignment work may also count toward your grade. This is called substantive content, check with your tutor or learning manager for further details.

The grading criteria outlined is a method of working for an advanced qualification. The best strategy for achieving a Merit or Distinction grade is to learn to design each assignment or project report to fulfil the criteria. The way GNVQ is assessed means that you can gradually learn to do this. Your very first work may not meet all the criteria; yet you can still achieve the desired grade if your final portfolio of evidence shows that you were able to provide evidence consistently for the grading standards. By

taking the grading criteria step-by-step they may be easier to comprehend.

The first three criteria may be fairly easy to build into assignment work. Before starting any written work you need a plan. An action plan can cover a whole range of issues: what books you should use, what people you could talk to, where and how you can collect evidence, when it should be done by. As well as drawing up plans you may have to prioritise what you do. Which books are the most important to read first? Which chapters or sections of books will give you the theory you need? Who must you work with to collect the evidence needed for the unit standards? Who should you speak to first?

As well as designing an action plan, you will need to monitor how well it is working and you can do this by including dates in your action plan records to review progress. Using dates for review should go some way toward meeting the grading criteria requirement to: 'independently identify points at which monitoring is necessary'. Revising action and assignment plans in the light of review will also establish the right 'methodology'. Never destroy an action plan that needs revision – simply produce a revised plan with dates. This provides evidence for your planning skills.

Writing a quality assignment will require an initial plan for the content, layout and the concepts and theory to be included. Few people can write effectively without planning and monitoring. The only new thing that the grading criteria for planning and monitoring require is records of the process.

Quality projects and assignments will require concepts, theory and information to be related to practical issues. Candidates will need to identify and use sources of information to plan and to develop assignment work. The action plan could record the identification of key texts, people to interview, places to phone for information and so on. A carefully laid out 'reference section', 'sources used' or bibliography at the end of the assignment will also provide evidence toward this criteria.

Look at the style of reference layout used in this book to help design the bibliography, or follow your centre guidelines if different. Identifying sources involves finding useful details and showing how these help meet the standards. Just copying a list of book titles at the end of an assignment is not evidence of using them for tasks or complex activities. As well as identifying sources of information in an action plan, and listing them later, you would need to include references to them in the assignment work. The usual way of doing this is to quote the author's name, put the date of the work in brackets and then put full details in your reference or bibliography section. When writing or recording details of information gained on visits, you may record details of how you identified appropriate information in a 'sources' section at the end of your assignment.

Naturally you will be given lists of references and guidelines on using information technology, libraries and so on. Your job as an independent researcher is to work out how to get the necessary information *out of* books, libraries, data bases or interviews. You have to work out exactly *what* information is needed: what quotations to use, what questions to ask people, what issues to write about. Using information is a skill – like all skills it will develop with practice and with reflective feedback from others.

The first three grading criteria have to be evidenced in a similar way in order to gain Merit and Distinction grades at Intermediate level. The second three criteria really distinguish Advanced level from earlier achievements.

Establishing the validity of information involves a depth of thinking about what is being written or recorded. How do you know you have got the ideas right? If you are using another author's theory, are you sure that what you have put down is valid – or a true representation of their ideas? If you are drawing conclusions from an interview, are you sure that they are reasonable? If you are writing your own views about a topic, how can you back your views up so that they are valid?

Identifying information which requires to be checked or supported involves self-assessment skills. It also involves being critical of what you write or record. The validity skill involves frequently asking yourself: '*How do I know that this is correct – what evidence could I use to support this point?*'.

Creativity is also important at advanced level, and each candidate may develop a range of methods for demonstrating and checking validity. Methods may vary between units. Checking validity in 'Application of Number' may involve double-checking of calculations; checking validity in Unit 8, 'Research', may involve checking a conclusion by using more than one research technique. Below are a few general ideas which you might like to develop into your own style of writing or recording.

— When writing about an author's views, quote the page numbers of your source and select some quotes on those pages which establish the validity of your interpretation. Use the author's own words to support your case.

— When interpreting views from interviewees, check what you have written with the people you interview. Ask them if your interpretation is correct – check the validity of your views.

— Suppose you were writing about placement, work or visit experiences, and you were quoting details like the number of clients or the size of the building. You might ask a workplace supervisor to check your statements and validate them for accuracy.

— *Always* quote the reference for any theories you write about. Quote more than one author or more than one set of statistics to support complex arguments you wish to make. This demonstrates a weight of evidence for your argument. It doesn't prove that you are right, but it *does* show that what you are saying is reasonable and appropriate.

— Cross-check any tables or statistics you quote. Explain that you have double-checked your reasoning.

Demonstrating that you have built validity into your assignment style is another **self-evaluation** or self-assessment task. One way of doing this is to write a short set of notes at the end of each assignment. These notes might explain how you have checked your work. The notes might also point out page numbers in your assignment where you have checked the validity of what you are arguing or saying. As a self-check you could put small pencil 'Vs' in the margin to note your performance. Whatever methods you use to demonstrate the validity of information, you might need to discuss this concept with your tutor or learning manager. Sometimes it may be necessary to use a reflective learning process like the Kolb cycle (page 14) in order to develop the right style of work.

 Evaluation is another self-assessment skill. As a higher education skill evaluation involves being able to make comparisons and see similarities and differences between ideas, theories or situations. It may involve contrasts between viewpoints. At advanced level, evaluation implies the ability to judge your own work. For example, you might evaluate whether you have enough evidence for validity in your assignment. Evaluating this would require you to analyse what you had done in relation to what you understand to be necessary. You would need to explain what validity was and then assess or *evaluate* your own performance.

When using care and social science theory, evaluation usually involves assessing a particular line of thought in relation to other theories, values or facts. It will be important to have a wide range and depth of knowledge in order to assess your own work effectively; like other grading criteria skills, evaluation may take time to develop into a regular part of assignment writing.

Evaluation means that when doing Advanced GNVQ assignments, it is not good enough simply to do a good assignment: you have to know that you've done a good assignment – and know *why* it's a good assignment! Then you have to explain what you

know; evaluate and 'own' your achievement. Evaluation skills involve taking control of your own assessment – at least in the first instance.

Providing evidence for evaluation might involve producing a set of notes at the end of each task or assignment that you complete. This set of notes would cover your own judgement as to how your work met the national standards – the element or unit standards that you were working towards. If, for example, you had written an assignment to cover Element 2.1, you might provide a contents page which would list where the performance criteria and range items were covered. Your contents page would enable you to check and evaluate how you had covered all the necessary issues. Because 2.1 involves a lot of practical work you might not have written a section about every term in the range statements; so not every term would be listed in the contents page. The evaluation or review section at the end of an assignment could explain that particular communication techniques had been recorded on video or audio tape, and that evidence for the range of behaviours could be found there.

As well as evaluating how an assignment meets assessment criteria, candidates need to evaluate *how* aspects of their performance worked. This will involve judging the outcomes of behaviour in terms of theory. So in an assignment for Element 2.1: what are supportive skills? How well were supportive skills used? What verbal and non-verbal behaviours convey them? What do different authors say about supportive behaviours? How good was a particular piece of recorded practice at providing support in relation to theory? Candidates will need to analyse their own ideas and performance in relation to alternative concepts and theories. A thorough knowledge of a range of concepts and how they can be used in practice will usually be needed for Distinction grades.

When a candidate evaluates their knowledge and performance, they are beginning to argue a case for their work; this will also call on the skill of 'justifying approaches'.

Justifying the approaches used and their alternatives, advantages and disadvantages, is the final self-assessment skill. Like evaluation, this skill will involve analysing approaches and techniques used in assignment and evidence-collection work. Like evaluation, it will involve a wide range and depth of knowledge if candidates are to be able to make an effective case for themselves. Justification involves the questions: *Why do this work, the way I have done it? What advantages are there in doing it this way? What were the alternatives? Why didn't I choose them?*

Justification involves producing an argument to support a candidate's design work.

Candidates will often need to use theory and value statements in order to be able to justify their approach. Again, concepts and theory will often provide a basis for considering 'alternatives' and relevant 'advantages and disadvantages'.

Providing evidence for justification might involve producing a set of notes at the end of each assignment. These notes might be written together with the notes on evaluation. Alternatively, they might be written under a separate subheading or written on a form supplied by the centre.

Candidates might evaluate how supportive they had been in order to evidence Element 2.1. They might go on to argue reasons why they used skills such as reflective listening at a certain point in their conversation. This review of their work would involve using theories of supportive behaviour to justify their approach.

When you pass a driving test, you have to demonstrate that you can drive effectively and answer a few questions at the end of the test. To pass an advanced driving test you have to be able to explain or evaluate your driving as you go along. Advanced GNVQs may be like advanced driving: both evaluation and justification skills are needed to demonstrate that you *really* know what you are doing. To get Merit and Distinction grades you have to review and evaluate your work. Even more

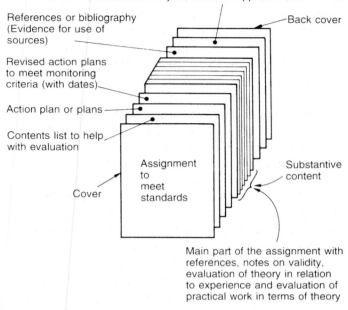

Sections of a written report or assignment designed to meet the grading criteria

importantly, you have to be able to explain and justify the way your work has been done.

Collecting evidence for the grading criteria might begin with each piece of written work, each report or assignment that you design. As you begin to pass a number of units, you will need to think about the presentation of your work in a final portfolio. The overall design of your portfolio might also be something which could be evaluated and reviewed to provide extra evidence of your skills.

Differences beteween Merit and Distinction grades

A table of the main differences is on page 23. Generally we can see from this table that Distinction grades require more independence and greater depth of knowledge. At Merit grade, candidates only have to describe alternatives; whereas for Distinction, candidates have to use their knowledge of alternative criteria for evaluation. At Distinction level, candidates have to understand advantages, disadvantages and alternatives when setting out their arguments around justification. At Distinction level, candidates have to justify their choice of information sources. For a Merit grade, candidates may have received some help and guidance with the design of all of their work. Independence, and perhaps confidence, need to be demonstrated for a Distinction.

Getting a Merit or Distinction grade suggests that a candidate has developed the advanced skills needed for study in higher education. Because these skills are 'advanced', it would not always be reasonable to expect the first project work to include them. Candidates will need time to develop and evidence skills of using validity, analysis, evaluation and justification. For this reason, 1993/94 regulations for GNVQ required that only one-third of the candidates' final portfolio needed to evidence the grading criteria for a Merit or Distinction grade to be awarded. Individual projects or assignments are not graded using the criteria, although evidence toward the grading criteria may be recorded. However, it is always best to attempt to develop and use the grading criteria skills as soon, and in as much work, as possible.

The portfolio

A portfolio is a portable folio – or a portable collection. A GNVQ portfolio is your collection of evidence for the award of the qualification. Evidence for the qualification will probably be contained in:

- assignments
- a record or log book
- extra notes and forms.

Evidence has to cover:

- mandatory and optional units
- core skills units
- grading criteria.

Assignments

Evidence for mandatory and optional units will mostly be found in assignment work. There may be one or more assignments per unit and they may be straightforward to present at the end of the course. Assignments will also probably contain most of the

GRADING: AN OVERVIEW		
	Merit	**Distinction**
Action planning	Independent design of action plans for **tasks**.	Independent design of action plans for **complex activities**.
Monitoring	Monitor plans independently. **Some help** with revision.	Independent monitoring **and revision**.
Identify and use sources	Collect information for tasks. **Some help** with additional sources.	Independent collection of information for **complex activities. Range of sources used with justification**.
Establish validity	Independent checking **using given methods**.	**Independent checking and selection of methods** for checking.
Evaluation	Evaluate outcomes. **Describe** alternative criteria for evaluation of success.	Evaluate outcomes and **apply a range of alternative criteria** in order to judge success.
Justification	Justify approaches. **Describe** alternatives.	Justify approaches with a **detailed consideration of advantages, disadvantages, alternatives and possible improvements**.

evidence for core skills units. However, the evidence for core skills will probably be spread *across* assignments.

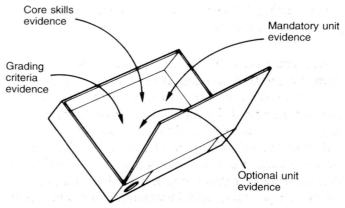

'*Standard' 12 Vocational Unit Advanced GNVQ*

Record or log book

Another way of collecting evidence for the unit standards, core skills and the grading criteria, is to use a log book. By keeping a diary of study activities it may be possible to provide evidence for monitoring, use of success and validity. A log book used on placement might provide evidence of the communication, information technology and even use of number core skills. Placement activities might often provide opportunities for demonstrating and evidencing skills. Records of performance might need to be signed by a supervisor or manager before they can count as evidence.

Notes

Sometimes candidates might prefer to use action plan forms for planning. Core skills in information technology might be demonstrated by designing action plan forms, or other record sheets. These sheets might be separate from the assignments or from other log books or notes.

What the portfolio might look like

By the end of the GNVQ programme, there could be a great deal of evidence to be reviewed for the award of the qualification.

All this evidence could be collected together, dumped in a bag and given to the assessors and verifiers. But no-one would be able to understand it all. A disorganised portfolio won't communicate quality and it won't suggest good planning, monitoring or evaluation. So a portfolio is more than a bag of bits!

Think it over

Imagine your assessor checking the quality of assignment evidence. What sort of things will he or she be looking for?

If you can use your imagination to reflect on and visualise this situation, then you have the planning skills to organise a good portfolio of your work.

Portfolios need to be carefully planned and organised. The planning of the portfolio might provide evidence for the grading criteria.

The portfolio might be a ring binder, an envelope folder or a file of some sort. The portfolio at the end of the programme might need more than one folder. What matters is that there is an explanation of how the evidence in the portfolio meets the standards for GNVQ, and the standards for a Merit or Distinction grade if this is claimed.

So, looking inside the folder there will probably be:

1 A *title sheet* stating the candidate's name, the centre's name (school or college) and the name of the qualification (Advanced GNVQ in Health and Social Care).
2 An *index of assignments, evidence and assessments* which have already been made.
3 A *statement or claim* explaining that the assignment work meets the unit standards and has been assessed as meeting the standards (dates of assessment and forms might be included here).
4 Photocopies of the *unit standards* which the work claims to demonstrate (or workbook containing the standards).
5 An *index of core skills evidence*. This index would explain where evidence could be found for Information Technology, Application of Number and Communication skills. Page numbers in assignment work might be quoted. Notes would be placed in order in the portfolio and numbered. Core skills demonstrated by other records (floppy disk, video, etc.) would also be noted, and disks and boxes labelled.
6 An *index of evidence for the grading criteria*. Most of the evidence would probably be in project reports, assignments or on forms. Page numbers should be quoted.

You don't have to supply evidence for the core skills of 'problem solving', 'working with others' and 'improving own learning'. It might still be worth putting in for these units, as they can go in your NRA; and evidence for these core skills might also count towards the grade for the GNVQ. The grading criteria often require 'problem-solving' and 'improving own learning' skills. Health and Social Care assignment work will often link with 'working

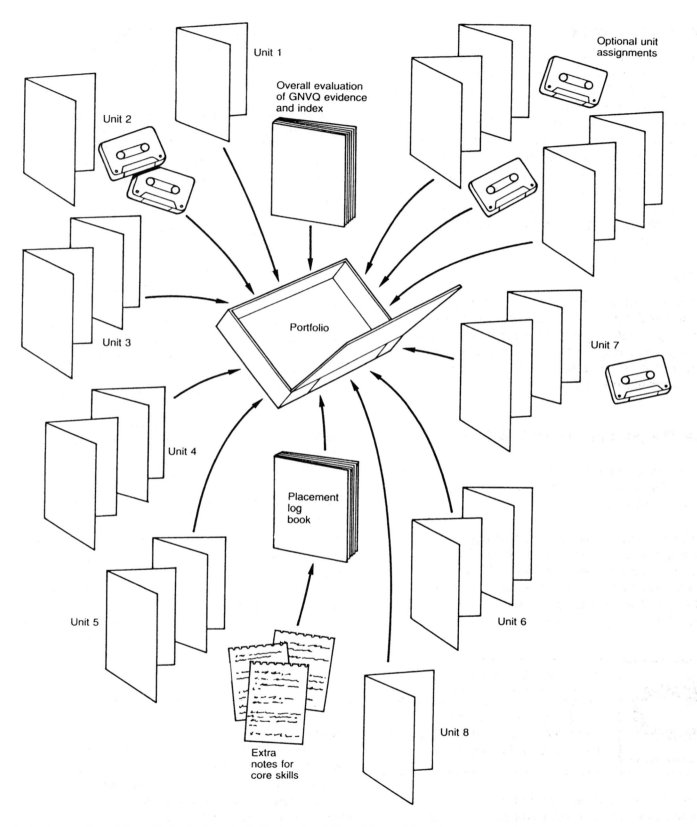

A visual map of portfolio evidence for 'standard' 12 Vocational Unit Advanced GNVQ

with others'. The act of designing a really good portfolio involves self-assessment of your own learning. A high-quality portfolio might supply evidence to claim the additional core skills linked with the claim for Merit or Distinction grades.

So, in summary, the portfolio will include indexing, the standards and the evidence. The portfolio can also contain explanations and arguments which support the claim for a Merit or Distinction grade.

Using icons to organise the portfolio

One idea to make indexing easier is to use symbols or 'icons' to label your evidence. A range of icons appears at the back of this book – these can be photocopied for use with GNVQ evidence, free of copyright restrictions. After photocopying, they can be cut out and stuck to notes or pages of assignment or log-book work. When an icon is stuck next to a piece of writing, or on a tape box, etc., it means that evidence is being claimed. An icon states, 'Look, this is evidence!'

Portfolio design

Designing a portfolio to achieve a Distinction grade will involve a good deal of self-assessment work. Usually, this work will have to be started *early* in the programme and developed as the programme goes on. Good grades may be difficult to achieve if portfolio design is left until the end of the programme.

Designing a portfolio of evidence will eventually require you to self-assess your own evidence. You will have to be able to show that:

1 The work is your own.
2 There is enough work to cover the performance criteria and range statements in the unit standards.
3 There is enough evidence to meet the grading criteria.
4 There is enough evidence to meet core skills standards.

Doing all this involves using imagination and checking ideas with tutors or assessors. Designing a good portfolio is a major learning task.

As you gradually put together your design for your portfolio you have opportunities to include new evidence to meet unit standards, to cover core skills or to meet the grading criteria. You are putting your own book together! The portfolio is the final record of your achievements. It can be more than just a box of assignment work. The portfolio can be the final review of all your learning. The indexing and the claim statements can make an argument for the grade of qualification that you are seeking.

Designing a portfolio is the final check that all the necessary evidence has been collected. The grade of the GNVQ qualification will be awarded in relation to the quality of the portfolio and its contents. Merit and Distinction grades may depend on good evidence presentation. Careful evaluation of your evidence shows that a great deal of learning has been done.

Getting started

Imagine trying to learn to drive a car by reading a book. Very few people could do it. To drive a car you have to *practise* doing it. Collecting evidence and designing projects, assignments and portfolios, will be the same kind of learning – try it, imagine how to do it better, listen to advice . . . Or listen to advice, imagine it and then try it. The order isn't important. What can't be done is to learn the whole idea in one go and then do it.

Evidence collection will look very complicated at first, there is so much that can go into a portfolio. It is important to get some ideas, think about them, try them out in practice and then get advice. If this is done over time, it should become much easier. Like driving a car, it gets easier once you've tried it for real.

Some of the ideas here might make more sense after evidence for the first assignment has been collected. So, if you are reading this before starting your GNVQ, why not plan to read it again in a month's time or in two months' time? Some of the ideas about assignment and portfolio design will make more sense when they are tried in practice.

What does it take to achieve an Advanced GNVQ?

It takes the obvious things like time, energy and good learning opportunities and resources. These are needed to develop and use reflective thinking skills, 'conceptual' or 'use of theory' skills and self-assessment skills. Linked with all of this is a broad range of knowledge and understanding. This will include understanding and working within the value base for Health and Social Care.

GNVQ is about researching and collecting evidence to prove that standards have been achieved. Evidence gets recorded in assignments, project reports, log books, notes and in test results. When all necessary tests have been passed, and all necessary evidence is collected in the portfolio, a GNVQ qualification is awarded.

Achieving success at GNVQ might be a little like achieving success at the game (see pages 28–29). The game is offered here as a reflective thinking opportunity. If you don't actually play it, at least have a think about the rules and the possible outcomes. You may gain some ideas by imagining how the game works. Have a look at the possible difficulties at the beginning and end of the game. Have a look at the potential of the star squares!

Tests

Most mandatory units were tested in 1994. Tests provide evidence that all the detail involved in the units has been covered. Some people think that test evidence will mean that GNVQ qualifications will be more valued and respected by the public and by future employers.

GNVQ tests should usually be taken after all the other evidence collection work for a unit has been done. Tests will ask a number of short questions about the unit and will probably last about one hour. Tests have to be passed in order for a unit to be awarded. If a test isn't passed first time, it can be

taken again. Indeed, it should be possible to take the test several times if necessary. Fear of failing often worries people when they have to take tests. GNVQ tests *shouldn't* cause fear because the tests can be retaken.

You will already have achieved lots of practical learning for the unit. Before you take the test, you will have planned evidence collection, reviewed your own knowledge, reflected on knowledge with others in discussion and written assignments or notes. All this work will have been assessed. It should mean that there isn't a lot of extra work and revision to do for the test.

Before doing the test, it might be worth organising discussion sessions with others so that practical work and information can be shared. *Talking* about knowledge can be one of the best ways of learning to remember it for a test.

The knowledge contained in this book should help cover the needs of the test. Fast Facts won't always cover every question possible for a unit, but they should cover many! Use Fast Facts for revision.

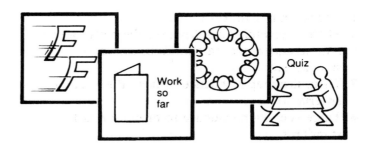

Another idea is to combine group discussion and Fast Facts to make up your own quiz game, along the lines of 'Trivial Pursuit'. Making revision fun can provide a good way of checking learning. Turning revision into a game may also remove anxiety.

Preparing for tests

You will need a lot of knowledge in your head to pass the test. Sometimes people imagine that getting this knowledge is like filling up a mug with water. The idea is to keep learning until the mug is full. Big mugs hold lots of water, little mugs can't hold so much. Sometimes people try to stretch their memory to hold lots of information – then try to become big mugs!

This idea of stretching memory is usually painful and it makes taking a test a very unpleasant experience. In caring, it shouldn't be necessary to 'strain' your memory.

For example, a candidate just starting a placement may have lots of clients' and colleagues' names to remember. One idea could be to stretch the memory and go around trying to list all the names over and over again until they stick. Usually carers don't do this. An alternative idea is to talk to each person and to get to know them one by one. After a while it becomes easy to remember all sorts of details about people. Their names become easy – and sometimes

---

Getting there: the Health and Social Care Advanced GNVQ Game

Goal

The object of the game is to get to Distinction grade as quickly as possible and in as few moves as possible. If you feel competitive you can try and get there before other players. If you want a short game you can aim for just a Merit grade or even for just a Pass grade!

Rules

1 Place your marker on the Start square at the start of the game.
2 Use only one six-sided dice.
3 Throw the dice and move up or sideways to the exact number thrown. You may choose to move in any up or sideways line, provided you stay on the board and you finish on the exact square that your dice throw indicates.
4 'Skills squares' give you an extra free go, and you can move diagonally to any square that is counted by your dice number. You may only move diagonally from a 'skills' square.
5 You must keep a list of the 'evidence' you collect, and which squares you landed on to collect that evidence. Other players must be able to check and see what you are recording; they are the 'verifiers' of your achievement.
6 Empty squares don't provide 'evidence' – try not to land on them.
7 Hazard squares cause you to miss a turn – try not to land on them.
8 You have to collect evidence for each element of every unit that you will need for a 12-unit GNVQ. So you will need to land on three squares (marked 'M') for each numbered mandatory unit, and three or four squares (marked 'O') for your four options (check how your awarding body has structured them). You will also need to land on five element squares for 'Information Technology' ('IT'), four element squares for 'Communication' ('C'), and three element squares for 'Number' ('No.').
9 Only when you have recorded landing on all these squares can you get through the 'pass' barrier.
10 You must land on the six different grading criteria squares marked Merit in order to get a Merit.
11 You must land on the six different grading criteria squares marked Merit, and the six different grading criteria squares marked Distinction to get to a Distinction.
12 As soon as you have all the evidence for Merit or Distinction grade, and all the evidence for the necessary units, you have to throw a number that will take you across the 'pass' barrier. You have then won.

In real life the game is a little more complicated and usually takes two years to play.

GETTING THERE: THE HEALTH AND SOCIAL CARE ADVANCED GNVQ GAME

DISTINCTION ESTABLISH VALIDITY				M 7.3	DISTINCTION USE INFORMATION SOURCES		SELF CONFIDENCE (skills)			⚠ NO CAREER PLANS	MERIT	DISTINCTION	
	M 6.1		M 7.2			02.1	I.T. ELEMENT 3	03.1		M 6.3	PASS	MERIT	
		USE OF THEORY (skills)								⚠ LEARNING ASSESSMENT TO THIERS 'YOU TELL ME'		PASS	
	DISTINCTION EVALUATION			02.3			APL SYSTEMS (skills)	NRA SYSTEMS (skills)	⚠ NO INDEX IN PORTFOLIO	⚠ NO CLEAR CLAIM FOR GRADE	⚠ NO CLEAR CORE SKILLS INDEX		
M 7.1			02.4	I.T. ELEMENT 2		M 6.2		03.3		04.1	⚠ NO LOG BOOK RECORDS		
			USE OF PLACEMENT EVIDENCE (skills)	M 8.1		No. ELEMENT 1	No. ELEMENT 2		DISTINCTION ACTION PLANS		04.2		
	M 5.2			M 8.2		03.4	No. ELEMENT 3			MERIT JUSTIFICATION		04.3	
		M 4.3			04.4		C ELEMENT 4				REFLECTIVE THINKING (skills)		
⚠ CAN'T FIND STANDARDS	I.T. ELEMENT 1		M 4.2	C ELEMENT 3	M 4.1		DISTINCTION JUSTIFICATION			MERIT EVALUATION		I.T. ELEMENT 4	
⚠ MISS A TUTORIAL			PORTFOLIO DESIGN (skills)		⚠ CAN'T FIND REFERENCES				MERIT ESTABLISH VALIDITY				
	01.2	C ELEMENT 2	M 3.3		M 2.3				MERIT USE INFORMATION SOURCES				
C ELEMENT 1	M 3.1	M 3.2		M 2.2		M 5.1		MERIT MONITOR ACTION			I.T. ELEMENT 5		
M 1.1	M 1.3	01.1	01.3	01.4			SELF ASSESSMENT (skills)			⚠ NO GUIDANCE ON PLACEMENT			
START	M 1.3	M 2.1		⚠ MISS A TUTORIAL	⚠ NO NOTE TAKING SKILLS			M 5.3			M 8.3		

Key:

- M = Mandatory unit
- 0 = Optional unit
- C = Communication (core skill)
- I.T. = Information Technology (core skill)
- N: = Use of Number (core skill)

- ⚠ = Hazard square
- ✺ = Skills square
- **APL** = Accreditation of Prior Learning
- **NRA** = National Record of Achievement

automatic – to remember, because names link to all the other details about the people. This kind of automatic knowledge feels natural; sometimes people feel that it just happens to them. It may be that this kind of learning is 'deeper' than the kind where a memory gets 'full-up'.

GNVQ tests won't be as natural as remembering people on placement, but the ideas about learning may still work. If you have done project work, written assignments, shared ideas with other people, taken notes from other people's explanations and so on, then learning may feel more real and natural. This deeper learning may be interesting. It could even make the tests feel like a fun challenge, rather than an unpleasant pressure.

Whatever the test feels like, it is important to avoid 'overfilling' the memory – cramming things into it for a test. It is usually a better idea to learn from practical experience and then to use Fast Facts to help revise. Fast Facts probably won't work very well as starting points for learning. They shouldn't be crammed into the memory for the test. One way that they might be useful is in helping candidates to recognise things that they already know. When a person looks at the Fast Facts list, the words should prompt thoughts. The thoughts should link with the details under each 'fact' heading. Experience of studying Fast Facts may make it easier to recall detail when actually taking a test for a unit.

Think it over

Experiment with this chapter. Use the Fast Facts – do they make sense first time?

An experiment using Fast Facts

There are no tests of knowledge for doing GNVQs, but if you wanted to check your understanding of this chapter you might need to be able to answer questions like:

- What is evidence?

- Why is it necessary to collect evidence in order to be awarded a GNVQ?

Some people feel mentally 'frozen' by such a question. No matter how long a person stares at it, there is no clue as to where to begin. So, what is evidence?

Fast Facts say these things about 'evidence':

1 It is the key to passing a GNVQ and getting good grades.
2 Evidence is information which confirms that a standard has been reached.
3 Evidence can be gathered in assignments.
4 There are many ways evidence can be presented, such as by video or tape recordings. Demonstrations of skill can be observed and recorded to provide evidence.
5 Tests provide evidence of knowledge.

If a person attempted to memorise all this, it would hurt! Or, at least, if someone went through Fast Facts and tried to commit it all to memory, very few memories could take it. So the five points above *aren't* the answer, they are too difficult to remember just as they are written.

- **Continue the experiment**: try to analyse the five statements above. What do they mean?

The five points above need to make sense. They need to feel real; they need to link with the practical know-how of doing a GNVQ.

Point 1 says evidence is the key to passing a GNVQ and getting good grades. Action planning is one example of evidence – it is written or recorded information. Point 2 states that evidence is information which confirms that a standard has been reached. This might remind someone of the types of information: videos, pictures, references; these are all types of records of things which have been done. These records are used to prove that a standard has been reached. Point 3 says that assignments are used to gather evidence. Records again, types of evidence again, and examples of assignments might come to mind. Point 4 talks about examples of evidence. Perhaps these inspire pictures in the mind? Point 5 says that tests provide evidence (a difficult point, but then the test is needed to get the award of most mandatory units); a test provides a record of knowledge. It's another example of information that confirms that a standard has been reached.

Is this the kind of thing that came into your mind? If not, have you done any practical work with evidence yet?

There is an old Chinese proverb:

I hear and I forget,
I see and I remember,
I do and I learn.

Collecting evidence is something which has to be done in practice. When it has been done, the Fast Facts will act as a reminder. The explanations come together *after* study.

- An answer to the question: what is evidence? Answer: evidence is information, records and details that show standards have been reached.

That question on evidence is different from questions to be set for tests; most test questions will be multiple choice and will only require you to recognise the right answer. Even so, practical work, reflection and evaluation will help to turn 'book ideas' into useful knowledge that may assist with tests.

Self-assessment of knowledge about GNVQs

1 What are 'standards'? Why are standards used in assessment?
2 Why are standards sometimes difficult to understand at the beginning of a GNVQ programme?
3 Why is it necessary to produce evidence in order to be awarded GNVQ units?
4 What are action plans? Why is it important to keep records of action plans?
5 Can a person plan to get a Distinction or Merit grade and be confident of getting it?
6 What is needed in order to get a Merit or Distinction grade?
7 What is a portfolio? When should work on a portfolio start?
8 How might candidates prepare to take a GNVQ test?

---

9 Why is it important for GNVQ candidates to assess their own learning?
10 Why is 'reflection' useful when learning in Health and Social Care?

Answers can be found at the back of the book.

Fast Facts

Action planning Evidence has to be collected in order to pass a GNVQ. The collection of evidence needs to be *planned*. What action will produce enough evidence to demonstrate (pass) the standard? 'Action plans' equal 'plans to get evidence'. Evidence of good action planning helps towards merit and distinction grades.

Assessors These are the people who assess evidence to decide whether it meets the requirements of National standards. In other words, they assess work to see if it should pass. Assessors will also assess the grade of a GNVQ qualification when the portfolio is presented for assessment. Assessors will often be tutors or learning managers. They must be very knowledgeable and qualified in the area they are assessing. By 1995, most assessors are expected to hold an NVQ award which demonstrates that they can operate to the NVQ/GNVQ assessor standards.

Assignments Assignments are one way of collecting evidence to demonstrate (pass) an element or unit of GNVQ. Assignments should be planned and negotiated with an assessor, tutor or learning manager.

Awarding body City & Guilds, BTEC or RSA will check the quality of courses and candidates' work. They award the GNVQ qualification (the National Council for Vocational Qualifications does not award qualifications – it designs and checks the national system).

Candidates People who collect evidence to get GNVQs are called candidates – they are candidates for assessment. Colleges call all people who study 'students', and 'students' and 'candidates' are the same; but the word 'candidate' emphasises the fact that these people are putting themselves forward for assessment – that they are very active, not just spending time in study.

Concepts Concepts are ways of thinking which enable people to understand and make sense of the world. Concepts also help us to recognise situations and predict or guess what will happen next. Concepts are expressed in words which help us to group experiences together and label them.

Core skills The skills of Communication, Application of Number and Information Technology are needed to get the GNVQ qualification. They are assessed using evidence gathered to pass mandatory and optional units. Core skills of Problem Solving, Improving Own Learning and Working With Others can also be assessed and recorded in a candidate's NRA.

Criteria Criteria is the plural of criterion. A criterion is a standard by which things are judged. Criteria are standards which things can be measured against.

Elements The smallest parts of standards to be assessed. *Units* are usually made up of between two and five elements. Once an element is 'passed' it has to be collected with other elements to pass a unit.

Evaluation Advanced level grading criteria. Evaluation will require a depth of knowledge and the ability to judge or self-assess work in relation to theory. Evidence should be *evaluated* by candidates in order to check that it meets the standards. Candidates' assignment and portfolio work should be self-assessed or evaluated in relation to appropriate ideas, concepts or theory.

Evidence This is the key to passing a GNVQ and getting good grades. Evidence is information which confirms that a standard has been reached. Evidence can be gathered in assignments. There are many ways evidence can be presented, such as by video or tape recordings. Demonstration of skill can be observed and recorded to provide evidence. Tests also provide evidence of knowledge.

Evidence indicators In GNVQ standards, evidence indicators are found at the bottom of element details. They give an outline of the kind of evidence needed to pass a given element.

Grading GNVQs are graded Pass, Merit or Distinction. GNVQs cannot be failed, but they are not awarded or 'passed' until all the necessary units are passed. Here, Merit or Distinction grades depend on extra evidence of performance to grading criteria standards.

Grading criteria At advanced level, these cover action planning, monitoring, use of sources, validity, evaluation and justification. Grading criteria require that students can self-assess and review their own performance. Skills of reflective thinking, use of theory, independent working and learning, will be required. Grading criteria enable GNVQ to be awarded with either Merit or Distinction grades. Distinction grades may generally require more independence and a greater depth of knowledge than Merit grades.

Justification Advanced level grading criteria. Justification requires the ability to design an argument which supports the approach taken in practical and assignment work. Justification might be written alongside the evaluation of a piece of work.

Knowledge The word covers information, facts, concepts, theories and also the way people use their ideas to guide their work. GNVQs in Health and Social Care will involve using knowledge in practical situations. Just remembering things won't be enough for most units.

Levels Both GNVQ and NVQ qualifications are structured in five levels: Level 1 is Foundational; Level 2 is Intermediate and equal to good GCSE qualifications; Level 3 is Advanced Vocational A-level; Levels 4 and 5 are graduate and post-graduate equivalents.

Mandatory unit Mandatory units are a fixed part of the GNVQ qualification. They have to be achieved or passed to get the GNVQ.

Methodology The approach taken, or methods used to organise or design outcomes. Candidates may design their own methodology for ensuring that assignment and portfolio work meets the grading criteria standards.

Monitoring Monitoring means checking what's happening. In GNVQs action plans have to be monitored, or checked, and developed, in order to get Merit and Distinction grades. Monitoring links with self-assessment, where individuals check their evidence before having it assessed. A log book or notes will often be needed to provide evidence of monitoring.

NCVQ The National Council for Vocational Qualifications. The Council controls the national framework of GNVQ and NVQ qualifications.

NRA A National Record of Achievement. Candidates should have an NRA in which to keep records of their units as they are awarded. The NRA provides a record of achievement which might be useful to an individual who did not complete the whole of a GNVQ qualification. The NRA can also record extra units, and extra core skills units, for individuals who get more than the standard GNVQ qualification.

NVQ National Vocational Qualifications are more narrowly focused than GNVQs. They are structured in different units but designed with the same qualification levels as GNVQs.

Optional unit Advanced GNVQs have four 'optional units'. These are not formally tested.

Performance criteria These define the performance necessary to reach the standard (or criteria) necessary to achieve an element. Performance criteria explain what is to be covered. They are rules to guide the assessors. Performance criteria should not be assessed separately. Evidence has to cover all the criteria when it is submitted for assessment.

Portfolio A portable 'folio' (or collection) of evidence. Action plans lead to the collection of evidence to meet unit requirements. All the evidence should be put together into a folder – or perhaps a file box if photos, tapes and videos are included. The portfolio can then be assessed and verified.

Programmes GNVQs are usually called programmes because units can be taken in any

order, and passed in any order. Individuals could – at least in theory – take different pathways to achieving a GNVQ. Many people call GNVQ programmes 'courses'; they can be courses, but this is a more old-fashioned idea which implies a fixed 'pattern of treatment' (like a course of drugs for an illness!).

Qualification The whole Advanced GNVQ in Health and Social Care. GNVQ Units are *not* qualifications.

Range Range provides details of what should be covered when providing evidence for an element. Issues in range have to be covered somewhere in the evidence. Range specifies what needs to be known for assessment purposes. Other knowledge may sometimes be needed in order to develop an appropriate understanding.

Reflection A skill which helps in the process of evidence collection, self-assessment and planning. It is a skill also necessary in health and social care work.

Self-assessment Achieving Merit or Distinction grades will require candidates to monitor, evaluate, justify and check the validity of their work. These skills all require candidates to assess their own approaches and work before formal assessment takes place.

Skills Abilities which people can demonstrate and do. GNVQ standards cover instances of knowledge, skills, understanding and values.

Sources Use of sources is one of the advanced level grading criteria. Candidates have to show evidence that they have identified books, articles, data bases, people to interview, places to visit, materials to use etc. Evidence will often require a 'references' or bibliography section at the end of an assignment. Further discussion of sources may also be required in review and action planning sections.

Standards The basis for assessment, national standards are all the unit, element, performance criteria, range and evidence indicator descriptions for GNVQ areas. Standards don't explain what must be studied, but they do explain what must be assessed.

Tests   Most mandatory units are tested at present. Tests will probably last about one hour, and will involve multiple choice questions.

Theory   Theories are systems of ideas which interpret and explain things. Theory will involve the use of *concepts*. In Health and Social Care work, it will often be necessary to use theory to interpret events. Theoretical knowledge will be needed to evidence the evaluation and justification grading criteria.

Tutorials   A term for the discussions with a tutor or learning manager which will guide action planning, evidence gathering and project work.

Understanding   Deep or thorough knowledge and skill that can be used in many different circumstances and settings; also, practical knowledge that can be used to solve problems. GNVQ evidence will often show that concepts and theories can be used in practice, or in practical situations.

Units   The building bricks of qualifications. Units are the smallest part of a GNVQ to be awarded. They can be recorded in the NRA. Units are made up of *elements*.

Validity   Advanced level grading criteria requiring candidates to check and self-assess their work. Validity requires evidence that details are checked and that arguments are supported. Evidence for validity might often be found within a candidate's assignment work.

Value base   The system of interrelated values or value statements that guide a profession. The NVQ value base in Care is defined within the 'O' unit.

Values   Viewpoints which are the foundation of professional practice. Values are part knowledge and part skill. They are partly a skill because they have practical applications in decision making. In Health and Social Care, values are emphasized because other caring skills don't work without them.

Verifier   A person who checks assessments. When assessments are made of people's evidence, these assessments themselves have to be checked. The *internal verifier* checks a sample of tutors' assessment work within a GNVQ centre. The *external verifier* checks the operation of systems in GNVQ centres on behalf of the awarding body.

Reference

Kolb, D., Rubin, I., and McIntyre, J. (Third edition, 1979), *Organizational Psychology: an Experimental Approach*. New Jersey, Prentice Hall

Substantive content

This is a fourth grading criteria which may be used to decide the award of merit and distinction grades from 1995 on. Details of how substantive content might be assessed were not available when this book was written. Substantive content will relate to the quality of assignment, project or portfolio work. Candidates who meet the current criteria for merit or distinction awards may often produce work that will also meet any new requirements for substantive content.

chapter 1 ACCESS, EQUAL OPPORTUNITIES AND CLIENT RIGHTS

This chapter focuses on the individual: it will demonstrate the impact of other people in forming identity and value systems. Case-studies illustrate the major factors involved when individuals are disadvantaged. The effects of disadvantage on individuals, their self-concept and their resulting ability to make full use of their rights to services in the health and care field are analysed.

· HUMAN NEEDS (PICES) ·

A very frequently heard quote comes from John Donne, about four hundred years ago: 'No man is an island' (c. 1600). To gain some understanding of what Donne meant, consider the birth of a baby. A human baby is totally dependent on their carer for warmth, food, shelter and protection, until such time as the child becomes physically and intellectually able to take control of their own life. Just as an island is separated from the main body of land, and is therefore isolated, so a baby isolated from its carers would fail to survive without their support. Why – what happens and why is the presence of people so important?

Human babies are obviously helpless, so it is easy to see the importance of physical care. But is that all that is necessary to enable this dependent baby to grow into an independent adult? It may be argued that in order to grow and develop into a well-balanced whole person a baby needs to develop in all of the following areas, which I will term PICES. This stands for:

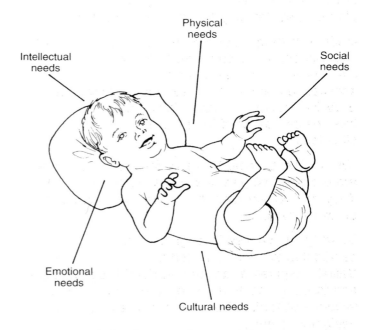

Figure 1.1 *PICES – the needs of a young baby*

Physical needs,
Intellectual needs,
Cultural needs,
Emotional needs,
Social needs.

Physical needs

Physical needs include appropriate food, in terms of nutritional and calorific value to facilitate healthy physical growth and development. They also involve warmth to maintain body temperature, cleanliness to preserve healthy skin and teeth as they form; and exercise to stimulate the development of muscles and co-ordination of movement.

The physical development of children is well documented in a range of specialised texts; a suggested reading list is provided at the end of the chapter. In addition it is worth noting the many studies undertaken to understand the effects of lack of appropriate food or exercise (*privation*) e.g. Bowlby (1969), Skeels (1966) and Tizard (1977), who look at the physical as well as emotional effects on a child. A child must be provided with physical care but also requires intellectual stimulation in order to function independently.

Intellectual needs

Intellectual development involves encouragement of the child's curiosity to enable them to learn about themselves and the world around them. Sociologists and psychologists are interested in the way children learn, albeit from their own disciplinary perspective. A sociologist will review the effect of society and the environment on a child's development; whilst a psychologist concentrates on the factors which contribute to the individual's experience.

Task

Observe a baby of nine-months old, either in life or by watching a video. Make notes to record the physical abilities of the child you are observing. Concentrate on the way the child tries to hold the attention of others, or deals with an object given to them. Look at the way they hold and explore any object – it is usually done by putting it in their mouths to 'feel'.

A psychologist would be interested in the way the child was learning about their environment and the influence they have on other people around them. Psychologists will provide several interpretations from observations of children, depending on their perspective. Someone belonging to the *Behaviourist*

school will watch the child's repeated movements to attract attention from the adult – in the form of signs which encourage the child to continue the movement; i.e. babbling noises and smiles from the baby are rewarded by a smile or 'conversation' from the adult (*reinforcement*) which the child enjoys.

A much older child who retreats into thumb sucking when distressed may be seen as reverting to the 'oral stage of development', from a psychodynamic perspective of psychology as expounded by Freud.

Looking at a different discipline, sociology, it is possible to gain an understanding of the ways in which a sociologist may use observations. Note will be made of the interaction in the context of a particular sociological perspective.

A sociologist from a *functionalist* perspective would believe that education strengthens (reinforces) the shared norms and values of society. Observing the interaction between carer and child, note will be taken of the methods adopted to encourage socially acceptable behaviour. In America, children learn about their history, sharing a common language in school, beginning their day by the Oath of Allegiance to the Stars and Stripes. This is to encourage commitment to society as a whole.

The equivalent in Britain has been the singing of the national anthem, or the singing of a school song, which reinforced a shared commitment to society.

Think it over

Did this happen in your experience of school? You may wish to discuss this issue.

An observation of a group of children in a school playground might include an interpretation of why individuals react to an argument over a ball. One child may wish to gain the ball to prove that they are the strongest or the leader; another to defend a younger or smaller child who has been left out; yet another because they are interested in finishing the game as they were winning; and another for the

opposite reason – no ball means no game, no winners and certainly no losers, so face saved!

Stimulation

Much research has been undertaken to try to determine the importance of other people in child development. Schaffer (1971) notes that a baby finds people stimulating, yet cannot in the early weeks distinguish them from inanimate objects. This was further analysed by Bushnell et al (1989) who noted that babies as young as two days old preferred the faces of their mother to the face of someone very similar. This implies that the baby is able cognitively to differentiate features and supports the feelings of Maurer and Barrera (1981), who noted that babies of two months old looked more at a schematic human face than at a scrambled face which had been matched for its pattern and complexity.

Stimulation is therefore essential for children to grow and develop and be equipped to take their place in the world. Play becomes the work of the child to help them to explore the world, their place in it and their ability to get along with others. There have been many studies on play. Fenson and Schell (1986) note how exploratory play gradually becomes more complex as the child increases their knowledge. Several studies note that play becomes more productive when an adult is involved, e.g. Collis and

Schaffer (1975), Bakeman and Adamson (1984), Duns and Wooding (1977) and Meadows (1986), to name a few.

Cultural needs

Cultural needs have two important aspects in that culture is not only learned but shared by the group. If this were not the case then confusion could result, as no-one would be sure of how another would behave or indeed what behaviour they should adopt in order to be accepted by others.

Think it over

Imagine that you are to move from an inner-city area to a small rural village some sixty miles away. The relative quiet of the countryside would be a marked difference, as would the number of people you will meet in the village and, possibly, the pace of life would be different also. All these things are clearly apparent (tangible) but the culture of village life is more abstract and less tangible, i.e. not so clearly visible.

A sad reflection of life in the 1990s for many city dwellers is the rising crime rate, resulting in a culture in some areas of not making eye contact with strangers as they pass and certainly not speaking to them. In many villages, by contrast, people are more openly friendly and expect eye contact and, at the very least, a verbal acknowledgement. Failure to elicit (or get) the expected response could lead to a feeling of rejection and an assumption made about 'townies' as being unfriendly. However, times are changing – not least because villages are becoming more cosmopolitan, as people elect to move out to the country, changing what had often been a relatively static population in country areas.

Culture has been defined by Ralph Linton (1945) in the following way: 'The culture of a society is the way of life of its members; the collection of ideas and habits which they learn, share and transmit from generation to generation.'

Culture is about the way things are done and the behaviour that is acceptable to the people with whom you live. For example, a young child is encouraged to behave in a particular way at mealtimes, i.e. to use cutlery or to eat with the right hand only. Another example may be in the respect that must be demonstrated to an elder or to follow particular religious practices.

Language

Human beings need to be accepted by others, so language can be an important issue in that certain words are considered to be unacceptable. Language is, however, also used by some social groups as a means to say we are different from most other groups. So, for example, in the 'youth culture' to be found in every generation different words are used, such as 'groovy' and 'far out' in the 1960s and 1970s and 'wicked' and 'brill' in the 1980s and 1990s! Those using such terms are seen as 'one of us', a kind of password to a bonding process for a particular group.

In a different social context, language may be used to proclaim a social class by a particular accent or even a profession by using *jargon*.

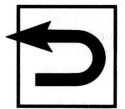

Think it over

Think of a time when you visited a hospital or visited a solicitor, or perhaps sat in a court to watch proceedings. Think about how it felt to be involved in a conversation with a professional using jargon. It perhaps felt awkward and as though you were being excluded, certainly disadvantaged, because you were not totally sure that you fully understood what was happening. Did it feel as though they were speaking a foreign language? Think then what it must be like to be in a country where you have limited understanding of the language; you may feel very vulnerable, even threatened by it all.

Norms and values

Culture may be expressed through clothes, music, language, art, food and behaviour – all of which proclaim to others that you belong to a particular group, that you accept the norms and values of that group.

Norms are the guidelines or rules for acceptable practice by a particular group. In all societies there are norms about the way two people greet each other, for example rubbing noses in Eskimo culture, shaking hands in some Western cultures, a formal bow in some Eastern cultures.

Figure 1.2 *The way people greet each other shows social norms*

Each culture has guidelines regarding personal space, i.e. how close one person stands to another to hold a conversation. Anglo-Saxon culture demands more personal space than, for example, a Middle-Eastern culture. Imagine what can happen when someone from an Anglo-Saxon culture meets someone from the Middle East. The person from the Middle East has learnt that it is acceptable to stand very close to the person being spoken to. Touching the other person during conversation is also acceptable. Imagine their feelings when the person from the Anglo-Saxon culture edges backwards to preserve the acceptable personal space! The person from the Middle East could feel rejected and the Anglo-Saxon threatened, yet each is responding to the norms of their own society.

It is important in health and social care practice to ensure that staff are aware of what is acceptable in different cultures, in order to avoid unnecessary misunderstanding and offence.

Different cultures have different expectations regarding eye-contact between strangers or between men and women. Many Eastern cultures would consider it disrespectful for a woman to make full eye contact with a man, whilst in a European culture fleeting eye contact is viewed with suspicion. It is easy to see how misunderstandings can occur and these have particular importance for those working in the health and social care field.

Respecting individual differences is a recurring theme throughout this chapter. Norms are the guidelines for what to do in particular situations, in order to be accepted by a given culture. Values are beliefs that something is desirable or good. Different cultures do have different value systems; for example, it may be argued that in Britain in the 1990s elderly people are not deemed to be valuable to society. In other cultures elders are respected for their wisdom and are cared for in a way that many Western elders may envy!

Success, in terms of academic or material achievements, may be a value for some cultures, whereas respect for the environment, or a search for enlightenment, may be a deeply held value for others. The value placed on human life is one which varies between cultures.

Norms and values may be seen as the means by which individuals learn to co-exist with others in their social group. Just as society at large (macro society) defines its own norms and values, so individual groups within that society (micro society) will develop their own norms and values.

Think it over

If you are working on GNVQ as a member of a group, you may or may not have known your new peer group. You will have all gone through a process of getting to know each other, the institution, the staff and the programme. Gradually, a way of working together will have evolved in order to get on with the business of learning. You will all have had different experiences of life to date, and may even find very different social norms and values initially. In time, you have learnt to define behaviour and attitudes which the majority – if not all – will accept; in other words, your group has developed norms and values to enable you to function.

This process will have involved individual reviews of the value systems taken from the culture you grew up in. One of the most difficult tasks faced by anyone coming into one of the health and care professions, is to review objectively the beliefs and values acquired over a lifetime of experience within a given culture. This sometimes leads to the realisation that the individual has unwittingly been racist or sexist, because of their experience to date. Care needs to be taken to support each other in an atmosphere which encourages raised awareness by learning from mistakes. Confrontation, where errors are made through lack of understanding, should be avoided.

Emotional needs

Emotional development is essential in order for an individual to grow and develop into a self-assured person with a positive self-image. It means being accepted and encouraged by those around us, starting with a bonding process at birth and continuing in one form or another throughout life.

Bowlby placed great emphasis on the role of the mother in what he termed a critical or sensitive period. Bowlby saw the close proximity of mother and child to be essential for the child's emotional development. He thought (hypothesised) that maternal deprivation would result in an inability to establish relationships in later life, with an increased risk of developing anti-social behaviour.

Rutter (1981) refutes much of Bowlby's theory of attachment and maternal deprivation. He points out that Bowlby uses the term 'maternal deprivation' to

Emotional development means being accepted and encouraged by those around us. (Winged Fellowship Trust 'Images of Caring' Competition by Joan Shannon.)

3 permanent separations, either because of death or adoption.

Both Bowlby and Rutter recognise the importance of the main carer in the socialisation of the child. This is supported by Richards (1987), who takes it further by noting that young children are equally affected by their interaction with peers and the extended family members in terms of their socialisation.

Read the poem, whose author is Dorothy Law Nolte.

Children Learn What They Live

If children live with criticism
   They learn to condemn.
If children live with hostility
   They learn to fight.
If children live with ridicule
   They learn to be shy.
If children live with shame
   They learn to feel guilty.

If children live with tolerance
   They learn to be patient.
If children live with encouragement
   They learn to be confident.
If children live with praise.
   They learn to appreciate.
If children live with fairness
   They learn justice.
If children live with security
   They learn to have faith.
If children live with approval
   They learn to like themselves.
If children live with acceptance and friendship
   They learn to find love in the World.

explain two very different types of experience: i.e. the lack of attachment, or loss, through separation from the mother, which Rutter terms *deprivation*; and the lack of any attachment (even with a mother present), *privation*. The effects of deprivation can usually be seen as short-term, while the effects of privation are long-term.

Rutter (1971) does agree, however, that long-term separation can lead to behavioural problems, identifying three categories:

1 working mothers, as they are not with the child full-time,
2 transient separations, for example mother or child in hospital so they are separated for a short time,

How does this assist carers to view their interaction with a child? Imagine that you are working with a young child with Down's Syndrome. (A disorder where a child is born with characteristic physical features and a degree of learning disability, Down's Syndrome is caused by an extra chromosome.) How could you use the message contained in the poem to show that this child is important and 'special' – in the way you would expect to demonstrate to any child that they are 'special'?

Each child is *special*; each child has the same need to be accepted by others for themselves. Each has the right to dignity and respect as an individual; so how can you as a carer ensure that right is upheld? Failure to demonstrate this will lead to low self-esteem in the child which may cause the child to take on the role of victim and/or learn to be helpless rather than becoming independent.

A sense of security and well-being help to form a positive self-image. (Winged Fellowship Trust 'Images of Caring' Competition by Susanne Radmann.)

Emotional development is, therefore, essential for the well-being of a child if it is to grow into a well-balanced adult with a positive self-image. A child who is cuddled and made to feel important develops a sense of security and well-being which can enable them to cope with new situations.

The close bond with a carer is important yet in many cultures the primary carer may not be the birth mother: it could be the father, aunt, grandmother, nanny or child-minder. The main concern is to provide warmth and security in terms of encouraging a positive self-concept.

Think it over

Imagine the child born with a disability. In the early years of life the child has limited experience and may not be totally aware of the difference between themselves and their peers. The difference becomes more apparent when the peer group become mobile or start school. How would you work to enable this child to develop a positive self-image – to feel valued without becoming over-protective?

A good way to review this would be to watch the film 'My Left Foot', a true story about a boy with cerebral palsy born into a large family in Ireland. Watch the way his family treat Christy – particularly when playing football! The boy has no speech and is unable to walk. The father makes a wooden go-cart for Christy, which the brothers push him around in as he grows. The incident with the football is about an older brother insisting that Christy be allowed to take a goal kick. Other players look on in amazement, seeing the silent twisted young teenager in the go-cart. The brothers lift Christy out and support him as he uses the only part of his body which he is able to control – deftly placing the ball in the centre of the net!

Can you imagine how important it must have been to Christy to have scored that goal – especially as others were watching? Think how important it is to value each person for what they are able to do. It is too easy to concentrate on what an individual cannot do, which leads to their feeling devalued. Christy's broad grin at his success is only matched by the brothers' loud cheers!

Think it over

Imagine what it must be like for a child from a different ethnic group to their peers, particularly if the child is subject to name-calling and is made fun of because of different dress, speech or habits. Again use your imagination to try and be that child (empathise). How does it feel? How might you react in that situation? And, most importantly, what effect do you think it will have on the way you see yourself and, indeed, on the value you place on yourself?

A way of getting in touch with these two situations might be to think of a time from school when you wanted to be part of the crowd but were left out (marginalised). What did you think and feel and what did you do to try and make yourself 'popular' or acceptable?

Have you ever experienced the situation when two members of your class at school were told to choose a team? Can you recall the feeling of unease as members of your group are gradually called to join one team or another? Do you remember the shuffling of feet, the pleading eyes saying 'do not leave me until the last'? Do you remember the feeling of relief when you were chosen? Perhaps even a sense of smugness as you look at the discomforture of the few remaining children left until last. Were they last because they were considered to be no good at the game to be played and therefore a liability? What effect do you think it had on the child who was always the one to be left until last? Why did you feel smug when chosen early on? People can be fickle and self-centred, even cruel – particularly, but not exclusively, in childhood.

You might have never had the experience of waiting to be picked for a team. Think then of a time when you had been put down by an adult; remember how it felt, particularly if you believed their actions were unjust in some way. Can you remember the anger and frustration, the feeling of powerlessness? As a child you were expected to do what the adult said. Adults had power to control situations, whereas you as a child did not.

Think it over

Imagine now some adult experiences: the worker made redundant, the individual made homeless, the couple going through a divorce process, the ending of a relationship you felt would last forever. All these would have a profound effect on the way the individual perceives themselves and the value they place on themselves. It takes time and support from others to rebuild a bruised and battered self-esteem.

Social needs

Social development involves learning to take a full and active part in society by learning the cultural norms and values acceptable to the group. This will only be fully appreciated by a child who feels confident about themselves because they have been supported and encouraged by the significant others in their lives. A child who has been over-protected, or one who has been deprived or has suffered privation, will lack the self-confidence to assert themselves in the group.

All humans have a need to be accepted by others, to feel valued and respected as an individual. Tizard (1977) studied children from a working-class background from London who were brought up in an institution or were adopted. The studies did *not* verify the claims made by Bowlby that there would be long-term psychological damage if children were deprived of maternal care. They did show that children from institutions found greater difficulties building relationships with their peers and were more demanding of adult attention than those who were

It can be hard if you're the last one chosen

adopted. Other studies have shown that children can develop and grow, long after the crucial early years outlined by Bowlby. Clarke and Clarke (1976) draw together several studies in their book to demonstrate a child's potential for growth, across life.

Play is an important feature of social development. By the age of 3 to 5 years, children often use fantasy play to replicate activities they have seen around them and so reinforce norms and values learnt from the immediate family during primary socialisation (see below). This may include playing house or shops, or hospitals, using any objects and clothes at hand to help in the fantasy.

Care must therefore be taken in playgroups and nurseries to make sure that equipment in the home corner and dressing-up box reflect the different cultures of the children. This is essential to ensure that children learn to value their own culture and respect that of others. If equipment and clothes are from a purely white Eurocentric culture, then the message to a child from a different cultural background is that their culture is not so important. It can lead to conflict for the child as they begin to understand about themselves and the world around them.

Equally it is important to recognise different languages, dress and religions; to ensure that pictures on the wall, books and religious festivals are deemed to be important. Valuing individual differences and respecting the individual does not mean taking on board someone else's culture; rather, it fosters understanding and tolerance from an early age whilst assisting in the development of positive self-images for all children.

Case-studies from a sociological perspective are often used to demonstrate the ability of a child to learn from those around them in order to be accepted and survive. Reports of two children apparently found living amongst wolves in Bengal, in 1920, noted their behaviour as 'wolf-like' rather than as one would expect children of two and eight to behave. This suggests the power of observation and mimicry of behaviour which is learned in order to be accepted by those around us – in this case it ensured survival for the children.

Reports on children who were socially isolated include the studies of Isabelle by Davis (1947) and of twin boys by Koluchova (1972 and 1976). Isabelle was found at 6 years old, living in social isolation with a deaf-mute mother; but gradually she was helped to reach normal development. The Czech twins had a disrupted early experience of life after being in care, cared for by an aunt and later abused by a stepmother from 18 months to the age of 7 years. Following adoption and very skilled help, the physically and mentally disabled boys learned to speak. Intellectually and emotionally the boys regained 'normal' development patterns.

· SOCIALISATION ·

Behaviour is learnt through a process which sociologists term socialisation. *Primary socialisation* takes place in the early years through a child observing and being taught the type of behaviour which elicits approval from the people around them, usually the immediate family.

Behaviour which is deemed acceptable is often rewarded with a smile, a word of praise or a cuddle. Unacceptable behaviour elicits a frown or a sharp rebuke. During their early years children are anxious to gain approval from the significant adults in their world, so they respond by adopting the norms and values of those around them. The world of the young child is usually concentrated around the home, so that all that is observed there is taken on board as the norm – or how the world is. The world for some children will be that of a nuclear family (children and two parents). Alternatively a child's world might be a family where roles are shared, for others it will be a single parent family or an extended family where grandparents and other relations share the household. Each child will accept the pattern they grow up with as the norm.

It is when the child becomes older and comes into contact with others who have a different perception of the world that *secondary socialisation* takes place. A child's peers and the media may become powerful influences on a child and how that child wishes to 'fit' into the world they find themselves in. (*Note*

Peers can be defined as people who are equal to each other, e.g. the members of a GNVQ group may or may not be of a similar age but all are equal to each other in sharing the experience of learning.) For example, a young boy brought up on a farm went home, after his first morning at nursery school, amazed that other people had daddies who went to work in a car rather than on a tractor. In his limited experience of the world, the boy had assumed that all dads went to work on a tractor because his did!

Social status

Members of society hold different positions within that society. These positions are known as social status, for example they proclaim the status in the family – such as son, daughter, mother, father etc. Other social status is associated with work, e.g. lecturer, nurse, social worker, cleaner etc. In some cultures status comes with age or knowledge, or by being the first-born son.

Figure 1.3 *Social status is associated with different roles*

Status can be related to biology as in gender (male or female) or race (nationality, black or white). Status can also be culturally defined in other ways such as the leader of a group or star of music or film.

Social roles

Along with each social status come norms. Norms provide a kind of blueprint as to the expected behaviour associated with that position or social role. The social status of a nurse is defined and associated with the role of the nurse, who wears a uniform as a symbol of the role. Patients expect the nurse to have specific knowledge to meet their needs when ill. They also expect the nurse to have certain qualities, for example to be calm, efficient, patient, understanding etc. In turn, the nurse will look to the person who is unwell to fulfil the social role of patient. In this way each is clear about the accepted norms for their role and the two are able to work together to aid recovery.

Social roles assist in the organisation of behaviour by regulating that behaviour in a way that is acceptable to society. They help individuals to be able to predict the probable behaviour of others, so that they can adopt the corresponding role themselves.

Task

Make a list of the many roles that you have played today; these may include son or daughter, parent, brother/sister, student, friend, customer. Write down against each role the possible behaviour that others would expect of you in that role; check your ideas out with others.

Then make a list of the behaviour you expect from a lecturer. Check your ideas out with one of the lecturers – any surprises? You might ask the lecturer to list the behaviour they expect from a student and compare your ideas!

A child will learn the different social roles that people play by watching those around them in their early years. Gender roles are learned by watching what Mum does or big sister, Dad or big brother. Children copy adults and through fantasy play re-enact the social roles observed in their world. On gaining wider experiences of life these ideas about roles may be challenged. A girl brought up to believe that her role is to be a wife and mother may socialise with other girls who have been brought up to be career-orientated. Conflict between different expectations may occur.

When boys brought up to view the male role as that of main provider, find women in that role, they may feel their identity is threatened. In the past, having a female boss may have been difficult for some men to cope with. This threat may come about purely because of the way men have been socialised into gender roles.

For example, an only son was brought up by a mother who considered that he could do no wrong. The mother did everything for her son, telling him that it was her job to cook his meal ready for him to come home to. On leaving school and going to college, the young man had a fixed idea of the role of men and women. Women were there to provide the home, do any sewing, cleaning and cooking; leaving the men to go out to do the 'real work'.

At college the son made friends with another young man and they decided to share a flat. All went well at first, but it soon became clear to the friend that he was the one who tidied up, shopped and cooked. An argument ensured and the son returned home confused and angry that he was expected to do what he considered to be women's work! On completing his business course at college, the young man joined a firm in the City. Imagine his feelings on finding that his boss was a woman. He was uncertain how to interact with his boss – how was he to take his directions from her, when she should be home raising a family rather than doing a man's job!

Research, e.g. Reed and Gavin (1983), has shown that men react in different ways to a female boss. Either they look on her as being 'butch and bossy', an iron maiden and therefore unfeminine; or they see her as a sex object to be patronised, an earth mother. By adopting one of these attitudes, the male feels secure in the knowledge that his social role as a man is not compromised by the female boss. It is the woman boss who is deviant, who has broken away from the accepted norm for the social role of a woman. He, on the other hand, has remained true to the norm for the social role of a male; i.e. a male social role is higher than that of a female! The young man in the example found it so difficult to cope with a female boss that he later had to move departments due to conflict with his boss, which nearly cost him his job. The moral of the story is that inflexible attitudes can and do lead to individual downfall. Carers of children must beware the power of primary socialisation of gender roles!

Experience of life has taught individuals that certain types of behaviour are expected by others when they undertake a particular role, so the individual conforms. If a doctor leaps over the desk and starts telling the patient about their own problems they break the expectation; the patient will leave feeling at best confused, and at worst disenchanted, with the medical profession!

A young child looks to the adult carer for security and information, as well as for their physical needs. But as the child gains a wider experience of life, they look beyond the members of the family to teachers at school. As a parent it is mildly disconcerting to find your role as information-giver is being pushed to one side by a child who now thinks that teacher (not parent/carer) knows best!

Knowledge is power and is an important aspect of social roles. For example, a TV health promotion on the dangers of drugs illustrates the power of peer groups to encourage young people to take drugs. The scene is of a bored, frustrated young man being loudly told off about the dangers of drugs by an unseen upset mother. He is thinking that she does not know what she is talking about – but his friends do. Teenagers will often listen to their friends, who are seen as being able to understand their problems, rather than someone older and therefore out of touch! The credibility of a social role is therefore seen to be important.

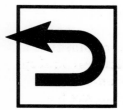

Think it over

Revising for a GNVQ end test you are unsure of a particular issue. You can discuss the issue with a member of your group, a lecturer who spends the sessions dictating from textbooks, someone who has passed this unit, or a lecturer who answers questions honestly and is an expert in the particular unit. Can you guarantee that the first three will give you the correct information to enable you to pass the test? You are more likely to get the correct answer by going to the person with the knowledge and experience of the subject matter.

Role conflict can arise when two social roles clash

Social roles may provide status which is reflected in power or money, for example a High Court judge is viewed by most people as having a powerful role to maintain order in society. The judge is respected for their knowledge of legislation and their ability to work within it to maintain law and order. The responsibility of this work is rewarded by society in monetary terms as well as in respect. In turn, society expects this person to be above suspicion themselves and to lead a blameless life! Doctors and nurses in their role to help the sick are seen as valuable, whilst other work roles are equally important for society yet little apparent value is placed on them, certainly in monetary terms, until something dramatic happens.

It is important to recognise that there are times when the roles an individual plays bring conflict. Role conflict may arise when one individual has the demands of two different roles placed on them at the same time. For example, a police constable stopping a driver for speeding discovers that the driver is a friend. The police officer has a duty to perform via the work role, yet may feel some moral duty to a friend.

The media act as an agent for secondary socialisation by portraying different social roles in different ways. Think of an advert for a perfume or after-shave that featured an elder or someone with a physical disability or learning difficulty. What does this say about the way society values these people?

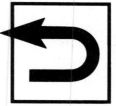

Think it over

Next time you watch an episode of a TV soap look for a range of age, ability, ethnic origin, attractive/unattractive people etc. among the cast of characters.
Television is one of the most powerful influences on life in the 1990s, bringing clear but limited images of the social roles in society.

Social values may be challenged by images of abuse and violence; gender roles may be reinforced; discrimination in terms of age, physical or cognitive ability, sexuality and ethnicity may be subliminally or unconsciously portrayed by the films and serials presented daily on TV.

Peers also play an important role during secondary socialisation: at school, social groups, college, work or religious groups. Wanting to be accepted by a given group may mean re-evaluating your perception of the world and the norms and values you hold.

Think it over

Look back on your own experience of life to date. What are the key points you feel you learnt from your family (primary socialisation) and from those from outside the home (secondary socialisation)? Think of your value system. What is important to you and why? Where did these values come from?

Attitudes, values and beliefs

Individuals develop attitudes, beliefs and values through socialisation. There are numerous definitions of an **attitude** but one you may find particularly useful is given by Petty and Cacioppo (1981): 'The term attitude should be used to refer to a general enduring positive or negative feeling about some person, object or issue.'

Psychologists have failed to agree on a definitive definition of an attitude because it is difficult to equate what people say and do. In other words, the feeling you may have about a particular person may be of intense dislike, yet on meeting you smile and behave most politely!

Values are more general than attitudes. You were polite when meeting the person you dislike because you value the social skill required to be polite to others. Values are principles which enable people to choose between alternatives and make decisions. Values guide behaviour in relation to what is judged to be 'valuable' or appropriate.

Beliefs are based on the knowledge or information an individual has about the world. An individual's perception of the world may be at variance with others; it is a personal opinion about something.

Attitudes, values and beliefs are hypothetical ideas or constructs and so cannot be measured but are guessed by others from our behaviour. It is thought that an individual may have thousands of beliefs, hundreds of attitudes but only a few tens of values.

Impression management

In an effort to be accepted by others, individuals control their behaviour to create the impression they feel will most closely match the expectation of others. Deux and Wrightsman (1988) suggest that there are five possible strategies to impression management:

- *Ingratiation* – to be seen as likeable, to offer to carry messages for friends or buy presents, give compliments to them in order to be liked and accepted.
- *Intimidation* – to control through power, the boss who threatens the sack, the bully who demands money or goods, the informer threatening to tell, goading someone to do something against their will by calling them 'chicken'.
- *Self-promotion* – to be seen as competent, always organised, able to answer questions, able to do a task so that others are aware of your capabilities.
- *Exemplification* – to be seen as moral, always doing the right thing, staying behind to help clear away when others leave, impressing others by your commitment, e.g. revising instead of going out before a test.
- *Supplication* – to gain sympathy, playing dumb to gain help or acting ill to gain support when things are difficult. Trying to win sympathy and attention.

The authors also point out that sometimes a self-defeating strategy is adopted; for example, saying that 'I know I will do badly in my test as I had to babysit last night and they came back so late I did not get much sleep or have time to revise'!

Theory into practice

Individuals amend their behaviour according to the expectation of others, which will also include the social setting. The people you care for will have clear expectations of how a carer should behave in a care setting. Which of Deux and Wrightsman's strategies would you adopt?

In a private setting with people who know and accept you, you will be able to relax and be yourself rather than consciously managing the impression you give to others – because you know that the others will accept you.

However, think of a time when you were going somewhere new, perhaps meeting the parents of a possible partner for the first time. You want to impress them and may be anxious to say and do the right things. As you get to know them, and they you, you gradually relax and show the 'real' you over a period of time.

Public settings may be interpreted as those public places where you are not known. These may include a job or college interview, a wedding or other social event where you are not well known by the majority, or a meeting in a care setting. Here you will very carefully manage the impression you give to others, perhaps watching the behaviour of those around who seem to be part of this new experience and copying what they do.

Think of answering the phone at home – how many people have a 'telephone voice' on picking up the phone, which quickly reverts to the usual voice on realising it is a friend and not a stranger on the other end! This is yet another form of impression management, to create what the individual perceives as being the acceptable manner to others.

Private, public and care settings are examples of *social contexts*. They are like a stage in a theatre on which you perform your social role in the manner which you believe is expected of you. You will find further information is provided on social context in chapter four.

To summarise this part of the chapter: it has been argued that our attitudes, values and indeed the perception of the world around us, are formed firstly during primary socialisation. Each individual learns from their family or carers what is acceptable behaviour as required by their social group. As the experience of the individual is increased by wider contact through school, clubs, friends and the media etc., the individual becomes aware of a range of attitudes and values, of different patterns of

Figure 1.4 *The individual performs a social role*

acceptable behaviour and different cultures, and so has to readjust to the new world – secondary socialisation.

This readjustment may lead to the individual reviewing the behaviour expected in particular social roles, and learning to manage the impression they give to others in a range of new social contexts. The attitudes that the individual holds may be inappropriate in the wider social context so new learning takes place. Failure to re-evaluate inappropriate social roles leads to a label of *deviance* and the individual being perceived as anti-social.

· DISCRIMINATION ·

It was seen earlier in the chapter that social status is either based on perceptions of biology, e.g. gender or race, or it is based on other cultural constructs e.g. occupational status. This section of the chapter looks at the effect on individuals whose social status is perceived by many as low.

Task

Arrange to interview two people who have had very different experiences of life. This may be because of a difference in their age, ability, gender, ethnicity, social class or region. Try to determine the factors which have led to the formation of their current view of themselves and the world. Who were key people in their lives and why? Look at the social roles they take and note the implications for those roles in different social contexts.

Individuals valued by society for their knowledge, experience, or authority gain high status and power. Those who are deemed to be of low status have little power and are disadvantaged by society. This is a difficult issue as the value placed on a particular social role varies between cultures, for example males are valued by many in Third World countries as they are the providers of food for the village. Sons also care for their elders in their later years, whereas daughters marry and go to a new family or village.

In Eurocentric cultures, value has been awarded to those who contribute to the economy. Those who are not able to contribute are deemed to be of little apparent value. Such people include those over retirement age (i.e. 65 years), those who are physically or mentally unable to contribute for whatever reason and those who are unable to find employment (in the recession in the 1990s). In Britain, society demonstrates the value placed on individuals by the monetary rewards made available, e.g. high salaries. Unemployed people rely on benefits set by the State, on the one hand, and on strategies devised to enable them to contribute in some way on the other, e.g. retraining schemes.

There is a problem when those in work become frustrated by rising taxes, necessary in order to support financially those who are not in work. The stage is set for one group in society to marginalise another. Those in work may construct a mental picture of those who are unemployed. The mental picture could include a range of characteristics (*stereotype*) which are applied to all unemployed people, for example, lazy, work-shy, inadequate, unskilled etc. This description is unfairly attributed to all unemployed people. A stereotype is an irrational and unfair series of labels. Some unemployed people may be unskilled but many are highly skilled; some may be content not to work, others write endless job applications. It should be clear that it is *discriminatory* to assume that such a range of characteristics may be applied to all in the same predicament.

Stereotyping is a way of making a collective sense of the world by grouping objects together into a fixed pattern or image; it makes life easier to organise. The word comes from the printing industry; but people are not words, people are unique individuals and cannot be grouped in such a way.

Discrimination is the ability to notice differences between things. In an equal opportunities context, discrimination means to notice differences between groups of people and then go on to deny one group the same quality of opportunity or service that a different group receives. Discrimination may mean favouring one group more than another when it comes to maintaining rights or access to services.

Positive action may be taken to redress an imbalance to ensure that equality of opportunity is afforded to disadvantaged groups. For example, special equipment may be provided in a college to enable a student with a hearing impairment to participate fully in all sessions; or special arrangements must be made for testing candidates who have dyslexia, so they are not disadvantaged.

Discrimination may involve basing decisions on attitudes acquired during socialisation. These attitudes are based on beliefs about people or prejudices. *Prejudice* involves the use of stereotypes to try to explain or categorise particular groups in society. Secord and Backman (1974) describe discrimination as: 'the inequitable treatment of individuals considered to belong to a particular social group'.

We have seen that attitudes, values and beliefs are formed in early life through primary socialisation. During secondary socialisation, the individual begins to reaffirm or change existing values in the light of wider experience and learning.

Discrimination in a health and social care context is seen as a negative practice. Discrimination involves the power of one group to place people in other groups at a disadvantage. Disadvantaged groups in current society include the young and the aged, and people with physical disability or learning difficulties. Others face discrimination because of religious beliefs, their gender, race, social status (class) or sexual orientation.

Discrimination may be direct (overt) or indirect (covert). **Direct discrimination** is obvious, for example: a child bullied at school because of an unsightly skin disorder, such as psoriasis; an Asian youth beaten up by a gang of white youths, as he waited for a bus, just because he was Asian; a black family suffering hate mail to get them to move from a mainly white district; an elderly resident handed clothes to wear, without being allowed the opportunity to choose for themselves.

Theory into practice

Visiting a dress shop with a disabled friend in a wheelchair, the assistant politely asked me about a range of outfits I might wish to see. The assistant assumed that I was buying for my friend as she was unable to make decisions for herself just because she was in a wheelchair! She was openly discriminating against my friend, by making assumptions about her abilities. This assumption led the assistant to ignore my friend – denying her the dignity of making her own choice. When people are regularly exposed to discrimination like this it may threaten their self-esteem, see chapter four.

This example shows how discrimination can occur unwittingly. The shop assistant was young and relatively inexperienced; she had never been in close contact with someone in a wheelchair before. The stereotype she had in her mind was that people in wheelchairs were cognitively disabled as well as physically! A gentle word in the assistant's ear helped her to understand the situation, and afterward she could not have been more helpful.

It would have been easy to get cross with the assistant and to have marched out of the shop in anger; but what would the assistant have learnt? That people pushing wheelchairs should be avoided at all costs because they were as difficult as the occupant of the wheelchair!

Individuals should not be blamed for making errors because of their lack of awareness. It may be a different story if the person does not change their behaviour, once their awareness of discrimination has been raised.

Think it over

A black woman, employed in a busy bank, was made to feel very welcome by her white colleagues who included her in all the social activities. It was a different story when opportunities for staff development and training came along. The woman was not included on such training, which meant no opportunity for promotion despite her undoubted capabilities. The woman successfully took her employers to an Industrial Tribunal and won her case under the Race Relations Act 1976.

Discrimination may be individual, as has been explained above, or institutional. Institutional discrimination includes any systems which disadvantage others, for example: shops with baby changing rooms in inaccessible places when the baby is in a pram or pushchair.

An example of institutional discrimination might include a firm employing many people with young children but not providing creche facilities; museums and galleries providing lifts and ramps for people in wheelchairs, but giving no thought to those with

BABY ROOM

sight or hearing impairment–just assuming that such people would not want to visit!

Covert or **indirect discrimination** is far more subtle and hidden. For example: not inviting someone with a disability to a party because you feel embarrassed by their disability; avoiding a friend who has been diagnosed as HIV positive; a restaurant set out so that people in wheelchairs will be unable to gain access; providing information in English only, when it is known that people using other languages might also benefit from the same information.

Psychologists are interested in why individuals discriminate against others. Minard (1952), looked at the co-operative interaction of black and white miners when relying on each other underground. This co-operation ceased for many of the miners as soon as they returned to the surface. The norms above ground meant separation not cooperation! Underground, co-operation could mean the difference between life and death; above ground there were no such concerns, only the need to be accepted in terms of the white group.

Studies have been undertaken to see if there is a personality type more likely to be prejudiced e.g. Adorno (1950); whilst others looked to see if competition for resources was a factor, e.g. Sherif et

al (1961), Tyerman and Spenser (1983), Brown (1988).

Discrimination in education

Psychologists studying the behaviour which contributes to predjudicial attitudes and discriminatory behaviour sometimes study what might be a fragment of a much wider picture. Factors to be considered include individual social, cultural, political and social policy issues.

Sociologists have undertaken research in a range of areas to gain insight into the way some groups are marginalised by others. Education is one such area where discrimination has been clearly demonstrated. The Swann Report (1985) highlighted a range of factors that led to the death of an Asian boy in a school in northern England. The factors ranged from systems and practices within the school to social factors within the locality.

Other studies look at the way different groups are perceived by teachers and the effect of low teacher expectation. Jackson and Marsden (1962), and Keddie (1975), noted that black children, in particular, were not expected to do well. These children were not stimulated to achieve their potential in the way that their white peers were.

Discrimination in education is about race and also gender and social class. Bernstein (1959) and Gould (1965) noted that children from working-class families were disadvantaged because they used a different 'language' code. Bernstein alleged that children from working-class families adopted a restricted language code from their carers. These children would use simpler language and were not encouraged to think in an abstract way. For example, in answer to a question, 'What is this?' (holding up a drinking glass), a reply would name the object (glass) and that would be the end of the conversation. Bernstein considered that children from middle-class homes used an elaborate 'language' code. A child from a middle-class group, asked the same question, was likely to give the name of an object and also describe the object's function 'it's a wine glass – for drinking wine'.

Such a difference between two groups means that whereas one is encouraged to think things through and explore, the other is not. This has implications for children in school as some teachers use an elaborated code. This elaborated code might disadvantage those who have only experienced a restricted code.

It is argued by some that the introduction of the comprehensive school system, following the Education Act 1976, was to offer wider opportunities for all. Prior to that, children sat an eleven-plus exam which determined whether they moved to a grammar school, and so to university and a profession with corresponding pay and social status; or, if they did not pass the eleven-plus, a secondary school, where the emphasis was on more practical trades for the future in business and industry, which meant lower status and lower pay in many instances. Some children did progress to higher education from secondary schools but they were the exception rather than the rule!

The emphasis in education since 1979 has been to better meet the needs of industry and business in a very competitive world market. The introduction of training schemes, the National Curriculum in schools and the emphasis on core skills in GNVQ is part of that movement.

The Warnock Report (1978) reviewed the educational provision for children deemed in the terminology of that time to be mentally or physically handicapped. The recommendations of that report helped to change the focus of provision for people with disabilities and indeed the terminology used. Children considered to have *special needs* were to be offered a range of options and, where possible, the segregation in special schools was to cease.

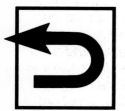

Think it over

Integrating children with special needs into mainstream schools has been slow; perhaps you have noticed this development during your own time at school?

Work is another area which sociologists investigate in order to review the issues where discrimination takes place. The introduction of a range of legislation to combat discrimination is given later in this chapter.

· USE OF LANGUAGE ·

Language is a uniquely human skill. Birds, fish and animals communicate by body language; some even make vocal sounds, for example the songs of a whale, or the clicks of a dolphin. But only humans have a complex language by which information is transferred.

Discrimination can take place in language through the choice of words and even the tone adopted during conversation. Calling people names that are aimed to make them feel bad or different is an example of the way language may be used to discriminate. For example, to call someone an imbecile implies that they are mentally less able; the term 'imbecile' was at one time used as a label to denote people who we would today say had learning disabilities.

Think back to the quotation at the beginning of this chapter. Some people may feel offended by it – can you think why? It has to be remembered that it was written around 1600, in a society where only men had any status in society. It is this status which is reflected in the quotation, i.e. no *man* is an island. Today we would say 'no person is an island'. This statement does not differentiate between the sexes, or discriminate in favour of men.

Think why others may take offence at certain words, for example most black people prefer to be called black and not coloured. However, many older people were taught to say coloured, as it was then more polite than black. Look at this poem, whose author is unknown; it gives an insight into why black is a more appropriate term.

When I was born
    I was black
As I grow up
    I am black.
When I go in the sun
    I am black
When I am cold
    I am black
When I am ill
    I am black
When I die
    I will be black.

When you were born
    You were pink
As you grow up
    You are white
When you go in the sun
    You are red
When you are cold
    You are blue
When you are ill
    You are green
When you die
    You are purple

And you have the audacity to call me coloured!

Anon.

However, there is a problem in that black has sometimes been seen as the colour to symbolise bad things in Western culture. When did you see a good fairy in a children's book dressed in black or the wicked witch dressed in white? This association has been so much part of Western culture that some people may accept it as the way things are. But this can cause offence to many of the population, so maybe the situation needs to be reviewed. Perhaps now is the time to be more aware of the power of language, in that it can be used to discriminate against others.

English is the most widely spoken language in the world. It is used in British schools and is taught as a second language in nearly every country worldwide. The result is that many British people have never seen the value of learning a second language themselves. The root of this view may lie in an imperial past, when Britain ruled many foreign

countries – imposing her language and culture on others.

It is easy to be trapped by language and to feel that one has to watch everything that is said, to be 'politically correct' in speech. A more sensible way might be, to be aware of the possible implications and roots of language; to check with people what they would prefer, so that offence is not unwittingly given.

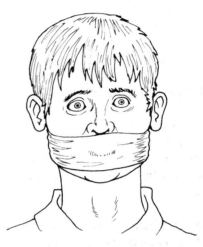

Figure 1.5 *An awareness of language does not mean that one has to feel trapped by it*

Today, those for whom English is a second language may well feel that in Britain their own language is unimportant. Being taught in English at school, spoken to in English at the doctor's surgery or at Social Services offices, means learning the language quickly to survive. Some young people can cope well with learning a new language, but other people may well find this difficult.

Think it over

Imagine falling ill on holiday in a foreign country. You are far from home, feeling unwell and unable to make people understand what you need. You are also unable to understand what they say to you and can only watch as they start any treatment. What emotions would you have? What would help to reassure you?

Children in school who need to learn English may well speak several languages. Those same children may be seen as slow learners by the teachers until their English improves. Think then what a teacher would think of an English-speaking child of the same age who could also speak fluent French, German or Spanish. That child would be seen as clever, but the Asian child of the same age who can speak Hindi and Gujerati but who has a poor command of English, may be viewed less favourably!

If little value is placed on original languages, children may begin to value original languages less favourably and so lose part of their culture. It is an undeniable fact that children do need to learn English. It will enable them to cope with life in Britain. But this does not need to be at the cost of losing their mother tongue.

Body language

We live in a hearing world, so what happens to those who are hearing-impaired? Since the Education Reform Act 1988, children with hearing impairment may be learning in a mainstream school with support. Some theatres have special performances with a person at the side of the stage signing. There has been an effort to sign for musicals and opera, so that people who are hearing-impaired can enjoy this form of art. BBC2 has news programmes with a signer but in the main little is done for those with hearing impairment. Try watching your favourite TV soap with the sound off. Is it not frustrating to miss half of what is going on? Especially if several people speak at once – who do you watch if you have to read their lips?

People who are hearing-impaired are perhaps more keenly aware of the signals people give with their bodies. Think again about feeling ill in a foreign country: you will be sensitive to people's facial expressions, tone of voice and body posture (body language).

We use body language to assist the verbal messages, to act as a reinforcer to help get the point across. Imagine a person angry with another: words will be used to express feeling but body language will also

send a message. The body will perhaps lean towards the other person, possibly pointing a finger at the other's face, or shaking a fist; the face will be contorted into a twist, the corners of the mouth down and the eyes staring directly at the other person. Even if you could not hear the words you would know exactly how the other person felt!

We also use body language to discriminate against others. It may be by turning your back on another, blocking them out of your sight. It may be by making a sign which shows your feelings; indeed body language may result in abusive gestures such as two fingers put up to show anger and contempt. Putting your finger to the side of your head and rapidly twisting it denotes that the other person is mad, or mentally affected in some way.

Body language sends messages

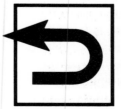

Think it over

Imagine that you are learning a new skill and the person demonstrating the skill makes the following gestures while you are practising, how will you feel?

Raising the eyebrows, looking to the sky, showing anger or impatience, given at the same time as a loud sigh.

Think it over

Think of a time when you said 'no' to someone. A soft 'no', accompanied by a smile, will be seen as playful, perhaps really a 'yes'! A sharp 'no' accompanied by a frown is clearly understood.

'You cannot do that, you are only a girl', said with disdain is a way of implying girls to be less able than boys. 'Real men do not do such things', said with a look of horror or a sarcastic smile, implies that you are less than the accepted norm of a man! In both instances you may feel a whole range of emotions, one of which will be hurt, as you have been discriminated against. If an individual is constantly put down by others, because they are seen as different, they may lose confidence. A child repeatedly told that they are 'stupid' or 'bad' may begin to believe it and stop trying; in addition, they may incorporate the idea of being poorly valued into their identity. A self-fulfilling prophecy may start to happen as the labelled person comes to believe that they are 'bad'.

Labelling a person may begin to create a self-fulfilling prophecy.

A young person facing name-calling, because of their skin colour, may begin to feel awkward and different. Such a person may become stressed if they do not get positive support for their identity. A person with physical disabilities, or with learning disabilities, may be told so often that they cannot do things for themselves that they begin to believe it. The individual takes on board the opinions and actions of others, incorporating those opinions into their perception of themselves.

Theory into practice

A young girl, badly scarred by a fire at the age of six years, is shy and withdrawn as a teenager. She is unwilling to go out to meet new people, because people show their horror at her scars even though most try not to stare. She feels ugly in a world that only values beauty and perfection. She knows that the world values such things because she has never seen anyone like herself on the TV or as a model in a magazine.

Perhaps part of the appeal of such plays as 'Beauty and the Beast', the 'Phantom of the Opera' and the 'Elephant Man', is that at last someone has seen below the surface to the real person: seen the ability not the disability!

Think it over

Think again of the time as a child when you waited to be chosen by someone in your group to join their team. Remember the feelings?

People who have faced perhaps a lifetime of discrimination will feel devalued which can lead to a feeling of powerlessness, feeling that it is not possible to change their situation. These feelings lead to a low self-esteem, i.e. I must be less valuable because that is what others think.

The concept of identity is dealt with in depth in chapter 4. Here it is important to recognise the importance of other people in the formation of the picture of ourselves as individuals. Other people matter: we all have a basic need to understand ourselves in relation to others.

How can an individual who feels less valued than others claim their rights in society? Such people may well feel that they are not entitled to any services and they probably will not have the confidence to assert their rights to such services. For example, it may be difficult to ask a doctor why a certain treatment has been prescribed, when the doctor is perceived as being of a higher status than you. Assumptions about social value lead to discriminating attitudes. Two discriminatory attitudes are listed below:

1 'What right has someone with a disability to ask for alterations to their home, when they do not work and therefore do not pay taxes?'
2 'What right has a woman to a job when many men are out of work, when the woman believes that men have a higher social status than women?'

Other assumptions about social status might include the mixture of apprehension and anger when a group of travellers settle in a field near a town or village. People draw on their stereotype of travellers rather than look at the individual. The power of the stereotype results in prejudicial attitudes and may result in discrimination. A further example might be a single parent putting up with unsuitable bed and breakfast accommodation because society currently sees single parents as a drain on resources. All these people may well feel unable to make full use of all services, particularly if – in their experience – they are put down when they do try.

Prejudice

A home carer who wears a mask and thick rubber gloves when working in the home of a person with AIDS; a nurse who is brusque with the person being treated for a drug overdose, because they consider it to be self-inflicted; the social worker who shows disdain for someone suspected of abusing others; the teacher who expects little from a black child but much from a white child in the same class. Such prejudicial attitudes from these people reinforce a feeling of inferiority in the individual, compounding the discrimination given by others.

Health and social care staff have a responsibility to ensure that they remain impartial and non-judgemental.

Think it over

Consider the following case-study: Mrs Ahmed, an Asian woman in her late seventies, was admitted to a residential home for elders. Mrs Ahmed had arrived in England from Calcutta twelve years previously. She lived with her son and family, rarely went out and had not learned very much English. The family had fallen on difficult times after the recent death of her daughter-in-law. Mrs Ahmed had been given a place in the residential home for three weeks to enable her son to come to terms with his new situation. The staff in the residential home had no experience of Asian elders.

Imagine what must have been going through Mrs Ahmed's mind: a strange land, language and customs, and no family to turn to whilst in the home. The staff, though concerned and caring, had asked about diet but not about customs such as different hygiene, dress etc. Mrs Ahmed was expected to conform to 'the way we do things here'. Unable to communicate, Mrs Ahmed became withdrawn, stopped eating, refused to get out of bed and was quickly labelled as 'awkward' by overworked staff. Frustrated staff showed their annoyance by the body language and tone used when working with her. Being unable to understand the language but interpreting the frowns and sighs of staff, did little to reassure a bewildered and frightened woman.

Imagine the horror of the son on finding his mother in such a state. The guilt of giving up his duty of caring for her by agreeing to respite care, would be reinforced by seeing her so unhappy and confused.

Theory into practice

The situation could have been avoided if the staff had ensured that as much as possible was learnt about Mrs Ahmed's culture before she arrived. The ideal would have been to have Asian staff but this may not be possible. An interpreter should be found and the staff could learn a few words of greeting to break the isolation. Learning about dress and hygiene codes would avoid offence. Checking about diet and any religious practice would also help. Ensuring that Mrs Ahmed had access to others who spoke her language, and people who could provide books or music for her, would be useful.

Staff would also need to watch for any possible discrimination from other residents – whether intentional or not. Pulling faces or exchanging glances at the dining table when Mrs Ahmed ate her food using her hands rather than the unfamiliar knives and forks; making comments about the smell of unfamiliar Asian food in a tone that would leave Mrs Ahmed in no doubt as to their disapproval; refusing to sit next to her, or turning away from her; all these things would show discrimination. Mrs Ahmed would feel very vulnerable and devalued, no wonder she did not wish to face such discrimination – apparently giving up the will to live!

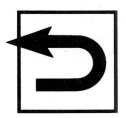

Think it over

Consider also the case of Robert, a young man aged 23, attending a Social Education Centre for adults with learning difficulties. Robert is the only child of an elderly couple who were in their forties when he was born. The joy of having a child, after nearly twenty years of marriage, turned to grief on discovering that he had Down's Syndrome.

Robert's parents over-protected him as a child. They felt guilty for producing a child whom they saw as being less than perfect. In their guilt they showered him with love and affection. The result, however, was to treat him as a young irresponsible child rather than as a growing adult. Robert was dressed in short trousers, led around by the hand and spoken to as if he was a young child even though he is in his twenties. Never allowed to go out alone, even to the shop next door, he was unable to

develop the skills required for independence. Robert was encouraged by his parents to 'play with his cars' and to read books more suited to a nine-year old child. But Robert's parents genuinely felt that they were giving him the best care possible.

Imagine the difficulties facing Robert at the Centre he now attends. The staff there will work with him to build his social and life skills required for independence. He will mix with a range of people and learn many new things which could bring him into conflict with his parents. The staff have a sensitive task to work with Robert and his parents to meet his needs as a man in his twenties.

Theory into practice

It is important for Robert to gain some independence, to encourage him to make the most of his abilities. It is also important that he has the support of his parents as his world begins to expand. The importance lies in his rights as an individual to reach his own potential within society.

Primary socialisation is very powerful, as we saw earlier. Robert has had limited secondary socialisation from his school. His experiences at the Social Education Centre will build on the socialisation process so that Robert can be accepted more readily in a wider society.

People often show sympathy to children with any form of disability. Generally, people feel protective of these children and tolerate behaviour from them which would be deemed unacceptable if they were perceived as being 'normal'. However, once the child grows to a physical adult, attitudes change. People may often think of other people like Robert as overgrown children – to be patronised – or as a threat – because their behaviour is considered unpredictable. Think of the confusion for the individual who has been allowed to do what they like as a child, because they were perceived as being less capable. But anti-social behaviour tolerated as a child is frowned upon in an adult world.

Primary socialisation is very powerful

One of the implications of the National Health Service and Community Care Act, 1990, is that large hospitals and institutions for people with learning difficulties are closing. The residents of these institutions are being prepared for integration into the community. Unfortunately, the community is not necessarily prepared to welcome them and discrimination may and indeed does take place. Comments from potential neighbours may show irrational fear for the safety of residents and the value of property. Only education and time, with support from professionals for all concerned, will see true integration.

Task

Choose a client group, perhaps the client group you are currently working with on placement. Identify any stereotypes associated with this group. Stereotypes may enable people to try to predict likely behaviour of anyone in this group. Many in the

group may have some of the characteristics, but rarely all!

Identify any areas of overt discrimination which are common in society against this client group. What effect does this have on the individual? Think of any more subtle ways in which people discriminate against this group. What action would you consider necessary to improve the situation?

Think about the different social contexts where discrimination takes place and note the possible effect this has on the individual. (Think about when someone is applying for work, housing, education or health care.)

What do you consider to be your personal responsibility to ensure that you do not discriminate against others? What, in your opinion should be done in the health and social care field to prevent discrimination?

To summarise this section of the chapter: it has been argued that attitudes and values are formed through the socialisation process. Stereotyping people, by attributing a range of characteristics to the members of that group, is a way of trying to predict behaviour. The dangers of generalisation may lead to discrimination and the formation of prejudicial attitudes.

Prejudice and discrimination treat members of other groups less favourably. Discrimination has been described as either being openly displayed or more subtle. All forms of discrimination may lead to an individual perceiving themselves as less valuable than others. Once an individual believes themselves to be devalued they are less able to claim their rights assertively in society.

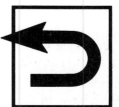

Think it over

It could be that you have faced discrimination in one form or another during your lifetime. If this has happened you will be aware of the emotions and feeling of powerlessness. Most people are resilient enough to cope with these feelings for short periods of time. But constant daily discrimination has a profound effect on the individual, requiring skilled support to combat the low self-esteem.

· EQUAL OPPORTUNITIES ·

This final section of the chapter will consider the strategies adopted by government to ensure that equality of opportunity is afforded to all.

Equal opportunity is a concept which rises from legislation to address issues around overt and covert discrimination. Originally the legislation was seen in terms of gender, race and disability issues in employment. This term is now widened to include discrimination of all types wherever it may be found; for example, discrimination against those who are HIV-positive or have AIDS, or on the grounds of age, or sexuality, to name but a few. It is important to note that only discrimination in terms of gender, race and disability in the workplace have legislation to support them.

In health and social care terms it may be argued that equal opportunities may be defined as *the right of an individual to have equal access to provisions and services*. All should have equal access to these services *irrespective of gender, ethnicity, age or ability*.

Earlier in the chapter it was stated that all individuals have a right to be valued for their unique individuality. This individuality arises from their biology and from their socialisation. (See Chapter 4.)

The historical background of equal opportunities legislation

A good starting point is 1942, when the **Beveridge Report** looked at the state of the nation. Remember that the Second World War continued until 1945. The role of women had changed dramatically in order to take over work in the factories and on the land while the men (and some women) were in the

forces. A radically new concept emerged from the Beveridge Report, which aimed to rid the country of what was termed the 'five giants' of *want, disease, ignorance, squalor* and *idleness*. The idea of the Welfare State had been conceived.

The Welfare State was set up to provide for the welfare of every citizen 'from the cradle to the grave'. The Education Act 1944 provided education for all from the age of 5 to 15 years. The National Health Service was created in 1948 to provide medical care and advice for all ages. This system included Social Services, dentists, general practitioners and pharmacists: no longer would poorer people suffer because of their inability to pay for medical help. Mothers would receive care and advice before, during and after the birth of their children. Children would be monitored by Health Visitors, and seen by doctors and dentists, to ensure appropriate development. Housing and social security benefits meant that those who were on low incomes, or were unemployed, had somewhere to go for advice and assistance. In all, the aim was to rebuild a nation following two devastating world wars: a nation where provisions and services were more widely available to all.

Many changes have taken place in the last fifty years, not least in the rise in population and the change in the population in terms of the ethnic mix. Britain in the 1990s is a multicultural society; industry has become more complex and competition from around the world is greater. The demands on the Welfare State are very great compared to those of the 1940s; social values and roles have changed as society evolves to keep pace with events.

There is not space here to go into the detail of the many changes, but it may be important to have a basic awareness of the historical context of the current changes. You may find it useful to read about the development of the Welfare State to gain a better understanding of the issues.

In order to ensure that all members of society have equal opportunities in the workplace, several pieces of legislation have been implemented over the last thirty years in particular.

Equal Pay Acts

The rising number of women in the workforce, in the late 1960s and early 1970s, saw the introduction of the **Equal Pay Act 1970**. This made it unlawful for firms to discriminate between men and women in terms of their pay and conditions in the workplace. This Act came about as a direct result of the Treaty of Rome (1957), Article 119, which stated that,

> 'Each Member State shall during the first stage ensure and subsequently maintain the application of principle that men and women should receive equal pay for equal work.'

Later, the Equal Pay Act 1975 and the Equal Pay (Amendment) Regulations (1983) made it possible to claim equal pay for work which was considered to be of 'equal value' to that done by a member of the opposite sex. This too came about following proceedings by the European Commission against the British government. This amendment to the original Act brought Britain further into line with mainland Europe.

Sex Discrimination Acts

The **Sex Discrimination Act (1975)** built on the Equal Pay Act of 1970 by further ensuring that women were not discriminated against in education or employment on the grounds of their gender or marital status. It is interesting to note that the provisions of this Act apply equally to discrimination against both sexes. Women are the major beneficiaries, as they are more likely to face inequality on the grounds of their gender in the workplace.

This Act is concerned with the recruitment, training and promotion of employees as well as other aspects of employment. In all these aspects it is essential that an employer does not discriminate against a person on the grounds of their gender.

The Act established two forms of discrimination – direct and indirect – both of which are unlawful. *Direct discrimination* arises when a person of one sex is treated less favourably than another purely on the grounds of their gender. So it is unlawful to refuse to employ a woman because a position is a 'man's job'; for example, the position of school caretaker has in the past been seen as a man's job. If a woman applied for such a post and fulfilled all the relevant criteria, then she should be given equal consideration for the job; failure to do so could lead to a case being brought before a tribunal if the evidence is clear that the woman was not appointed solely because she was a woman.

Discrimination is illegal on the grounds of marital status for either sex. In the past, women who have childcare responsibilties were often seen as a potential liability to a firm or business. Under the Act it is illegal to take this into consideration to the detriment of the individual; for example, no questions should be asked at an interview regarding domestic or childcare arrangements. It has to be assumed that the person would not have applied for the job without considering the implications for their personal and family life. If an employer considers such a question to be important then they must ask all applicants and not just women; this is, however, most unlikely. Equally it is good practice to try and gain a gender balance on an interview panel where possible.

Indirect discrimination arises when conditions are applied which favour a person of one sex rather than another. If these conditions cannot be justified, then the employer is deemed to be acting illegally. For example, in 'Hurley v. Mustoe', the applicant for a waiter/waitress job was a woman with four young children. The manager decided to give her a trial but on the first night the proprietor of the restaurant asked her to leave. He said that it was against his policy to employ women with young children as he thought they were unreliable. The woman took her case to a tribunal, who ruled that she had been directly discriminated against on the grounds of sex contrary to Section 1(1)(a) and indirectly discriminated against on grounds of marital status contrary to Section 3(1)(b).

Equal Opportunities Commission (EOC)

At the same time as the Sex Discrimination Act was passed, the Equal Opportunities Commission (EOC) was set up to monitor, advise and provide information regarding the Sex Discrimination Act and its implementation. Individuals have the right to bring proceedings before an industrial tribunal should they face discrimination under this legislation. Help and advice is obtainable from the EOC should an individual feel that they have a case.

The EOC has issued a document, 'Guidance on Employment Advertising Practice'. This document helps employers to consider appropriate wording for advertising jobs. Appropriate wording is essential to remain within the law. It is unlawful to advertise a post in such a way as to discriminate against one sex in favour of another. The use of terms such as waitress, barman, steward and postmistress imply that applicants should be either male or female.

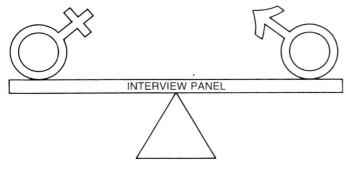

Figure 1.6 *Achieving a gender balance on the interview panel is one of the principles of good recruitment practice*

Following the EEC Equal Treatment Directive (76/207/EEC), major amendments were made to the Sex Discrimination Act 1975. These amendments affected discrimination in collective agreements, employment for the purpose of private households, employment in firms with five or fewer employees and retirement age. All were brought together to widen the scope of the original Act and to bring Britain in line with mainland Europe through the **Sex Discrimination Act 1986**. This EEC Directive also means that decisions made by the British courts and tribunals are subject to the overriding views of the European Court of Justice applying Article 119 of the Treaty, and the Equal Pay Directive. In the event of any disputed interpretation of these issues, it is European law which will apply.

In 'Worringham v. Lloyd's Bank', female clerical officers under the age of 25 were not required to contribute to a pension scheme. However, male clerical officers under the age of 25 were required to contribute 5 per cent of their salary to the scheme. To compensate for this, male staff were paid 5 per cent more than female staff. The Equal Pay Act (Section 6)(1A)(b) excluded terms relating to death or retirement, or any provision made in relation to death or retirement. Contributions to a pension scheme are therefore outside the Equal Pay Act.

The female clerical officers took their case to the European Court of Justice as they considered that they were not being afforded equal pay and conditions. The European Court of Justice ruled that under Article 119, there was an enforceable Community right on all individuals within the EEC. This right to equality of pay meant that the Bank was in violation of Article 119 and took precedence over the Equal Pay Act: the female staff won their case!

Race Relations Acts

Just as Europe influenced British social policy in terms of discrimination on the grounds of sex, so it did with race. The Treaty of Rome 1957 made it unlawful to discriminate against EEC workers on grounds of nationality and citizenship.

The British government introduced the **Race Relations Act 1965** which made it unlawful to discriminate on the grounds of colour, race, ethnic or national origins in places of public resort. The Act also made it an offence to incite racial hatred. The Race Relations Board was set up to enforce the law, acting as a 'watch-dog'. A Local Government Act 1966 made money available to local authorities for work with 'immigrants' from the New Commonwealth. Some of this money was used to create 'section eleven' posts to meet specific need, for example to pay for staff to support learning in schools and colleges.

The 1965 Act was replaced by the **Race Relations Act 1968**. The provisions under the Act were widened to include areas of employment, education, and the provision of housing and services.

This law was repealed by the introduction of the **Race Relations Act 1976**. This law, currently in force, seeks to close several loopholes left by previous legislation. Modelled closely on the Sex Discrimination Act, the Race Relations Act 1976 identifies direct and indirect discrimination in the area of race.

Direct discrimination occurs when a person treats another person less favourably because of their 'group membership'. In the case of racial discrimination, the actual race of the person discriminated against is immaterial. It is possible, for example, for Jonathan to discriminate against Stuart on the grounds of Jamal's colour: i.e. Jonathan may dismiss Stuart in order to give Jamal a job because Jamal is black. Stuart would win his case for unfair dismissal at a tribunal under Section 1(1)(a) of this Act.

Equally it is unlawful to segregate a person on racial grounds, as this constitutes less favourable treatment. Providing separate facilitates for black and white staff is unlawful. However, if a group of black care staff negotiate to work together on a particular shift that is acceptable – unless the manager states that all black staff should work a specific shift. The former is negotiated by choice, the latter imposed by reason of race.

Indirect discrimination occurs when a condition(s) is applied which places people from one race in a more advantageous position than people of another race. Any criteria for a job which an applicant 'must' have is deemed discriminatory if it disadvantages a person of one race in favour of another. If a firm can demonstrate that the requirements or conditions are justified, then the complaint will not succeed. For example, in 'Panesaar v. Nestle & Co Ltd.' a factory rule prohibited beards and long hair. This was seen as indirect discrimination against the applicant who was a Sikh. The Court of Appeal held that the condition was justified on the grounds of hygiene and safety.

The Act makes it unlawful to discriminate on *racial grounds*. The Act defines racial grounds as being colour, race, nationality or ethnic or national origins. A House of Lords ruling in 'Ealing Borough Council v. Race Relations Board', held that the term national origins meant race rather than citizenship. This is now overruled, being replaced by the term 'nationality' to cover both meanings.

This is a complex issue, as was demonstrated by a much publicised debate about an advert for a 'Scots cook'! It was ruled that it was unlawful to advertise in this way and it was suggested that the advert should read, 'a person skilled in Scottish cooking'!

The debate was whether Scotland is a separate nation, or an ethnic or racial group. This is a matter of concern for several groups. The Act does not appear to cover religion as such, which can cause confusion. Are all Muslims deemed to be of the same racial, ethnic or national origins? What about Hindus, Christians or Jews? The law as it stands is not very clear.

In 'Mandla v. Dowell Lee', the House of Lords held that the term 'ethnic' was appreciably wider than 'race'. What constitutes an ethnic group? Under the Act, such a group must be able to demonstrate particular characteristics:

a they must have a long history shared and kept alive by all its members

b a cultural tradition with shared social traditions and customs

Other factors which may be relevant include:

- a common geographical origin or common ancestors
- common language (this may not necessarily be peculiar to the group)
- common literature
- common religion different to their neighbouring groups
- being either a minority or a dominant group within a large community.

An example of a racial group using these criteria would be Sikhs. They share common religious beliefs, have social customs and traditions which are shared by all.

The 1976 Act denotes important exemptions, such as 'positive action'; for example, a Social Service Department wishing to recruit a social worker to have responsibility for meeting the needs of a particular ethnic group. It is perfectly acceptable within the law for positive action to be taken to advertise the post by stating that the post is for someone from that particular ethnic group. The rationale for this is that a person from the same ethnic group will have a better understanding of the needs of the group. The person will therefore be in a more favourable position to identify and meet those needs. This is covered by Section 5, 'genuine occupational qualifications'.

Commission for Racial Equality (CRE)

The Race Relations Act (1976) abolished the Race Relations Board and set up the Commission for Racial Equality (CRE). This body monitors the Act, acts as an adviser and has extensive powers to investigate discrimination. Individuals have new rights to bring proceedings before an industrial tribunal should they be the victims of discrimination. The CRE may be asked to give information to an individual who wishes to take a case to a tribunal.

Industrial tribunals

If an individual wishes to make a claim in respect of discrimination in employment, they must do so within three months of the discrimination taking place. Such a claim is lodged with an industrial tribunal. The time limit for such a claim may be extended if there is just and equitable cause; i.e. a distinction has to be drawn between an act of continuing discrimination and an act which has continuing consequences.

In 'Clark v. Hampshire Electro-Plating Co Ltd', an individual applied for a supervisor's job with his employer. The black applicant saw his employer on 25 April and was told that he would not be considered. On 4 September a white man was appointed to the post. The black employee submitted a complaint on the grounds of discrimination due to race. The industrial tribunal held that the complaint was out of the three-month time limit and turned the complaint down. The man appealed and his complaint was upheld as the applicant's cause of action crystallised when the white man was appointed in September and not from his original application for the job in April. In other words, it was not clear that there was proof of discrimination on the grounds of race in April. The employer may have had many reasons for not considering the black worker for the supervisory role. In September, when a white man was appointed to the job in question, there was the potential for a case to be answered on the grounds of racial discrimination. The tribunal was therefore justified in extending the time limit for making a complaint.

Once a complaint is lodged with the tribunal, a copy of the complaint is sent to a conciliation officer. If this officer fails to achieve a settlement, then the case goes to a tribunal for a hearing. If the complaint is deemed to be 'well-founded', the tribunal will make one of the following orders:

1 a declaration of the rights of the complainant.
2 a monetary award for compensation, to include damages if there was loss of earnings. Damages may also be awarded for injured feelings, humiliation and insult.
3 a recommendation that the respondent (employer) should take the necessary actions to improve the situation within a specified timespan.

It is important to note that the burden of proof lies with the person bringing the complaint, i.e. the person who has been discriminated against has to provide the evidence for the complaint. This is often very difficult, so the tribunal has the power to draw inferences from primary facts. For example, if an employer's replies to a questionnaire sent by the CRE are evasive, the tribunal is entitled to infer that discrimination has taken place. (See, 'Virdee v. EEC Quarries'.)

A complainant may be able to draw on existing statistics to support the complaint; for example, the number of people from different ethnic groups attending training programmes, or gaining promotion in a particular organisation. A tribunal does not have the power to order such data from an employer.

The CRE has the power to carry out formal investigations into the practice of an organisation or an individual. Investigations may be at the request of a Secretary of State or by its own volition. If such an investigation is of a named person, that person must have the opportunity to make a written or verbal response. A report is usually issued which may make recommendations. If it is considered that an unlawful act has taken place, a **non-discriminatory notice** may be served on the individual. This requires the person to cease any and all acts of discrimination, and to inform the Commission of any changes to practice intended. The Commission must inform the individual of the specifications prior to issuing a notice. This is to allow time for the individual to make a verbal or written reply.

If the individual discriminates again during the next five years following a notice, the Commission may take out a County Court injunction against the person. This injunction restrains the individual from committing further discriminatory practices.

An appeal may be made within six weeks of a notice to an industrial tribunal. The industrial tribunal may quash any requirements within the notice but substitute their own. It is the responsibility of the individual who has been served the notice to challenge any points made in the notice during an appeal. A public register is maintained for all non-discriminatory notices.

Disabled Persons Acts

Legislation is also available for people with disability. The **Disabled Persons (Employment) Act 1944** and **1958** lay down the main provisions for the legal obligations placed on employers towards people with disabilities. The Acts initially arose to support the many people who returned from the Second World War with disabilities.

The Acts produced a requirement that all companies employing twenty people or more should ensure that 3 per cent of the workforce were registered as disabled. A register of disabled people was set up, as were records to demonstrate that the Act was being complied with. Designated employment by the Secretary of State included car park attendants and lift attendants.

Certain exemptions were made to the Act. This included special industries where the employment of people with disabilities might be hazardous, for example the steel and mining industries, steeplejacks etc. It is also possible for a special permit to be obtained if a firm can show that the work is unsuitable for people with disabilities, or that the firm has not reached its quota because few people with disability had applied. Few cases have ever been brought under this Act. A special Advisory Committee hears the case from the employer before deciding whether to prosecute. Persuasion is considered to be a better policy than compulsion!

The Acts of 1944 and 1955 were followed by the **Chronically Sick and Disabled Persons Act 1970**. The main focus of this legislation was to ensure physical access to public buildings and educational establishments, to maintain parking spaces, provide toilets for people with physical disabilities, and to provide appropriate signs.

This Act was amended by the Chronically Sick and Disabled Persons (Amendment) Act 1976 to ensure that the provisions outlined above were extended to places of employment.

The Companies (Directors' Report) (Employment of Disabled Persons) Regulations 1980, states that companies which employ more than 250 people (on average over a year) must include a statement in the Directors' Report regarding company policy on recruitment, training, career development and progression of people with disability within the company.

What was then the Manpower Commission produced a Code of Good Practice on the Employment of Disabled People in the 1980s. This document had no legal status but it did foster good practice for the employment and training of people with disability. It set out clear aims and objectives which could be incorporated into company policy.

The **Disabled Persons Act 1981** places a responsibility on the providers of premises to comply with standards set by the Code of Practice, for access for disabled people in buildings (British Standards

Institute). This legislation also covers highways, placing an obligation on highway authorities to '. . . have regard to the needs of disabled and blind persons'.

The EEC Recommendation (OJL 86/225/43) states that appropriate measures to '. . . provide fair opportunities for the disabled in the field of employment and vocational training', should be made. This led to the **Disabled Persons (Services, Consultation and Representation) Act 1986**. This Act requires that people with disability, or their representatives, are involved in planning their care. The person with disability or their carer have a right to request an assessment of their need for services. It gives the person with disability the right to representation by another person, for example to have an advocate. It places the responsibility on the local authority to provide the necessary resources to meet the needs of people with disability within their area.

Theory into practice

Heather, a black woman in her mid-twenties, has multiple sclerosis, which is a degenerative disease affecting the covering (sclera) of the nerves supplying muscle. The condition means that Heather experiences weakening of some muscle resulting in loss of movement. Heather does go into remission from time to time, when all symptoms disappear. Currently the condition has worsened, resulting in Heather having difficulty in speaking and moving as the muscles in her legs and larynx are affected.

Under the current legislation Heather has the right to request an assessment of her physical needs by a social worker, who will liaise with an occupational therapist to identify her need for a wheelchair and any adaptations in her home to allow for her independence.

The social worker will liaise with the district nurse to ensure that Heather's physical requirements are met in terms of hygiene and medical care. A bath attendant may be called to assist with personal hygiene, and a home carer to offer support with

getting up and going to bed if there are no family members able to assist Heather. 'Meals on Wheels' may be organised, or a stay in respite care facilities, to relieve relatives for a week or two during the year.

A plan of action to meet Heather's physical and social needs will be drawn up to include the above network of support. Her cultural, intellectual and emotional needs will need to be addressed by any such care plan. (Care plans are discussed in greater detail in Chapter 7.)

As Heather has difficulty in speaking because of her condition, she may nominate a relative, friend or request a social worker to act on her behalf as an advocate. This person works with Heather to gain help and advice, attending hospital or meetings with her to speak on her behalf. Any decisions are made by Heather in conjunction with her advocate, she does not give up any of her legal rights.

The **NHS and Community Care Act 1990** builds on the legislation outlined above for people with disability. It is widened to take into account all people in need of care in the community. The Act ensures that all individuals in need of care have the right to be assessed for services to meet their need. A care manager works to meet individual need by providing a 'care package' for each individual. The Act also ensures that all individuals have a right to complain about services. Greater detail regarding this far-reaching legislation is given in Chapter 6.

Children Act 1989

Children have rights within the law. The Children Act 1989 followed several well-publicised cases of child abuse. It seeks to simplify the great complexity of child care law. The law applies to all statutory and voluntary organisations providing care for children and their families. It is essentially a balancing act between the rights of the child, the parents and the duty of the state to protect children deemed to be in need or at risk.

Children in need are defined as, '. . . children whose health and welfare may suffer significantly without support from social services'. Any child with a disability is automatically deemed to be in need. The local authority must provide services to meet identified need, for example nurseries and family centres.

Race and culture is for the first time recognised as an essential factor to be given consideration. Local authorities must carefully consider a child's race, religion, language and culture when deciding on fostering, day or residential care services. Department of Health guidelines state that day care services should promote the self-esteem and racial identity of the child. Any provider of child care services must be able to satisfy the local authority that they are able to meet the racial and cultural needs of the children in the area, in order to gain registration.

The Act requires local authorities to 'take preventive steps', to ensure that children may live as normal a life as possible. Care must be taken to ensure that children are safe from suffering and that disabilities are minimised. Care must also be taken to ensure that children do not commit offences, so avoiding the need for placing them in secure provision.

Other key features of the Act lie in a principle termed **paramountcy**. This term means that the child's welfare is paramount (the most important issue). Any decision made about the child has to be in the child's best interest. Where a child is either mature enough or old enough, they have a right to be consulted about their wishes. These wishes must be given priority.

The Act requires caring agencies and parents to work in partnership. Both work to plan and organise to meet the needs of the child at all stages. Parents are also still responsible for their child, even when that child is living in a local authority establishment. Any person may apply to be deemed responsible for the child, such as a friend or relative if it is appropriate; for example, the grandmother of a boy orphaned whilst his parents were on holiday in Eastern Europe.

A child's own wishes must be given priority. (Winged Fellowship Trust 'Images of Caring' Competition by David Gibson.)

Collaboration between parents, child care agencies and the child is essential to meet the needs of the individual child at all stages.

The Department of Health produces a useful series of booklets about the Act:

The Children Act and Local Authorities – A Guide for Parents (CAG1)
The Children Act and You – A Guide for Young People (CAG3)
The Children Act and Getting Help from Social Services (CAG5)
The Children Act and the Courts – A Guide for Children and Young People (CAG6)
Living Away from Home, Your Rights – A Guide for Children and Young People (CAG7)

The UN Convention on the Rights of the Child was formalised by international agreement to protect the rights of children. This was in response to concerns raised across the world about the rights of children being ignored or forgotten.

The articles (statements) identify the rights of all children in the world, whether rich or poor, up to the age of 18. Three main rights were stated:

1 All rights apply to all children whatever their race, sex, religion, language, disability, opinion or family background. In other words, there will be no discrimination.
(*article 2*)
2 Adults must always consider the best interests of the child when making decisions for them.
(*article 3*)
3 Children must be listened to carefully and their opinions heard. Courts must take note of a child's wants and feelings.
(*article 12*)

Other rights include civil and political rights, economic, social, cultural and protective rights. All are important issues which should be part of good child care practice. For example, Article 24 states that children have the right to live in a safe, healthy and unpolluted environment. Article 18 notes that children should have proper care from day to day with the family, but with government support if necessary. Article 20 looks at the day-to-day care with other families, or in a children's home if there is no family. Due respect must be taken of a child's race, religion, culture and language when a new home is sought.

Think it over

Does this sound familiar? You can clearly see how important this UN Convention was when looking again at the Children Act 1989!

You may wish to obtain a booklet, *The Rights of a Child – A Guide to the UN Convention* (CAG9), from the Department of Health, to further your understanding.

The implications for those working in health and social care are great. Children must be provided with a safe environment where they may grow and develop to their full potential. That environment must acknowledge the child's race and culture, religion and language. This is essential for the child to develop a positive self-esteem. Positive self-esteem will enable the child to grow into a confident adult, able to take their place in society.

Charters

The British government has produced a series of *charters* which aim to improve a wide range of services. A **Parents' Charter** looks at education, denoting performance indicators which a school must make public; for example, exam results and truancy rates. It looks at the rights of parents when they consider the education they require for their child.

The **Patients' Charter** looks at the Health Service, again noting performance criteria; for example, the waiting time in an Out-Patients' Department. It sets targets in order to improve the quality of care available. The Charter outlines complaints procedures throughout the hospital. An ombudsman for health can be contacted if there is concern about administration, but they do not deal with complaints against professional malpractice. In such a case there will be an independent review, with reports sent to the Regional Health Authority.

Concerns about doctors (GPs), dentists, opticians and pharmacists go through the Family Health Services Authority. The Community Health Council is available for advice on matters concerning community health. If required they will attend a tribunal to support a complainant.

There is a **Citizen's Charter** which aims to work for better quality in public services: to offer more choice and to ensure that all know the kind of service that they have a right to expect. Each charter also states what can be done if the service provided does not meet the expected standard.

Other Charters cover **further education** and **higher education**. Each outlines the criteria to ensure high quality services are provided. They look at the way each service identifies and works to meet the needs of its service users. It reviews the complaints procedures.

Most professional bodies have a code of practice for their staff, perhaps one of the best known is the Hippocratic Oath taken by doctors. The British Association of Social Workers, the United Kingdom Central Council and the British Institute of Psychologists all provide such guidelines for staff, to name just a few.

Residential care, too, has seen a series of reports and codes of practice to ensure clients' rights and the quality of service are maintained. The **Wagner Report** stated that people moving into residential care should have real choices. These rights and choices include: the continued right as a citizen, for example to vote in local and government elections etc; having access to community services and the right to complain if need be; the right to manage their own affairs including their pension; the right to make decisions and, where this is not possible, the right to a six-monthly review; the right to have their cultural needs met.

In 1986 **Home Life: A Code of Practice for Residential Care** was introduced. This stated that clients have the right to: individuality, dignity, esteem, fulfilment, autonomy, be able to take risks, have a quality of experience and have emotional needs met through personal/intimate relationships, if they wish.

Community Life 1990 went a step further by saying that all care packages should reflect the informed choice of the client. Individuals should know their rights and responsibilities. They have the right to an advocate, and to make complaints if required. This placed responsibility on the providers of services to

People in residential care have rights and choices

ensure that a complaints procedure was implemented and that provision for advocates was made. Providers have to ensure that all the service users are aware of possible choices and the potential outcomes of those choices. This also meant that clients could decide to take a calculated risk, for example, to make their own cup of tea despite some physical difficulty. The provider should take all necessary steps to minimise the risk but not prevent it.

Complaints procedures are made available to all service users; for example, a complaint regarding the service in a residential home would be made to the manager. Should the service user remain unsatisfied, they may refer to the Social Services Department or to the Registrar of Residential Establishments (the person who registers such establishments).

If it is a member of staff who feels they have a complaint, they would address this to the immediate line manager. The staff member may wish to take the matter to their union for advice and guidance before taking the matter up with their employers. Should the case be one of discrimination on grounds of race or gender, then the matter may be referred to a tribunal as described earlier.

Task

Choose one client group, perhaps the group you are currently working with. Identify the clients' rights and responsibilities laid out by legislation and/or codes of practice. Identify the ways in which the service meets these rights. Identify your responsibility as a care worker. Give details of the complaints procedure and the agencies involved to rectify the situation.

In this chapter, emphasis has been placed on the unique qualities of the individual: the importance of valuing each person for their uniqueness, which has arisen from genetic inheritance and socialisation. The many changes in society have been briefly reviewed to place the current legislation into an historical context. The range of issues addressed to raise the quality of service and, therefore, the quality of life for all in society, have been noted.

You are embarking on a career working with others. This places you in a very responsible position to ensure that all have equal rights and access to services. Improved quality of life starts with *you* and the service you provide. In turn you will gain greater job satisfaction, it is worth the effort: you are the future.

Self-assessment test

1 A young child first learns the norms of society from:
   a peers
   b family
   c Health Visitor
   d Social worker

2 Which of the following is *not* an agent for secondary socialisation?
   a school
   b media
   c peers
   d family

3 It is important for health and social care staff to be aware of a client's culture because:
 a staff may better meet client needs.
 b staff may be less intolerant.
 c staff may help the client to integrate better.
 d staff may learn something new.

4 Respecting the culture of a client will:
 a demonstrate tolerance.
 b demonstrate flexibility.
 c reinforce self-esteem.
 d reinforce own learning.

5 Health and social care staff have important social roles because:
 a they are able to ensure equal access to services.
 b they have a range of knowledge and skills.
 c they have control over the care setting.
 d they are able to provide a safe environment.

6 Direct discrimination means:
 a subtle ways of showing respect.
 b failing to monitor an equal opportunity policy.
 c hiding true feelings about a given group.
 d blatant ways of showing disrespect.

7 Where would you get advice regarding complaints about GPs?
 a Regional Health Authority.
 b Local Hospital Trust.
 c Community Health Council.
 d Family Health Service Authority.

8 If a male colleague at work considers that he is treated less favourably to the female staff, where can he go for advice?
 a Equal Opportunities Commission.
 b Commission for Racial Equality.
 c Citizens' Advice Bureau
 d Industrial tribunal.

9 In relation to Question 8, under which legislation may he make a claim?
 a Race Relations Act, 1976.
 b Equal Pay Act, 1975, 1983.
 c Sex Discrimination Act, 1975.
 d Treaty of Rome, 1957.

10 Covert discrimination takes place when:
 a You move your seat when a person with learning difficulties joins your table.
 b You avoid inviting your black friend to a party where all the rest will be white.

 c You give a look of disgust and comment about a person at the bus stop with severe scarring on their face.
 d You speak to the person pushing the wheelchair about the occupant and ignore them.

11 Language may be used to discriminate by:
 i tone of voice.
 ii choice of words.
 iii body of words.
 iv assumptions.
 Which of the following applies:
 a Putting milk and sugar in tea for an elder because they are labelled as being confused.
 b You are *only* a girl!
 c Pulling a face and laughing at a person with learning difficulties when they are muddled with their money.
 d He is the black sheep of the family!

12 State which of the following is true and which is false.
 i An appeal may be made following a decision made by an industrial tribunal.
 ii Decisions made by British courts and industrial tribunals are subject to the European Court of Justice.
 a F, T
 b T, F
 c F, F
 d T, T

13 Consider whether the following are true or false.
 i A firm may have an industrial tribunal decision over-ruled if they can prove that their decision was based on health and safety grounds.
 ii A firm may refuse to employ a person with disability if they can justify their decision on the grounds of hazardous occupation.
 a F, F
 b T, F
 c T, T
 d F, T

14 An applicant was turned down for a job as a telephonist as he was in a wheelchair. Under which legislation may he make a claim?
 a Sex Discrimination Act, 1975.

b Chronically Sick and Disabled Persons (Amendment) Act 1976.

c Disabled Persons Act, 1981.

d Disabled Persons (Employment) Act, 1958.

15 To whom would you officially address a complaint about the care given to a relative in a residential home?

a The Officer in Charge.

b The care staff.

c The Director of Social Services.

d The Inspector of Residential Establishments.

16 As a support worker in the NHS, to whom do you complain regarding possible malpractice on the ward?

a The patient's relatives.

b The hospital management committee.

c Your union representative.

d The ward manager.

17 Social role is:

a the value placed on a given individual.

b the area of work or leisure an individual is involved in.

c the part a person plays to fulfill the expectations of others.

d an act one puts on for others to make them like you.

18 An individual may adapt their behaviour to meet the expectations of others in a particular social context. Decide whether it is true that **i** and **ii** below are examples of adapting behaviour to meet the expectations of others.

i A Home Carer patiently repeating a question several times for an elderly man who is confused.

ii A teacher swearing at a child because they are slow to understand the topic for the lesson.

a F, F

b T, T

c F, T

d T, F

19 Institutionalised racism is:

a racism through violence on the streets.

b racism through the culture of an organisation.

c racism through verbal attacks.

d racism through failure to employ black people.

20 Equal opportunity means:

a to treat everyone the same.

b to ignore individual differences.

c to give the same rights in law and society to all.

d to protect and feel sorry for people who are different.

Fast Facts

Attitude Socially-learned reactions to and likes and dislikes of people, objects or situations.

Belief Ideas which we draw upon to make sense of our own particular view of the world.

Black A term used to describe physical characteristics, e.g. skin colour and racial features. The term is also used in a political context to include all people who are oppressed by racism and discrimination because of skin colour or ethnic and cultural background. Much work has been undertaken in the last two decades to redefine the term to highlight positive issues.

Culture A collection of ideas and habits shared by a given group, i.e. the norms and value base for the group. These help to reinforce the identity of the group, making it different to other groups. Individuals learn the roles acceptable to others within their culture.

Discrimination To be able to distinguish between things. In health and social care, it refers to a decision to deny one group the same rights as another.

Discrimination, direct Very open and obvious methods of disadvantaging a person or group of people, e.g. name calling, refusing to employ someone because of their age or religion etc.

Discrimination, indirect Subtle ways of disadvantaging an individual or group, e.g. not providing access to people in wheelchairs, or selecting people only from certain housing areas, in order to discriminate.

Empathy A conscious effort to try to see the world as another person sees it. Empathy is an attempt to gain a closer understanding of another's feelings.

Equal opportunity   Aims to ensure that all people are afforded equal access to services and have equal rights in law and society. Ensuring that all have an equal right to develop to their full potential.

Ethnic group   A group who share the same cultural tradition, perhaps a common ancestry or geographical place of origin. The group may share a common language, literature, music etc.

Ethnic minority   A commonly used term in Britain to describe groups from the black community. The term also covers such groups as Chinese, Greek, Turkish people etc. This broad term covers a range of factors e.g. race, religion, culture and language.

Eurocentric   Viewing the world solely from a white European value base. This does not address issues raised within other cultures and may assume the superiority of European culture.

Hypothesis   A projection or idea which is proposed and then tested out to see if the idea is valid or not.

Marginalise   In health and social care terms it is to push a group to the outer edge of society and social concern, and so disadvantage them. Such groups may be oppressed due to age, ability, gender, race, religion or social class.

Norms   The accepted attitudes and values which underpin the behaviour of a particular social group, i.e. the 'rules' by which the group functions.

Peer group   A group who share a common purpose or who are in a similar situation. For example, a youth club or a study group may have members of different ages but all have come together for a specific purpose.

Positive action   A positive step which aims to benefit individuals or groups who face discrimination, e.g. employing an interpreter to assist a student with hearing impairment in the classroom. In this way the student is not disadvantaged by the hearing loss

Prejudice   An attitude which is based on pre-judgements made about others leading to

discrimination. Prejudice is often based on ignorance and stereotypes of an individual or group.

Primary socialisation   The socialisation that takes place during early childhood when the rules and norms of the society into which an individual is born are acquired. Through the family a child learns the patterns of acceptable behaviour expected by their social group. The attitudes and values of the culture of that society are also formed.

Race   The idea of a group based on biological differences between people. In practice, a person is assigned to a particular race on the basis of the subjective impressions of others, not on the basis of measurable biological differences.

Racial discrimination   Unequal treatment on the grounds of being a member of a particular racial group.

Racial prejudice   An unfavourable attitude towards another because they belong to a particular race. This attitude may be based on negative stereotypes of that particular race.

Racism   Attitudes and procedures (economic, political, social and cultural) which advocate and seek to maintain the superiority of one racial group or groups over others.

Secondary socialisation   Wider experience of the world outside the home exposes the child to different attitudes and values in society. The main agents of secondary socialisation are the media, education and peer groups.

Sexism   Attitudes and procedures (including economic, political, social and cultural factors) which seek to maintain the superiority of one gender over the other.

Social context   A particular social setting in which individuals have a preconceived notion about acceptable behaviour. There is clear definition of the roles and the behaviour associated with those roles in this setting. For example, in a hospital ward, the nurse is expected to behave in a caring and professional manner.

Social role   The 'part' that an individual plays in a given situation. The accepted behaviour expected by others of that role, e.g. a college student being ready to learn, asking questions etc.

Social status   The value a group places on a particular social role, giving credibility and respect. For example: the leader of a teenage group because they can organise others or perhaps control the group through fear; a judge because of the knowledge they hold and the power to uphold the laws of society. Status may be due to money or possessions and will vary depending on the culture of groups within society.

Stereotype   A way of grouping people, objects or events together, attributing individuals with the same qualities and characteristics. Stereotyping can help the individual to make sense of the world by making predictions easier. Stereotyping may have positive or negative consequences.

Values   Learned principles or thought systems which enable individuals to choose between alternatives and make decisions. Values guide behaviour in relation to what is judged to be 'valuable'. Values are learned in a cultural context and will develop in relation to the beliefs and norms which exist within a cultural group.

References

Adorno, T.W., et al (1950) *The Authoritarian Personality* Harper

Bakeman, R. and Adamson, L. (1984) Coordinating Attention to People and Objects in Mother-Infant and Peer-Infant Interaction. In *Child Development*, 41, 291–311

Bernstein, B. (1959) A Public Language: Some Sociological Determents of Linguistic Form. In *British Journal of Sociology* 10

Bowlby, J. (1969) *Attachment and Loss: Attachment* Hogarth Press

Brown, R. (1988) *Group Processes* Blackwell

Bushnell, I., Sai, F., and Mullin, J. (1989) Neonatal Recognition of the Mother's Face. In *British Journal of Developmental Psychology*, 7, 3–15

Centre for Policy on Ageing, 1990 *Community Life: A Code of Practice*

Clarke, A. and Clarke, A. (1976) *An Early Experience: Myth and Evidence* Open Books

Collis, G. and Schaffer, H.R. (1975) Synchronization of Visual Attention in Mother-Infant Pairs. In *Journal of Child Psychology and Psychiatry*, 16, 315–20

Davis, K. (1974) Final Notes on a Case of Extreme Isolation. In *American Journal of Sociology* 52, 432–437

Deux, K. and Wrightsman, L.S. (Fifth edition, 1988) *Social Psychology* Brooks/Cole

Donne, J. (?1600) *Holy Sonnets*

Duns, J. and Wooding, C. (1977) Play Learning and Interaction with the Mother. In Tizard, B. and Harvard, D. (eds) *The Biology of Play* Heinemann Medical Books

Fenson, L. and Schell, R. (1986) The origins of Exploratory Play. In Smith. P, (ed) *Children's Play: Research Developments and Practical Applications* Gordon and Breach

Fridd and Weddle, 1989 *Basic Practice in Courts and Tribunals Waterflow*

Gould, J. (Ed) (1965) *A Socio-linguistic Approach to Social Learning* Social Science Survey, London

Jackson, B. and Marsden, D. (1962) *Education and the Working Class* Routledge Kegan-Paul.

Keddie, N., (1975) *Knowledge and Control* M. Young Ed.

Koluchova, J. (1972) Severe Deprivation of Twins: A Case Study. In *Journal of Child Psychology and Psychiatry*, 13, 107–144

Koluchova, J. (1976) A Report on the Further Development of Twins after Severe Deprivation. A chapter in Clarke, A. and Clarke, A. (eds) *Early Experience: Myth and Evidence* Open Books

Linton, R. (1945) Present World Conditions in Cultural Perspective. In Linton, R., (ed) *The Science of Man in World Crisis* Columbia University Press

Maurer, D. and Barrera, M. (1981) Infants' Perception of Natural and Distorted Arrangements of a Schematic Face. In *Child Development*, 52, 196–202

Meadows, S. (1986) *Understanding Child Development* Hutchinson

Minard, R. (1952) Race relationships in the Pocahontas coal field. In *Journal of Social Issues*, 8, 29–44.

Petty, R.E. and Cacioppo, J.T. (1981) *Attitudes and Persuasion: Classic and Contemporary Approaches* William C. Brown

Richards, M. (1987) Parents and Kids: The New Thinking. In *New Society*, 79, p. 14

Rutter, M. (1971) Parent-child Separation: Psychological Effects on the Children. In *Journal of Child Psychology and Psychiatry*, 12, 233–60

Rutter, M. (Second edition, 1981) *Maternal Deprivation Reassessed* Penguin

Schaffer, H.R. (1971) *The Growth of Sociability* Penguin

Secord, P.F. and Backman, C.W. (Second edition, 1974) *Social Psychology* McGraw-Hill

Selurge, 1993 *Law of Employment* Chapter 4

Sherif, M. et al (1961) *Intergroup Conflict and Cooperation: The Robbers' Cave Experiment* University of Oklahoma Book Exchange

Skeels, H.M. (1966) Adult status of children with contrasting early life experiences. In *Monographs of the Society for Research in Child Development*, 31, 3 (Serial no. 105)

Swann, Lord (1985) *Education for All: A Brief Guide* HMSO

Tizard, B. (1977) *Adoption: A Second Chance* Open Books

Tyerman and Spenser (1983) as cited in: Gross, R. (second edition, 1991) *Psychology: The Science of Mind and Behaviour* Hodder and Stoughton, page 289–290

Warnock, M. (1978) *Warnock Report* HMSO

Community Life A Code of Practice for Community Care

(1990) Centre for Policy on Ageing

Legislation

Disabled Persons (Employment) Act 1944 and 1958
Treaty of Rome 1957
Race Relations Act 1965
Local Government Act 1966
Sexual Offences Act 1967
Race Relations Act 1968
Chronically Sick and Disabled Persons Act 1970
Equal Pay Act 1970
Sex Discrimination Act 1975
Equal Pay Act 1975
Race Relations Act 1976
Education (Handicapped Children) Act 1980
Disabled Persons Act 1981
Equal Pay (Amendment) Regulations 1983
Mental Health Act 1983
EEC Recommendation (OJL 86/225/43)
Disabled Persons (Services, Consultation and Representation) Act 1986
Sex Discrimination Act 1986
Data Protection Act 1986
Children Act 1989
National Health Service and Community Care Act 1990
Medical Records Act 1990
The Criminal Justice Act 1992

Charters and Codes of Practice

Home Life: A Code of Practice for Residential Care 1986
A Positive Choice. The Wagner Report 1988
Homes are for Living In (1989 DOH Inspectorate)
Code of Practice for Social Care
The Citizens' Charter 1991
The Patients' Charter 1991
The Parents' Charter 1991
Community Life 1990
A Code of Good Practice on the Employment of Disabled People
Black Community Care Charter, 1991
The UN Convention on the Rights of the Child 1992
The UN Universal Declaration of Human Rights
12 Principles of Social Work Practice, 1991

2 INTERPERSONAL INTERACTION

This chapter aims to help you consider how you relate to other people, in both your working and private lives. Someone who has good interpersonal skills may be more successful in their relationships than someone who is ignorant as to how their own actions and speech affect the way others respond to them. Unless you live alone on an island, life is built around interaction with other people and, if your work is in the field of social care, relationships are vital. In order to understand other people's responses it is necessary to examine how you are likely to be perceived by others, and to be honest with yourself about your interaction with them.

Think it over

Think of someone you know who is really popular. What is it about them which draws other people to them? Make a list of the qualities you think they possess.

It is likely that people who are popular are seen as warm, friendly, good listeners and cheerful. But how do we arrive at such judgements?

Communication is divided broadly into two parts: what we say and what we don't. Initially it may be thought that the words we use are of the greatest significance, and we often take great trouble to 'say the right things'; but is this enough? Have you ever been in a situation where someone says 'the right thing' but you don't believe a word they are saying?

For example, imagine a middle-aged woman meeting a man for the first time. He gazes into her eyes and swears that he thought her daughter was her sister. She would have to be very gullible to believe what he was saying (and he would have to be very accomplished for his non-verbal communication to support his words).

We use more than words to 'say' what we mean. We use non-verbal messages either to support our spoken words or undermine them. Using non-verbal signals involves using our eyes and our bodies to send messages. We can think of them as signs associated with sight, sound, touch and smell.

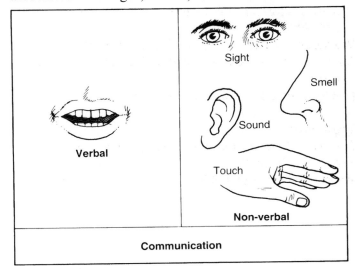

Visual communication

How we *perceive* someone is influenced greatly by how we *see* them. Think of someone you have met recently, perhaps a member of your course group, and try to think of how what you first saw of them influenced the way you first thought of them.

You were probably influenced first of all by the clothes they wore and their hairstyle. We make conscious decisions about these things because we are very much aware that they portray us in a certain way – how we wish people to perceive us. This is probably why there may be friction between adolescents and parents. Adolescents are trying to assert their own views and project an independent image of themselves to the rest of the world. They often adopt images exactly opposite to those of their parents to accentuate their difference. This may cause much family unease in the process!

We are sometimes constrained by circumstances to project a 'suitable' image, often in terms of a more formal one than we would wish. Does the way we present ourselves influence the way we behave?

Think it over

Do you behave differently when you are presenting yourself in a formal or non-casual way?

There has been much discussion about whether, for example, pupils at school should be required to wear uniforms, because it is thought that wearing specific clothes influences the way people behave. Even reminders of authority can influence people; for example, cardboard figures of policemen in supermarkets are known to reduce petty theft. Certainly, appearing in court in front of a judge wearing robes and a wig is likely to give the occasion, and the judge, much more authority than if the meeting took place in an ordinary room with the judge wearing casual clothes. Clothes certainly give messages; for example, the victim of an accident might feel comforted by, and confident in the ability of, someone approaching who is wearing a nurse's uniform.

Task

Perhaps you wear a uniform at work. If you do you may like to speak with the people you work with, both colleagues and clients, and ask them whether they think the uniform inhibits or helps personal interaction. If you write a report of your findings you may be able to use it as portfolio evidence for Communication Core Skills Elements one and two.

Facial expressions

We often make judgements about a person based on their physical appearance. Included in this is their facial expression. Because the face is such a sensitive guide to a person's feelings we often try hard not to let ourselves reveal too much by our expressions. Only when we are overcome by our feelings do we allow our faces to 'say' what we feel.

Can you remember an occasion when you felt very strongly about something but managed not to let your feelings show? Perhaps you were furious with a customer but had to remain polite, or felt amused by a child with whom you were trying to be stern.

Our facial expressions reveal our emotions in several ways – such as, by the pupils of the eyes expanding and contracting, by our blushing or sweating. Our eyebrows will raise or fall and the mouth smiles, raising upwards, or tightens with anger, turning down to show displeasure. A nervous person's mouth may twitch and they may feel a need to lick their lips. Even the muscles in our face and neck tighten if we feel angry or tense.

Different cultures may have different ways of behaving in terms of displaying feelings. Japanese people, for example, often do not display – or expect others to display – facial expressions showing anger or displeasure.

Gaze

An important part of our facial expression is how we use our eyes to gaze at others. The very act of making or having eye contact implies recognition of some sort.

Have you ever used gaze to tell someone how you were feeling? You have probably used gaze to tell people you were annoyed with them. For Europeans, refusal to meet someone's glance at you is a very powerful means of rejecting them. Long gazes of more than six seconds indicate high degrees of intimacy or liking. However, long gazes can also be used to intimidate and show aggression – 'to stare someone out'. Ellsworth (1975) found that staring motorcyclists at traffic lights caused motorists to move off much more quickly than usual.

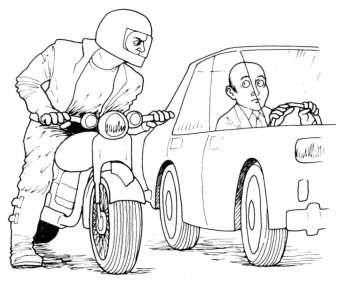

Gaze can be used to intimidate!

Glances are used in conversations to indicate a wish to enter into the discussion or to signal agreement. People look more when they are listening than when they are talking. So if you look at someone while they talk it is an important way of supporting someone's views and letting them know you are interested in what they are saying. Amongst Europeans, if someone is attempting to lie, or find what they are saying difficult, they are likely to look away from the people they are talking with: they will break or avoid eye contact. However different cultures use gaze differently and it is important to check the cultural norms of an individual before interpreting their non-verbal behaviour.

When you are communicating with clients it is important to take their individual needs into account. If someone cannot see well the use of *gaze* will be impaired. Parents of blind children may sometimes find it difficult to establish a bond with their child because much early communication between babies and adults is in eye contact. It is important to use other communication skills when gaze is not available.

Children suffering from autism have been found to avoid the gaze of others. They use short glances of up to 0.5 seconds. They will turn away to avoid a gaze or pull a cover over their eyes. Clancy and McBride (1969) suggest that one cause of autism may be due to failure to form an initial attachment with a care-giver, which has led the child to develop cut-off skills to continue its isolation.

A number of studies of people with schizophrenia note that they look at psychologists on average only about 65 per cent as much as non-schizophrenics. However, a study by Rutter (1976) showed that when talking to another person about impersonal problems their gaze was of normal level. They, and people suffering from depression, may avoid eye contact when talking about personal matters related to their illness.

Think it over

Have you ever been instructed on 'correct' gazing or found yourself instructing others?

Again, gaze is also subject to cultural interpretations. Most people in Northern European and Asian cultures will have been told that it is rude to stare at strangers. Parents tend to demand that their children look at them at certain times, notably when they are being told off for a wrongdoing! ('Look at me when I'm talking to you!') Too much gaze, however, is seen as insulting, disrespectful and threatening (Watson, 1972). By way of contrast, in Southern European, Arab and Latin American cultures too little gaze is seen as being insincere, dishonest or impolite. There may also be rules about who to look at or not, as well as how to look. Some Kenyans may not look directly at their mother-in-law or Nigerians at a person of high status. Some South American Indians must look at outside objects during a conversation and Japanese people prefer to have the gaze directed at the neck rather than the face (Argyle 1983). Remember that a client is an individual and individuals have different experiences. Carers need to learn to 'read' people and understand their different responses.

Gestures

Gestures vary from society to society and from groups within society. In Britain there are about twenty commonly used gestures while in Southern Italy there are about 200!

Can you think of cultures where gesture is extensively used to communicate? Specialist gesture languages have been developed in certain working environments, for example, in broadcasting where speech would interfere with the work being staged, or at race tracks to send messages over a distance. Noisy mills and mines are also places where workers will use signs to supplement mouthed words. Gestures in general usage are often involuntary, and of no particular use, for example, pointing to give directions when on the telephone! However gestures can sometimes betray emotions, such as clenched fists indicating aggression or anxiety.

Deaf people use signs to communicate and the British and American Sign Languages have been developed to a high level of sophistication. As with spoken languages, sign languages are constantly evolving. For example, the signs to indicate full breasts for women and a moustache for men have been changed to a tap on the forehead for men and on the cheek for women. These changes reinforce the status of sign languages as evolutionary and responsive to the societies in which they are used.

Other elements of non-verbal communication which can be seen are **proximity**, **orientation** and **posture**. The nearness or distance, **proximity**, between people may be a good indication of how they feel towards one another. The ritual of shaking hands may have evolved as a measure of a polite distance between two people meeting formally (to keep someone at arm's length). It is interesting to note that within some cultures, such as the Southern European, Arab and Latin American culture, greeting may often involve a hug and kiss rather than just a handshake. You may have experienced the person who needed less personal space than you did – and had the feeling of being edged into a corner as you moved away from their closeness. In Northern European culture this may be a way of intimidating people, standing too close can make others very uncomfortable!

Orientation means organising your own or others' positions in the space available. Consider the court-room again. It is no accident that the judge is placed physically on a higher level and apart from the rest of the court. Judges are automatically perceived as 'higher' and in control. All variations of positioning make statements about the participants' roles. An interview with the bank manager or head teacher will often take place with a desk between the participants, which forms a barrier; while a counselling session is more likely to be between people seated on the same level, with no barriers between them. The way you organise your environment will support or obstruct your communication.

Posture is the way a person sits or stands, and it gives messages about how they are feeling. Tension in the back and shoulders indicates stress, as do arms clasped around the body. Someone with an 'open' body posture, leaning slightly forward towards the speaker, indicates a relaxed, non-threatening listener. But someone sitting with hunched shoulders, folded arms and crossed legs might not be so relaxed!

In addition to what we can see of a speaker we also rely on what we smell, feel or touch, and hear: i.e. olfactory, tactile and auditory communication.

Olfactory communication

Newborn babies recognise their mother by her smell and people with visual disabilities may distinguish landmarks in buildings and towns by their particular odours. Whilst the smell of fish and chips may be enticing or otherwise to sighted individuals, to a visually disabled person it might be an essential part of the geography! Smell is also very powerful in evoking memories of past events. The mind will respond to a certain smell by conjouring up vivid images and events associated with that particular odour – perhaps the smell of a dentists' surgery is one of the most unpopular!

To some extent, smell may be a much weaker influence in communication than it was to our prehistoric ancestors. Without the benefit of deodorants it was all too easy to tell when people were frightened or anxious by the smell of their perspiration. Psychologists believe still that humans are attracted to each other by the presence of *pheremones*, barely detectable smells which either attract or repel. However, generally these days it is not socially acceptable to have 'natural' smells and there is a large market in covering them and projecting different images of ourselves by the way we smell. Manufacturers of washing powders compete to produce the 'cleanest smelling wash', so, commercially at least, a person's status can be defined by their smell – provided it is unnatural!

Figure 2.1 *Tactile communication can be important. (Winged Fellowship Trust 'Images of Caring' Competition by Camilla Maia.)*

Tactile communication

The use of the sense of touch is one which is surrounded by cultural taboos. Many Northern Europeans are not inclined towards body contact, except formally when shaking hands or within a close relationship. In the British culture tactile messages are most often concerned with aggression, greeting, guiding or caressing. Depending on how comfortable a client feels about touch, tactile contacts can be very important.

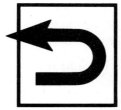

Think it over

Have you worked with or seen a client benefiting from tactile contact? Perhaps a touch or a hug or holding hands?

Many disturbed or severely disabled people may find massage comforting or soothing. Elders who no longer have close friends or relatives may lack the comfort of touch. However, remember that it is essential to gauge the client's reaction to a tentative touch, say on the arm, and caution must be exercised when working alone with clients.

It is also important that your touch is appropriate to the client's culture and age. It would obviously be abusive to pat a middle-aged person with learning difficulties on the head as one might with a very small child.

Auditory communication

The last type of non-verbal communication we need to be aware of is auditory communication. Although this involves using words, it's not the actual words but the way in which they are used which is important.

Certain clients may give the answers they think they should give, either because they don't want to be thought a nuisance or because they fear what will happen if they complain. It is the carer's job to listen to the tone, timing, accent, speed of delivery and rhythm to judge whether the words mean what they say. If, for example, you were to say, 'YOU LOVELY LITTLE THING' to a baby in a loud and threatening voice it would probably cry. The baby makes a judgement about your attitude based on how the words are said, because it doesn't understand their meaning. The opposite is often true with adults: they will use the right words but their meaning can be obscured by the way they say them. Can you remember saying, 'Sorry' because you were made to – not because you were sorry? It is likely that you didn't sound it!

· SUPPORTIVE SKILLS ·

Having identified the main types of verbal and non-verbal communication we need to examine strategies for supporting others during interaction.

Task

Sit with a partner and ask them to talk to you about, say, how they are finding the course and any problems they are having. Concentrate hard on really listening to them and do not interrupt except to clarify a point or prompt their thought process. After about five minutes, without further discussion between you, you should each write a list: one of how, as the listener, you tried to show you were listening; and one about how the speaker perceived the listener to be attentive or not.

Encouraging communication

The following are all positive behaviours which should encourage effective communication:

- The listener gives evidence of total concentration: does not look around the room, out of the window or at other material, e.g. a file on the desk; does not fidget.
- The listener looks at the speaker and gives their full attention to what is being said. The listener does not allow themselves to be distracted by other happenings around them; does not adopt a faraway expression or look bored.
- The listener assumes a posture which is relaxed and 'open' to encourage the speaker to continue.
- The listener looks warm and concerned, and tolerates silences.
- The listener accepts what the speaker is saying without interrupting or making negative non-verbal comments. The listener gives verbal or non-verbal signs of encouragement, such as nods, smiles, 'umms', 'ahs'.
- The listener notices the non-verbal signs the speaker is sending.

Just as these behaviours will encourage communication the ones listed below will create barriers:

- The listener lets their mind wander on to other matters.
- The listener stops looking at the speaker. (Of course, an unbroken gaze would be threatening, but try to maintain intermittent eye contact to let the speaker know you are interested.)
- The listener looks cold or disinterested, or over-serious.
- The listener thinks of a reply while the speaker is still talking or has preconceived ideas before the person says what they feel.
- The listener shows disagreement with what the speaker is saying, either verbally or non-verbally.

- The listener uses a negative body posture, either sitting or standing above the speaker, or showing apathy or lack of interest.
- The listener concentrates on verbal information to the exclusion of body language.

Evaluate your conversational skill

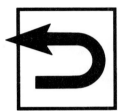

Think it over

Now ask yourself the following questions (cover up the scores – there is no point in fooling yourself!).

When someone tells you something, do you:
1 a note the content of what they say?
b watch their face, gestures, posture etc.?
c think of the context in which they are saying it?

Score: a = 1; a and b = 2; a, b and c = 3

2 a pick up on something that interests you, and reply straight away?
b listen to all of what is said, then reply?
c think of what the speaker is wearing?

Score: a = 0; b = 2; c = 0

3 a start thinking of a reply before the speaker has finished?
b allow the speaker to finish before beginning to think of a reply?
c interrupt with your own view?

Score: a = 0; b = 2; c = 0

4 a look around you?
b nod and give eye-contact?
c position yourself appropriately to the speaker?

Score: a = 0; b = 2; c = 2.

Interpreting your score

If you have scored between 7 and 9 in total you have a high level of conversational skill. The questions covered some of the most common listening problems.

In part 1 it is important to take account of all the clues the speaker has provided. This means taking notice of the *context* in which the conversation takes place and the non-verbal clues available, as well as what is actually said. (You will realise from this that communicating by telephone means it is much more difficult to get a full 'picture' of what the speaker is meaning.)

Part 2 deals with the way we can allow ourselves to be side-tracked into picking up mainly on what interests us, by hearing only what we want to hear. This is sometimes called 'selective hearing'.

Part 3 identifies a tendency to start thinking of a reply before the speaker has actually finished saying everything. This is a very common fault and we can all remember the frustration of talking with someone who finishes our sentences for us!

Sometimes we do this because we want to avoid silences or gaps in the conversation. Sometimes we are more interested in what we ourselves want to say than in what the speaker is saying. Sometimes we are bored and want the speaker to get to the point. However, the point is that we must give the speaker space to make their point and say what they mean, not assume we know what they mean.

Part 4 deals with the importance of letting someone know you are listening to them, by looking at them and being in an appropriate position. If you are gazing around and not giving eye-contact, it is difficult for them to judge what your reactions are.

CONVEYING WARMTH, UNDERSTANDING AND SINCERITY

The NVQ value base for care requires that carers can 'value others with appropriate communication'. Valuing others may involve simple acts like remembering things a client has said, such as 'Oh your son's coming to see you today isn't he?', said to a client in a care setting. Sometimes, just a gesture or a wave of the hand is enough to acknowledge a client. When a conversation gets going, valuing a client is likely to involve much more than these basic skills.

Carl Rogers (1902–1987) identified three necessary conditions for creating a *safe* conversational atmosphere which *valued* a client. Originally these were seen as a basis for counselling relationships, but they have since become adopted as a basis for any befriending or supportive relationship. The three conditions for a caring supportive conversation are that the carer must show (or convey) a sense of warmth, understanding and sincerity to the client. The *conditions* for valuing others sometimes have other names:

- warmth (sometimes called acceptance)
- understanding (originally called empathy)
- sincerity (originally called genuineness).

Conveying warmth

Conveying warmth means being seen by the client as a warm, accepting person. In order to influence another person to view you this way you will need to demonstrate that you do not stereotype and label others. You will need to demonstrate that you do not judge other people as good or bad, right or wrong. This is sometimes referred to as a *non-judgemental attitude*. Warmth means not even comparing people to see who is best!

Conveying warmth means being willing to listen to others. It means being able to prove that you are listening to a client because you can remember what they have said to you. Warmth involves using reflective listening. That is, you give your attention to the client when they talk, and remember what they say. You can then *reflect* the words back again.

Client	'I hate it here, you don't know what it's like, there's no one to talk to, they're all too busy, no one cares about me.'
Carer	'I suppose they are busy and you feel that no one cares.'
Client	'That's right, they don't – you aren't so bad, but you won't be here tomorrow.'
Carer	'Well that's right, I can't come in tomorrow but we could talk for a while now if you would like that.'

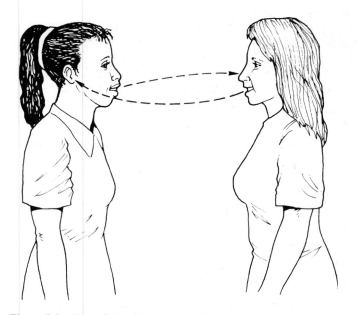

Figure 2.2 *Warmth involves using reflective listening*

The carer is able to show the client that they are listening by repeating some of the things that the client has said. The repetition is not 'parrot fashion', the carer has used their own way of speaking. The carer has also avoided being judgemental. When the client said that no one cared, the carer did not argue with them. The carer might have felt like saying, 'How can you say that – don't you know how hard we work for you? You want to think yourself lucky, there's plenty of people who would be pleased to be here, other people don't complain'. This advice to think yourself lucky and comparison with other people is judgemental, it does not value the client, it is not warm. If the carer had said these things it would have blocked the conversation. *Warmth* makes it safe for the client to express their feelings. Warmth means that the carer could disagree with what a client has said, but the client should feel safe that they will not be discriminated against or putdown.

As a care worker you will come across a wide range of clients, many of whom will have ways of thinking and life experiences completely different from your own. You will usually choose as friends people who have views similar to your own, but you will not be able to choose your clients.

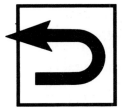

Think it over

Even within a group of friends or a family, there are likely to be areas of disagreement. Write down three areas in which you disagree with your friends or your family.

You have probably found that you have differences of opinion in areas such as:

- choice of clothing and hairstyles
- choice of foods – vegetarian, non-vegetarian, dietary etc.
- choice of leisure activities
- responsibility for household chores.

So, even our family or people we choose as friends do not always think or feel as we do ourselves.

In developing the skill of showing warmth, it is important not to judge, not to compare yourself with others. Carers accept that clients have the right to be the way they are, and to make their own choices. While you may disapprove of a client's behaviour, you must show that you do not dislike them as an individual person. This is particularly important when working with clients with difficult behaviour. It is essential that clients know it is the behaviour which is disliked, not them as a person.

Conveying understanding

Understanding means learning about the individual identity and beliefs that a client has. Carl Rogers saw the idea of understanding or empathy as 'the ability to experience another person's world as if it was your own world'. The key part being the 'as if'. We always keep an idea of our own world and we know that the clients have different experiences from our own. It is important to try to really understand clients' thoughts and feelings.

Reflective listening provides a useful tool to help carers to gradually learn about their clients. By keeping a conversation going, the client may feel that they are understood; the carer is warm and non-judgemental, so it becomes safe to tell the carer

something about their life. If the carer checks that they understand the client, the client may feel valued. As the client gets value from the conversation so they may talk more. The more the client talks, the more the carer has a chance to learn about their views.

Client	'So anyway, I said to the doctor look these pills are only making me worse, I don't want them.'
Carer	'So you told him to stop them.'
Client	'That's right, I don't believe in pills – you end up rattling round with all that lot inside you – if you're meant to get better you will, that's what I say.'
Carer	'Have you always believed that pills don't help?'
Client	'Yes, well ever since I was young, I put my faith in God.'

By listening and conveying warmth the carer is being given the privilege of learning about the client's religious views and perhaps even needs. Understanding can grow from a conversation which conveys value for the client.

If you can get to understand your clients a sense of trust may develop. If the client is understood and not judged they may consider it safe to share thoughts and worries with their carer.

Conveying sincerity

Being *sincere* means being open about what you say and the way that you speak. It means not acting, not using set phrases or professional styles which are not really you. In some ways being sincere means being yourself, being honest and real! Being real has to involve being non-judgemental though, trying to understand people rather than trying to give people advice. If being honest should involve giving other people your advice – don't do it! However, when you listen and learn about other people, do use your own normal language. Think about ways you might describe yourself and occasionally share details of your own life with clients. Sometimes it is necessary to share your thoughts to keep a conversation going.

Sharing information from your own life might help to convey sincerity or genuineness in some situations.

> **Client** 'But what's the point in talking to you, I mean you don't really care, it's just your job.'
>
> **Carer** 'It is my job, but I do care about you, and I would be pleased to talk with you. I chose this work because I care and because I can make the time to listen if you want to talk about it.'

Understanding, warmth and sincerity have to be combined in order to provide a safe, supportive setting. Ideally, carers might combine these approaches with the broader caring value base to develop a *personal style* of working with clients.

Learning to create a supportive relationship with clients will involve practice and a great deal of self-monitoring and reflection. It will be necessary to get feedback from colleagues, supervisors and most importantly clients, when you practise conveying warmth, understanding and sincerity. You may be able to tell if your communication is effective because the client may reflect your behaviour. That is, if you are warm and understanding and the client comes to trust you; then you may find that the client

is warm and friendly toward you. If you are honest and sincere, your clients may be honest and sincere with you. The quality of a supportive relationship can become a two-way process. You may find working with clients more enjoyable because you become skilled at warmth, understanding and sincerity.

The following are ideas for developing supportive skills.

1 Work with a friend. Take turns in imagining that you are upset or sad whilst the other person uses reflective listening skills. Tape record the conversation. Play the tape back and evaluate your performance in terms of warmth, understanding and sincerity.
2 Watch videos of conversational skills or counselling situations where warmth, understanding and sincerity are demonstrated – discuss how this is effective and how you might develop your own conversational skills.
3 Think about your own conversations with clients – keep a log book to reflect on your own skills development.
4 Practise being warm, understanding and sincere with your supervisor or tutor – ask them for feedback!
5 Work on supportive behaviour as part of a group project. Practise being supportive whilst undertaking some problem solving work.

Think it over

Think of someone you don't know well and ask yourself these questions. How would you let them know they were valued? How do they let you know they value you?

Figure 2.3 *All of these are involved in learning to create a supportive relationship with clients.*

People let others know they are valued by being able to distinguish them from other people. A good communicator will listen carefully to what someone has to say and remember it. Next time they meet they will have a point of reference, that is, there will be something from their previous meeting that can be developed. This is likely to be very simple everyday things such as asking someone how their driving lessons are going or if they have moved house yet. It tells the person that the enquirer valued their last conversation (and them!) enough to remember what was happening in their life.

Think it over

Imagine a situation where two care assistants are bathing a client. This sort of practice was common in the past. The two care assistants are talking about the new shift rotas that have been devised. All the toiletries for the bath are assembled. The room is warm and private. Clean clothes are ready for the client. The assistants help the client to remove her clothes and carefully lower her into the bath. She is able to reach the soap and wash herself.

The staff continue to talk between each other, allowing the client five minutes to soak in the water. One of the assistants wonders if another will exchange shifts with her and carefully hoists the client out of the water. She is wrapped in warm, dry towels and helped to dry and dress. When she is finished one of the assistants clears up the bathroom while the other escorts the client to the lounge saying 'There, that was lovely wasn't it, you look nice and fresh now'. The client in this situation is likely to be feeling worthless or, at the best, unfulfilled by the experience. When her family ask if she is being well treated, kept clean and warm the staff can say she is. Why then is she not happy? If she decided to complain could she say:

- *the care assistants did not have all she needed to hand?*
- *the room lacked privacy?*
- *the room was cold and uncomfortable?*
- *she was rushed and not given time to enjoy relaxing?*
- *she was not allowed to be independent as far as possible?*

All these criteria were in fact met. The client had access to a warm room with all her needs to hand. She was given the opportunity to retain her dignity by washing herself and time to relax and enjoy the bath.

The answer to the client's underlying feeling of misery is that the care assistants ignored her existence. She was a body that was being skillfully helped to remain hygienic. She was undervalued as an individual and likely to feel unhappy. The use of phrases such as 'There you look nice and fresh now' could be used with anyone and cease to have meaning for an individual. As well as this they could be patronising, implying that the staff have power over the client. It would be better to talk to the client, 'I hope you have a good day out later, don't spend all your money!' This lets the person know the care assistant has remembered what would be important to them and will probably be interested in hearing about the outing. Half the pleasure of doing things is remembering them afterwards and that is more fun if there is someone interested to hear what we have to tell them.

Think it over

Did you notice any problem with the idea of having two care assistants bathing the client? Unless the client specifically requested this level of help, two people are likely to intimidate the client. It is easier to have a conversation with one carer. With one client and two staff the client will probably not feel safe to talk about personal things. Confidentiality may not seem possible with two care assistants. No wonder the two staff ignored the client, perhaps the client was glad that they did!

· MASLOW'S HIERARCHY OF NEEDS ·

It is almost impossible not to interact with others constantly. However, as a professional in one of the caring occupations it is important to understand some of the theories of interaction in order to work positively with clients. Good interpersonal communication may take place incidentally, but as professionals it is necessary to be aware of different needs and ways of helping people.

In 1954 a humanistic psychologist called Maslow put forward his theory of motivation. The basis of the theory is that individuals have a series, or hierarchy, of needs to motivate them. These range from the very basic physiological needs of satisfying thirst, hunger and the need for shelter, through a range of higher level needs. Maslow believed that once a need had been satisfied it no longer served to motivate a person. The diagram below shows the hierarchy of needs, from the basic through to the higher level needs, which help to realise potential, to 'become everything one is capable of becoming' (Maslow 1970), especially intellectually and creatively. Achieving one's full potential is known as self-actualisation. Skilled communication is important in meeting many of the needs suggested in Figure 2.4.

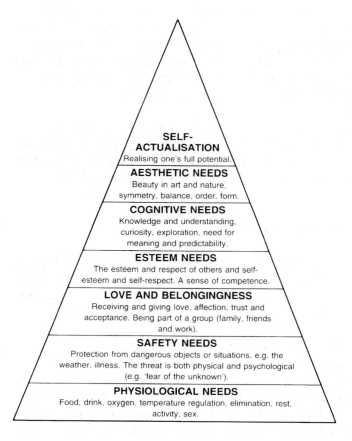

Figure 2.4 *Maslow's hierarchy of needs*

You may have noted that meeting 'Esteem Needs' and 'Love and Belongingness' needs might require good communication skills. If you are able to convey warmth, sincerity and understanding, use supportive skills and avoid factors which inhibit interaction, you will be helping clients to satisfy their needs in these areas. If you treat all clients as individuals and are aware of their physical, cognitive, social, emotional and behavioural needs you will be able to provide skilled care. Only the very poorest forms of social care would fail to meet the basic physiological needs, although there is often confusion or ambivalence (mixed feelings) regarding clients' rights to sexual activity. However, many providers give little thought to their clients' higher level needs.

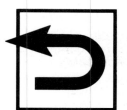

Think it over

Look at Maslow's hierarchy of needs and think about clients you have met in placements. Can you think of any instances of needs being met or remaining unmet?

Task

1 Write up an exchange you have had which you feel demonstrates your communication skills. Include evidence – where possible – of how you selected an appropriate method of communication, used supportive techniques, let the other person know you valued them, and say how you avoided negative behaviour which may have interfered with communication. This exchange may have been with a client, possibly someone with a disability, or with a colleague, boss, friend of member of your family. When you have written your exchange, use Maslow's hierarchy of needs to evaluate where you think you were (or were not) able to meet some of the needs.

2 Analyse a placement you have been on and relate the clients' experiences to Maslow's hierarchy of needs. You may want to concentrate on one client in particular, to evaluate how the staff in the establishment helped them. Write a short report.

When you have completed these tasks you may be able to use them as portfolio evidence for Unit 2.

· TYPES OF BEHAVIOUR ·

It is inevitable that when considering others' behaviour and interaction there will also be a need to consider the way we ourselves behave and why. There is a need for honesty and self-evaluation if we are to understand and control the way we act.

Task

Make a list of: a my strengths and skills; b things I like about myself are; c positive things others say about me are. When you have made your list, find a partner and each go through your lists saying each one confidently. (Think about how you can support your partner in doing this)

When you have done this, find one strength you feel comfortable about saying to the whole group.

We often feel uncomfortable about admitting we are good at something. We might feel anxious not to be thought of as vain or pompous, and so tend to state our faults openly. However, it would be difficult to find someone about whom it was impossible to find something good. Sometimes people neglect opportunities to convey the positive value of others and usually only make critical personal comments. While we should look for opportunities to be positive to others we must also learn how to respond to criticism from others.

The way we respond to criticism will depend on how justified we feel it was, our level of self-respect and

confidence, and probably our mood at the time. Typical reactions are:

- **Aggressive** – immediately deny the fault, refuse to listen or attack the critic immediately
- **Indirectly aggressive** – take no action, but vow revenge
- **Submissive** – feel self-pity, guilt, loss of confidence and accept the criticism
- **Assertive** – listen, ask for more information and then decide whether the criticism is valid.

Aggression

Being aggressive refers to actions which threaten someone or make them feel inferior to you. It may seem a useful strategy in the short term, but it has negative effects – both on others and on you. Responding aggressively may make you feel better. You may feel a sense of power over the other person and be glad to release your anger. However, in the long term you may feel guilty and feel the need to apologise. You may feel you have made yourself unpopular and expect revenge from others. This may mean you are on a constant look-out for attacks, which will be exhausting, and you may even imagine unintended slights. Aggression may result in your becoming isolated from other people.

Your aggressive behaviour can affect others by making them avoid you. They may be humiliated or angry and retaliate openly, or they might wait for an opportunity to undermine you at a later date.

Indirect aggression

When someone is indirectly aggressive they do not explode immediately, but store their anger until later or direct it towards someone who is unconnected to the original event. They may be manipulative.

Although in the short-term being indirectly aggressive means not having to confront people directly, perhaps plotting behind the scenes or letting off steam on somene else, in the long term it may result in stress – from not dealing with anger at the appropriate time. People may distrust someone who behaves in this way.

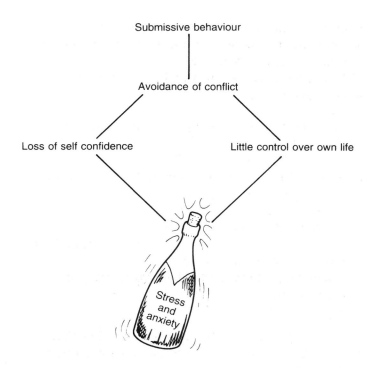

Submission

Being submissive may be based on the belief that other people's needs are more important than your own. Such people may be over-apologetic, helpless, and timid, reinforcing the notion to others that they are in fact of little importance.

Initially others may feel sorry, or guilty, that they have taken advantage of a submissive person; but eventually there is the danger they will feel irritated and lose respect for the submissive individual. Initially submissive people will be relieved at having avoided a conflict situation. They may enjoy playing a martyred role in putting others first. However, in the long term they could suffer a growing loss of self confidence and may feel that they have little control over their lives. This might increasingly cause stress and anxiety.

Assertiveness

Being assertive means accepting the importance of both your own, and other people's needs. It is important to acknowledge the value of feelings and emotions. By being assertive feelings are dealt with

before they become bottled-up tensions. Being assertive means being aware of your reactions and taking them into account when making decisions. It is necessary to speak simply and directly, saying how you feel and expressing your views and wants.

Despite being confident about stating your wants, being assertive is not about getting your own way or putting people down. It means accepting and respecting other people's rights as being equally important as your own. Assertion also means trying to ensure that situations are fair for everyone, so that people can take part on an equal basis.

When you are working with possibly vulnerable clients it is important for you to be able to recognise their needs and try to help clients by behaving appropriately.

Theory into practice

Read the short case-study below and make notes about the behaviours Harold adopts. Why do you think he behaves in this way? How does Sylvia respond?

Harold is a 32-year old factory worker. He works permanent night shift. He lives in a tower block with his wife and three children aged 2, 3 and 6. His wife is expecting a fourth child in three months. Before he was married, Harold worked with a travelling fair. His parents had split up when he was a child and his father remarried. There were younger siblings and Harold felt unwanted. He spent much of his time truanting from school and playing in the open spaces of the woods. He was interested in the wild life and enjoyed the freedom he had in the forest. Harold took the first opportunity to join the fair and travel the country. He enjoyed the work but it was not suitable for a family. He does not enjoy his work at the factory and has recently been in trouble for not keeping up with production targets.

Recently Harold has been mistreating the eldest child, a girl. He is anxious she should do better than he did at school and tries to teach her to do her sums. When she gets one wrong he becomes very angry and shouts. She becomes frightened and often wets herself. Recently he has lost control when this happens and beaten the child. He is sorry afterwards but the beatings have continued for several months now. Sylvia comforts the child afterwards but does not interfere. The child avoids her father when possible.

An interpretation

Harold is being indirectly aggressive. He is probably frustrated by his indoor job, unable to sleep properly during the day in a flat full of small children and has been in trouble at work. Instead of confronting his problems he is bottling up his anger and taking it out on his small child.

Sylvia is behaving submissively. She may not understand Harold's aggression or know how to react. She may adopt the idea that she cannot interfere with her husband's behaviour. Whilst she is sorry for the child she does nothing assertive to help.

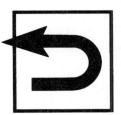

Think it over

If you are going to use assertive skills you will have to accept certain responsibilities. Read the list of 'Assertiveness rights' below and make a list of responsibilities which would need to go with the rights. An example might be: 'To treat other people with equal respect and confront situations where I see people being discriminated against.'

Assertiveness rights and responsibilities

I have the **right** to:

- be treated equally regardless of my age, race, class, sex, sexuality and disability, and whether my work is paid or unwaged
- express my feelings and opinions
- ask for a response
- be listened to and to disagree
- have different needs and wishes from other people
- say no

- criticise others in a constructive way
- know of, and have the opportunity to respond to, criticism made about me
- have time to think when making a decision
- change my mind
- make mistakes
- say I don't understand and ask for more information
- ask for what I want
- judge if I am responsible for finding solutions to others' problems
- be responsible for my own actions
- not depend on others for approval
- set my own priorities as a person, independent of any roles others see me in
- challenge attitudes and behaviour which puts others down
- enjoy myself

If you are going to behave assertively rather than aggressively you may have decided on some of the **responsibilities** below:

- to listen to other people's views and opinions when they disagree with me
- to accept that some of my requests will be turned down
- to accept that others have the right to criticise my actions if they do so in a constructive way
- to be understanding when others make mistakes.
- to check own attitudes and behaviour and ensure that these do not put others down

Dealing with criticism

It is important to be able to receive and give constructive criticism. This is criticism given with foundation and with the intention of improving a situation or response.

The first step when receiving criticism is to ask for more information. This gives you more time to evaluate the situation and means you are able to respond with a full account of the situation. If you feel you need more time you have a right to ask for it. This would mean you were able to talk the problem through with a friend.

"OK, I agree my table manners could be better!"

When you are in full possession of the facts, and have had time to consider them, you must decide whether the criticism is justified or not. If it is, accept it. Remember we all have the right to make mistakes; but we should also learn from them and not make the same ones over and over again. It may be that you accept other people's criticisms but not other people's advice on how you should remedy it. You have the right to negotiate with other people.

If you believe that criticism is unfounded, then feel confident in rejecting it. Find out more about the cause of the criticism; it may not be really to do with you. You may want to ask if the critic is angry about someone or something else. If you talk it through the real reason may emerge. Remember that constructive criticism can be useful, but even valid criticism needs to be made appropriately. It should never put down the person to whom it is directed.

· TRANSACTIONAL ANALYSIS ·

The first section of this chapter considers how we can analyse communication by observing people's verbal and non-verbal signals. This section now explores a theory devised by Eric Berne (1964) called 'Transactional Analysis'. As its name implies, Transactional Analysis (or TA) attempts to analyse the ways people behave very closely. It is based on the assumption that all our experiences from birth onwards are stored in our minds and can be 'replayed'. Children are continuously experiencing new feelings and events and these become significant in our adult memories. As adults we are very influenced by the way we were treated as children and by the experiences we had. TA theorises that we frequently respond as adults in the way we observed our parents responding, or in the way we were taught to respond by adults.

However, Eric Berne believed that we all have the capacity to behave the way we choose to and we are free to make new choices and break away from past patterns of behaviour.

If we consider the way we are feeling psychologically, the very simplest response would be either OK or not-OK. As we become more self-conscious and responsible for our own lives many people spend much of their time feeling not-OK.

It is likely that beneath the surface even in the most apparently smooth and effortless lives people have feelings of shyness, lack of confidence, worry, embarrassment, apprehension, fear and other feelings which can result in feeling not-OK. Mostly these feelings are mild and we can cope, but occasionally they may become dominant and cause problems.

The skill in good interpersonal relations is not only being aware of how you are feeling, but how the other person is feeling. If we spend much of our time feeling not-OK it is likely the people we work with do too. Of course, there are sometimes genuine reasons for feeling not-OK such as, for example, knowing that someone close to you is seriously ill. However, not-OK feelings can be distinguished from genuine feelings in that they become repetitive, manipulative and inappropriate.

Theory into practice

Below is a list of not-OK feelings. Read them and think about one which is particularly familiar to you. If you work with another person you may want to discuss why you think this is the case.

anger	guilt	hurt	frustration
anxiety	loneliness	stupidity	inadequacy
depression	rejection	fear	clumsiness

The same experience will set off very different feelings in different people. Some people may be very familiar with a feeling of rejection but hardly ever of anger. For example, someone accidentally dropping a bottle of milk at breakfast may experience feelings of clumsiness, anger or anxiety, depending on how they had learned to feel as a child. These types of feelings are inappropriate to a trivial situation and must be distinguished from genuine feelings related to external reality.

Berne's TA model

Berne believed that if we look at the way people behave we can observe them existing in three separate states: the Parent, the Adult and the Child states. The diagram below shows the three states and the behaviours associated with them. The three states are always present and were learned by each of us as we grew up and experienced the world.

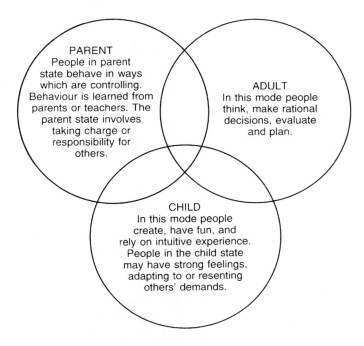

Figure 2.5 *Berne's three states of being*

TA theorises that when a child begins life it experiences everything by feeling – the satisfaction of a full tummy and a cuddle, the misery of a wet nappy and no attention. This is the *natural child* and is a state we will return to throughout life. As a child grows it realises that it must adapt its behaviour to what is demanded by others. These behaviours, such as being polite and obedient, are learned by the *adapted child* alongside not-OK feelings of guilt and anxiety. The growing child learns to behave in the way which will get the right response. Being in *intuitive child* (TA) mode helps the child to behave without working out (logically) why. TA theory suggests that it is in this mode that artists create. They know the techniques but it is intuitive feeling which makes the design original.

When someone is in the adult (TA) state they think logically – are not influenced by emotions. They process information and make judgements on that basis. This state has been referred to within TA theory as the computer within us.

The parent (TA) mode is one where people feel responsibility for others. Children incorporate the views of right and wrong they learn from others around them. There are two aspects: one is of the *critical parent*, which defines the systems under which they feel people should operate, 'the rules', expecting them to be obeyed; the other is the *nurturing parent* which cares for people. Both of these states have their place but can cause problems if over-used.

Think it over

If a parent were constantly in the critical parent *mode what effect might it have on a child? Perhaps the child might begin to feel guilty or stupid, and these feelings might become not-OK feelings in adulthood. If a parent was mostly in* nuturing parent *mode how might this affect a child?*

Sometimes, not allowing others to take responsibility for themselves can be done in order to make the 'rescuing' person feel good. It can result in over-protection and an adult who may feel inadequate and not-OK.

It is possible to observe people's states by watching their non-verbal communication and listening to their tone of voice.

Task

Look at the pictures in Figure 2.6 and decide what mode each participant is in.

a

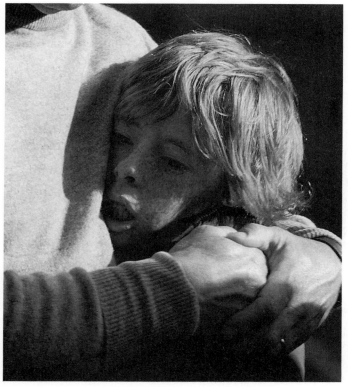

b

c

Answers

a The child enjoying the feeling of a cuddle was in *natural child* mode.
b The adult annoyed at the broken cup was in *critical parent* mode.
c The woman trying to win the man's attention was in *intuitive child* mode.

A well-balanced adult will move between the states, using the one most appropriate at the time. It may be that we have a favourite state and others which we rarely use.

Theory into practice

John Dusay, who worked with Eric Berne, developed a means of exploring our own behaviour. If you carefully record your behaviour, either in all situations or in certain ones, such as at home or at college, you can draw a graph to indicate which behaviours you used most. You could draw a graph using your IT skills (called an Egogram) showing which states were used most and least. This might help to analyse your behaviour and could be used for your portfolio as evidence for Information Technology.

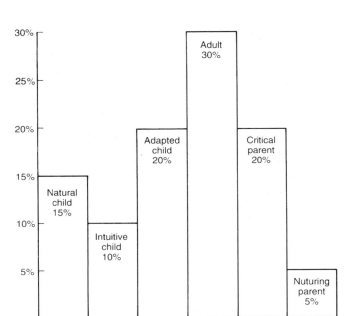

Figure 2.7 *Example of an Egogram*

Stroking

'Strokes' are a term for the calming pleasure that we may get from others, like the feeling of pleasure that comes from being stroked. Strokes need not always be physical. They can be any sort of recognition one person gives another. Without stroking babies will fail to thrive, or to grow as expected.

In an ideal situation, strokes relating to all three states, i.e. child, adult and parent, are positive ones – both when given and when received. Examples might be the child state requiring physical contact, or hugging. The adult might want recognition for a successful piece of work, perhaps putting up a shelf or writing a report. The parent might want thanking for picking up their teenage

son late at night from a party. We all need recognition for what we do in our three states. As well as receiving strokes we must remember to give them. Often we feel embarrassed about saying positive things to one another and find it difficult to receive compliments. However, if we never express our gratitude how can others know how we feel?

Task

Keep a record over one day, or longer if you wish, of all the positive and negative interactions or strokes given by you to others and received by you. You could show this as a graph and use it as evidence for your Information Technology unit.

Sometimes these different strokes are given currency value, i.e. 1p for a Ritual, 5p for Pastimes, 20p for Activities, £1 for Intimacy. Everyone needs a certain number of exchanges to accumulate enough currency to feel they have a value as an individual.

Remember: we need strokes for all three states. The strokes children receive during the first few years of their lives will determine how they feel about themselves as adults. If they are continually put down and criticised they may carry inadequacies throughout their life. Sometimes these not-OK feelings could take the form of dominating others, forever getting angry with their children or partners or subordinates at work. Their behaviour is theorised to have the effect of making others feel not-OK and in conjunction with their own not-OK feelings this becomes a downward spiral of despair, culminating at worst in suicide.

Transactional Analysis describes the ways we use time by a range of choices:

- **Withdrawal**. Basically this is not communicating with others, just watching the world and thinking.
- **Rituals**. These are exchanges with others which have little meaning such as, 'Hi, how are you?', 'Fine, thanks, see you later.'

- **Activities**. These include work, gardening, cleaning etc.
- **Pastimes**. These include general conversation with little depth such as, 'Cold today, isn't it?', 'Where are you going on holiday this year?' This is the sort of conversation you might have in the hairdressers. You are recognised as an individual but the content of the conversation is 'safe', non-controversial.
- **Games**. These are psychological games played by winners and losers.
- **Intimacy**. This recognises warmth and respect. It involves commitment on the part of participants and is sometimes avoided for this reason.

Think it over

James' grandfather functioned in Critical Parent mode much of the time. James now behaves badly and is often in trouble with his own father who often puts him down and makes him feel inadequate. Why does James' father behave like this and why does James continue to behave badly?

Explanation

James' father is patterning his behaviour on the not-OK feelings generated by his own treatment as a child. He has no experience of receiving positive strokes and so cannot give them. He is likely to produce the same feelings in James. However, James continues to seek a response from his father and if the only means of getting it is negatively, he will behave badly. A negative response will be preferred to no response at all.

The theory of Transactional Analysis can be used to 'read' or interpret other people's communication and gain an understanding of what they are hoping to achieve. People might adopt a state which they believe will be beneficial to them. For example, an insecure person may use the Child mode and seek a strong and dominant person (in Adult or Parent mode) with whom to form a relationship. Supposing the insecure person then had the following conversation with a friend:

'I'd love to get a job but John wouldn't let me. He hates the idea of his wife working.'

This person actually does not want a job. She is insecure and lacking in confidence. However, rather than admit this, to herself or her friend, she adopted a Child state in relation to her husband. It was convenient to allow him to support her financially and adopt the Adult role thus preventing her having to face the job market.

Take the example of Paul in a meeting. Paul has recently been passed over for promotion and he refuses to come to terms with it. In the meeting he rejects all plans put forward by the new management on the grounds that 'they won't work'. He refuses to offer any positive alternative suggestions when asked. He is immature, helpless and spontaneous in his anger. He is adopting the Child state in response to a situation over which he has no real control, but by remaining with the Child role he is refusing to function as an adult.

Scripts

Much of what we have looked at concerns the importance of how our interaction with others affects the way they value themselves. When Eric Berne was researching his Transactional Analysis theory he attempted to discover how children make sense of the world and decide what is their place in it. He called this process forming a *script*. Berne believe there are three important ways in which children are given messages about themselves, and thus how they develop their self-concept: modelling, attributing and suggesting.

Modelling

The child observes the way in which people close to them behave. The child forms their opinions on what people and their roles are by what it sees. Modelling is particularly concerned with gender-defined roles and with how children and adults are expected to behave towards one another.

Figure 2.8 *Berne has suggested that there are three ways in which children develop their self-concept*

Think it over

Observe and listen to children talking and playing together. See if you can find evidence of modelling *in their exchanges.*

The play-house in a nursery school is an interesting place to observe children modelling themselves on their experience. Often the roles are very gender-specific, for example a little boy may walk in and sit down and say, 'What's for dinner?'. Psychologists use play-therapy techniques with disturbed children to see how they model themselves in an attempt to discover what is causing their distress. If, for example, a child is being abused, he or she will often 'play out' with dolls what is happening to them and how they perceive their own and others' roles.

Attributing

We all continually receive messages from others 'telling' us what they think of us. Of course, not all messages are given verbally but we form opinions of ourselves by the way others respond to us. Children form their original self-concept by hearing messages like, 'Hurry up, you're so slow' or, 'I knew you'd win' every day of their lives. It would be amazing, therefore, if children did not come to the conclusion

that they were in fact how others described them – slow or bright, attractive or boring. What is so important about the way we respond to children is that once a negative self-concept has been learned it may be very difficult to change. The child may become an unconfident adult with a negative view of themselves. (See Chapter Four.)

Suggesting

Because a child is so vulnerable, powerless, and dependent on adults for survival, it is easy for adults to give messages about what they expect from the child. If a parent or care giver is preoccupied and gives out messages that suggest, 'You are in the way' a child may conclude it is unwanted and withdraw. If a carer adopts a martyred attitude of always being over-worked the child could feel that they should give up their own needs and look after the parent.

The scripts formed in childhood are thought to influence the people we become as adults. In helping people achieve their potential it is important to realise that we all have the power to change our scripts. In order to change we need to analyse where we think our experiences have brought us and what messages we are currently bound by. If you want to do this you can complete the exercise below which will give you some insight into where you are now. If it reveals parts of your experience which you think have contributed negatively to your script, remember that it is possible to change the original messages and give yourself a new set of ambitions about your life. This will not be easy, because of the powerful messages absorbed in childhood, but it can be done. Eric Berne believed that a baby was born with trust in the world. It is only the receipt of negative messages that makes the adult unable to give unqualified love and to think without confusion. Those who decide to rewrite their scripts can rediscover that potential.

Theory into practice

Ask yourself the following types of question. You need not feel you have to have an answer for all of them but the more answers you have, the more clues there will be to your script.

1 *What are your memories of your grandparents?*

2 *What kind of person was your mother or female carer?*

3 *What kind of person was your father or male carer?*

4 *Where and when did you come into the world?*

5 *Do/did you have a 'pet' name?*

6 *What memories of your carers do you have from your childhood?*

7 *What is each/either of your carers saying to you?*

8 *What was your parents' or carers' ambition for you?*

9 *Think of when you felt really good with your father or male carer.*

10 *Think of when you felt really bad with your father or male carer.*

11 *Think of when you felt really good with your mother or female carer.*

12 *Think of when you felt really bad with your mother or female carer.*

13 *What was your favourite story as a child?*

14 *Did you have a favourite hero? Was it male or female?*

15 *What do you think you will die of?*

16 *How old will you be when you die?*

17 *What will be written on your tombstone – and on the back?*

18 *Write down about 30 things you remember your parents or carers passing on to you, for example, 'A little bit of what you fancy does you good', 'Everything in moderation'.*

As you work through this exercise key elements of your script will come through. You will need to concentrate but you should be able to establish the pattern which has given you your adult script.

· WORKING IN GROUPS ·

Just as we almost constantly interact with others on an individual basis so, in a work situation, most people are required to work at least some of the time in groups with other workers. For a group to be

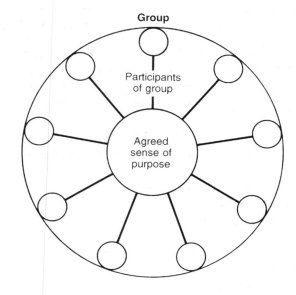

Group

Participants of group

Agreed sense of purpose

successful, all the participants must co-operate with an agreed sense of purpose.

Think it over

Are all people in the same situation a group? Would you say that a number of people at an airport waiting for a flight to be announced is a group in the same way that an air-rescue team is?

You probably came to the conclusion that a number of people waiting for the same flight is very different to a rescue team. Although a group can be defined as 'more than three people together', they also need to be co-operating in an enterprise, psychologically aware of each other and they must perceive themselves as a group. Interesting as people-watching at an airport can be, it is unlikely that the individuals involved would perceive themselves as part of a group in real terms.

Advantages and disadvantages of groups

If you are taking a course or working in a social care environment it is likely that you will often be asked to work as part of a group.

Theory into practice

Make a list of the advantages of working in a group during a course for: (a) the individual; (b) the groups as a whole.

You may want to do this in groups!

Below is a list of advantages of working in groups. Compare it with your own and decide which apply to the individual and which to the group as a whole.

- Broader base of knowledge/skills (shared between people)
- Motivated by others (having company and support)
- Shared responsibility (having others around you)
- Security (safety with others)
- Confidence (in the group, and in their view of you)
- Role models (people whose behaviour can be copied)
- Power (the group may have more power collectively than a single person has)
- Division of tasks (between people; people can do what they are best at)
- Able to work to own strengths (people do the things they are best at)
- Improve weaknesses (people to help you)
- Question assumptions (people to check your ideas)
- Give feedback (people can give advice and help with learning)
- Fun (groups can be!)
- Synergy (the whole is greater than the parts, interacting parts fitting together)
- Richer decisions (better analysis and evaluation)

Think it over

As can be seen there are many advantages to working within a group but, in an imperfect world, there can also be disadvantages. From your own experience of working with others, now make two lists of disadvantages you have experienced: one for individuals and one for groups. You may decide to work alone or with others!

For a group to work and gain the advantages identified earlier, its members will have had to go through a process of learning to work with each other. If this does not happen the following problems may arise:

Individual's difficulties which may occur in group work

- One person may dominate the group
- The leader may 'lean' towards one or more person's views
- There may be confused aims
- Insecurity if individual feels they don't 'fit'
- Loss of own identity
- Specialist jargon might be used
- Excess risk-taking
- Co-leaders may create a power point, making it difficult to challenge their assumptions
- Peer pressure (others might put pressure on you to agree with them)
- Difficult to challenge group values
- Individuals might shelve personal responsibility
- Group pace may differ from own pace
- Lack of personal satisfaction
- Roles could be forced upon individual
- Individual may be tired or overworked

General problems which may exist for groups

- Groups might be inclined to greater risks
- Badly used space, crowded or 'split', inappropriate seating
- Factions/disagreements may occur
- Inertia
- Conflict of aims
- Time wasting discussion
- Power struggles
- Unequal commitment
- The group may refuse to take responsibility

You may have worked in groups which have been very successful – but why was this so? Success does not always happen automatically; so to ensure it does, it is necessary to consider what conditions are ideal.

For a group to work it is often necessary for it to have a common aim. After all, this is probably why the persons concerned came together in the first place. Remember the group discussed earlier who were waiting for a plane? Suppose they had boarded the plane, but had had the misfortune to be involved in a crash during their journey. They would immediately have had to reassess their identity as a group and form much stronger bonds than those of people who were merely in the same queue. Indisputably, their common aim would be to survive the experience, but what else would be needed for the group to work?

The group would need to co-operate, be supportive, and be open with each other. Gradually it would be important to adopt a group identity, become cohesive, stable and, in order to plan, dynamic (or full of energy).

Of course, most groups are not formed in response to such a drastic emergency, but within social care, groups such as support groups are often formed to help those in need.

Creating a successful group

When a group is formed its purpose or objective has to be defined. This is sometimes known as its **mission statement**.

Think it over

Some of the organisations you have worked for on placement will probably have mission statements. Do you know what they are? Do they do what they say they will?

Within a mission statement the objectives have to be realistic, clear and understood by all. There is no point writing mission statements in language most people don't understand, or writing things which are desirable but not achievable. Unfortunately, establishments often have very admirable mission statements, for example about client dignity, but workers do not always abide by them. There is no point in having mission statements about respect and dignity and then barging into people's rooms without knocking! Conversely, while objectives should not be unattainable, they should be ambitious – otherwise no progress would be made.

Groups need to be of an appropriate size and have people with the right skills and training. They also need members who are likely to remain with the group. It is demoralising to have to restart a group because people leave. It is important, therefore, when you are working as a team member, to know that others are depending on you and not to let them down (for example, do not be away when you have some important material for the group's presentation!). The members of a group need to know what is expected of them in order to carry out their part of the task. Many groups also need a leader who is experienced, skilled and committed to the group's aims.

Finally, resources are important. It is difficult to achieve much without such basic resources as place and time to meet, support, materials and finance. Power is an important factor, but sometimes, as in the case of support groups, their very function is to *create* power to achieve unmet ends.

Once the objectives have been defined and values identified, the members of a group need to analyse their strengths and weaknesses and decide on roles to work together. Tasks have to be allocated to decide who will do what and, eventually, progress reviewed.

It is important that there is a balance of personalities within a group, although all members should take an active role. A certain amount of flexibility is needed in the sharing of tasks. If the group is mutually supportive members should feel able to make mistakes and fail without blame. If this is not so, the dynamism (or energy) of the group is curtailed with everyone 'playing safe' so as not to take risks. The group will then be less proactive (able to plan) and will achieve less in the long run. Finally, members must be committed to attend meetings and show good timekeeping.

If a group consists of people working towards common goals (for example, surviving the air crash), and if a group which works well together can accomplish much more than one person alone, why don't all groups work? Much research has taken place on this subject and many people feel that groups have to go through a process of maturing before they function efficiently. Tuckman (1965, pp. 384–99), divided the process into four stages shown in Figure 2.9.

Performing As people become more comfortable within the group there can be more flexibility and less directive leadership. The group shares a common system of norms and values. Morale is high and the group is successful.

Norming During this stage a culture is established around shared norms and values. Roles are defined, with members specialising in areas, and trust is created

Storming There may be leadership challenges during this stage and debate as to the group's objectives. Eventually a realistic 'mission statement', purpose or objective should emerge.

Forming During this stage the group gets together and a strong leader emerges. Members are unsure of the objective and may be subject to scapegoating by other members.

Figure 2.9 *Tuckman has suggested that groups go through a process of maturing before they function efficiently*

In an ideal world, all groups would progress through these stages to successful outcomes, but not all do. Woodcock (1979) says that some groups get stuck in the *Forming* stage and need to be pushed through the next two stages before becoming mature and reaching a *Performing* stage.

Think it over

Within an educational situation the aim of a group might be to help people learn. How can you, as a group member, help yourself and others?

You may decide that groups can help the learning process by:

- offering information and advice
- listening to problems
- careful questioning
- summary and reflection
- encouragement
- providing opportunities.

Group interaction

In any form of group interaction individual people will adopt different ways of behaving. The same person will probably behave differently within different groups. As a group goes through its maturation process, individuals will adapt their behaviour. Bales (1970) observed groups in action and defined the following types of behaviour:

1 Proposing – a behaviour which puts forward a new concept, suggestion or course of action.
2 Building – a behaviour which extends or develops a proposal which has been made by another person.
3 Supporting – a behaviour which involves a declaration of support or agreement with another person or their ideas.
4 Disagreeing – involves a declaration of difference of opinion, or criticism of another's ideas.
5 Defending/attacking – a behaviour which attacks another person or defensively strengthens a person's own position. Defending/attacking behaviours tend to involve open value judgements and often contain emotional overtones.
6 Blocking/difficulty stating – a behaviour which places a difficulty or blockage in the path of a proposal without offering an alternative proposal, or which states a difficulty without full reason.
7 Open – a behaviour which exposes an individual who shows it to the risk of loss of status or to ridicule. Admissions of mistakes or inadequacies made in a non-defensive manner.
8 Summarising – a behaviour which summarises, or otherwise restates in a compact form, the ideas of previous discussions.
9 Seeking information – a behaviour which seeks facts, ideas or clarification from another member.

10 Testing understanding – a behaviour which seeks to establish whether or not contributions have been understood.

11 Giving information – a behaviour which seeks facts, ideas or clarification from another member.

12 Bringing in – a behaviour which offers facts, ideas and opinions to others.

13 Shutting out – a behaviour seeking to exclude another.

Task

In order to begin to analyse how you and others function in groups you will need to identify the types of behaviour used. A method known as the 'goldfish bowl' technique enables an observer to record on a chart each person's behaviour within a group discussion. Imagine that the people at the airport we discussed earlier boarded their plane, but that it crashed as it crossed the desert. Fifteen people survived the crash, as did a motorcycle which was in the hold of the plane. The temperature in the desert was very high and the survivors were not likely to last more than a few hours without water. Only two people can be selected to board the motorcycle and head for an oasis twenty miles to the south. There is a working compass on board.

Form into two groups. The discussion which follows should last for fifteen minutes. One group will discuss which of the fifteen passengers described below should go for help. The other group will select one member each of the first group and monitor their part in the discussion by marking the boxes on the chart (below). Do not say who is monitoring who.

List of survivors
 1 *Pilot, appears to be in shock.*
 2 *Doctor*
 3 *Army sergeant (female)*
 4 *Mother of ten children*
 5 *Priest*
 6 *Man in remission from cancer*
 7 *Orienteering expert, wanted by police for murder*
 8 *World-renowned plastic surgeon*
 9 *Taxi driver*
10 *Old-age pensioner on way to see newborn grandchild*

Chart to profile individual's interaction

Group member: _____

	Time intervals										Minute by minute: 10 to 15 minutes				
Proposing															
Building															
Supporting															
Disagreeing															
Defending/attacking															
Blocking/difficulty stating															
Being open															
Testing understanding															
Summarising															
Seeking information															
Giving information															
Bringing in															
Shutting out															
Total															

Figure 2.10   *The 'goldfish bowl' technique*

11 *Manual labourer, native of desert*

12 *RAF (engineer), male, accompanied by person number 13*

13 *Eleven-month old son (of RAF engineer)*

14 *Air hostess*

15 *Long-distance runner*

Group polarisation

Much research has taken place as to whether decisions reached by groups of people differ radically from those made by individuals. Bem, Wollach and Kogan in a number of studies between 1962 and 1965 believed that groups were more inclined to take greater risks than individuals and this became known as the 'risky shift' effect.

However, subsequent studies found that groups may not necessarily be less cautious but that they tend to be more extreme either in caution or risk than the individual. If the individuals were initially cautious, the group would become more cautious. If the individuals were inclined to take risk, the group would take greater ones. It is the norms or values which become adopted by the group which cause 'polarisation'. The group becomes more extreme or polarised when people focus on shared beliefs.

Think it over

Why might individuals take a more or less cautious view than their own original one when formulating a group response?

You probably realised that there are two basic reasons:

- people tend to be influenced by others
- they gain more information on a topic after discussion.

These two effects have been classified as:

- the normative influence and
- the informational influence

The group provides a forum in which the person can get extended information and can re-evaluate their position. Studies have shown that either the informational influence or the normative influence can work independently, but that the informational effect is greater.

Task

You could test out these ideas by having a group discussion.

Firstly, read the scenario below and on a scale of 1–10 write down a score each for Peter and the assistant on the justification of stealing drugs. (10 is high and 1 is low.) Do not tell the rest of the group what the scores are. When you have read the scenario discuss your views and reach a group score each for Peter and the assistant. You can then compare your individual scores and see if they have been influenced by the group.

Peter's fiancee Thelma has lung cancer. She is twenty eight and they have a six month old son. Thelma has seen a hospital consultant who tells her the pharmacy at the hospital has a new, very expensive drug which could treat her. The drug could at best hold the disease in remission for around ten years.

However, the consultant refuses to treat Thelma unless she agrees to give up smoking. The hospital cannot afford to treat everyone and there are other people who do not smoke needing the drug. Thelma has smoked since she was a child and feels, with the pressure she is under, she would not be able to do this.

Peter knows the assistant at the hospital pharmacy. The assistant has a disabled mother who needs extra support, more than he can afford to give her on his wages. Peter persuades the assistant to steal a week's supply at a time for payment and to continue doing so until the consultant confirms the disease is in remission. This is likely to take at least a year and the cost to the hospital of the stolen drugs will be many thousands of pounds.

Is Peter justified in asking the assistant to steal for him and Thelma?

Is the assistant justified in stealing the drug?

Task

From what you have learned about yourself and seen of groups operating make a list of what you feel makes groups succeed or fail. You can do this alone or in a group.

Some of the reasons for groups succeeding are listed below. You may have thought of others – there are many reasons, which vary depending on the circumstances of the group.

Success in groups

- composition of group – right people
- agreement as to objectives

- outcomes agreed, even if it is not what the individual might want
- openness about agendas etc.
- agreement as to way of operating
- good quality information
- experience of respect for others, active listening, feeling valued
- not feeling pressurised
- ability of individuals to pick up signals and respond
- role of leader (to be discussed later)

Failure in groups

- no clear agenda or objectives
- participants not feeling equally valued, balance of contribution
- lack of trust, suspicion, hidden agendas – individual or organisation
- avoidance tactics, avoiding work
- different power levels within group
- too much time or not enough time

Chairing a group

Obviously one of the key persons in a group is the person who chairs it. They are responsible for making sure that the meeting covers the agenda and progresses as it should.

Task

Make a list of what you think a chairperson needs to do within a meeting.

A chairperson can have a long list of duties – no wonder many people avoid chairing meetings! Some key points are listed in Figure 2.11.

Remember that both the chairperson and group members can positively or negatively influence people's feeling of inclusion. All members of groups

- define objectives, set a time-scale and keep to it unless it is renegotiated

- pay attention to the process and people as much as to the task/content

- keep the session moving

- involve people in the discussion, control any 'dominators'

- clarify points of discussion

- bring people back to the point if things start to drift

- summarise progress

- check out the views of non-contributors

- ensure an outcome to any discussion

- summarise points, identify key issues, check for agreement, action

Figure 2.11 *Key duties that a chairperson may have*

Actions to prevent difficult behaviour			
	Before (meeting)	During (meeting)	After (meeting)
Self			
With other person			
With the whole group			

Task

Taking each of the four types of behaviour, brainstorm how you might deal with the difficulties they present.

positively and negatively influence the feeling of openness, and thus trust, experienced by their colleagues, as well as people's feelings of control and ownership.

Difficult behaviour in groups

Despite being aware of the roles you and others play when working in groups, almost everyone will experience difficult behaviour from group members at some time. It is impossible here to predict what form this might take, or the reasons for it, but the grid that follows offers one strategy you might adopt to try to work through the difficult behaviour. Enter your ideas for handling the difficulty in the boxes.

Types of difficult behaviour may include: (1) people who are unmotivated or reluctant to join in; (2) those who put others down; (3) aggressive people; (4) those who are dominant or just talk too much.

People who are reluctant to join in can be encouraged in the following ways:

- encourage contributions and reinforce their offerings
- try to find why they are resistant or reluctant to join in
- allow them to choose their task
- offer alternative work
- give time
- give responsibility
- encourage others in the group to respond to the reluctant person's suggestions
- get them to work with a supportive group member
- attend to what they offer
- be patient
- work on relationships within the group
- challenge if appropriate
- if appropriate, invite to leave the group.

People who put others (or the task) down can be helped towards less difficult behaviour. You might:

- set ground rules
- give the group responsibility – use others to rebuff criticism
- build a contract for membership
- support/reinforce/model other behaviours

- give feedback
- confront behaviour
- allow time out for the group.

To help deal with aggressive people in the group you could:

- confront behaviour
- give feedback
- focus on difficulties and feelings produced by behaviour
- reinforce more appropriate behaviour
- discuss effect on group
- set ground rules
- seek causes for behaviour
- discuss with person outside group.

Dominant or talkative people can be encouraged to work better with others. You might decide to:

- agree to share time for discussion
- divide into small groups – to give less opportunity for dominance
- discuss the effect on the group
- give specific task, e.g. taking notes for group!
- encourage others to contribute more
- seek others' views about confronting the culprit in the group
- speak with the person outside the group situation.

Group values

Groups can form around all sorts of purposes and values. Some people just want to belong to something and will go along with anything. Some groups create a sense of belonging by breaking social rules (taking drugs and so on). Other groups unite around values, like opposing fox hunting – they share a common value in being opposed to something.

In care work it is important that groups respect and value individual group members. Valuing individual people is part of the unwritten rules for working together.

Group work in social care should reflect the NVQ value base. (See box below). 'Promoting individual rights and choices' and 'maintaining confidentiality' may not always be easy to demonstrate, but the other areas of the NVQ value base should come into all individual and group communication.

Demonstrating respect and value for others and demonstrating supportive behaviour are not just skills; they also provide the value base for creating the sense of 'belonging' among individuals in a discussion group.

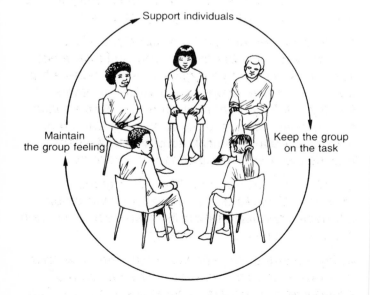

Maintain the group feeling · Support individuals · Keep the group on the task

Figure 2.12 *The dynamics of a care group*

> **All individual conversations, group work and professional care work have to demonstrate these values:**
> - Support individuals through effective communication.
> - Acknowledge individuals' personal beliefs and identities.
> - Promote individual rights and choices.
> - Maintain confidentiality.
> - Promote anti-discriminatory practice (which includes identifying and challenging discrimination based on race, gender, culture, religion, age, physical appearance, physical ability and mental ability).

Getting care groups to work

Most care groups have a purpose or task to work on. Children get together to play games, adults may get together in recreational groups. Groups often need a focus – a game to play, an activity to join in or a topic to discuss.

1 If individuals are going to join in a supportive group meeting, then someone will need to introduce the activity – start the conversation. From time to time when the conversation wanders, someone will need to steer it back to the right topic.
2 Occasionally group members will need to clarify, or make sense of, what is being said.
3 Throughout the group meeting people will need to exchange ideas on the activity or topic being discussed.
4 Towards the end of a meeting, group members will need to agree on what has happened or what the group has decided. The group will come to some kind of conclusions.

As well as performing their tasks, groups have to be 'maintained'. Group maintenance consists of encouraging a sense of belonging and keeping the whole meeting enjoyable. The following are some behaviours to maintain group discussion in a caring setting:

a A bit of laughter can help to relieve tension and create a warm, friendly feeling that everyone can join in.
b Show interest in the people in the group – learn about the 'identity' of group members.
c Be 'warm' and show respect and value when listening to people who are different from yourself or who have had different life experiences. This behaviour makes it safe to be in the group.
d Express feelings honestly and with sincerity. This will help others to understand *your* identity. Help others to understand you as well as trying to understand others.
e Take responsibility for everyone having a chance to speak and contribute. Some people may need to be encouraged or invited to speak, some people may need organising, so that turn-taking works!
f If necessary get people to explain what they have said, and to talk through disagreements. Group

members need to feel that their shared values will make it possible to arrive at solutions when people disagree.

A group leader must keep reflecting on what is happening in the group. Does the group need to come back to the task? Is this the right time for a funny story? Should I make it clear that I am listening and that I value what is being said by this person? Every other group member who really wants the group to work will also monitor how the group is getting on with its task.

To summarise: care groups need to provide a task, keep a sense of belonging going and make sure each individual is supported and valued.

Task

The best way to learn about supportive behaviour in groups is to take part in practical group activities. Try to organise a discussion group with colleagues or friends. If you can, arrange to have the meetings video-taped or tape-recorded. Naturally you will need to check issues of confidentiality and plan the discussion task before doing any recording.

Once you have recorded a group discussion, analyse your own behaviour. How good were your listening skills? Did your questions and non-verbal behaviour convey respect and value for others' identity? Did you contribute to group maintenance, by showing understanding, conveying warmth or sincerity? Above all, was the group a pleasant experience, was there a sense of belonging?

Check your evaluations with another group member. What did he or she make of the group and your part in it? Reflect on what happened, then organise another group meeting.

Doing several observations should help to develop your own self-awareness and understanding of supportive conversation techniques in groups. The final observations should help to produce much of *the evidence you might need for an assignment on 'Group communication'. This work will also provide evidence for the core skill of Communication.*

. CLIENTS' RIGHTS IN INTERPERSONAL . SITUATIONS

If you consider for a minute the clients you have worked with, you will realise that many of them are vulnerable. They have a part of their lives which is dependent upon others' help. If this help is not given impartially it would be very easy for their lives to be manipulated – to live how others think they should, rather than as they themselves want to. Because someone needs help in certain areas it does not mean they should lose their freedom to choose how to live.

Think it over

What do you consider to be your rights? Brainstorm your own views, or work with a group.

There have been many attempts to define client rights by working parties, such as the Human Rights Convention in 1950. Many of them have been adapted for their own purposes by care settings which use them as a value base. All in some form will consider **freedom from discrimination, respect for identity, confidentiality, choice, independence, privacy**, and **dignity**. As we work through these areas compare them with your list of rights. There will be obvious differences for people living in residential care, but some of the things you may have taken for granted may not be so automatic for clients.

Freedom from discrimination, confidentiality and respect for identity

A 'good' care setting will seek to:

1 ensure that clients are not subject to abuse including inhuman or degrading treatment, whether physical or mental or compelled to undertake domestic or other tasks against their will.
2 encourage freedom of consience, thought and religion, and facilitate participation in political process and in chosen activities, religious or otherwise.
3 encourage freedom of expression – meaning the right to complain, to hold opinions, and to receive and impart information and ideas, particularly regarding personal care and treatment.
4 maintain the right to liberty, including from participation in care and treatment.
5 respect private and family life, confidentiality of personal affairs and personal space.
6 permit and facilitate close personal relationships, sexual or otherwise and including marriage, between residents and between residents and other acquaintances.
7 permit and facilitate opportunities for social and other gatherings for whatever purpose, inside and outside the home, and place no restrictions on participation.
8 supply information to residents and apply appropriate types and levels of support to encourage and enable them to exercise their rights.
9 safeguard individual rights without discriminating on any grounds, including gender, age, race, colour, language, religion or other status, or political or other opinion.
10 ensure that where it is deemed necessary to interfere with or restrict an individual's rights, for the protection of that person or the rights and freedoms of others, or for any reason, such actions are recorded, explained to the individual and other interested parties, and reviewed regularly according to an agreed procedure.
11 have mechanisms for monitoring the care setting's performance in safeguarding residents' rights.

Choice

A 'good' care setting will seek to:

1 recognise the inherent value to clients' well-being of their being able to exercise some choice about the content of their daily lives.
2 have a clear picture of clients' physical and mental capacities and knowledge of the extent to which each person wishes – and is able – to make choices.
3 ensure that clients have adequate information on which to base decisions.
4 promote a care regime which facilitates and encourages clients to exercise choice regarding personal affairs, care and lifestyle in the context of an agreed notion of acceptable risk and the constraints of communal life.
5 create a physical environment in which clients can choose to use a variety of spaces and facilities, and one which is safe from hazards and has aids for people with physical disabilities; so that inaccessibility or fear of accidents should not limit scope for exercising choice.
6 monitor each client's condition and behaviour so as to ensure that a reasonable balance is achieved between self-determination, degree of risk involved and impact on other people.
7 create safeguards to ensure that any limitations placed on residents' right to exercise choice are explained, justified and reviewed regularly.

Independence

This is defined as, 'opportunities to think and act without reference to another person, including a willingness to incur a degree of calculated risk'. A 'good' care setting will seek to:

1 have some knowledge of clients' previous lifestyles and consult with them and their relatives/advisers so as to understand their expectations and wishes regarding independence.
2 help and encourage clients to think and act independently as far as this is compatible with their own abilities, their impact on other people, the constraints of communal life and the risks involved.

3 encourage and enable clients to participate in making decisions about home-life in general, insofar as they wish and are able to do so.
4 provide a physical environment which enables clients to do as much as possible for themselves without having to rely on staff assistance or having things done for them.
5 monitor each client's condition and behaviour so as to ensure that a reasonable balance is achieved between independence and risk taking.
6 create safeguards to ensure that any limitations placed on clients' scope to act independently are explained, justified and reviewed regularly.

Privacy and dignity

This is defined as, 'the right of individuals to be left alone or undisturbed and free from intrusion or public attention into their affairs'. A 'good' care setting should:

1 have some knowledge of clients' previous lifestyles so as to understand their expectations regarding personal privacy.
2 identify clients' preferences regarding the extent to which they wish to associate with other clients and in what circumstances.
3 ensure that clients can meet people, have conversations, make or receive telephone calls, correspond and receive visitors, without being overlooked or overheard, and without having to account to anyone for their actions.
4 ensure that clients can bathe, wash and use the toilet without being overlooked or overheard, and that they are protected from intrusion whether accidental, deliberate or routine.
5 ensure that where staff assistance is required to enable clients to dress, bathe, wash or use the toilet this is kept to the minimum commensurate with the residents' abilities and is performed with due regard to the need to safeguard the privacy of the individual.
6 make suitable arrangements for clients to discuss personal matters with staff and visitors in private.
7 ensure that staff deal discreetly with the affairs of clients and safeguard the confidentiality of information held about them.

8 ensure that essential housekeeping and administrative procedures intrude as little as possible on the privacy of individuals or groups.

9 create safeguards to ensure that any erosion of privacy that is considered by 'management' to be necessary in order to provide essential care for individuals, is explained, justified and reviewed regularly.

10 create a physical environment which protects people from the public gaze, which allows the choice of whether to be alone or in company, which provides personal and private spaces for every individual, which provides for security of information and personal possessions, and in which shared facilities such as bathrooms and toilets are designed to ensure that personal activities can be conducted in complete privacy.

The maintenance of identity and meeting higher order needs

Maslow's hierarchy suggests a need for personal fulfilment. Fulfilment is defined as 'the realisation of personal aspirations and abilities in all aspects of daily life.' A 'good' care setting will seek to:

1 know some of the things that clients have done in earlier life, and the skills and interests which they can retain.

2 help clients to continue to use such skills and follow such interests, if they so wish, and to aspire to new ones.

3 further the maintenance of established personal relationships and create conditions which facilitate the development of new ones where so desired.

4 build on clients' experience and knowledge, rather than merely 'manage' negative features such as confusion or physical incapacity.

5 help clients to use their physical and mental faculties, within the limit of their abilities and wishes, but recognise and cater for those who have no wish to be active or sociable.

6 understand and cater for the emotional and spiritual needs of clients.

7 encourage and enable clients to participate in making decisions about their own lifestyles insofar as they are willing and able to do so.

8 create a stimulating environment and provide appropriate supporting services.

9 create a lifestyle which is flexible and which can adapt and develop as clients change.

As you read through the above criteria you may see that the basis is, wherever possible, a client should be able to choose what they wish to do and only be constrained by safety and concern for others' needs. If clients are prevented from doing something they wish to do the reasons must be carefully explained, recorded and reviewed. It should not be a 'once and for all' *no*. Like many things in life, this is easier to say than to do!

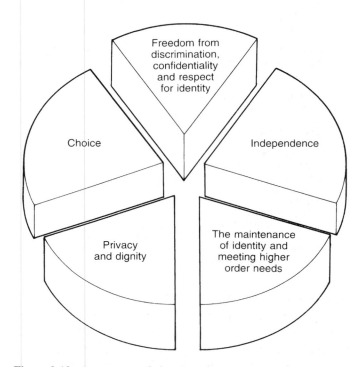

Figure 2.13 *A summary of client's rights in interpersonal situations*

Below is a well-known charity's own interpretation of the value base which is used with young people with learning difficulties. Against the policy they match the evidence they have to show how it is put into practice. This matching practice takes place on a daily, weekly, termly and annual basis. From your

own experience of social care placements, try to complete the second half of the chart with examples you know take place. If you have had involvement with the practice you may be able to use this as evidence for your portfolio; check with your tutors.

Value base	Practice
continuity and consistency	
choice	
dignity	
confidentiality	
Respect – empowerment	
communication	
access to relationships	
open access to records	
challenging disadvantage	
independence	
fulfilment	
Potential development	
hope	
creating opportunity	
partnership	
working together	
Membership sharing and caring	
responsibility	
the environment	
privacy	
Rights – empowerment	
involvement in decisions (participation)	
health and safety (protection, welfare, care)	
access to education	

You may see from the value base examples, that attempts are made to give individuals control over their lives in as many ways as possible. The examples are broken down into daily, weekly, termly and annual examples to remind staff that this is an on-going process and not something which is documented at an annual review and then not practised.

If, for example, a pupil arrived at the school they would immediately begin to be encouraged to make choices and be independent within the daily structure. They are offered choices about food, going to bed and getting up. In order to foster community responsibility they will negotiate certain chores to be done by individuals. They will be offered opportunities for privacy by having their own personal space in their bedrooms and the use of bathrooms. Leisure activities will be individually planned with the opportunity to participate in a

---

Value base – examples of practice

Daily
– individual interactions between young people and staff
– access to – daily planning and decisions
    – documentations e.g. daily diaries, incident reports
– access through complaints procedure
– participation in academic and social skills programmes
– food, mealtimes
– waking up
– going to bed
– work activities
– personal space, use of bedrooms, bathrooms etc.
– sharing, participation, certificate presentation
– weekend activities

Weekly
– in house meetings/team meetings
– shares
– access to agenda, planning, decisions
– contact with range of people
– money management – pocket money/ allowances etc

Termly
– participation in planning regarding:
– activities
– holidays
– celebrations and special events
– leisure
– cultural events
– home visits
– places of worship
– medical issues
– money, clothing grants
– transitions – new young people joining
    – new staff joining
    – moving base house
– decision making through – school council planning discussions

Annually
– annual reviews
– annual reports

group or not. They will see people valued as individuals by the presentation of certificates. Each pupil will be shown the records kept about them and know that they have access to the planning and decision making process. They will be aware of how to complain if they feel they are being unfairly treated. By itemising examples in this way every opportunity to use this value base is maximised.

Stereotyping

If base values are not used in caring, there may be a danger of sterotyping clients. Stereotyping basically means we make fixed assumptions about people or things.

Many studies have taken place relating to stereotyped responses. Dion et al (1972), for example, found that people perceived as physically attractive were thought to be happier, nicer and more able than physically unattractive people. This has obvious disadvantages for people who happen to be physically unattractive! It is wrong to stereotype people because our assumptions can influence the way we actually treat them. This can, in turn, become a *self-fulfilling prophecy*. A self-fulfilling prophecy occurs when someone's behaviour is so influenced by others' expectations that they actually behave as was predicted. All clients are vulnerable, children especially. Meichenbaum et al (1969) told teachers of juvenile offenders that six out of a group of 14 had unrealised academic potential. The teachers were so influenced by the prediction that they raised their expectations of the six who, in turn, did significantly better than the other eight. They had fulfilled the prophecy to succeed even though it had no foundation!

If we are not careful, stereotyping people can lead to discrimination and judgemental behaviour. It is important, therefore, to involve clients in planning all areas of their lives as far as possible. If the clients themselves are not able to enter fully into discussions their needs are sometimes represented by a person known as an *advocate*, who can be a friend or professional social worker.

· MEETING INDIVIDUAL NEEDS ·

Most social care agencies plan each client's care individually. As well as helping them to identify and meet the client's needs, this process also provides information about the need for future development of services and helps monitor service provision.

Any process which is designed to meet the needs of an individual must be adaptable to enable the identification and recording of a huge range of needs. The needs will be long and short term, and it is unlikely that they can all be met immediately. It is necessary, as with most plans, to prioritise. A person's needs change as they develop, so it is necessary to update and review plans regularly.

Task

If you were planning to meet the needs of a person with a learning difficulty what type of issues would you need to consider?

It is likely that the following areas of a person's life would need consideration:

- a place to live – independent/sheltered?
- occupation – open or part of a scheme?
- income
- leisure/education and training
- social contacts and social and emotional needs
- support and any physical needs
- cultural needs

When identifying a person's needs it is important to inform resource managers of needs which cannot be met because of lack of provision; for example, the local college of further education may not run suitable courses. This information can be used when developing new resources. It is also useful to discover how existing services are meeting the needs of an individual, or whether they may need changing or developing.

The basic principle is that the individual concerned should be involved as much as possible at all stages in identifying needs and saying how they should be met. The process must be introduced in a form which will enable the person to have the greatest input into the process which will affect their life.

When the person is able to make a decision about their life *and* understand the consequences, that decision must take priority over other people's views. This means the care-worker must be non-*judgemental*. Even if the client is taking what the care-worker considers a wrong decision, when the position and consequences have been explained fully the client must decide for themselves. Non-judgemental behaviour means not judging a client using our own norms and beliefs. Non-judgemental behaviour means not discriminating against people because they operate from different norms. It may often be important to challenge clients' behaviour. Being non-judgemental means that we challenge the behaviour rather than criticising the individual. Non-judgemental behaviour provides a way of challenging without needing to threaten a client's identity.

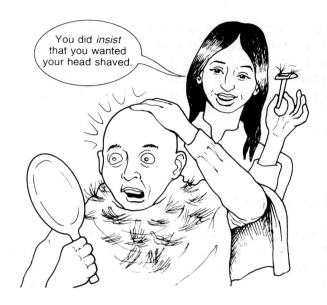

> You did *insist* that you wanted your head shaved.

Think it over

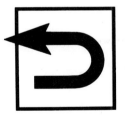

Have you ever made a decision which others have considered foolish? Or refused to take advice? You may want to share this with a colleague.

Most of us can easily recall times when we have stubbornly insisted on doing what we wanted against others' advice. This is important because it gives us the opportunity to learn from our mistakes.

Everyone is entitled to make mistakes and most of us learn from them. Unfortunately, people in care situations are often protected to the extent that they never have these chances. This is to deny them learning opportunities. Unless something will put a client or others in danger, they should be allowed to make their own choices even if it is not what we would choose.

Preparing for a planning meeting

Individual care or programme plans are sometimes developed in care settings – see Chapter Seven for further details.

Before an individual planning meeting takes place the care-worker involved should spend time with the client, getting to know them and gathering as much information as possible. A statement of *strengths* and *needs* might be drawn up to present at the meeting.

Think it over

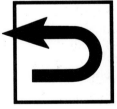

What sort of skills do you think a care-worker helping a client plan for a meeting would need?

The worker should:

- have the ability to get to know the client
- be able to convey supportive skills (warmth, understanding, sincerity)
- be able to observe and identify Strengths and Needs
- record information in an organised manner
- present information clearly and concisely

- prepare the client for the meeting
- work within the NVQ value base

If you look at the list again you will see that many of the skills needed are those in the Core Skills Communication unit of the GNVQ.

Assessment of strengths and needs

Before the meeting the client and worker should discuss together a list of the client's strengths and short/long-term needs. These must reflect the circumstances of the individual and *not* the availability of a particular set of resources or services already in existence. Needs should take into account wishes, desires and aspirations and not just be geared to daily living requirements. However, they should be realistic and not over-ambitious to prevent disappointment.

Individual planning meeting

The person concerned, together with their parents/advocate if appropriate, will decide who should be involved in order to meet the individual's needs. Friends and other workers may be invited, or someone who has an input into the individual need. For example, if the meeting were for a partially-sighted student it may be helpful to have someone available who could discuss computerised aids to learning. At this meeting specific, realistic goals should be developed; some of which would be attainable before the next meeting. Priorities for longer term needs would be identified.

After the meeting relevant records should be completed. The care-worker will be responsible for monitoring progress and a data base may be updated.

Support strategies for clients during a meeting

In order for clients to feel confident and able to state their needs and make choices, it is important to ensure effective communication can take place. Remember that care staff may be well used to attending meetings, but to clients and their families they may seem intimidating. It helps to reduce the level of stress to have someone outside the meeting room to come in with them. It is easy for them to see the professionals as a group which excludes them, e.g. chatting, drinking tea. The meeting should take place at a venue where the client feels most comfortable – not where it is most convenient for staff.

If the client and their family are to be called by first names, then the professionals in the team should be too. The person chairing the meeting should introduce everyone or let them introduce themselves. Clients should understand that they are the most important people and the meeting is for them.

Do not use jargon: initials may not be understood by everyone present (including some of the staff probably!) Be clear about the purpose of the meeting and the setting of *goals*. It is important to word the goals carefully. They are specific and ought to be attainable before the next planning meeting. Other goals may be set as longer term goals or objectives. *Strengths* may be used to set goals. The *needs* are the things the person needs to learn, or which they would like to learn, to make them more independent.

· CONFIDENTIALITY ·

All information relating to a client and their circumstances is confidential and may not be shared without that person's permission. This is one of the base values of social care and one which may cause conflict when the worker feels something has been or is about to be divulged, which they would feel obligated to act upon. Say, for example, a client seemed about to tell a hostel worker they were taking drugs. Now, if the rules of the hostel clearly stated that no-one should enter the premises while under the influence of, or possessing, drugs or alcohol, the worker would have a dilemma if the client continued. At this point the worker should stop the client and explain that if the conversation continued the worker would have to take the information further and that may result in the client being asked to leave.

If, however, a client told a worker they were taking drugs, the worker could ask the client if they would allow someone else to be told who might be able to offer help. If the client agrees the worker is able to proceed. The worker would need to inform their supervisor of any serious information such as a client taking illegal drugs. Confidentiality is not always as important as health and safety principles or the need to work within the law.

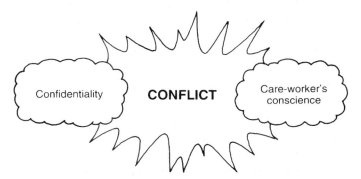

Figure 2.14 *Conflict can occur between issues of confidentiality and the worker's conscience*

There is often conflict between issues of confidentiality and the worker's conscience. If something potentially harmful to the client is kept completely quiet the worker may be liable for disciplinary action. There can be no such thing as complete confidentiality. If, for example, a client tells a worker that they are being abused by someone and the worker does nothing out of respect for confidentiality, the client is at risk. However, if the client tells a worker that a relative is breaking the law, this would not have implications for the client and so confidentiality could be preserved.

Task

Suppose an older woman was having her hair done by a care worker when the worker noticed she had a scalp infection. What should the worker do?

The worker could not possibly go into the staffroom and say 'Hey did you know Mrs So-an-so has a nasty infection on her scalp'! This would be breaching the client's right to privacy. The worker should mention to the client that she has a scalp infection and say it would be a good idea for the doctor to look at it. The worker should then request that the officer-in-charge asks the doctor to see the client, if the client agrees to this. Should the client ask for it to be kept confidential, the worker might have to explain that they must inform the manager.

The basic rule of thumb is to ask yourself if the client will be put at risk by preserving absolute confidentiality. If this is so, the worker's duty to themselves and the client has to be to refer the issue to a supervisor who can decide what to do.

Self-assessment test

1 There are two methods of communicating with other people, what are they?
2 What does body language involve?
3 Which of the following is gaze not indicative of?
   a Attraction
   b Anger
   c Rejection
   d Feeling cold in winter
4 Which of the following would indicate that a listener is not paying attention?
   a Assuming an open body posture
   b Smiling, nodding
   c Reorganising their file
   d Tolerating silences
5 What did Maslow define as the basic physiological needs?
6 The best way to deal with criticism is:
   a To be aggressive and deter the critic.
   b To be assertive – ask for the reasons for the criticism.
   c Be submissive and accept it's your own fault.
   d Do nothing but vow revenge – be indirectly aggressive.
7 An example of being assertive is:
   a 'I am entitled to do what I want'.
   b 'I should expect other people to agree with me'.

c 'I have the right to have different needs and wishes from others'.

d 'I can say what I like'.

8 A parent constantly in the Critical Parent mode would be likely to:

   a produce self-confident children.

   b have children who often feel guilty or stupid.

   c allow their children freedom from restrictions.

9 List five advantages of working in groups.

10 Which of the following is an essential component that a group could not function without?

   a A room to meet

   b Someone to take minutes

   c A common aim

   d Money

11 Which of the following would be least effective if a chairperson was experiencing difficulties with a group member?

   a Build a contract within the group to support each other.

   b Tell the person the chairperson is the boss and they must do as they are told.

   c Discuss the matter with the person outside the group.

   d Reinforce or support acceptable behaviours.

12 Which of the following reasons is least likely to cause a group to fail?

   a Lack of trust, suspicion.

   b Members avoiding work.

   c Meeting when football is on television.

   d Not having enough time or having too much time.

13 Non-judgemental behaviour means:

   a not making decisions.

   b always going along with the client.

   c not helping a client.

   d not judging someone by their appearance or views.

14 Being independent means:

   a clients should do everything for themselves.

   b we should not ask or expect others to help us.

   c we should have the opportunity to make our own choices and decisions.

   d teenagers should be allowed to go anywhere they want.

15 Which of the following does a client's entitlement to privacy not include?

   a Having regard for the extent to which they wish to associate with other residents.

   b Having somewhere for visitors and telephone calls which is private.

   c Ensuring that clients can use the toilet and bathe without being seen or heard.

   d Having an en-suite bathroom.

16 If an older client is confused how might their carers aim to offer opportunities for supporting their identity and fulfillment?

17 A self-fulfilling prophecy occurs:

   a where there is an ancient proverb which explains what could happen.

   b when a person can accurately predict the future.

   c when a person has religious views which should be valued.

   d when a husband tells his wife she is sure to fail her driving test (even though she is a good driver) and she does, because this undermines her self-confidence.

18 Name seven areas of a person's life which would need to be considered in a client's care plan.

19 Why should people be allowed to make mistakes sometimes?

20 When is it necessary for a care worker to share confidential information relating to a client with their line manager?

Fast Facts

Assertiveness Accepting that both your own and others' needs are important, being aware of reactions and being able to negotiate with other people so as to resolve a situation. Assertiveness is not about winning! Attempting to win and defeat others is aggressiveness.

Auditory The form of communication taken in through the ears (hearing).

Constructive criticism Useful comments designed to help someone improve. Constructive behaviour involves a willingness to listen.

Culture The collection of values and norms that are associated with specific groups. Cultural interpretation and cultural needs are key issues in communication work.

Gaze Allowing our eyes to meet with other people's eyes and exchange looks. Gaze is part of the non-verbal system of eye-contact which is a central component of non-verbal communication.

Gestures Signs made with the body or hands to convey a message. Gestures are especially sensitive to cultural interpretation. A hand signal can mean 'everything is fine' in one culture, and can be a serious insult in another.

Ideal self The image of the kind of person we would like to be.

Indirect aggression To store anger and direct it later at someone unconnected with the original cause of the anger.

Individual Planning Meeting A meeting between a client, maybe a friend or relative, and a range of professionals to help plan short and long term goals.

Mission statement A group or establishment's statement about its aims, objectives and methods of operating.

Non-verbal signals Using our eyes, faces and bodies to send signals. Messages which do not involve words. Tone or voice is often regarded as non-verbal, because verbal relates only to the words used in a message.

NVQ value base The defined value system for competent practice in caring.

Olfactory Our olfactory sense is the ability to smell.

Orientation Organising your own or others' positions in the space available. The way people face or look when communicating. (Orientation relates to direction.)

Personality traits Qualities which are attributed to a person such as clever, generous, miserly.

Pheremones Barely detectable scents which may attract or repel.

Posture The way someone sits or stands which can give messages about how they are feeling e.g. an 'open' body posture indicates someone is relaxed.

Preconceived ideas Decisions made before listening to the facts surrounding an issue.

Script Eric Berne's term for how children make sense of the world and their place in it. He called this forming a script.

Self-actualisation To become everything one is capable of becoming, to achieve an inbuilt potential.

Self-esteem This expresses how good or bad a person feels about themself – how the person values their own individuality. High self-esteem may help a person to feel happy and confident. Low self-esteem may lead to depression and unhappiness.

Self-fulfilling prophecy When someone's behaviour is so influenced by others' expectations that they actually behave as expected.

Self-image The kind of person we think we are. If there is a big gap between our ideal self and our self-image we are likely to have a low self-esteem.

Sincerity A supportive skill which involves being honest and open. Sincerity may involve some self-disclosure.

Social role The behaviour adopted by individuals when they are in social situations. Group norms and individual status help to define a role such as mother, sister, engineer etc.

Stroking Forms of recognition given by one person to another, not necessarily physical.

Submissiveness Feeling others' needs are more important than your own, giving in to them so as to avoid trouble.

Supportive skills Warmth, understanding and sincerity have to be used together to create a safe, caring conversation.

Tactile Something which can be touched.

Transactional analysis A theory devised by Eric Berne which analyses the way people interact with each other.

Understanding A supportive skill which involves learning about the client's world. Understanding may require reflective listening skills like 'warmth'; understanding would lead to a sense of trust.

Values Values are learned thought systems which enable individuals to make choices and decisions. Values may guide communication skills.

Valuing others Promoting a sense of self-esteem in other people.

Warmth A supportive skill which displays the ability to be non-judgemental and to listen to clients. Warmth may help to create a safe conversational atmosphere which may lead to a sense of trust.

References

Argyle, M. (1983) *The Psychology of Interpersonal Behaviour* Pelican

Atkinson, R., (1993) *Introduction of Psychology* Ted Buchholz

Bales, R. (1970) *Personality and Interpersonal Behaviour* Holt, Rinehart and Winston

Bem, Wollach & Kogan (1965) *Journal of Personality and Social Psychology*

Berne, E. (1964) *Games People Play*, Grove Press

Berne, E. (1975) *What Do You Say After Hello?* Penguin

Clancy, H. and McBride, G. The Autistic Process and its Treatment. In *Journal of Personality and Social Psychology* volume 36

Dion, K.K. (1972) What is good is beautiful. In *Journal of Personality and Social Psychology*

Ellsworth, P. (1975) *Direct Gaze as a Social Stimulus* Plenum

Human Rights Convention (1950) World Health Organisation

Kuhn (1966) – see Gross, R.D. (1987) *Psychology, The Science of Mind and Behaviour* Edward Arnold

Maslow, A. (1962) *Towards of Psychology of Being* Van Nostrand

Meichenbaum, D.H. (1983) *Stress Reduction and Prevention* Plenum

Rogers, C.R. (1951) *Client Centred Therapy, Its Current Practices, Implications and Theory* Houston

Rutter, D. (1976) Visual Interaction in Recently Admitted and Chronic Long-Stay Schizophrenic Patients. In *British Journal of Social and Clinical Psychology* volume 5

Tuckman, B. (1965) Developmental Sequence in Small Groups. In *Psychological Bulletin*, LX111(6)

Turner, C. (1990) *Transactional Analysis* FEU

Watson, J.B. (1972) Conditioned emotional reactions. In *Journal of Experimental Psychology*

chapter 3 PHYSICAL ASPECTS OF HEALTH

This chapter focuses on the structure and functions of two important organ systems in the body: the **cardio-vascular** and **respiratory systems**. They work together to provide body cells with the materials necessary for their metabolism. Changes caused by lifestyle choices and the natural ageing processes are considered with respect to these two systems. This chapter also considers disease processes and examines, in detail, three infectious diseases which are still problematic in modern society. Finally, we investigate the basic constituents and practices of diet, examining some special diets and the procedures for monitoring nutritional balance.

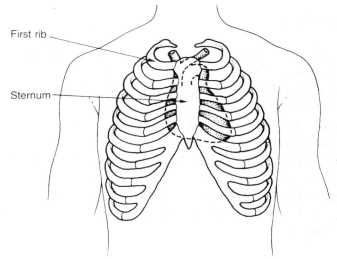

Figure 3.1 *The position of the heart*

· CARDIO-VASCULAR SYSTEM ·

The cardio-vascular system comprises the heart and its associated blood vessels, i.e., arteries, veins and capillaries.

The heart

The heart is about the size of a clenched fist, situated in the chest or thoracic cavity. It lies behind the sternum and in front of the oesophagus, protected on either side by the ribs and their cartilages (see Figure 3.1). The heart is surrounded by a tough double-layered fibrous sac called the *pericardium*. There exists a thin fluid film between the two layers of the pericardium and this fluid reduces the friction of the heart's movement.

At first sight, the heart appears to be a single organ but, in reality, it consists of two muscular pumps working side by side. It will help us to understand the way the heart works if we consider these pumps to be separate to begin with.

Imagine that the heart is sliced vertically through its central partition, which is known as the *septum*. Each pump now has an input tube or vessel and an output vessel. *Note*: an important point to remember with any textbook diagram is that the heart drawn on a page is opposite to the way it is sited in the body. To place the diagram as it is in the body you could lift the book or page and place it in front of your chest, facing outwards – the sides now correspond to your left and right sides.

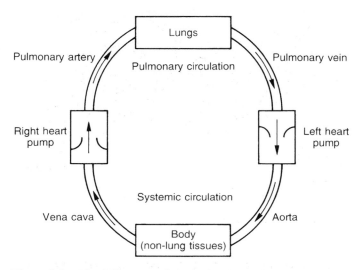

Figure 3.2 *Blood flows round the body in a circle*

Each pump consists of two chambers: an upper chamber called the *atrium* (plural, atria) and a lower, the *ventricle*. Atria have veins supplying them with blood and ventricles have arteries taking blood away from them. The right pump receives blood from the body or non-lung tissues and sends it to the lungs. The left pump receives blood from the lungs and sends it to the body. In this way (as you can see from Figure 3.2), blood flows round the body in a circle.

Blood vessels taking and receiving blood from the lungs are said to form the *pulmonary circulation*, whilst those concerned with the non-lung tissues form the *systemic circulation*. Arteries carry blood away from the heart, so there is the *pulmonary artery* serving the lungs and the aorta delivering blood to the rest of the body. Veins bring blood back to the heart, so again we have pulmonary veins from the lungs, but *vena cava* from the body. In fact, there are two venae cavae: the *superior* from the head and neck, and the *inferior* from the trunk and lower limbs.

The term *double circulation* is often used in human physiology because there are two circulations and the blood passes through the heart *twice* (through each half pump). The function of the pulmonary circulation is to allow the blood to release carbon dioxide and take up oxygen to supply the tissues. The systemic circulation acts in the opposite way: to

release oxygen to the tissues and take up carbon dioxide to carry to the lungs. Following this through, the right side of the heart carries blood poor in oxygen, called *deoxygenated* blood, whilst the left side distributes oxygen-rich, or *oxygenated*, blood to the body or *somatic* tissues. The two pumps can now be imagined working side by side – see Figure 3.3 below.

As blood flows in a circle, it must flow at the same rate comparatively through the blood vessels, whether they are large, near to the heart, or very small, supplying a group of cells. If the flow of blood was not at the same rate serious 'traffic jams' of blood could occur – causing a lack in other parts of the body. This might prove fatal if the part of the body concerned was a vital organ such as the heart itself, the brain or the kidneys. There are about five litres of blood in the human body, more in males than females, and resting blood flow is approximately five litres every minute. So, on average, all the blood in a person flows around the body once every minute. There will be more details about blood flow later in the chapter.

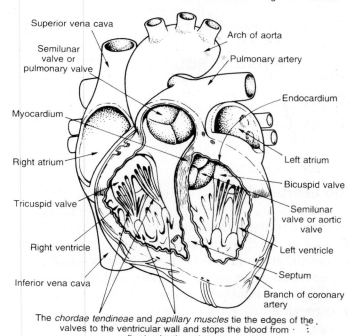

Figure 3.3 *Section through the heart*

You can understand that with such importance attached to these circulations, blood could not be permitted to flow in a reverse direction – particularly through the heart. To ensure this never happens, the heart is fitted with four *one-way valves*. Two are located deep inside the heart, between the atria and the ventricles on each side; and two more are situated just inside the major blood vessels which carry blood away from the heart. The one-way valves cannot operate on their own; they are relatively flimsy and do not contain any muscle. They open and close due to the forces which push them from either side. This force is called *blood-pressure* and it is the force which blood exerts on the walls of the heart or the blood vessels. There will be more details of this later on in the chapter.

The valves between the atria and the ventricles are often termed *right* and *left atrio-ventricular valves*, but you will find their older names more commonly in textbooks. The left-hand valve is known as the *bicuspid valve* and the right-hand one the *tricuspid valve*. (A cusp is the meeting point of two arcs, so 'bi' means two meeting points and 'tri' means three.) The valves lie in a fibrous ring which separates the atrial muscular wall from that of the ventricles. The valves are tethered to the walls of the ventricles by *tendinous cords* and small lumpy *papillary muscles*. These exert tension on the valves and prevent them being turned inside out during periods of extreme pressure; rather as an umbrella can do in a high wind! They function like guy ropes on a tent. The other two valves take their names from the vessels in which they are found, namely the *aortic* and *pulmonary valves*.

Cardiac muscle

The muscle that makes up the heart is of a special type found only in that place and, not surprisingly, is named *cardiac muscle*. Its fibres interconnect to form a network, along which the nerve impulses can pass rapidly to make the heart beat. This muscle, however, is capable of contracting without nerve impulses and this is called being *myogenic*. (See Figure 3.4.)

Cardiac muscle cannot rely upon the blood flowing through for its essential raw materials; it has a

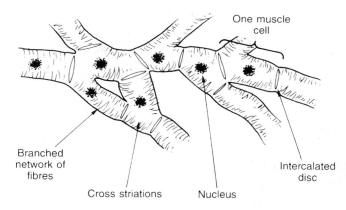

Figure 3.4 *Cardiac muscle tissue*

special blood supply from the *coronary* arteries and veins. These can be seen running over the external surface of the heart. They bring dissolved oxygen and nutrients to the heart muscle and carry away carbon dioxide, water and other waste products.

The atrial muscle beats at a faster rate than that of the ventricles so, practically, nervous control is important in making the heart contract in a co-ordinated and purposeful way. Sometimes, if the nervous route is not functioning correctly or is even interrupted, the heart can adopt an irregular pattern; this usually occurs as part of a disease process.

Nervous conduction through the heart

A cluster of special cells lie in the upper part of the right atrium and every few moments they become excited, sending nerve impulses across the branching network of the atrial muscle fibres to cause contraction. This cluster is called the *sino-atrial node* (shortened to the S-A node) or more commonly termed the *pacemaker*, because this is indeed what these cells do. These impulses are caught by yet another group of cells forming the *atrio–ventricular node* (A-V node) and relayed to a special band of tissue made of large *Purkinje fibres*, adapted to conduct impulses efficiently. The A-V node delays the transmission to allow the atria to complete their beat. The Purkinje fibres form the *Bundle of His* (or A-V bundle) which crosses the fibrous ring separating atria and ventricles, and then divides into *left* and *right bundle branches* running either side of the septum before spreading over the ventricles.

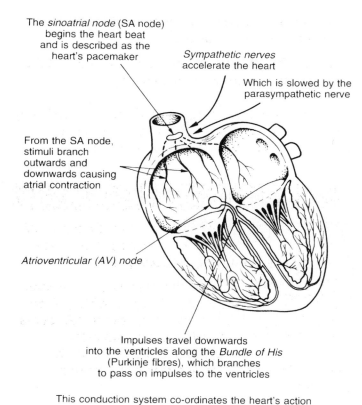

The *sinoatrial node* (SA node) begins the heart beat and is described as the heart's pacemaker

Sympathetic nerves accelerate the heart

Which is slowed by the parasympathetic nerve

From the SA node, stimuli branch outwards and downwards causing atrial contraction

Atrioventricular (AV) node

Impulses travel downwards into the ventricles along the *Bundle of His* (Purkinje fibres), which branches to pass on impulses to the ventricles

This conduction system co-ordinates the heart's action

Figure 3.5 *The heart's conduction system*

Impulse conduction is very fast so that the two ventricles beat together to force the blood around the body organs.

If the conduction system fails **artificial pacemakers** can be fitted which supply electrical stimuli from their batteries to stimulate the cardiac muscle direct.

Nervous control

Despite this elaborate conduction system, the heart also has a nervous control to allow for an almost instant response to the dangers and stresses of everyday life. There are two sets of nerves constantly making a play for control over the heart's rate by influencing the S-A node, which is only rarely allowed to beat at its own pace. Both nervous commands form part of the *autonomic nervous system* which co-ordinates and controls the internal organs or viscera of the body. One set continuously tries to calm the heart down, slowing its pace and lessening the strength of the beat. This is the

parasympathetic branch of the autonomic nervous system, which unceasingly aims for peace and contentment. The other branch is the *sympathetic*, aiming for increased strength of heartbeats and a stirring of pace. It is called into action during muscular work and stress (see Figure 3.5). The sympathetic branch is closely associated with the release of the hormone *adrenaline*.

Cardiac cycle

The events which take place during one heartbeat form the cardiac cycle. If the heart-rate, at rest, is counted at around 70 beats each minute, then the time for each beat is $1 \div 70$ minutes or $60 \div 70$ seconds. This works out as approximately $0 \cdot 8$ seconds for each beat of the heart.

If this is represented by 8 small squares each to the value of 0.1 second then we can produce a diagram as shown in Figure 3.6 (below). If we wish to show events happening in the atria and ventricles during this period, we can have two 'timelines'. The shaded squares represent when the cardiac muscle is contracting and the plain squares, relaxation. Contraction phases are called *systole* or *systolic periods* and relaxation periods *diastole* or *diastolic periods*. (See Figure 3.7 on the following page.) These names are also used for the two figures in a blood-pressure measurement.

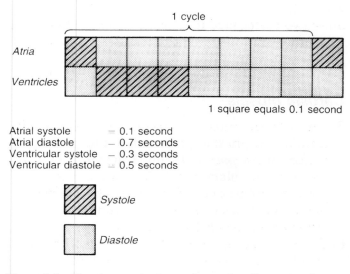

1 cycle

Atria

Ventricles

1 square equals 0.1 second

Atrial systole = 0.1 second
Atrial diastole — 0.7 seconds
Ventricular systole — 0.3 seconds
Ventricular diastole = 0.5 seconds

Systole

Diastole

Figure 3.6 *Timed events in the cardiac cycle: allocations of systole and diastole*

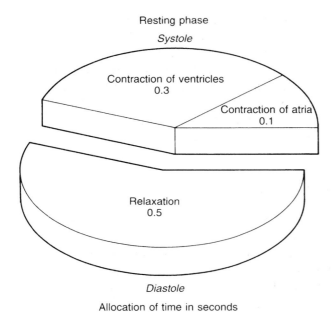

Resting phase

Systole

Contraction of ventricles
0.3

Contraction of atria
0.1

Relaxation
0.5

Diastole

Allocation of time in seconds

Ventricles relax while atria contract and vice versa

Figure 3.7 *Cardiac cycle: resting phase*

The events in the cardiac cycle can be simply listed as follows:

1 Atria contract, blood pushed into ventricles under pressure.
2 Ventricles bulge with blood, pressure forces the tricuspid and bicuspid valves shut. This causes the first heart sound to be heard with a stethoscope; it sounds like 'lub'. Atria relax and begin to fill with blood.
3 Ventricles begin contraction, pressure in blood rises and forces open the aortic and pulmonary valves.
4 Systole in the ventricles pushes blood into the aorta and pulmonary artery, these are elastic walled and begin to expand.
5 Ventricles begin to relax and blood falls back with the effect of gravity for a few moments and catches in the pockets of the semi-lunar valves, of the aorta and pulmonary artery pressing them together and closing off the opening. This causes the second heart sound which, through a stethoscope, sounds like 'dupp'.
6 Tricuspid and bicuspid valves are forced open and blood rushes from the filled atria into the ventricles during their diastolic phase. On being filled to about 70 per cent capacity, atrial systole

occurs and the heart has completed the cycle at the point where it started.

Note: in a healthy heart, both the two atria and the two ventricles contract simultaneously.

You now have learned substantial cardiac physiology and should be able to research and investigate further to generate evidence for your portfolio.

Task

a Write an illustrated account of the actions taking place in one heartbeat during rest.

b Compare this with the actions occurring during exercise; if the heart-rate increases to 120 beats per minute, produce similar diagrams to those shown in Figures 3.6 and 3.7 to illustrate timing during exercise.

c) Relate the electrical conduction of nerve impulses through the resting heart to the systolic and diastolic events.

d) Some pressure changes during a cardiac cycle are shown below. Give a brief explanation of the shape of the graph.

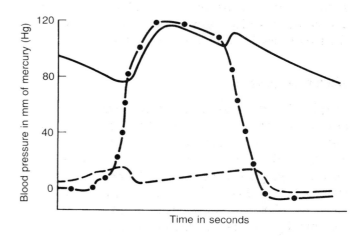

Time in seconds

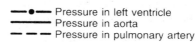

—●— Pressure in left ventricle
—— Pressure in aorta
--- Pressure in pulmonary artery

ARTERIES	VEINS	CAPILLARIES
Functional differences:	**Functional differences:**	**Functional differences:**
Carry blood away from heart to organs Carry blood under high pressure	Carry blood to heart from the organs Carry blood under low pressure	Connect arteries to veins Arterioles and capillaries cause greatest drop in pressure due to overcoming the friction of blood passing through small vessels.
Usually contain blood high in oxygen, low in carbon dioxide and water	Usually contain blood low in oxygen, high in carbon dioxide and water	Delivers protein free plasma filtrate high in oxygen to cells and collects up respiratory waste products of carbon dioxide and water.
What are the exceptions? Large arteries close to the heart help the intermittent flow from the ventricles become a continuous flow through the circulation.		
Anatomical differences (see diagrams)	**Anatomical differences**	**Anatomical differences**
Large arteries close to the heart are almost entirely made of elastic tissue to expand and recoil with the outpouring of blood from the ventricles during systole. Arteries have thick walls with corrugated lining and round lumens. Walls consist of three layers, endothelial lining, muscle and elastic tissue, and outer tough fibrous layer.	Veins have thinner walls than arteries Veins have oval spaces in centre (lumens) Veins over a certain diameter contain valves which prevent blood flowing backwards under the influence of gravity. Veins usually lie between skeletal muscles which squeeze blood flow onwards during muscular activity. Walls have three coats but far less muscle and elastic tissue and more fibrous tissue.	Capillaries have walls which are only one cell thick. Capillaries have leaky walls (permeable) enabling small molecular nutrients and dissolved gases to exchange with cells. No cell can lie more than a few cells from a capillary. Capillaries often smaller than red blood cells which must distort to pass through.

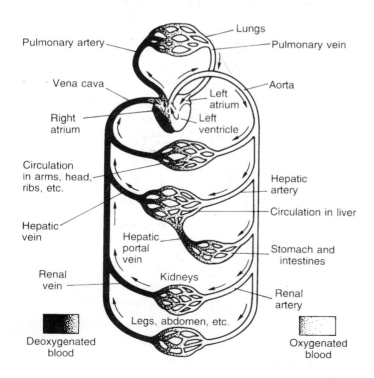

Diagram of human circulation

Blood vessels

These tubes together with the heart compose the *circulatory system*. There are three main types of vessels with intermediate types in between. The basic plan is shown in the diagram above with the intermediate vessels in small print.

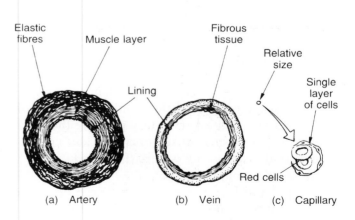

Blood vessels, transverse sections

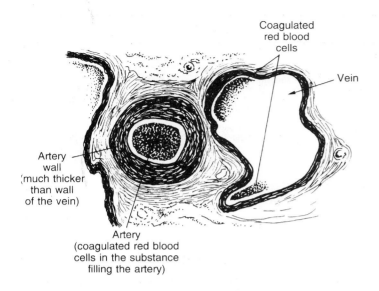

Transverse section through a vein and an artery

· THE RESPIRATORY SYSTEM ·

This body system consists of two lungs, their associated air passages and blood vessels. See Figure 3.8 below.

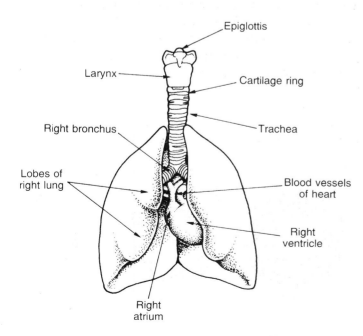

Figure 3.8 *Diagram of lungs showing position of heart*

Each lung is filled with tiny air pockets called *alveoli*, each of which is surrounded by capillaries from the pulmonary artery and vein. Alveoli are usually collected together in small clusters, each of which is served by an air passage or bronchiole. The bronchioles branch off much larger air passages called bronchi, one of which serves each lung. (See Figure 3.9 below.) The two bronchi join and the combined larger tube runs upwards to the back of the throat; this is the *trachea* (also commonly called the windpipe). The top of the trachea has a special adaptation for voice production, called the *larynx* (voice box).

The respiratory system so far described is enclosed in the airtight chest or *thorax*. This is bounded by the

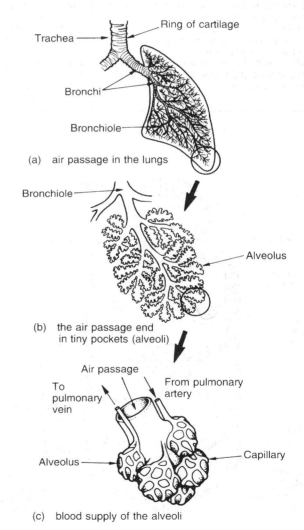

Figure 3.9 *Lung structure and alveoli*

chest wall, composed of ribs and intercostal muscles, and a musculo-fibrous sheet below–the *diaphragm*. The diaphragm is dome-shaped and when it is relaxed it is high in the chest. On contraction the diaphragm moves downwards, expanding the volume of the thorax.

Ventilation

Ventilation is the movement of air in and out of the lungs to refresh the air deep inside them. In order to keep a high concentration of oxygen and to remove the accumulated carbon dioxide and some of the water vapour, this occurs at least 16 times every minute. During exercise this rate increases considerably – up to 30 times, depending on the severity of the activity.

Volume and pressure are inversely related. This means that when one increases the other decreases. On *inspiration* (taking air into the chest), the diaphragm contracts and moves downwards at the same time as the intercostal muscles contract – pulling the ribs upwards and outwards. The whole effect increases the volume of the thorax, causing the pressure inside the lungs to drop below the atmospheric pressure of the air outside. As the thorax is an airtight cavity, the only way to equalise the pressure again is for air to rush in through the trachea. In this way the lungs become inflated with fresh air. *Expiration*, the expulsion of air, is the opposite. The diaphragm relaxes and becomes dome-shaped again, the ribs fall back to their original position and the lungs, being highly elastic structures, recoil to expel the air.

Friction produced by these movements is reduced because the lungs and the inside of the chest wall are lined with a thin layer of moist membrane, called *pleura*.

Gaseous exchange

This involves the exchange of dissolved gases between the alveoli and the blood in the capillaries of the pulmonary vessels. The exchange depends on a process called *diffusion*.

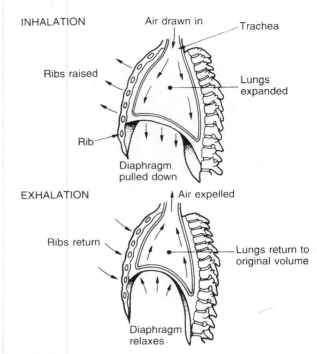

Figure 3.10 *Inspiration and expiration*

Diffusion is defined as the movement of molecules from a region of high concentration to one of low concentration. (In the respiratory system the important molecules are dissolved gases – oxygen and carbon dioxide.) In reality, this is sound commonsense: if one starts with a lot of anything in one place and few in another, after a period of time and random movement the numbers should become more even! This is exactly what happens in the lungs. Air, with a high percentage of oxygen molecules, is inside the alveoli; while pulmonary artery blood in the capillaries surrounding the alveoli is low in oxygen molecules. Diffusion occurs because the two single cell layers of the alveolar and capillary walls allow the molecules to 'even up' and oxygen passes into the blood.

Exactly the same process happens with carbon dioxide (and water vapour) but in the reverse direction, because the high concentration is in the capillary blood and the low concentration is in the air in the alveolus. Atmospheric air contains 0.04% carbon dioxide, i.e. virtually none. This exchange means that air breathed out contains less oxygen and

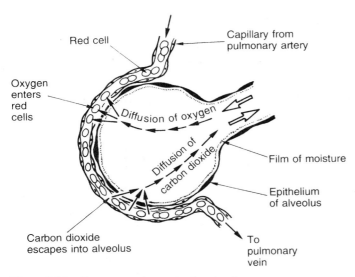

Figure 3.11 *Gaseous exchange in the alveolus*

more carbon dioxide and water than inspired air (as can be seen in the table below).

The composition of breathed air

Content	Inhaled %	Exhaled %
Oxygen	21	16
Carbon dioxide	0.04	4
Water vapour	Variable	Saturated
Nitrogen	79	79

The lungs are well adapted to this function because:

a they have a very large surface area due to the millions of alveoli present inside them

b they have an intimate association with the pulmonary capillaries; only two single cell layers separate them

c the constant refreshing and removal of air maintains the concentration gradients between the diffusing molecules

d the capillaries amalgamate to form the pulmonary vein which takes away the diffused oxygen via the blood. You may realise that the pulmonary vessels are opposite in their oxygenation to other arteries and veins!

Carriage of dissolved gases

Blood is also well adapted for this function of gaseous exchange. There are five million tiny red blood cells or *erythrocytes* in every cubic millimetre of blood. Average blood volume is 5 to 6 litres, depending on the gender and size of an individual.

Task

Calculate how many red blood cells there are in a person with a blood volume of 5.3 litres. If 1 per cent of this individual's red blood cells are replaced every day, how many red blood cells will need to be replaced and therefore made in a week?

Erythrocytes (or red blood cells) contain a very special pigment called *haemoglobin*. This is able to form a compound with oxygen known as *oxyhaemoglobin*. It does this very readily in the conditions of high oxygen concentration which exist in the lungs. Even more remarkable, oxyhaemoglobin breaks down to release its oxygen under the low oxygen conditions which exist in cells. Cells are low in oxygen because oxygen is continually being used up in the process of cell respiration. Thus oxygen is carried to body cells by the red pigment, haemoglobin, found in the erythrocytes.

Carbon dioxide is carried in the watery part of the blood – the plasma – and only briefly has contact with red cells. It uses parts of water molecules to form hydrogen carbonate (HCO_3), and on reaching the lungs breaks down to form carbon dioxide and water again.

CELL, TISSUE OR INTERNAL RESPIRATION

The description of the processes so far comprise external respiration and have involved both cardio-vascular and respiratory systems. True respiration only begins *inside* cells, and it is an *energy-releasing* process.

Digested food leads basically to the production of glucose in the blood. Glucose contains energy bound up in its molecular structure. This energy is vital to all living cells to enable them to carry out their metabolic processes. However, the energy can only be released by the chemical breakdown of glucose: using oxygen to combine with the fragments of glucose to make the waste products carbon dioxide and water.

Glucose + Oxygen → Carbon dioxide + Water + Energy

The equation above is much simplified and ignores the contribution played by the intracellular enzymes without which life could not exist. It is also the equation of **aerobic respiration**, which infers that oxygen is always freely available in large quantities. Alas, this is not always the case. Humans cannot store oxygen, although the other respiratory raw material, glucose, can be stored easily as *glycogen*, in liver and muscle cells. There is an irony then, as one can be stored but the other cannot; does this mean that respiration stops if oxygen becomes in short supply? Fortunately for the human race, it does not. There is a contingency arrangement in the form of **anaerobic respiration**! (See Figure 3.12 a and b adjacent.)

Anaerobic respiration occurs only in muscle cells because those cells are the ones which suffer oxygen depletion during severe exercise. Imagine that glucose is a molecule which can break itself down in small steps, many of which release a small parcel of energy. Only at the end is oxygen needed for the final burst of energy, in the production of carbon dioxide and water. In circumstances where oxygen was in short supply, the breakdown could occur until that final step – the energy released would then be much smaller and the products would not be carbon dioxide and water. This is exactly what happens, and the product is *lactic acid* which still contains 'locked-up energy'. This energy cannot be released until the exercise is over and oxygen is plentiful again to convert the temporary lactic acid back into glucose, or into carbon dioxide and water. The extra oxygen needed to carry out this task is ~~r~~ and above our normal needs, which is why

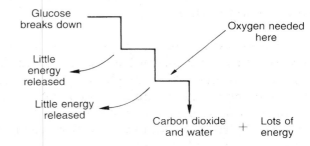

(a) *Aerobic respiration*

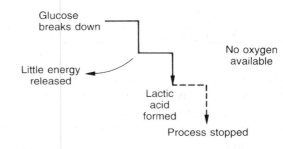

(b) *Anaerobic respiration*

Figure 3.12 *Aerobic and anaerobic respiration*

breathing is still rapid for some time after the exercise is finished.

The difference between the amount of oxygen an individual requires to carry out a muscular activity, and the amount actually taken in (even with both raised heart and respiratory rates) is termed an *oxygen debt*. The raised respiratory rate after the exercise is over, is equal to and repays this debt.

Effects of exercise

To gain benefit from exercise it must be taken regularly; three times weekly is the recommended level. It must be sufficiently strenuous to increase the pulse rate (to a level agreed with fitness or medical experts) and last for at least 20 minutes. Such activity is likely to cause:

- the heart to deliver more blood at each stronger beat (may increase blood flow to the heart itself)
- muscles, ligaments and tendons all to become stronger and therefore less liable to injury
- muscle tissue to become more efficient at energy production
- joints to become more flexible.

Lack of exercise is thought to be a risk factor in coronary heart disease.

The cardio-vascular and respiratory systems are also threatened by other choices and changes in our lives. The ageing process obviously plays a part, but poor diet, smoking and stress are important contributory factors over and above this. We will go on to consider the diseases that can result from changes caused to these body systems.

· CORONARY HEART DISEASE ·

From quite an early age most of us develop fatty patches on the linings of our arteries; the patches become more numerous and each becomes larger with advancing years. These patches comprise what is known as *atheroma*. We are not aware of these changes until the atheromatous patch has narrowed the blood vessel so much that the part of the body it serves begins to suffer. For example:

- the heart – leads to pain on exertion (known as *angina pectoris*)
- the brain – causes periods of confusion and poor memory (called by doctors *transient ischaemic attacks*)
- skeletal muscle – pain on walking short distances (called *intermittent claudication*). The Roman emperor Claudius suffered with this!

After many years, when atheroma has become extensive, the previously smooth inner arterial lining may be roughened and the usually streamlined blood flow turbulent. These two factors possibly influence the next stage of the disease process. (See Figure 3.13 below.) A clot or thrombus forms on and within the atheromatous plaque until the whole vessel becomes blocked. Blood flow is suddenly cut off to that part of the organ. If this is a small vessel, the area served might be quite small and after a period of illness the individual will return to normal physical health or near to it. However, this attack should serve as a warning that the circulation is in a poor state and a change of lifestyle will be strongly recommended by medical advisers. If, on the other hand, the vessel is medium to large in diameter, then severe disablement or even death may occur.

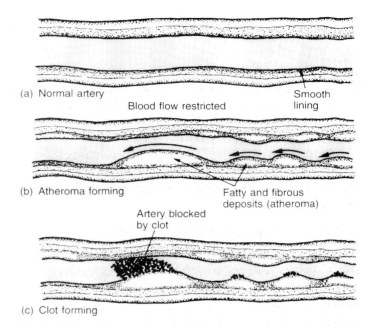

(a) Normal artery

Blood flow restricted — Smooth lining

(b) Atheroma forming

Fatty and fibrous deposits (atheroma)

Artery blocked by clot

(c) Clot forming

Figure 3.13 *Atheroma and clot formation*

Atheroma occurring in the heart or brain is most likely to result in death; in other less vital organs survival is more likely. Such a blockage in the heart is known as *coronary thrombosis* or heart attack, whereas in the brain it is a *cerebral thrombosis* or stroke.

Heart disease tends to run in families so it is described as having a *familial tendency* but families also tend to eat the same foods. As Western countries became richer so the incidence of heart disease has risen. People with diets high in animal fats tend to be at greater risk of developing heart disease. More recently, larger number of people have been having their blood cholesterol levels measured, and it has been found that some families have what is considered to be abnormally high levels of blood fats (*hyperlipidaemia*). Such families are being advised to consume diets low in cholesterol, i.e. cutting down on foods such as dairy fats, fat meat and meat products.

Many commercial companies have had business successes in food manufacture by using vegetable fat sources in their products and claiming a 'healthy eating' label. (See Figure 3.14 on the next page.)

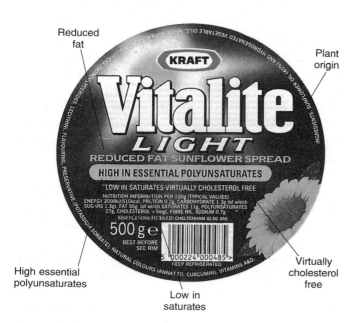

Figure 3.14 *Example of a 'healthy' spread*

Hypertension

Elevated blood-pressure (increased levels of either systolic or diastolic blood-pressure) is a major contributor to coronary heart disease. Afro-Caribbean races are nearly twice as likely to have hypertension and heart failure than white Caucasian races. Hypertension is also age-related. Over half of elderly people are hypertensive. This causes increased risk of both coronary heart disease and stroke.

Atheroma, coupled with so-called 'hardening of the arteries', is known as *atherosclerosis*. There is strong evidence that increased blood-pressure and hyperlipidaemia contribute to progressive atherosclerosis. Screening for raised blood-pressure is recommended annually for people over the age of 65 years and every five years for younger healthy people.

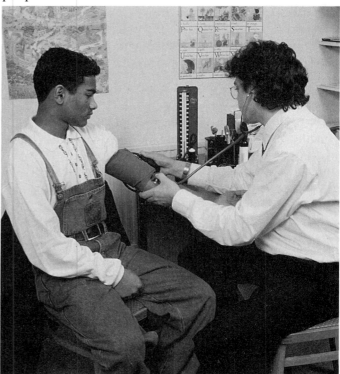

Screening for raised blood-pressure is recommended

Theory into practice

What advice would you give to a friend or relative about dietary changes to reduce the incidence of heart disease or stroke with increasing age?

Stress

Emotional stress and overwork are also high risk factors for heart disease. Stress releases the hormone

Other risk factors in heart disease are considered to be:

- Smoking
- Obesity
- Stress
- Lack of exercise

Heredity, gender and ageing account for approximately 50 per cent of cardio-vascular deaths. Lifestyle choices such as smoking, diet and drug treatment accounts for the remainder.

adrenaline which has an effect on heart function. Adrenaline also acts to trigger many of the effects of the stress response described in Chapter 4.

Task

Using the information from Chapter 4 and your knowledge of the heart, write a report on the effects of stress on the cardio-vascular system. Illustrate your answer wherever possible and cross reference it to both units in your portfolio.

Effects of ageing

This has been one of the most researched subjects in history and there are many theories proposed which are still largely unproven. There is a myth that a fortune can be made if the ageing process could be halted. Some experts believe that the cells of our bodies are pre-programmed with a life span. Some other theories propose that cell replacement cannot keep pace with cell death or that cell replacement processes wear out. Whatever the reason, we know the facts: we do age, metabolism slows, cells do not work as efficiently and that means the functions of organs and organ systems decrease. The two systems we have studied work together and are said to be interdependent, so when the functions of one system deteriorate the other does also.

Cardio-vascular system

Atheroma and atherosclerosis have already been discussed; there is one other similar condition which you might meet – *arteriosclerosis*. This is, as its name suggests, simply a reduction in elasticity and an increase in hardening of the walls of the arteries. The arteries are unable to expand with the flow of blood during systole and therefore carry less blood to the organs. The flow might be adequate for light everyday tasks but not with sudden emergencies which demand extra blood volume.

The heart itself has a similar problem of being unable to respond to extra demand. Cardiac muscle fibres become smaller and replaced in part by connective tissue and fat cells. The muscular pump is handicapped and able to deliver less blood to the waiting arteries. Stroke volume, or the volume of blood delivered at each beat, is reduced. The heart is said to have less reserve, as it copes with unchanging situations but not with stressful change or increased activity.

Valves in both the heart and veins also function less well due to loss of flexibility. This interferes with the onward flow of blood through the heart and in the return of venous blood. The latter often leads to a damming-up of blood in the venous side (right side) of the heart and can lead to heart failure and congestion. Failure of valves in the veins can lead to the all-too-familiar problem of varicose veins. This is worse in some families which might have inefficient or damaged valves from birth and in people who have any condition which increases pressure in the abdomen. Women are more prone to varicose veins as a result of pregnancies, but varicose veins can also be troublesome as a result of obesity and smoking (due to persistent coughing) in men and women.

Smoking

It is considered that smoking increases the rate at which cells age, possibly due to lowered oxygen delivery to cells.

As well as leading to heart disease, hypertension and chronic lung disease, smoking is well known for being a major cause of *lung cancer*. Less well known is that it is a major cause of other cancers such as those of the throat, stomach, oesophagus, pancreas and bladder. Smoking kills 300 people each day in the UK and of the 250 million children alive in Europe today, 20 million will be killed before their time by tobacco. (Action on Smoking, November 1992.) The risk of lung cancer from passive smoking is small but it is still 50 to 100 times greater than from exposure to asbestos. Smoking habits are decreasing in British males but, unfortunately, increasing in females, particularly in the 15 to 35-year-old age group.

Cigarette smoking, in particular, is a major risk factor in angina and heart disease. It is recognised that the greater the number of cigarettes smoked and the longer the exposure, i.e. the younger a person begins to smoke, the greater is the risk of serious smoking-related illness. When hypertension and high cholesterol levels are associated with smoking, deaths from coronary disease are high. It is interesting to note that in Oriental countries many males smoke but the number of deaths from heart disease is quite low. This occurs when traditional diets are consumed, which have low animal fat content and high levels of fish oils etc. When a typical European diet is taken by Orientals who smoke, the incidence of heart disease and lung cancer rises dramatically and approximates to that of the West.

Children of parents who smoke have increased chances of both cot death and developing asthma. They are also smaller than other children, do less well academically and have more time off school. (See also Chapter 5 Health Promotion.)

Asthma

This is a lung disease which can affect adults but occurs mostly in children. Most children stop attacks after puberty.

There are muscles in the walls of the bronchi which run in a circular fashion around the tubes. If these muscles contract the bronchi become narrowed, and in an asthmatic person this happens in response to substances to which they are particularly sensitive. Some substances which cause asthmatic attacks in people are: pollen, pollutants, dust, mould, animal hair or certain foods. When the bronchi narrow it becomes difficult for the person to breathe out and they appear to be fighting for their breath. Fortunately attacks are often not serious and effective drugs are available in many forms. Inhalers containing muscle relaxants are the most common and asthmatics take 'puffs' to prevent attacks and for treatment. Asthmatic attacks are more common during lung and bronchial infections, such as bronchitis.

Bronchitis and emphysema

This can present either as an acute illness or a chronic disease. The *acute* condition is characterised by a cough, fever and sore throat. The organisms responsible are usually viruses or bacteria. It can cause distress in the young and the old who have little in the way of reserve function.

Chronic bronchitis is a disease caused usually by exposure to dust, smoke or particles over a length of time. Sticky mucus is produced by the lining of the air passages in abundance and this gives rise to a 'productive' cough. Gradually the interconnecting walls of the alveoli break down so that they become much larger spaces. The result of this is that the exchange of gases becomes much less efficient and some people's skin may look permanently bluish due to lack of oxygen. This widening of the alveoli is known as **emphysema**. A sufferer is far more prone to infection and heart disease as the heart and lungs have to work faster in compensation. The individual with this disease appears breathless and stressed.

Victims of bronchitis and emphysema should give up smoking and avoid breathing in particle-laden air.

· CLASSIFICATION OF DISEASE ·

There are several ways of classifying diseases. One definition of disease is that it is a disordered state of an organ or organism. Disordered states can arise from several causes: infections, inherited or degenerative diseases, or mental or physical illness.

Infectious diseases

Infectious diseases are usually caused by viruses, fungi or bacteria, producing poisonous products (often called *toxins*) which cause illness. The organisms travel from sick to healthy people in several ways; these will be discussed later.

Examples of infectious diseases are: influenza, bronchitis, measles.

Inherited diseases

These are passed on via a fault in the individual's genetic material, that is, the *genes* which comprise the *chromosomes* in the nucleus of the body cells. A large number of diseases have a genetic origin. If present at birth, you may also hear that the condition is *congenital*, but these two words are not interchangeable because some genetic diseases do not show themselves until many years after birth. Genetic diseases often run in families and are sometimes called *familial*.

Many disorders of this nature exert their effects because genes control the making of important proteins in cells, including enzymes. If the 'blueprint' for making the enzyme is faulty then the correct substance will not be made. This means that there is likely to be a malfunction of the body's biochemistry in every cell. This is often known as an *inborn error of metabolism*. Examples of genetic disorders are cystic fibrosis, phenylketonuria and haemophilia.

Degenerative diseases

This is a blanket term, covering disorders with ongoing deterioration of structure and function of a particular part of the body. It is meant to exclude diseases with other causes and also the natural ageing processes. Degenerative disorders begin earlier than normal and are very rapidly more extensive. It may well be that many degenerative disorders are merely those we have at present attributed to no known cause. Many of the specialised cells in organs become replaced by fibrous or scar tissue for no apparent reason.

Examples of degenerative diseases are Parkinson's disease, Alzheimer's disease and motor neuron disease.

Mental illness

Often confused by the public with mental handicap or those with learning difficulties, mental illness is a term which describes psychiatric disorders. Largely, these fall into two groups: *neuroses*, where the client remains in touch with reality and understands their own illness; and *psychoses*, which are far more serious, with a loss of reality and understanding of the illness.

Examples of neuroses are obsessions, mild depression and anxiety disorders, whereas psychotic illness may include schizophrenia, manic depression and mania.

Physical illness

Physical illness is a bodily ailment not related to one of the causes already described. Gastric ulcer, chronic renal (kidney) disease and heart attack could be termed physical illnesses.

. CONTROL AND PREVENTION OF . DISEASE

General considerations

Micro-organisms surround us and generally live in harmony with us, preventing opportunistic harmful microbes (*pathogens*) from gaining a foothold. We tend to stay healthy because of our own defence mechanisms:

- Intact skin is a barrier to most microbes
- Acid gastric juices destroy swallowed microbes
- Harmless bacteria on skin exclude most pathogens
- Cilia, mucus and coughing expel inhaled microbes
- Diarrhoea rushes pathogenic microbes through the gut
- Blood has special defence characteristics:
  - White blood cells (phagocytes) devour and destroy invading microbes
  - Clotting process traps and limits invaders
  - Special proteins called antibodies neutralise antigens on invaders and prevent replication and reproduction within the body (see section on influenza).

Infectious disease process

There must be a pool or reservoir of causative agents (causes) to produce an infection (see Figure 3.15

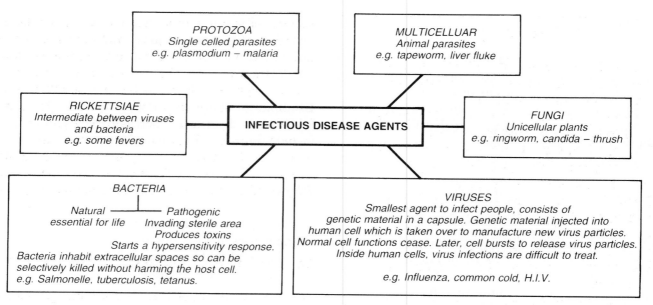

Figure 3.15   *Possible causes of infectious disease*

above), together with exit routes to other possible hosts (so the disease is passed on to other organisms and/or cells). (See Figure 3.16 on infectious disease process.)

Exposure to a microbe does not always cause illness; sometimes their numbers are too small. The 'dose' varies with different organisms, for example, 100,000 Salmonella bacteria are required to cause disease compared to only 100 Shigella organisms. Both cause food poisoning illnesses. However, less than one gram of faeces contaminating food will contain that large number of Salmonella organisms – a very small amount!

Some strains will cause severe illness, others less so (see page 139 on different types of Influenza). This is often known as *virulence*. The infecting microbe must have some means of entering the host to cause illness; just being in the presence of an organism does not necessarily mean the other person will become infected, e.g. being in the same room with an HIV-positive person will not transmit the disease. If a causative agent can be eliminated, then the disease will no longer exist in the natural state (for example, smallpox).

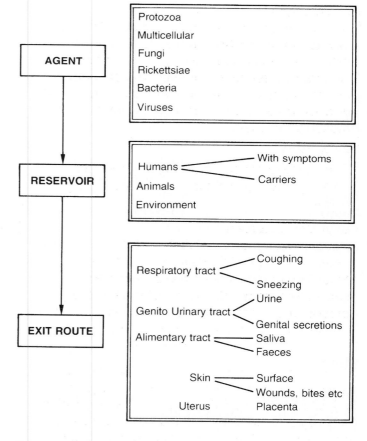

Figure 3.16   *Infectious disease process*

How diseases are spread

Disease-causing agents must be transmitted from one place to another and may indeed have more than one mode of travel.

When the reservoir and host are closer than 2 metres the spread is said to be **direct**.

This can be by **contact** such as skin-to-skin or person to person, e.g. gonorrhoea or environment to skin, e.g. tetanus

Droplet spread occurs when coughing, sneezing or talking to susceptible hosts. It is limited in the distance travelled to about 2 metres. The particles are pulled downwards under the effect of gravity. e.g. mumps, the common cold.

Indirect spread occurs when the host and reservoir are over 2 metres distance apart. The distance may be several thousand miles apart or as little as 2.1 metres. There are three main types of indirect spread:

a) By vectors.
A vector is an animal which transmits infectious disease from one host to another. Fleas, ticks, mites and mosquitoes are the most important vectors of disease to humans. The causative agent may actually live in the body of the vector or stick to the wings or legs of the vector; e.g. mosquito, housefly

b) By vehicles.
This is transport on non-living objects such as bedding, toys, equipment, milk or water; e.g. measles

c) Airborne spread.
Very small particles which can float on currents of air over large distances for variable lengths of time. The particles have come from talking, singing, sneezing, dentist's drill or laboratory procedures. This is probably the most difficult spread to stop; e.g. influenza, common cold.

Hosts may also have characteristics which may influence the transmission of disease, e.g. some individuals with a particular genetic configuration (heterozygous) to sickle cell anaemia have some resistance to malaria. Age is also an important factor; children are more likely to get acute diseases (diseases with a sudden onset and outcome) whereas adults are more prone to chronic conditions (diseases which are persistent). Children often suffer diseases sub-clinically, which means being generally ill with the disease but not showing the specific symptoms. We tend to say that a child must be 'fighting something off'. Adults are often immune to infections they have been exposed to earlier in life. Biological factors like these cannot be modified but other factors, such as socio-economic factors, can.

Socio-economic factors

Diseases can be influenced by relationships, lifestyle, travel, place of residence, geographical area and occupation. Children living in the UK now have vaccinations against poliomyelitis, measles and (for girls) rubella amongst many others. In other less developed countries these infections still exact their toll of disablement, deformity and even death. Treating drinking water, and so modifying the environment, has been responsible for saving more lives than antibiotics; but there are still many places in the world where clean drinking water is not available. Typhoid fever, once the scourge of many countries, has been largely eliminated by separating drinking water from sewage systems.

Tuberculosis, pneumonia and food poisoning, to name only a few, are more prevalent in damp overcrowded housing. There has been a long-standing association between poverty, unemployment, drug, solvent and alcohol abuse, violence and physical and mental illness. Individuals of low socio-economic status are more likely to be malnourished, including suffering various forms of anaemia due to inappropriate diets because of poverty or ignorance.

Many studies are being carried out worldwide on socio-economic factors and the incidence of disease. A large number are as yet inconclusive, others produce conflicting and controversial data, but some are giving clear messages to populations and, more importantly, their governments.

Some interesting statistical studies have shown that:

– Development of breast cancer is associated with high socio-economic status, being over 40 years of age and having had an early onset of menstruation.
– Cervical cancer is linked to social class and partner's occupation. Partners of non-circumcised men are more at risk; cervical cancer is low in Jewish women.
– Married men have higher frequencies of prostatic cancer than single men, but rates are even higher in divorced or widowed men.

Task

Research and investigate how socio-economic factors influence patterns of two diseases from those named above or choose two of your own. Make an action plan, detail the information you will need and evaluate your work.

We will now look in detail at three infectious diseases which still cause problems in modern society: gonorrhoea (a sexually transmitted disease), salmonella (food poisoning) and influenza. Each is transmitted in different ways. Taken together they can affect a cross-section of the population, from babies to elderly people, and – despite modern medical advances – in some cases they can be life-threatening. The strategy for control of these diseases is therefore crucial and we will consider this for each of the diseases in turn.

· GONORRHOEA ·

Sometimes called the 'clap', gonorrhoea is the second most common sexually transmitted disease in the UK, after *non-specific urethritis*. Some 50,000 cases are reported annually from STD clinics (so the actual figure is probably higher still). STD clinics are now referred to as GUM clinics, Genito-Urinary Medicine.

'The Health of the Nation' document (1992) described an upward trend for the years 1988–1990 (from 18,738 cases to 19,086) whereas previously the trend had been downwards. The document highlights the need for continued publicity and sex education, as well as early diagnosis and treatment of those with symptoms and also their partners. It continues to describe the STDs as a major cause of public ill-health with long-term consequences of infertility, ectopic (tubal) pregnancies and genital cancers. The government has issued a main health target to reduce the incidence of gonorrhoea among men and women aged 15 to 64 by at least 20 per cent by 1995. (See Figure 3.17 below.)

The cause of gonorrhoea is a bacterium called Neisseria gonorrhoeae, often given the alternative name of Gonococcus. (See Figure 3.18 on the next page.)

The highest number of cases occur in individuals between the ages of 15 and 24 in large cities. There are now several different strains known including one which, after originating in the Far East, is now responsible for 12 per cent of cases. This is penicillin-resistant and found almost everywhere. Different strains of the organism circulate in different sectors of the community and have different

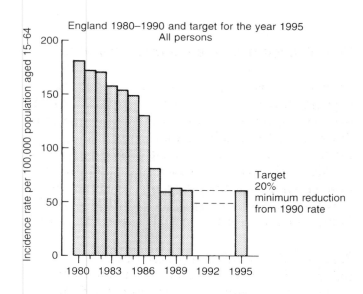

Source: Forms SBH60 and KC60 (from 1988)

Figure 3.17 *New cases of gonorrhoea at GUM clinics*

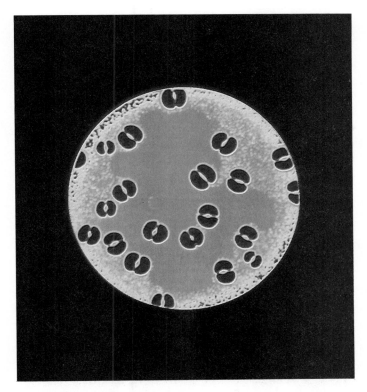

Figure 3.18 *Neisseria gonorrhoeae*

characteristics. A fairly resistant type has been located more commonly in gay men, while a strain likely to cause symptomless disease is more common in white races than non-whites.

The disease process – symptoms and signs

After an incubation period of between two and ten days the disease may or may not give symptoms. In **men** – the symptoms can be pain on urination, often described as like passing broken glass, and a discharge from the urethra (main exit from the bladder in the penis). In **women**, 60 per cent of caes have *no* symptoms and may pass the disease on unwittingly; otherwise, symptoms are similar to those in men – pain on urination and vaginal discharge.

Anal sex with an infected person causes inflammation of the lower bowel and anus but, again, in only about 10 per cent of cases. Oral sex leads to *Gonococcal pharyngitis* which gives a sore throat without other symptoms. A baby born to an infected mother may develop inflammation of one or both eyes.

Diagnosis is confirmed by laboratory tests on the discharge or swabs from infected areas.

Complications

Gonorrhoea is frequently undetected because of symptomless sufferers and it may spread to other parts of the body. In males it can affect fertility by infecting the testes, their tubes and the prostate gland. In females, the untreated disease often reaches the Fallopian tubes causing repeated bouts of PID or *pelvic inflammatory disease*. This may produce infertility and increases the chances of ectopic pregnancies.

Occasionally, the disease may spread to the bloodstream causing septicaemia with fever and malaise. This can also lead to gonococcal arthritis – painful swollen joints.

Treatment

Antibiotic treatment, usually penicillin, is effective and other antibiotics are available if resistance or sensitivity is a problem. Tests are repeated after treatment to make sure the disease has been cleared. However, in the USA 40 per cent of infected treated patients return to GUM clinics within a year and 20 per cent are back within six weeks!

Strategy for control

Treatment is effective for that bout of infection but not for the next! All partners of infected individuals must be traced and treated as infected, even if symptom-free. Case histories should be followed by appropriate tests, e.g. if an individual has oral sex with an infected person, then tests for pharyngeal gonococcus should be carried out. Screening should be carried out for sexually active women in high-incidence areas. Male partners of women with PID and recurrent gonorrhoea should be traced and treated, because 50 per cent of them may have the infection.

Theory into practice

You could investigate national or local patterns of gonorrhoea infection by inviting a local health visitor, GUM clinician or similar person to speak to your group.

· FOOD POISONING ·

This is a term used for an illness of sudden onset caused by eating contaminated food. It is characterised by abdominal pain, nausea, vomiting, diarrhoea and general feelings of being unwell (known as malaise).

Most cases of food poisoning are caused by bacteria, viruses, fungi or chemical contamination.

One group of organisms causing bacterial food poisoning is **Salmonella** and the most common type within that group is *Salmonella typhimurium*, which is commonly found in farm animals and poultry. Salmonella and another group, the *Campylobacter*, are responsible for most serious outbreaks of food poisoning in the UK. It is also interesting to note

that another member of the group, *Salmonella typhi* is the cause of a serious food-borne illness, i.e. *typhoid fever*.

Diagnosis of salmonella food poisoning is usually made by laboratory tests of vomit or faeces to isolate the bacteria. As the symptoms described above develop 12 to 24 hours after consuming the food, it has usually been consumed or thrown away.

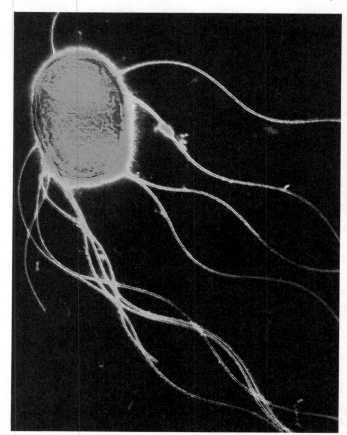

Figure 3.19 *Salmonella bacteria*

The symptoms decrease after 2 or 3 days and tend to be life-threatening only in the very young, sick or elderly who are unable to cope with the fluid lost as a result of the vomiting and the diarrhoea. Some individuals in these groups may develop blood poisoning or septicaemia. However, salmonella can also be a danger for pregnant women.

The incidence, or number of cases, of salmonella food poisoning increased dramatically during the 1980s in the UK and many cases appeared to be due to infected poultry and poultry products. Hens' eggs and chicken meat were blamed, as infection can start from the hens' ovaries or bowels.

Treatment

Treatment is mainly aimed at correcting the *dehydration* caused by the fluid loss. Plenty of fluids should be given but no solid food for at least 24 hours; in the high-risk groups already mentioned, intravenous replacement of fluids may be necessary. Cases developing septicaemia will need antibiotic treatment.

Carriers are people who, having recovered themselves from the infection, continue to harbour the salmonella bacteria in their bowels. As a result they excrete the organisms in their faeces, often many months after the original infection. This is particularly dangerous if the individual is in an occupation dealing with food and has poor personal hygiene practices. Food workers must report any personal illness, especially intestinal upsets, to their supervisor and refrain from work. Special tests will be performed to determine the time when they will be allowed to return to normal work.

Strategies for control

Simple but strict personal and kitchen hygiene measures can abolish most cases of salmonella food poisoning. (See table opposite.)

Task

One day after a wedding reception, 46 of the 65 guests became ill with nausea, diarrhoea and vomiting. The menu had consisted of the following: prawn cocktail; chicken a la king with roast potatoes, broccoli, carrots and peas, sage and onion stuffing with gravy; cream trifle; coffee and mints.

Salmonella organisms were isolated from over half (55 per cent) of those who were ill and one-eighth (12 per cent) of those who still felt well. On examination the hotel kitchen refrigerators contained raw fish and chickens, cooked chickens and trifles. Most guests recovered within two or three days. The bride's 90-year-old grandmother had to be taken to hospital for treatment but, regretfully, did not survive the illness. A nine-month-old weaned baby was also hospitalised but did recover.

Write a report of the outbreak detailed above. Include possible causes of infection, likely treatments, follow-up of individuals and preventative strategies for the hotel to follow to ensure such a tragedy could not occur again. Also include research statistics where possible and where necessary give reasons for your answers.

Hygienic practice	Rationale
Hands should be thoroughly washed: (i) After going to the toilet (ii) After touching raw meat (iii) Before touching any food.	Salmonella bacteria live in human, animal and poultry intestines.
Wash all equipment including knives and chopping board after using with raw meat	Raw meat may be contaminated.
Thaw meat and poultry thoroughly before cooking. Do not allow the water to drip over surfaces or other food.	Colder parts of meat will not reach the high temperatures needed to kill any bacteria present. Water will be contaminated from intestines.
Do not drink or use unpasteurised milk.	Harmful pathogenic bacteria will be present.
Cook meat, poultry and eggs thoroughly.	High temperatures kill the bacteria.
Avoid products containing raw or only lightly cooked egg e.g. homemade mayonnaise mousses meringues ice cream	Any bacteria present will not be killed.
Avoid cooking or preparing food if ill with intestinal upset.	Any bacteria present may be transferred to food and may infect others.
Never return to an occupation working with food after intestinal illness, however mild, until you have been officially cleared by laboratory testing.	You might have become a carrier without knowing it.

· INFLUENZA ·

Influenza, often popularly called 'flu', is a common viral disease which occurs sporadically (infrequently), in local outbreaks, in epidemics (existing for a time in a wider community) and pandemics (outbreaks crossing continents). Often a few isolated cases herald the sudden onset of an epidemic which peaks two to three weeks later and is over five to six weeks after that. The severity of any epidemic is measured by absenteeism in schools and industry, the number of pneumonia cases admitted to hospital and the number of associated deaths.

It is difficult to locate the influenza virus between epidemics and, although one strain usually predominates during an epidemic, several strains may be found in the population.

Nationwide epidemics tend to occur every two to three years, but intervals between world-wide

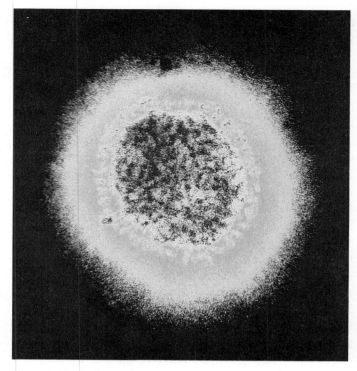

Figure 3.20 *Influenza virus*

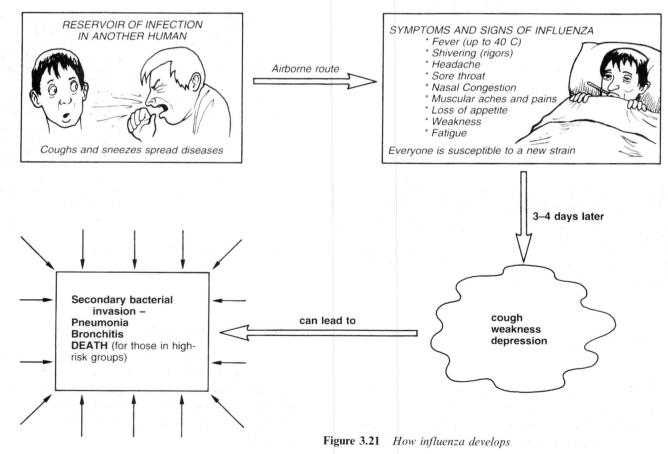

Figure 3.21 *How influenza develops*

outbreaks are longer and preceded by major changes in the virus strains (see section on antigenic nature below).

In the UK, worldwide infections tend to occur in the last three months of the year, while more localised disease strikes between January and March. Between 10 and 50 per cent of the population suffers from the disease at any one time. The highest rates are found in schoolchildren who have not built up any immunity from previous exposure. The greatest number of deaths occur in the elderly and those with chronic heart and lung diseases.

There are three distinct strains of the influenza virus: types A, B and C. Their individual characteristics can be seen in Figure 3.22 below.

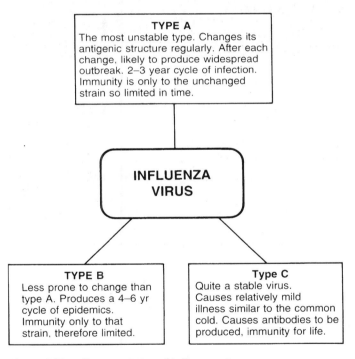

Figure 3.22 *Characteristics of influenza viruses*

Antigenic nature

Antigens are substances which stimulate the formation of antibodies from special cells found in our lymph nodes. It is useful to imagine them as partial or whole proteins inserted into the bacterial (or other micro-organisms) outer coat. Antibodies

produced by an individual's own lymphatic system confer specific immunity to a disease known as *active immunity*. This is usually permanent, or certainly long-lasting, provided that the antibody level reaches sufficiently high levels.

Antibodies produced in another's body, be it human, bacterial or animal, and then transferred to an individual is called *passive immunity*. This is only temporary and can be used as treatment or prevention for a limited time period.

The influenza virus contains two main antigenic structures, called the H and N spikes. It is thought that the H spike is the place where the virus attaches itself to the host cell (the body cell being attacked by the virus parasite) and the N spike is where the newly copied virus particles are released to attack other cells of the host. Both of these spikes can change their antigenic structure and this is more likely to happen with type A virus than any others. (See Figure 3.22.)

Active immunity	Passive immunity
1 Antibodies produced after recovery from natural disease	1 Antibodies passed from mother to foetus across the placenta.
2 Vaccination with dead or weakened forms of the micro-organism produces anitbodies in the same way.	2 Antibodies received from colostrum and breast milk.
	3 Antibody containing serum prepared from blood of animal or human previously exposed to the infection
Permanent or long lasting immunity	Temporary immunity lasts about three months. Needs to be followed by vaccination.

Naming of influenza viruses

The constant antigenic shifting has led to a special system for the naming of this virus. Each name includes the virus type, the geographical origin, year of occurrence and laboratory reference number; the antigenic nature of the H and N spikes follows in brackets.

Treatment

Although everybody is vulnerable to a new strain of influenza virus, it is rarely serious enough to threaten life in young healthy people. It is, however, much more likely to incapacitate severely and/or cause death in the elderly and chronically sick.

The recommended advice is bedrest in a warm, well-ventilated room, plenty of fluids and pain killers if required for muscular pains. The elderly should call for medical advice and antibiotics may be prescribed if there is a risk of secondary bacterial infection. It is important to note that antibiotics will not have an effect on the virus infection.

Strategies for control

Many of the characteristics of the influenza virus make it uncontrollable. Scientists are constantly trying to keep up with the changes in the virus and sending the data ahead to other countries to allow the preparation of suitable vaccines. This is coordinated by the World Influenza Centre and the World Health Organisation. The former has two laboratories in London and Atlanta (USA) which collaborate with at least 70 other countries in monitoring strains circulating around the world.

If the antigenic changes which precede the pandemics can be detected, then countries yet to be infected have time to modify the vaccines available. However, sometimes the virus changes again before arriving and the vaccine is ineffective!

Influenza vaccine

This is a mixture of the killed strains of virus circulating the previous year, thus the vaccine is always a year behind! This is why there is the constant rush to analyse any new strains which might appear. Note that although the virus is not alive its H and N spikes still exist and therefore promote antibody formation. The vaccine gives about 60 to 70 per cent protection against infection. It is generally offered in Western countries to individuals considered to be high risk or those working in the care services who might transmit the infection to high-risk individuals, for example:

– The elderly
– Chronically sick with cardio-vascular or pulmonary disease
– Medical, nursing and care staff
– HIV positive individuals
– Immunosuppressed individuals.

Drug treatment – **prophylaxis** (precautionary treatment to try to prevent illness): Amantidine will reduce the severity of an attack if taken within the first 24 hours of infection. If taken for the 'influenza season' it will confer some protection against type A virus.

· DIET ·

Macro-nutrients

The term nutrient refers to parts of food, solid or liquid, which have the following functions:

a to provide material for growth and repair
b to provide energy for body processes
c to supply materials which control a or b.

A macro-nutrient is a nutrient with a large molecular structure. Precise definitions can vary but here it is taken to mean **protein**, **fat** or **carbohydrate** substances. **Diet** is a combination of foods actually eaten (usually as calculated per day). The desired mixture is one which provides enough of each nutrient without too much of any one item.

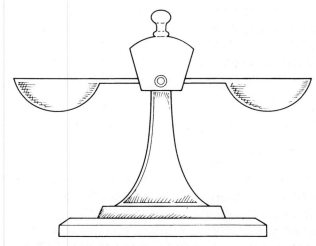

Balance is achieved within diet by ensuring there is enough of each nutrient without an excess of any one item.

Proteins

These substances provide materials for cell growth and repair. It can be useful to have a visual concept of our body cells, imagining them as being tiny bags of a watery protein mixture.

If there is too much protein in the diet, proteins become converted to carbohydrates and fat and used to supply energy requirements.

The chemical elements always present in proteins are carbon, hydrogen, oxygen and nitrogen. Many proteins also contain elements of sulphur, iron and phosphorus. These are combined in specific combinations known as **amino acids**. Each protein consists of hundreds, even thousands, of amino acids joined together by chemical bonds called *peptide links*.

There are only about 20 different amino acids *known* but these can be combined in more ways than anyone could count.

Theory into practice

Make a model using strips of coloured paper to represent four different amino acids. Label them with letters of the alphabet or use four different coloured papers.
Make three strips for each amino acid represented. Now, making pretend-proteins only four amino acids long with your strips (remember that in reality proteins are very, very much longer), see how many proteins you can make. For example:

A – A – A – A,   A – A – A – B,
A – A – B – B,   A – A – B – A, etc

You haven't exhausted two amino acids yet!

Each one of the 'proteins' shown above would have entirely different properties to its neighbour. You could discuss with your tutor (core skills – application of number) whether you could devise a formula for calculating the number of possibilities.

Amino acids are divided into two types:

- **Essential amino acids**
  As the name suggests, these must be present in our diet and we have no other means of obtaining them. Of the 20 known amino acids, 8 are essential for adults and 9 for infants.
- **Non-essential amino acids**
  These are equally important in our diet but can be made from excess essential or non-essential amino acids. The remainder fall into this category

Proteins in the diet

Main sources are meat, fish, milk and dairy products, poultry, eggs, nuts and pulses. Study the table below and think about why much of the Third World population is protein-starved.

Average protein content of foods as bought, g per 100 g

Milk, whole	3.2	Baked beans	4.8
Milk, skimmed	3.4	Beans, red kidney, dry	22.1
Cheese, Cheddar	26.0	Beans, soya, dry	34.1
Cheese, feta	16.5	Peas, frozen	5.7
Beef, average	16.6	Potatoes	2.0
Lamb, average	16.2	Apples	0.3
Pork, average	16.9	Peanuts, roasted	24.3
Sausages, pork	10.6	Bread, white	8.2
Chicken	19.7	Bread, wholemeal	9.0
Turkey	22.0	Flour, white	9.4
Fish, white	17.1	Cornflakes	8.6
Prawns	22.6	Spaghetti	12.0

The main sources of protein in the diet are meat, milk, bread and other cereals. (By permission from *The Manual of Nutrition*, HMSO)

The amount of protein needed in a healthy diet varies according to the different stages of life and occupation/activity. Average levels are:

Infancy – under 1 year of age, 18–19 g daily or 1.53 g per kg bodyweight.
Childhood – depending on age and development, 30–50 g daily or 0.8 g/kg body weight.
Adolescence – 55–75 g daily or about 1g/kg bodyweight.
Pregnancy – 60 g daily. 1.2g/kg body weight.
Adult – Men average 70g daily – 1g/kg body weight
          – Women average 54g daily – 1g/kg body weight
Old age – Recent studies and recommendations from WHO/FAO/UNU concluded that a 'safe' intake of protein should not be lower than 0.75 g/kg

bodyweight in older adults and elders. Munro et al (1987) suggested that the needs of healthy elderly people would be better met by 1g/kg bodyweight due to altered protein use in the elderly as a consequence of changed body composition.

Adult – minimum 40 g per day would be very unattractive and 70 g daily is a more acceptable level.

For the life stages other than adulthood and old age, i.e. in infancy, childhood and adolescence, and obviously in pregnancy for women, these are periods when pronounced growth is taking place and an increased intake of protein is required.

Approximately 33 per cent of the average British diet comes from fruit, vegetables and nuts leaving 67 per cent from animal foodstuffs. Vegetarians and vegans can obtain their proteins adequately providing their vegetable diet is varied; vegetarians can also obtain good sources from cereals, beans, eggs and cheese.

Biological values

Plant proteins are said to have **low biological value** because this is linked to the ability to supply all the essential amino acids. Although they are useful sources of amino acids, plants generally do not contain all of them. This is why a diet from vegetable sources only must contain a wide variety of plant proteins to ensure that all the essential ones are supplied by the combination.

Most proteins from animal sources are of **high biological value** but their main advantage lies in the nutrients which are also found in the same or similar foods. These are iron, and vitamins B12 and D.

Storage and use of protein

Surplus amino acids cannot be stored in the body and must be regularly broken down. This is carried out in the liver, with the nitrogen-containing amine group being converted into *urea*. Urea is poisonous to the body if it is allowed to build up, so it is constantly removed from the blood by the kidneys and passed into urine. The rest of the protein molecule is respired to produce energy or converted into glucose by the liver for storage as glycogen. If the diet does not provide sufficient carbohydrates or fat for energy then proteins will be respired for this

purpose, wasting valuable nitrogen-containing material (which is much more expensive to buy as food).

Soya protein can be used to make products which resemble meat (e.g. soya 'mince' or 'sausages') and combined with vitamins and minerals to suit vegetarian diets.

Fats

These food materials are compounds of carbon, hydrogen and oxygen and are three *fatty acids* linked to a molecule of glycerol. Such a combination is often called a *triglyceride*.

Many different fatty acids are known, but the most well known forms are chemically called *saturated* and *polyunsaturated* fatty acids. This chemical division is based on the number of double links between the atoms making up the acid: saturated fats have none while polyunsaturated have two or more. (For further details it is worth consulting a text on organic chemistry.) Some unsaturated fatty acids can also be classed as *essential fatty acids* because they are necessary for our diet and we have no other means of obtaining them.

Fats in the diet

According to recent studies, the ratio of polyunsaturated fat to saturated fat (the P/S ratio) is thought to be increasingly important. This ratio has risen in the last twenty years from $0 \cdot 2 : 1$ to $0 \cdot 3 : 1$ as people become more aware of the differences in fats and the likely benefits in the reduction of heart disease. In the Western world, fat contributes about 40 per cent of our energy requirements as it is a highly concentrated source of energy. In poorer countries this can fall to 10 per cent or less.

Fats provide interest and variety in our diets. Foods such as butter, margarine, cream, egg yolks and meat supply most of our animal fats. Oily fish provide a source of beneficial fat; this group of fish includes herring, tuna, sardines and salmon. Plant sources of fats are nuts, seeds and some fruits. In the

Typical fatty acid composition of some foods as bought

	Fat g per 100 g edible portion	Fatty acids, per cent of fat by weight[1]		
		Saturated	Monounsaturated	Polyunsaturated
Milk, cows'	3.9	64	28	3
Milk, human	4.1	48	39	8
Cheese, Cheddar	33.5	63	27	4
Eggs	10.9	31	39	11
Beef, average	27.4	41	47	4
Pork, average	25.5	35	42	15
Chicken	12.8	30	45	20
Liver, lambs	6.2	28	29	15
Mackerel	22.9	20	49	20
Butter	82.0	68	23	4
Margarine, hard	81.0	39	47	10
Margarine, soft	81.0	30	41	26
Margarine, polyunsaturated	81.0	17	27	52
Corn (maize) oil	99.9	13	25	58
Blended oil	99.9	8	52	36
Potato crisps	35.9	34	40	21
Peanuts, roasted, salted	49.0	21	38	37
Biscuits, chocolate	27.6	65	26	4
Chocolate, milk	30.3	58	33	4

[1]The total percentage of fatty acids is less than 100 because of the glycerol and other fatty compounds which are present. To calculate the total fatty acid content of a food, multiply the percentages of the various types of fatty acid by the amount of fat. Thus the total polyunsaturated fatty acid content of 100 g of beef is $\frac{1}{100} \times 27.4 = 1.1\,g$.

(By permission from *The Manual of Nutrition*, HMSO)

table above you will find the average fat content of the main fatty foods in our diets.

Fats are a source of energy, 1 gram of fat providing 37 kJ of energy. However, fats may also contain the valuable fat-soluble vitamins A, D, E and K, and cholesterol, which is the basic ingredient for many materials in the body, including steroid hormones.

It is a strange irony that people wishing to eat a healthier diet in affluent countries are advised to reduce the quantity of fat in the diet, while those in poorer countries have recommendations for increased consumption.

Volumes needed during life stages

There are no strict guidelines for either fat or carbohydrate intake (other than often recommending reductions) but rather for energy requirements. These daily energy requirements are as follows:

Infancy: 3000–3250 kJ
Childhood: 4,500–9,500 kJ
Adolescence: 8,500–12,000 kJ
Pregnancy: 10,000 kJ
Old age: 7,000–9,000 kJ

Generally, males have a greater energy requirement than females. Elders require less due to reduced activity.

Carbohydrates

Like fats, carbohydrates supply energy and are chemically composed of the elements carbon, hydrogen and oxygen. The second two are in the same proportion as they exist in water, thus carbo-n-hydrate or carbon water. All are based on a simple common unit which we can consider to be the *glucose* molecule. There are linked together by special *glycosidic* bonds in various combinations numbering up to thousands.

Carbohydrates are considered to be *sugars*, *starches* or *cellulose*-type materials.

Sugars are of the very simplest single molecule arrangements – *monosaccharides* – or two units linked together, the *disaccharides*. Glucose and fructose are the best known versions of the former and sucrose (the sort of sugar you put in tea) of the latter. All of these occur naturally in plants, particularly in fruits.

Starches are *polysaccharides* and, as the name suggests, are composed of long chains of glucose molecules. They are not sweet tasting like the mono and dissaccharides. They are the storage form of glucose in plant cells, forming an insoluble compound which can be tucked away conveniently in granules. Glycogen is related to starch, but is to be found serving the same purpose in animal cells, particularly liver and muscle.

Cellulose is another plant polysaccharide forming, in this case, the rigid cell walls and the fibrous structures in plants. It forms the main component of roughage or dietary fibre.

All of these carbohydrates, except cellulose, form part of our food supply, being digested after various enzymatic processes to make glucose, which can be absorbed by the gut wall into the blood. Glucose is the energy form required by body cells for the process of respiration. Although it is indigestible, cellulose has a very important role to play in the balanced diet. It provides bulk and helps retain water for the muscular bowel walls to act upon and propel the food, and food residues, along the alimentary tract. Various forms of protection have also been claimed for fibre-rich diets, such as reducing the incidence of bowel cancer and hindering the absorption of more harmful fats.

Carbohydrate in the diet

Flour, bread, jams, honey, fruit and vegetables, sugar, potatoes and various drinks are all carbohydrate providers in our diets. See the following table.

The amount of carbohydrate needed in our diet is related to energy requirements. See the previous page in the section on fats for daily energy requirements.

Micro-nutrients

Remember that the role of nutrients in the diet is to provide material for growth and repair and to

Average carbohydrate content of selected foods, g per 100 g edible portion (Available carbohydrate, as monosaccharides)

	Sugars	Starch	Total
Milk	4.6[1]	0	4.6
Ice cream	19.7	1.0	20.7
Meat	0	0	0
Sugar	105.3[2]	0	105.3[2]
Honey	76.4	0	76.4
Jam	69.2	0	69.2
Baked beans	5.8	9.3	15.1
Potatoes, boiled	1.0	17.0	18.0
Yams, boiled	0.2	29.6	29.8
Bananas	16.2	3.0	19.2
Oranges	8.5	0	8.5
Peaches, canned in syrup	22.9	0	22.9
canned in juice	12.9	0	12.9
Biscuits, chocolate	43.4	24.0	67.4
Bread, white	2.8	45.8	48.6
Bread, wholemeal	1.8	39.8	41.6
Flour, white	0.5	76.2	76.7
Cornflakes	7.4	77.7	85.1
Muesli, average	26.2	40.0	66.2
Porridge oats	1.1	64.9	66.0
Orange squash undiluted	26.1	0	26.1
Soup, canned, tomato	2.6	3.3	5.9
Tomato ketchup	22.9	1.1	24.0
Chocolate, milk	56.5	2.9	59.4
Beer, bitter	2.3	0	2.3
Wine, medium, white	2.5	0	2.5

[1] Lactose
[2] Equivalent to 100 g of sucrose:
  1 g disaccharide is equivalent to 1.05 g monosaccharide
  1 g starch is equivalent to 1.11 g monosaccharide
The main sources of sugars in the diet are sugar, sweets and chocolates, milk (as lactose), fruit and fruit products, and biscuits and cakes. The main sources of starches in the diet are bread, potatoes, cakes, biscuits, and other cereal products.
(By permission from *The Manual of Nutrition*, HMSO)

provide energy for body processes. Micro-nutrients are needed only in small quantities to enable chemical reactions to take place.

Vitamins and minerals

Roughly classed as being either water-soluble or fat-soluble, vitamins are diverse agents both in their chemical make-up and in their function. Vitamins are an essential part of our diet and their common link is that they all cause general and specific symptoms if not present in adequate amounts. (See the table on the next page.)

Minerals are another essential group of nutrients. They are needed to help form bones and blood, and to aid energy transfer. Minerals and trace elements

Vitamins

Name	Source	Function	Deficiency/Excess
Vitamin A • retinol • carotene precursor Vit. A	Animal foods only – fish liver oils, liver, kidney, dairy produce and eggs, carrots, spinach, cabbage, added to margarine.	Essential for vision in dim light. Healthy skin and lining tissues	Night blindness and eye conditions leading to blindness. Excessive doses can cause death by poisoning
Vitamin B • Thiamin B	Milk, offal, pork, eggs, fruit and vegetables, breakfast cereals, bread	Release of energy from carbohydrate	Beri beri
• Riboflavin	Milk (destroyed by sunlight) offal	Release of energy from food	Sores at corners of mouth
• Vitamin B_6	Meats, fish, eggs, wholewheat, some vegetables	Metabolism of protein and formation of haemoglobin	Very high doses are dangerous. Deficiency rare
• Vitamin B_{12}	Liver, eggs, meat, milk, cheese, fish, fortified cereals, yeast	Required for healthy red blood cells	Pernicious anaemia and nerve cell degeneration. Vegans are susceptible and individuals with malfunction of stomach
• Folic acid	Offal, raw green leafy vegetables	Required for healthy red blood cells	Type of anaemia. Pregnant women on poor diets susceptible
Vitamin C Ascorbic acid	Fruit and vegetables, particularly rosehips, strawberries, citrus fruits, blackcurrants	Maintain healthy connective tissues. Antioxidant	Slow healing of wounds, bleeding gums. Scurvy followed by death if prolonged. Destroyed by storage, preparation and cooking
Vitamin D Calciferol	Action of sunlight on human skin. Dairy produce, liver, oily fish, Added to margarine	Regulating plasma calcium levels. Helps absorption of calcium from gut and deposit calcium in bones	Rickets, lack of calcium in bone Osteomalacia – bone softening in adults. Fractures likely. Children and pregnant and lactating women susceptible, also invalids and others not in sunshine. Asian toddlers. Too high an intake dangerous, calcium deposited in kidneys
Vitamin E Tocopherol	Most foods especially oils, cereals and eggs	Associated with fertility in rats, not proven in humans. Antioxidant	Rare, possibly anaemia in very young
Vitamin K	Intestinal bacteria manufacture K. Vegetables, spinach, cabbage etc	Essential for normal clotting of blood	Rare

include calcium, phosphorus, iron, zinc, sodium, potassium and magnesium. All these are needed in very small quantities so supplements are not usually necessary – they are naturally present in a good mixed diet. (See Figure 3.23 on the next page.)

Iron
Found in haemoglobin of red blood cells and used to transport oxygen. Stored in liver (important in baby), Insufficient iron in diet produces anaemia. Needs are greatest in the child, pregnant and menstruating women. Most iron in diet comes from meat, but also from offal, apricots, corn-flakes and cocoa.

Phosphorus
Dietary deficiency is unknown due to widespread occurrence. Main sources are milk, bread and meat products.
Uses are:
a) With calcium, in bones, teeth
b) In proteins
c) Release of energy from food
d) Part of nucleic acids in nucleus
High levels in newborns may be linked to low levels of calcium, producing muscular spasm called tetany.

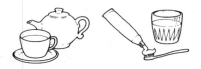

Calcium
More of this than any other mineral stored in compounds with phosphorus in skeleton, teeth and also found in a different form in blood and muscle.
Used for clotting of blood, enzyme action and contraction of muscles.
Very insoluble substance so goes hand in hand with Vitamin D which assists absorption. In U.K. the main sources are milk, cheese and bread (added), so it is very important that children and pregnant and lactating women get plenty of these foods as their needs are greatest to supply the growth of the skeleton.

Fluorine
Another compound associated with healthy bones and teeth, noted for increasing resistance of tooth enamel to decay.
Important sources are drinking water (variable amount), tea and seafoods. In areas of fluoride deficiency, some groups or individuals may add fluoride to their diet through treated drinking water, toothpaste or simply extra tablets.

Zinc
Has come into focus more recently. Needed for enzyme action and wound healing. Like calcium, zinc salts are often poorly absorbed. This is further decreased if large quantities of whole cereals are consumed so vegetarians could be vulnerable to zinc deficiency. Zinc is usually linked to protein foods such as meat and dairy products.
It has a role in the metabolism of insulin. Most of the body's zinc stores are in the skeleton.

Figure 3.23 *A variety of minerals are needed for a healthy diet.*

· BALANCED DIETS ·

At least one meal each day should be 'balanced'. This means it will contain a variety of foods in the right combination and amount to keep the body working healthily. Meals must look attractive and taste good but more importantly they should:

- provide sufficient energy to suit the body requirements at various life stages
- give adequate amounts of protein for growth and repair
- provide sufficient quantities of minerals and vitamins to suit body needs
- contain enough dietary fibre to promote health
- be limited in fat, sugar and salt

Generally , 55 per cent of energy in the diet should come from carbohydrates and no more than 35 per cent from fats; leaving about 10 per cent for protein and the micro-nutrients. Many people feel that this is too high a value for fats and that 33 per cent would be more acceptable.

Fats

In the 'Health of the Nation' document the government set targets for fat consumption. See box right.

It also stated that, 'excessive dietary intake of saturated fatty acids results in raised plasma cholesterol levels and that this is a main risk factor for Coronary Heart Disease and Stroke.' See box on following page.

Sugar

We need a certain amount of sugar, in the form of cabohydrates, in our diet. But too much sugar, usually the refined white sort, can have harmful effects on our bodies. The most obvious and highly visible damage occurs to teeth. We do not often realise we are taking sugar because it can be a hidden ingredient in many foods such as biscuits, cakes, sweets, some baked beans, ice cream, soft

Diet and Nutrition
- To reduce the average percentage of food energy derived by the population from saturated fatty acids by at least 35% by 2005 (from 17% in 1990 to no more than 11%).
- To reduce the average percentage of food energy derived by the population from total fat by at least 12% by 2005 (from about 40% in 1990 to no more than 35%).

(*Note*: Regular data are already collected through the National Food Survey on average population intakes of fat and fatty acids.)

Action to achieve health and nutrition targets involves the dissemination of information about healthy eating and encouraging and enabling changes in the population's diet. A whole diet approach is crucial if the balance of the diet is to be sensible. To reach the targets in a diet that also matches COMA's wider recommendations, patterns of food consumption will need to change very considerably.

In pursuit of this the Government will, in collaboration with others as appropriate:

- continue and enhance research into the links between diet and health, and into influences on consumer choice;
- continue to secure expert advice on nutrition and health;
- continue national surveillance of diet, nutrition and health of the population;
- seek ways of improving and targeting information and advice on healthy eating and weight control;
- seek ways of improving information on the nutritional content of food;
- produce and disseminate voluntary nutritional guidelines for catering outlets.

Co-ordinated action is needed from a range of interested parties. The Government proposes to set up a joint Nutrition Task Force, which would be a partnership of officials from relevant Government Departments and representatives from other sectors

(From *The Health of the Nation*, 1992)

drinks and so on. It is possible to consume these foods and not feel 'full-up', so we carry on eating long after our energy needs have been met. This results in being overweight, or even obese, with all the possible consequent problems such as diabetes, painful feet, backache, heart diseases etc. Sugar is a concentrated soluble form of energy, often taken almost without our knowing.

· SPECIAL DIETS ·

Vegetarian and Vegan diets

Much controversy exists over the nutritional value of diets based mainly or entirely on plant products. The articles on the following pages plus the example of a healthy food leaflet distributed by a large supermarket chain are reprinted with permission so that you may examine both and form your own opinion.

DIETARY FATS AND HEART DISEASE

Before looking at different dietary fats and how they affect blood fats (lipids), it is helpful to have an understanding of how fats circulate in the blood.

Briefly, fats circulate as particles called lipoproteins, and these are classified according to the type of fat they contain:

- Chylomicrons and very low density lipoproteins (VLDL) transport triglycerides
- Low density lipoproteins (LDL) contain most of the cholesterol in blood plasma
- High density lipoproteins (HDL) also carry cholesterol but are involved in removal of it from sites where it has accumulated for disposal by the liver.

Obesity and diets rich in saturated fatty acids can result in raised plasma LDL cholesterol in susceptible people. Total cholesterol, or LDL cholesterol (often known as 'bad' fat), is related to coronary risk, whereas HDL cholesterol ('good' fat) is a protective factor.

In general, fat in food from animal sources (dairy products, meat and so on) is mainly in the form of saturated and monosaturated fatty acids).

Vegetable oils and fats (such as polyunsaturated margarines) contain a small amount of saturates but mainly monounsaturates and the polyunsaturated fatty acid linoleic acid.

Saturates

There is well-established evidence that certain saturated fatty acids raise the level of LDL in the blood and therefore increase the risk of development of heart disease (particularly if an individual also smokes and is hypertensive). Individuals should be encouraged to cut down on foods high in saturates, including fatty meats such as lamb and pork, visible fat on all cuts of meat, meat products such as sausages, pies and burgers, full-fat dairy products such as whole milk, double cream, butter and cheese, as well as foods containing 'hidden' fat such as savoury snacks such as potato crisps, cakes, biscuits, shortbread and confectionery.

Monounsaturates

For many years monounsaturates were thought to have little effect on blood cholesterol, but recent studies have shown them to be just as effective as polyunsaturates at lowering LDL cholesterol levels without also lowering HDL cholesterol. The most common monounsaturate is oleic acid, which is found in olive oil, rapeseed oil, nuts, seeds and meat.

In Mediterranean countries, where intake of olive oil is relatively high, the incidence of coronary heart disease is low and this may, in part, be explained by the apparent benefits of a diet rich in monounsaturates. However, intakes of fruit and vegetable are also high in these countries, and these may also have a protective role against the development of heart disease. Other non-dietary factors may also be involved.

Small amounts of monounsaturates may be included in a healthy diet – such as rapeseed oil for cooking – to replace some saturated fat.

Polyunsaturates

Small amounts of polyunsaturated fatty acids (PUFA) are essential in the diet and are known as essential fatty acids. The two essential fatty acids are linoleic acid (omega 6), found mainly in vegetable oil, soft margarines, some nuts and seeds, and alpha linolenic acid (omega 3), which is found in oil-rich fish. PUFA in vegetable oils have been shown to lower LDL cholesterol. However, at very high intakes they may also lower the protective HDL cholesterol.

Alpha linolenic acid and its derivatives in oil-rich fish do not lower LDL cholesterol, but recent studies have shown that they may have an effect on reducing the 'stickiness' of the blood (that is, its tendency to clot). This has been demonstrated in middle-aged men who had already had a heart attack. Eating oil-rich fish at least twice a week appeared to reduce deaths more successfully than adhering to a low-fat or high-fibre diet. Clients should be encouraged to eat oil-fish once or twice a week, such as herring, mackerel, sardines, salmon or trout.

It is important to remember that all fat, whether saturated or unsaturated, is a concentrated source of energy (calories). So total fat and saturated fats should be reduced, with only a small amount of mainly unsaturated fats included as part of a healthy diet.

Another area of current research is the role of anti-oxidant nutrients in health and disease. Anti-oxidant vitamins have been shown to exert a protective role against heart disease and some cancers. A number of studies are under way to determine whether high dietary intakes of vitamins E, C or beta carotene (vitamin A) are related to a reduction in the incidence of heart disease.

All types of fruit and vegetables should be eaten as much as possible – at least five portions every day, which probably means an increase for most people.

Reproduced by kind permission *Community Outlook* where this article was first published Nov/Dec 1993

GOOD HEALTH!

We do not need to consume animal products in order to live well. Dispensing with them is part of our healthy future.

Recent research into dietary causes of ill health has dramatically increased interest in vegan diets, which have been followed successfully in many countries for nearly half a century and been shown to be health-promoting in a number of ways.

In 1983 the National Advisory Committee on Nutrition Education (NACNE) echoed the conclusions of numerous other expert committees worldwide in recommending changes in our eating habits: a one-third reduction in the intake of fats, especially those in meat and dairy products, which together supply three-quarters of all the saturated fats in our diet; and an increase in the intake of fibre from wholefoods, especially fresh fruit and vegetables. The NACNE report has become a turning-point in British eating, finally prompting government action to help people switch to a healthier diet.

A catalogue
Heart disease kills more people than any other illnesses. Britain tops the world league with about 180,000 deaths each year. It's no coincidence that we consume more meat and dairy products than other European countries, whose death rates from heart disease have dropped markedly in the last 20 years, while the British have continued to fall like ninepins from this largely preventable disease. Cancers of the breast and bowel, also major killers, have similarly been linked with a high-fat, low-fibre diet.

Another danger of an animal-based diet is food poisoning. Despite the image of clean, healthy farm animals promoted by the meat and dairy industries, the reality is quite different. When animals are slaughtered, meat can be contaminated with gut contents, faeces and urine, leading to bacterial infection. Four-fifths of all food poisoning incidents can be traced to infected meat, with milk and dairy products accounting for many of the rest. In an attempt to counteract infection in their animals farmers routinely inject them with doses of antibiotics. These, in addition to growth-promoting drugs and pesticide residues in their feed, build up in the animals' tissues and pose yet another threat to the health of those people still on a conventional diet.

Eating for health

A vegan diet starts at birth, with breast-feeding naturally taking the place of cow's milk formulas. Breast-fed babies are actively protected from infection by antibodies in their mother's milk, whereas allergy to cow's milk can cause asthma, eczema, diarrhoea and colic, and has also been linked with some cot deaths. But the real time bomb lies in the lifelong build-up of fatty layers in the arteries which can lead to heart disease – a process which starts in childhood with a diet high in milk and meat.

Fat in a typical vegan diet is at the level recommended by NACNE, and most of it is unsaturated. Consequently vegans not only have less cholesterol in their blood, thus reducing the risk of heart disease, but are less prone to gallstones and gout. Medical research has shown that a vegan diet can reduce high blood pressure in patients otherwise obliged to resort to drugs with unpleasant side-effects.

Staple vegan foods are high in natural fibre, lessening the risk of cancer of the colon, constipation, varicose veins and piles. There is no fibre in meat, milk or eggs. The low-fat, high-fibre vegan diet means that vegans tend to be slimmer than average, and so again less at risk from heart attacks, and also from diabetes and even arthritis. A report published in 1985 (Journal of Alternative Medicine June 1985) concluded that a vegan diet comes closest to the dietary goals set by NACNE.

A varied and balance vegan diet will provide all of the essential nutrients for all age-groups, including during pregnancy and breast feeding. Vegan children grow up fit and healthy, and there are third-generation vegans to prove it! There are now vegan marathon runners, long-distance swimmers, triathletes, professional footballers and doctors.

The prevalence of ill health in Britain, even in a century of so-called 'miracle cures', highlights the vital contribution veganism can make towards correcting harmful eating habits and improving the nation's health.

© *The Vegan Society*
November, 1992

SHOULD MEAT BE PART OF MY DIET?

Yes, but of course a balanced diet should consist of both meat and vegetables and a wide variety of other foods. No one food contains all the nutrients we need for good health. Meat offers many nutritional benefits (as explained later) and should be eaten together with foods such as bread, rice, pasta (especially wholemeal) and potatoes. These foods contain carbohydrates which provide energy. They help us feel full and are a source of dietary fibre. Also include in your meal plenty of fruit and vegetables.

These provide vitamins, especially Vitamin C. This combination will ensure you will receive all the nutrients necessary for good health.

Meat has many nutritional benefits, so for anyone cutting meat from all their meals, special attention must be given to adequate sources of iron and also Vitamin B12. For example, meat is an excellent source of iron and iron deficiency can lead to anaemia – a common problem in many women. The recent report on Dietary Reference Values (COMA 1991) 'cautioned that iron in diets containing little or no meat is less well absorbed and that people habitually consuming such diets may need a higher iron intake.'

What about the fat in meat?

Red meat has become leaner over the last decade as a result of changes in farming, production, consumer purchasing preferences and cooking practices. Farmers are now breeding much leaner animals and supermarkets and butchers are trimming meat so as to provide the consumer with leaner cuts of meat. Apart from this, meat has one obvious advantage over other foodstuffs; most of the fat on meat is visible and therefore can be removed by the butcher or consumer. Some customers believe that fat imparts great flavour to the meat and prefer to use it in the cooking process and then cut it off before serving or on the plate. The muscle (or lean) part of the meat which is left contains relatively little fat. Indeed, the majority of lean beef and pork, that is meat trimmed of all visible fat, contains less than 5% fat (McCance and Widdowson 1991, MAFF/MLC).

We are all concerned about fat in our diet and in particular saturated fat. Only half the fat in meat is saturated. The rest is unsaturated, some of which is in the form of essential polyunsaturated fatty acids. Indeed, carcase meats only provide around 11% of the total saturated fat in the British diet so the contribution of other sources is more important (National Food Survey). One more significant fact – Britain has the highest rate of heart disease among EC countries, but the second lowest meat consumption per head. France has the highest meat consumption and the lowest heart disease rate (World Health Organisation 1989)!

© *Meat and Livestock Commission*
December, 1992

TEENAGERS AND FOOD

Change and challenge

The school years through to the late teens are an important time for change. Physically, the teenage years are a time of growth and development – leading to an increased need for most nutrients. At the same time, the 'growing up' process can involve rejecting 'traditional' values and eating habits as a way of showing newfound independence.

Slimming
About 6% of girls aged 14–15 go on weight-reducing diets. The wrong kind of diet will not only decrease the energy, but can also lower the nutrient intake. So sound advice on low-energy, nutrient-dense eating is needed. Lean meat – being both low in energy and nutrient-dense – can be an important part of any young person's healthy food consumption plans.

Vegetarianism and veganism
Teenagers attempting – even if only temporarily – to take up vegetarian or vegan lifestyles may face problems. This can happen if animal products are omitted and not replaced with nutritionally equivalent foods.

For example, teenagers' iron intakes often fall short of the recommended levels. In girls, insufficient intake may be combined with high menstrual losses or pregnancy which can deplete iron stores. A lack of iron can lead to tiredness, apathy and in extreme cases anaemia.

Red meat is a rich source of vitamin B-12 and iron, in a form readily used by the body. The iron absorption from meat is at least twice that from plant foods. So for anyone cutting meat from all their meals, special attention must be given to adequate sources of iron, and also vitamin B-12.

School meals
The Education Act 1980 declared that local authorities no longer had to provide school meals (with the exception of free school meals) nor conform to set nutritional standards. The effect of the new arrangement for school lunches was monitored by a Department of Health Study on the diets of school children.

This highlighted that some children, particularly teenage girls, consumed the lowest amount of many nutrients, notably iron.

Attempts to improve the balance of school meals has been helped by active health education programmes in schools and the introduction of healthy eating menus. However, even if teenagers do miss a lunch time meal (or eat 'unbalanced' lunches) this does not necessarily mean their total daily food intake is inadequate. But it then places additional importance on nutrient-dense foods being included in their other meals.

Snacking
Snacking is popular with young people – with 11–13 year olds often having 5–6 meals or snacks a day. Eating meals away from home decreases the parental influence. Often it is foods that are high in fat and sugar that are chosen – with the parents' knowledge! (As a recent TV study of our eating habits showed.) But let's be clear – not all snacks provide so called 'empty calories'. In some cases, healthy eating advice may be more acceptable and realistic if given in terms of sensible snacks.

For example: A bag of chips and ketchup and an apple provides 2247kj (537kcals) – approximately 45% of which is derived from fat, but it provides very little protein, iron or zinc. Whereas: A meat sandwich means less energy and fat – but more protein and minerals.

© *Meat and Livestock Commission*
November, 1992

DIET, HEALTH AND NUTRITION

For many years, meat was considered essential for good health. Yet recently, red meat and meat products have been singled out as items to avoid in putting together a healthy diet. Like most things in life, the truth lies between the two extremes.

Meat eating and health
It shouldn't even need saying – but in view of all the scare stories, we'd better make it clear – meat eating itself is not an unhealthy activity.

It has to be remembered that meat eaters are not carnivores – but omnivores. Meat and meat products only provide about 15% of our total energy intake. And most meat eaters also consume large amounts of fruit, vegetables and cereals.

Nutritional benefits
Meat has many obvious nutritional benefits and can make a very positive contribution to a balanced diet. Not only is it an excellent source of protein, it is also important for B vitamins and minerals such as iron and zinc. Much of the iron in meat is present in a form (haem iron) which is particularly well absorbed by our bodies. Other foods contain iron too, but in a form which is less readily available.

Its biggest disadvantage appears to be its natural fat content. But most of this is visible fat (unlike the 'hidden' fat in so many food products, like biscuits and cakes!) – which can easily be trimmed or otherwise removed. The link between meat and fat is not, or need not be, as negative as some people are led to believe.

Food preparation and hygiene
The anti-meat pressure groups have attempted to claim that meat causes food poisoning and other ills – based on some outbreaks of food poisoning in canteens and restaurants. These occurred because some catering outlets failed to observe the required standards of hygiene when preparing the meals. But it's the caterer – not the meat – that's to blame.

Meat and heart disease: it doesn't add up
One more fact which might make you stop and think – Britain has the highest rate of heart disease among EC countries but the second lowest meat consumption per head. France has the highest meat consumption rate and lowest heart disease rate. C'est la vie!

© *Meat and Livestock Commission*
November, 1992

A HEALTHY VEGETARIAN DIET

A vegetarian diet can mean a healthy balanced diet as long as some basic principles are understood.
There are several types of vegetarian, all of whom exclude different animal foods from their diet.

Vegans
Avoid all animal products, including honey. In addition they do not use products which have been tested on animals.

Lacto vegetarians
Eat milk and cheese but *nothing* which has been produced as a result of an animal being slaughtered, eg meat, fish, poultry, or by-products such as gelatine, whey or rennet.

Ovo-lacto vegetarians
Eat eggs (often free range) as well as dairy products.

Demi-vegetarians
Choose to exclude red meat but may occasionally eat poultry and fish. To help vegetarians make the right food choices, we use

a symbol on the pack, space permitting, to indicate which Tesco Brand products are suitable for ovo-lacto vegetarians.

Look out for the symbol on our range of vegetarian products such as ready meals, quiches and cheese. You can be assured that they contain:

(a) No animal products or by-products (with the exception of eggs, milk products and honey).

(b) No products or by-products of the fishing industry.

A sensibly planned vegetarian diet will pose no health problems. Many of the myths surrounding a vegetarian diet arose when food choices were more limited. Some of the most common concerns are answered in this leaflet.

Can a vegetarian diet provide enough protein?

Yes it can. Meat, fish and poultry provide a substantial amount of protein in the meat-eaters diet. In reality the majority of us, vegetarians and non-vegetarians alike, eat more protein than we actually need. Protein deficiency is not a problem in this country. Any protein which is surplus to our bodies' requirements is simply turned into energy (calories) or stored as fat.

There are many interesting sources of protein apart from fish and meat. In a vegetarian diet most sources of protein, such as pulses and grains, have the added advantage of being low in fat and saturated fat. In addition they are good sources of vitamins and minerals and can often be high in fibre too.

- Pulses such as beans, peas and lentils are a good source of protein, low in fat and high in fibre. They can be made into burgers, casseroles, vegetable bakes and croquettes.
- Nuts are a good source of protein for non-meat eaters but are high in fat. Use them in moderation combined with pulses or grains which are low in fat.
- Grains such as rice, wheat, rye and corn are both high in fibre and protein and are excellent for bulking out casseroles and vegetable stuffings or serving cold as part of a salad.
- Quorn® is high in protein and fibre and low in fat. It is made from myco-protein which is related to the mushroom and is a vegetable

product. Available chilled, it resembles cubes of meat and has a lean and tender texture which has the ability to absorb flavours from other ingredients. It can be used in recipes in which you would use cubed or minced meat.

- Soya beans are a very good source of protein. They are also available processed into textured vegetable protein which can be made into a variety of savoury dishes.
- Tofu or soya bean curd is a valuable source of calcium. It is also low in fat and can be used in soups, stir fries and casseroles or blended for pâtés and desserts. Tofu also has the ability to absorb flavour from other ingredients.
- Cheese made from non-animal rennet, milk, yogurt and other milk-based products are also good sources of protein for lacto, ovo-lacto and demi-vegetarians.

What about vitamins and minerals?

An adequate supply of vitamins and minerals should not be a problem if the diet is carefully planned.

As well as being a good source of protein, meat provides much of the iron and many of the B Vitamins in the non-vegetarian diet. However, there are alternative vegetarian sources of virtually all these nutrients. These include wholemeal bread and wholegrain cereals, pulses and nuts. Leafy green vegetables are a good source of iron. Vegans may, however, need to take vitamin B12 supplements as this nutrient is found mainly in foods from animal sources such as meat and dairy products.

Quorn® is the registered trademark of Marlow Foods.
©Tesco Stores Ltd., 199-

Low-salt diet

There are good reasons for adopting a low-salt diet – see box on the next page on the health risks of salt. There are four simple steps in lowering the amount of salt in the diet:

1 Remove the salt cellar from the table – this cuts down between 10 and 40 per cent of an individual's salt intake.

2 Don't add salt to cooking – your taste buds will soon adjust.

3 Avoid foods with added salt – these will mainly be processed foods.

4 Eat more home-cooked food – you are more likely to know the salt content.

Salt is a flavour-enhancer and at first a low-salt diet may cause food to taste bland, but this will soon pass. Alternatives to salt can be the use of potassium salts, which are often rejected as rather bitter tasting, or a mixture of sodium and potassium salts. However, anyone with kidney, liver or heart problems should consult their doctor before taking potassium as a salt substitute.

SALT

While some salt is essential to life, evidence is mounting that most people are eating too much of it for their long term health.

In an unusually definite statement in a learned journal, researchers at St Bartholomew's Hospital, London, told readers of the British Medical Journal (April 6 and April 20, 1991) that three grams less salt a day, the equivalent of half a teaspoon, would save thousands of lives.

They estimate that such a reduction in the daily diet would prevent one in five strokes, one in six cases of heart disease and would halve the number of people taking drugs to reduce their blood pressure.

And if food manufacturers were to reduce the amount of salt they put into processed food, around 70,000 deaths a year could be prevented in Britain. Even without that change in commercial practice, the reduction of three grams a day itself could prevent 6,000 premature deaths in the under-65's and 40,000 deaths a year overall.

'Labelling of the salt content of foods and the reduction in the amount of salt added by manufacturers to processed food is a vital public health objective' the researchers state.

The work was conducted by the Department of Preventive Medicine at St Bartholomew's and led by Dr Malcolm Law. They analysed the data from 78 trials of the effect of lowering dietary salt on blood pressure, and 24 studies involving 47,000 people worldwide.

What they found led them to conclude that the usual rise of blood pressure with age in Western countries could be reduced and that the relationship between salt and blood pressure was much stronger than has been accepted. They also found that the higher the blood pressure the more readily it responded to reduction in salt intake.

Dr Law said that the blood pressure of, say, 110/75 of a healthy young adult ought, ideally, to be maintained throughout life. 'In our society people tend to increase their body weight, drink more alcohol and take less exercise as they get older, all of which can increase their blood pressure'.

'The effects of a salt reduction on risk of stroke would be almost immediate, but the effect on heart disease may take several years', he said.

It takes a few months for people who like to taste a lot of salt to adjust their palate to a less salty diet. His advice is to avoid obviously salty foods like nuts and crisps and to stop adding salt in cooking or at the table. He also recommends switching to salt substitutes which contain mixtures of sodium chloride and potassium chloride.

'There are few measures in preventive medicine which are so simple but which could achieve so much', he said.

A statement from London University at the time of the publication of the findings said the work 'not only conclusively confirms the previously suspected link between salt consumption and blood pressure, but shows the link is even more important than was previously thought'.

Monitoring of blood-pressure after moving on to a low-salt diet is essential, as it may necessitate reducing medication or abandoning it altogether. Of course, this should only be done on medical advice.

Diabetic diet

The aims of treatment for diabetes is to enable the diabetic to lead as normal a life as possible and to prevent long-term complications. To do this, it is necessary to keep the level of glucose in the blood to as near normal as possible. Steady weight, regular exercise, careful management of the diet and necessary medication at regular intervals will help to ensure this.

The carbohydrates in the diet must be spaced out at regular intervals so that fluctuations in glucose levels can be avoided. Diabetics must avoid obesity as this reduces still further the body's ability to metabolise glucose. Asian diabetics manage to obtain 60 per cent of the carbohydrate in their diets from rice or chapattis.

Monitoring is essential to prevent extremes of hypo and hyperglycaemia developing, as both these conditions can be life threatening. Diabetics have kits for monitoring their own urinary glucose excretion. They are also taught how to recognise hypoglycaemia and prevent it deepening by taking sugar.

Weight controlling/reducing diets

Individuals often monitor their own weight using domestic scales and check this against some form of chart or table. For example, see Figure 3.24 opposite.

In healthy adults, weight remains fairly steady because the energy intake from the diet matches energy expenditure in terms of activities or work done by the body. If this match is upset, and imbalance occurs, then the scales will register weight loss or gain.

The most efficient way for a person to lose weight is simply to consume less food (about 2,000 to 4,000 kilojoules) than their energy needs. This could produce a net loss of between 0.5 to 1 kg per week. More weight loss occurs at the beginning of a diet due to water loss. Food-controlled diets are even more effective when combined with a regular exercise or activity programme which helps to burn up food more efficiently.

There are many, many diets which promise rapid weight loss but most of these work in the short term only to disappoint the individual later as weight is gradually regained. The most effective way is to change eating habits permanently: for example, cutting out puddings and eating fruit instead; instead of chips, jacket potatoes; eating a healthy breakfast and not resorting to snacks etc. mid-morning For every 'bad' habit, a 'good' one can be substituted, so that an individual is not tempted to fall back into old ways of eating. The occasional treat can be allowed if the bulk of the diet consists of healthy foods such as fruit, vegetables, wholemeal bread and cereals, and so on. Monitoring is done by regular weighing, recording and checking against height/ weight charts.

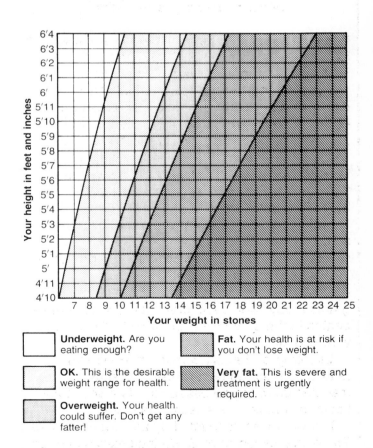

Figure 3.24 *Weight/height chart*

. FACTORS INFLUENCING CHOICE OF . FOOD

While all human beings have similar needs for survival, including a diet which provides the basic nutritional and energy requirements, the ways in which these needs are met can be vastly different. They are influenced by social, economic and cultural factors, which can mean enormous differences in what, where, how and why we eat.

Social factors

The edges are often blurred between strictly social, religious and secular factors, each one contributing to the others.

Food consumption in groups implies friendship and concord among the members of that group. Almost every society marks major events in life stages by communal eating, e.g. wedding feast, funeral wake, bar mitzvah etc. The importance of prominent calendar events is enhanced by special foods for the occasion, such as the Christmas (or Thanksgiving) turkey, Easter eggs, unleavened bread at Passover and so on. Families often develop their own rituals for special meals on birthdays or other occasions.

Family groups also enjoy meals together to exchange social intercourse after the working day; mealtimes may often be the main opportunity for communication. People go out for meals in order to spend time together – meals are the focus of many leisure activities. They can also be used for working purposes in the developed world, for example 'working lunches' or 'business breakfasts'.

Most groups would share food with others who visit, in order to indicate acceptance of one another. The sharing of food has significance for societies all over the world – and has done for thousands of years.

The types and quantities of food consumed will often convey social and economic status, for example, at a simple level, banquets of many courses for the rich but a simple rice dish for the poor. Knowledge of wine and food from different cultures also involves social status, as poor people may not be able to afford the travel implied, the extra money and books to acquire the information or to experiment with cooking.

Eating habits also imply social status: restaurant eating is not for those on limited budgets and, in some societies, for those of different race or caste. Having servants to prepare and serve food also confers high status. Many people in Western culture may hire others on special occasions to supply food and enjoy the enhanced status for special occasions (e.g. caterers at weddings or parties). The choice of eating companions, outside the family group, may convey messages about the work status or ambitions of an individual. Thus, traditionally, inviting your superior to dinner has been far more common amongst younger individuals wishing to move up the career ladder than older individuals, stationary or on the way down. The location of the meal can convey even greater prestige. The more inaccessible the place, the greater the status achieved, e.g. dinner on a yacht, an island etc.

Increasing your choice of food, like getting new possessions, can often provide an escape from the grinding effects of poverty. Individuals are frequently criticised, by more affluent people or various media experts, for choosing inappropriate meals, with little understanding about the uplifting effects a one-off 'spend-up' can have.

Food is also associated with fashion – it can provide one of the major opportunities to show 'trendiness'; for example, cooking in a particular style or visiting particular restaurants. Consider also the fashions which have existed between unrefined (brown) and refined (white) sugar and similar fashions with flour (bread), rice and pasta. Despite overwhelming arguments in favour of breastfeeding babies, the use

of artificial formula milk (rather than breastfeeding) continues to swing with fashion, and the health and financial implications of this in some parts of the world can be severe. Current concern is also expressed over teenage diets, junk and fast foods, as well as cola and similar drink intakes.

Task

Write a short report investigating three different social influences on dietary choice.

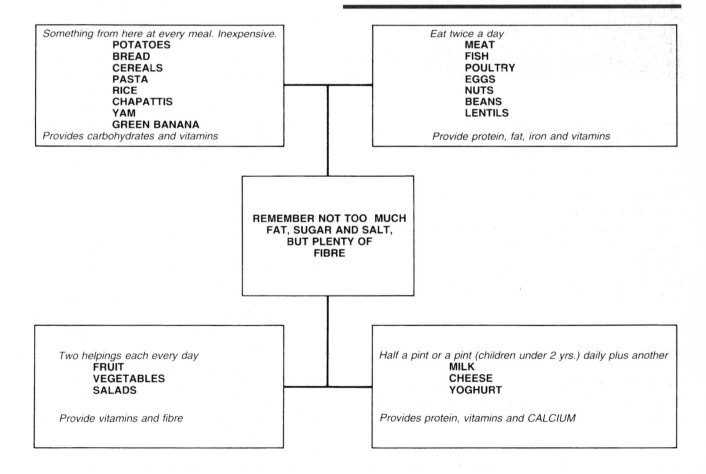

Figure 3.25   *The four food groups*

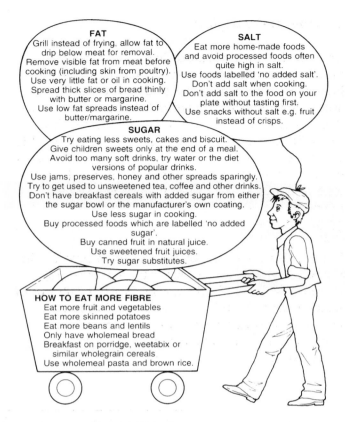

FAT
Grill instead of frying, allow fat to drip below meat for removal. Remove visible fat from meat before cooking (including skin from poultry). Use very little fat or oil in cooking. Spread thick slices of bread thinly with butter or margarine. Use low fat spreads instead of butter/margarine.

SALT
Eat more home-made foods and avoid processed foods often quite high in salt. Use foods labelled 'no added salt'. Don't add salt when cooking. Don't add salt to the food on your plate without tasting first. Use snacks without salt e.g. fruit instead of crisps.

SUGAR
Try eating less sweets, cakes and biscuit. Give children sweets only at the end of a meal. Avoid too many soft drinks, try water or the diet versions of popular drinks. Use jams, preserves, honey and other spreads sparingly. Try to get used to unsweetened tea, coffee and other drinks. Don't have breakfast cereals with added sugar from either the sugar bowl or the manufacturer's own coating. Use less sugar in cooking. Buy processed foods which are labelled 'no added sugar'. Buy canned fruit in natural juice. Use sweetened fruit juices. Try sugar substitutes.

HOW TO EAT MORE FIBRE
Eat more fruit and vegetables
Eat more skinned potatoes
Eat more beans and lentils
Only have wholemeal bread
Breakfast on porridge, weetabix or similar wholegrain cereals
Use wholemeal pasta and brown rice.

Figure 3.26 *Eating a healthier diet*

Cheap sources of energy and nutrients (in approximate[1] order, with the cheapest first)

Energy	Lard, margarine, vegetable oil, sugar, white bread, butter, brown or wholemeal bread, old potatoes, pasta, rice, biscuits, breakfast cereals.
Protein	White bread, brown or wholemeal bread, pasta, liver, eggs, baked beans, cheese, milk, chicken, rice, frozen peas, old potatoes.
Carbohydrate	Sugar, white bread, old potatoes, rice, pasta, brown or wholemeal bread, breakfast cereals, new potatoes, biscuits, baked beans, ice cream.
Calcium	Milk, cheese, white bread, brown bread, wholemeal bread, carrots, ice cream, biscuits.
Iron	Liver, fortified breakfast cereals, brown or wholemeal bread, white bread, baked beans, new potatoes, old potatoes, eggs, biscuits.
Vitamin A	Liver, carrots, margarine, butter, eggs, milk, cheese.
Thiamin	Fortified breakfast cereals, old potatoes, new potatoes, brown or wholemeal bread, white bread, frozen peas, pork, liver, bacon and ham.
Riboflavin	Liver, fortified breakfast cereals, milk, cheese, brown or wholemeal bread, old potatoes.
Nicacin	Liver, breakfast cereals, white bread, old potatoes, new potatoes, chicken, sausages, frozen peas.
Vitamin C	Fruit juices, oranges, old potatoes, new potatoes, tomatoes, fresh green vegetables, frozen peas.
Vitamin D	Margarine, fatty fish, eggs, fortified breakfast cereals, liver, butter.
Dietary fibre	Dried beans, All bran, wholemeal bread, baked beans, white bread, potatoes, whole grain breakfast cereals and pasta.

[1]When harvests are badly affected by weather conditions, the nutritional value for money provided by some of these foods may decline.
(Taken from *Manual of Nutrition*, HMSO)

Peer pressure is an important social influence within any group. Peer pressure is often associated with places to meet, such as the pizza bar or hamburger restaurant. To be both seen and participating in one of the 'in places' is to be part of the gang. People tend to choose the same type of food, the same number of courses and roughly the same priced food when out in a group.

Food is used for reward and punishment even in today's most modern societies. Children are particularly prone to being given forbidden foods, such as sweets, for being good and having these withheld as punishment. They are also not expected to have the likes and dislikes that older family members enjoy. The family meal can too often develop into a battleground on which: parents find principles difficult to uphold; and where negative attitudes are fostered and can spread into other aspects of family life. Children can develop a dislike of a food because of one unhappy mealtime experience which will last into adulthood; later in life they may find that they do, in fact, like that food after all!

Healthy eating on a budget

Many people believe that healthy food costs more but it can be available to those on a tight budget, with some forethought and planned shopping. The right 'healthy' foods, as seen by most nutritionists, help protect against heart attacks, strokes, being overweight and for fighting infection. Children and unborn babies get the best start in life and most individuals feel and look better on healthy diets.

'Variety is the spice of life' is an old saying, but it is also true of food choices. Eating a good variety of different foods goes a long way to avoiding dietary imbalance and deficiencies of certain nutrients. Many experts divide nutritious foods into the four groups shown in Figure 3.25 above. However, it is not sufficient merely to consume foods as the guidelines indicate, but it is also necessary to heed the warning in the central box. The diagram (Figure 3.26) above suggests ways in which this can be done

Task

Using the guidelines provided, suggest inexpensive meals for a vegan, vegetarian, an individual with hypertension on a low-salt diet and an individual from a different culture (stating which culture). Provide reasons for your choices and cost-out the meal at today's supermarket prices.

Culture and religion

Each of the world religions has its own beliefs, morals, ceremonies and rituals. The practices and laws of each religion relate to the worship of 'god' and followers confirm their beliefs by adherence to them. Many religious laws involve food or dietary restrictions, some of which appear to be designed to set the religious group apart from others. The origin of other practices comes from sacred or holy writings, such as the Torah in Judaism (Jewish religion). (See table below.)

Practising dietary restrictions can often provide the followers with a sense of security and belonging, shared with others in the group. A strict follower of religious laws is said to be *orthodox*; but many people today often ignore, or are more relaxed about, certain practices, including dietary restrictions.

Dietary practices

Food restriction	Time of year	Time of day	Preparation of food	Fasting practices
Judaism 1. Eat only animals with cloven hooves and which chew the cud, e.g. cattle, sheep, goats, deer. *Not* pig or camel. 2. Eat forequarters (must not eat sciatic nerve down back of leg). 3. Eat only fish with fins and scales *not* shellfish. 4. Must not mix meat and dairy foods at the same meal. 5. No blood eaten.	No food preparation on Sabbath.		Ritual slaughtering of poultry and animals to drain maximum possible amount of blood. Meat koshered by soaking in water and salt mixture then drained. Separate utensils used for meat and dairy foods. Separate utensils and preparation of fish dishes.	After meat eating 6 hours should pass before dairy foods can be eaten and up to 1 hour between dairy and meat eating. Artificial dairy products have freed this up. Fasts commemorate sad days in Jewish history. All girls over 12 yrs and 1 day and boys over 13 yrs and 1 day must observe the fasts. Many fast days incorporate eating special foods which symbolise events in Jewish history, e.g. celery and parsley represent the poor food during the years of slavery.
Islam (Muslim) (800 mill. people) 1. No blood eaten. 2. No pork (pig) eaten. 3. No alcohol.	During Ramadhan from sunrise to sunset.	9th lunar month for one month. Strict Moslems fast Mondays and Thursdays, and 13th–15th of each month.	Animal must be ritually slaughtered by a blow to the head during which certain words are spoken. No food or water in daytime, light meals only during Ramadhan.	For all who have reached the Age of Responsibility (12 years in girls, 15 years in boys) except for elderly in poor health, menstruating, pregnant and nursing women, the sick, long distance traveller and those in hard physical work. Eat only with right hand (left, unclean).
Hinduism Must not kill or eat any animal. **Sikhism** No beef No alcohol	Varies with caste, family, religion, age and sex.		Ritual bathing and clean clothes before food preparation, some avoid fish, fowl, onions, garlic, mushrooms, salted pork and turnips.	Very complex, cannot eat with members of lower castes.

Dietary restrictions may take the following forms:

a) Selection of foods to eat or not to eat
b) Selection of food to eat on certain days of the year
c) When in the day to take food
d) Preparation of food
e) Fasting – time of year and duration.

Lowenberg et al (1979).

Self-assessment test

1 The cardio-vascular system includes the following:
  a heart, brain, kidneys
  b lungs, brain, heart
  c heart, arteries, veins
  d heart, capillaries, lymph

2 The superior vena cava is a vessel which:
  a delivers oxygenated blood to the tissues
  b takes deoxygenated blood back to the heart
  c takes oxygenated blood to the tissues
  d takes deoxygenated blood to the lungs

3 Changes brought about by the ageing process may affect the cardio-vascular system in the following way:
  a quantity of blood expelled from the heart at each beat is reduced
  b heart valves become more flexible
  c capillaries act like steel tubes
  d blood clots more readily

4 A middle-aged woman has raised blood-pressure and is overweight. Her doctor may advise her to:
  a reduce the amount of fluid in her diet
  b reduce the amount of salt in her diet
  c reduce the amount of fruit and vegetables in her diet
  d reduce the amount of roughage in her diet

5 Salmonella is an example of a disease which is:
  a inherited
  b infectious
  c degenerative
  d mental

6 How is gonorrhoea transmitted?
  a By air
  b By water
  c By food
  d By person to person

7 Salmonella organisms are most likely to be found in the:
  a nose
  b reproductive tract
  c intestines
  d kidneys

8 A vegan is a person who:
  a only eats meat
  b only eats meat, fish, eggs and milk
  c only eats plant products
  d only eats plant products, milk and eggs

9 Anaemia can result from:
  a lack of iron in the diet
  b lack of salt in the diet
  c lack of saturated fat in the diet
  d lack of glucose in the diet

10 A vegan diet could be low in:
  a vitamin B
  b fibre
  c sodium
  d iron

11 Which vitamin is essential for good vision at night?
  a Vitamin C
  b Vitamin K
  c Vitamin A
  d Vitamin D

12 Which macro-nutrient contributes the greatest number of calories per gram to the diet?
  a Starch
  b Fat
  c Sugar
  d Protein

13 Potatoes are considered to be a good source of:
  a vitamin C
  b protein
  c iron
  d fat

14 If a friend shows signs of anaemia, which of the following foods would you recommend your friend to increase in the diet?
  a Vegetables
  b Milk

c Red meat

d Potatoes

15 Which of the following foods would be the best way for a vegan to obtain high biological value protein?

a yoghurt

b eggs

c spinach

d soya beans

16 Coronary heart disease is more likely to occur in people who are:

a overweight, hypertensive, smokers

b overweight, anaemic, smokers

c underweight, non-smokers, anaemic

d underweight, alcoholic, asthmatic

17 Systole is the name given to:

a contraction of the atria or ventricles

b relaxation of the atria or ventricles

c the measurement of blood pressure

d the taking of the pulse

18 The name of the blood vessel taking blood to the lungs from the heart is:

a aorta

b pulmonary artery

c pulmonary vein

d inferior vena cava

19 A lack of vitamin D in the diet can lead to:

a Anaemia

b Scurvy

c Rickets

d Night blindness

20 The first heart sound 'lub' heard in the cardiac cycle is caused by:

a heart valves closing

b heart valves opening

c ventricles contracting

d ventricles relaxing

Fast Facts

AIDS Acquired Immune Deficiency Syndrome.

Anaemia Deficiency in the oxygen carriage in the blood.

Antibody Part of plasma protein fraction of blood. Formed in lymph nodes to neutralise antigens.

Antigen Foreign substance entering body which stimulates the formation of antibodies by lymphocytes.

Arteriosclerosis Loss of elasticity and hardening of walls of arteries.

Artery Blood vessel carrying blood away from the heart e.g. aorta.

Atheroma Fatty plaque or deposit on arterial lining.

Capillary Smallest blood vessel, has walls only one cell thick. Delivers raw materials to cells via tissue fluid.

Diffusion Movement of molecules from a region of high concentration to one of low concentration.

Epidemic Local outbreak of disease.

GUM Genito-Urinary Medicine – a hospital department (often deals with sexually transmitted diseases).

HIV Human Immuno-deficiency Virus.

Hyperlipidaemia Person with high content of lipids in the bloodstream.

Hypertension Raised blood-pressure.

Immunity The ability of the body to resist disease.

Macro-nutrient Large molecular substance which provides essential nourishment, e.g. protein, fat, carbohydrate.

Micro-nutrient Substance needed in tiny quantities to provide essential nourishment.

Pandemic Outbreak of disease which crosses more than one continent.

Pathogen A micro-organism which causes disease.

PID Pelvic Inflammatory Disease, which can occur as a result of an infection like gonorrhoea.

Polyunsaturates   Chemical term used in fat chemistry which relates to having vacant carbon atoms in chain – generally taken to mean vegetable fats.

Saturated fats   Chemical term used in fat chemistry which relates to having no vacant carbon atoms in chain – generally taken to mean animal fats.

STD   Sexually transmitted Disease, such as HIV or gonorrhoea.

Vector   An animal which carries pathogens from one person to another.

Vegan   Person who does not eat any foods from animal sources, not even eggs or milk.

Vegetarian   General term used to describe an ovo-lactovegetarian, i.e. a person who does not eat meat or fish but will eat eggs, milk and milk products.

Vein   Blood vessel carrying blood towards the heart. Usually carries deoxygenated blood.

Ventilation   Movement of air into and out of the chest.

Reference

Brett Cassens (1992) *Preventive Medicine and Public Health* Harwal Publishing

Eastwood, Edwards and Parry (1992) *Human Nutrition* Chapman and Hall

Fieldhouse, P. (1986) *Food and Nutrition* Chapman and Hall

Manual of Nutrition MAFF HMSO

Swales and de Bono (1993) *Cardiovascular Risk Factors* Gower Medical Publishing

Suggested reading

Clegg and Clegg (199-) *Man against disease* Heinemann

D.G. Mackean, John Murray (1988) *Human Life*

Issues for the Nineties series Independence, Cambridge

Manual of Nutrition (1985) MAFF HMSO

Simpkins and Williams (1987) *Advanced Human Biology* Unwin Hyman

Stoyle J. (1991) *Caring for older people*

Useful addresses for information

Action on Smoking & Health,
109 Gloucester Place,
London W1H 3PH.

Age Concern,
Astral House,
1268 London Road,
London SW16 7.

Brook Advisory Centre,
29A North Street,
Belfast BT1 1NQ.

Brook Advisory Centre,
233 Tottenham Court Road,
London W1P 9AE.

British Safety Council,
National Safety Centre,
Chancellors Road,
London 6 9RS.

Health Education Authority,
Hamilton House,
Mabledon Place,
London WC1H 9TX.

Health Promotion Wales,
Ffynnon-Las, Ilex Close,
Ty Glas Avenue,
Llanishen,
Cardiff CF4 5DZ.

Health and Safety Executive,
Library and Information Services,
Broad Lane,
Sheffield S3 7HQ.

Help the Aged,
16–18 St James Walk,
Clerkenwell,
London EC1R 0BE.

MIND,
22 Harley Street,

London W1N 2ED.

National Aids Helpline,
Tel. 0800 567 123 (24 hr).

Quit,
102 Gloucester Place,
London W1H 3DA.

Royal Society for the Prevention of Accidents,
Cannon House,
The Priory,

Queensway,
Birmingham B4 6BS.

Terrence Higgins Trust,
52–54 Grays Inn Road,
London WC1X 8JU.

Ulster Cancer Foundation,
40 Eglantine Avenue,
Belfast BT9 6DX.
(smoking)

4 PSYCHOLOGICAL AND SOCIAL ASPECTS OF HEALTH AND SOCIAL CARE

· CARING ISN'T ALWAYS EASY ·

Imagine you are caring for each of the following three people. During your conversation with each person they make the following statements:

- *A 17-year-old*: 'You don't know what it's like where I live. It's horrible! Everyone gets by on social security and on nicking things. Just do a few cars or homes and you've got the money you need for drugs. There's no work, there's nothing in the future, like, but sex, drugs and drink make you feel better. There isn't much to life – no point in life really!'
- *An adult*: 'When I came round after the accident, I didn't believe what they told me. They said that I'd never walk again, and I thought what's the point of going on? If I can't live my life the way I want, if I can't do everything like I used to, well I'd rather be dead!'
- *An elder*: 'I don't mind you coming to talk, but do you think it will do any good? I've got nothing left to live for – what's the point? My family don't care about me, I'm no use any more!'

These three characters are not simply unhappy. Each of these people is expressing a feeling that life isn't worth living. They are not saying that they are afraid, or that they have pain, or that there is some service that they want. The three people each feel that their lives are not really theirs to control: life isn't worth much – what's the point of living?

Many people experience this feeling of a lack of purpose or meaning in life at some point. Clients of health and care services are particularly likely to experience this stress.

Think it over

Imagine yourself working with these three people. What answer could you give them? As a carer, how would you set about helping these people? How would you understand their statements about life not being worth living?

This chapter focuses on how individuals make sense of their lives. The concept of **personal identity** is used to explain some of the issues that may lie behind feelings of meaninglessness and lack of purpose. 'Identity theory' may help carers to understand some of the social and emotional needs of clients. Theories of personal identity might also help individuals to understand why and where they fail to be supportive to others. Understanding how caring situations can go wrong may be as useful as getting ideas for helping clients.

Candidates who are working for NVQ qualifications have to demonstrate that they can perform within a value system. This value system requires candidates to be able to 'acknowledge individuals' personal beliefs and identity' (see page 5). The study of identity provides a central focus for understanding other people. The ability to assess others' needs, the ability to support other people in a caring conversation may be strongly influenced by the carer's understanding of a person's identity.

So, the study of identity may help carers to understand difficult situations and it is a central part of caring practice and values. The most important reason for exploring personal identity may be that a person's identity may control what they can do, what they are confident in, how happy they are and how good their life is! Understanding identity may provide ideas for evaluating personal life and life goals.

· WHAT IS IDENTITY? ·

At its simplest, a person's identity is how they understand themselves and how they make sense of their life in relation to other people and society. The statement that identity is about 'how people understand themselves', means that identity is worked out, or even *invented*, by individuals. You will develop your own sense of identity using your own thoughts. The idea that individuals have to make sense of their life in relation to other people, means that identity is not just worked out or invented by people on their own. Identity is learned from life and social experiences – it changes as new social experiences happen. Your identity is influenced by the way people behave toward you. Other people's views and attitudes might influence how you see yourself.

Your sense of identity develops through your own thoughts but is influenced by the way people behave towards you.

Think it over

Read and answer the questions on social context which follow.

Spot-check on social context

1 Do you have any friends, or do you belong to any clubs, groups or organisations where other people's opinions of you matter to you?
2 Are there any special individuals who you really care about and who care about you?
3 Do you have a part-time or full-time job? If so, do you take notice of your colleagues' or manager's opinion of your work?
4 If you are studying, are you concerned about others' opinions of your work and whether you will achieve your goals?
5 Do you take an interest in things reported in the news – do any local, national or international events (including sport) interest you?
6 Are there any TV or radio programmes that you regularly watch and enjoy?
7 Do you have any sports, hobbies or interests which involve meeting other people?

If you answered 'No' to all of these questions, you are obviously socially isolated and you need to sort this out before caring for others. Alternatively, maybe you have only just arrived from somewhere far away: did you do any of these things before? If you answered 'Yes' to all of these questions – then congratulations, you sound a very interesting person. Most people will answer 'Yes', or 'Yes, maybe' to just some of the questions. The areas to which you answered 'Yes' give a clue to your **social context**. A context is the situation or setting that something or someone is in. Social context is the setting for people and activities which may have an influence on your life.

Glynis Breakwell (1986) explains identity as, 'A dynamic social product, residing in psychological processes, which cannot be understood except in relation to its social context and historical perspective' *(page 9)*. Breakwell's theory is that people can only make sense of their lives in relation to the social setting that they find themselves in. Making sense of life is a *dynamic* process. Dynamic means that there are forces at work which constantly change things. Psychological thinking and learning processes actually create our awareness of identity. It isn't possible to understand life fully just in terms of thinking and learning theories. Psychological theories have to be understood in relation to social context and changes in social context over time.

Is it necessary to understand life?

Most people would not recognise the term, 'identity'. Many people do not try to evaluate themselves or explain their concept of 'self' in words. This does not mean that the area of theory is not important. For example, everyone has kidneys in their body which are vital for life; we die without the service that they provide. But, quite correctly, very few people bother to think about how their kidneys work. We don't need to think about them – they just do their job of filtering toxic substances out of us. The kidneys carry on working whether we understand them or not! There are two situations where people become very interested in the theory of kidneys. The first is where people work as health care professionals. People may seek professional knowledge and advice. The more the professional understands about body systems, the more effective they can be in their career. The second situation where people get interested in how kidneys work is when something goes wrong. A person with a kidney infection may be extremely motivated to understand how the kidneys work, what can be done to get them right and what can be done to preserve their health.

It is possible to draw an analogy (or similarity) between the concept of kidneys and the concept of identity. If the social and psychological processes involved in identity are working well – why study them? The need to understand identity arises if the processes are not working well. People providing care for distressed or threatened individuals may also need to make sense of the situation; and, of course, there are always people who are just curious. The more you know, the more you can safeguard your own health and happiness – if you have the resources. However, as with all analogies, it is important just to see the similarities. 'Kidneys' are very different from 'identity' in that kidneys are physical, a fixed part of the body. Identity is not necessarily fixed; it changes and develops with life

experience and it certainly has no physical location in the body!

Glynis Breakwell (1986) explained that her theory of identity was developed from a wide range of previous ideas in the social sciences. In some ways her theory includes ideas like self-concept, self-image, real and ideal self. Her purpose in developing a theory of identity was to provide a framework of explanation for threatened identities. So, the key idea behind understanding 'identity' is to understand what might be happening when people become distressed and threatened by events in their life.

What does an identity do for an individual?

The results of effective identity processes, according to Breakwell (1986), are, 'To produce uniqueness or distinctiveness for the person; continuity across time and situation; and a feeling of personal worth or social value.' *(Page 24.)*

So, our learning and thinking processes enable us to make sense of our life within a social context. If we feel that we do understand who we are and, perhaps, if we feel in control of our lives and have a sense of 'self', then we should have:

- *A sense of distinctiveness*
- *A sense of continuity*
- *A sense of self-esteem*

Distinctiveness

Distinctiveness is about feeling that there is something special about us. Distinctiveness is our own sense of individuality. We are different from everyone else; there is no one exactly like us. Without this feeling of individuality, it may be difficult to make personal choices or decisions. Without a feeling of distinctiveness, it may be difficult to assert personal rights. People who become de-individualised are often prepared to see themselves simply as one of a crowd. They will take direction from other people or from people in authority. Clients who become institutionalised or disempowered may lose their feeling of distinctiveness and individuality. This means that they may be easy to control or manage as they are undemanding. However, institutionalised, de-individualised clients may experience psychological threat and dissatisfaction with life.

Continuity

Whilst our experience of life changes with time, our learning experiences might enable us to feel that we are growing and developing rather than simply being shocked with dramatic changes. Most people will develop the idea of a 'self' that has roots in the past. This self has a personal history; whilst it may change, this change is gradual and meaningful. Without a sense of continuity, or continuation across life, the social world might seem difficult to understand and difficult to predict.

Self-esteem

If we understand our own idea of self, this understanding will include evaluation of our identity. For example, how well regarded are we by others? How good are we at activities which other people value, and so on? Our evaluation of ourselves will create a level of self-esteem or self-value. Low self-esteem may lead people to feel a lack of confidence in their abilities to cope socially. High self-esteem may encourage a sense of 'empowerment' where an individual has the confidence to assert their needs and their views.

Whilst distinctiveness, continuity and self-esteem are the key outcomes of personal identity in Breakwell's theory, it is important to recognise that there are many different perspectives on life within the social sciences. An earlier theory of identity developed by Eric Erikson (1963) suggested four main outcomes of a person's sense of identity. These were:

1 A sense of *individuality* (rather like distinctiveness).
2 A sense of *wholeness*. This sense of wholeness integrated, or brought together, different life experiences to make one complete sense of self.
3 A sense of *continuity* (as above).
4 A sense of *social solidarity* or social *meaningfulness*. This idea links to self-esteem, in that an individual's identity has to satisfy the values of other significant people. The way that people understand themselves has to fit with, or have solidarity with, their social context.

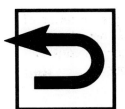

Think it over

Read and answer the questions which follow on personal identity.

Spot-check on personal identity

1 Think about your social context – the people you mix with, the activities that you do: is there anything about you that you think is special? Is there anything that makes you different from most other people? Is there any detail of personality, any way in which you behave, any way in which you dress, which is just you – a way of expressing yourself?
2 Think back over your past life: do you have a history? Can you picture yourself at different ages? Can you remember how happy or sad you have been over your life since you were ten years old? Do you have a sense of yourself growing, learning, living and developing?
3 Can you imagine an image of yourself? Can you picture your 'face', or can you picture your name? Do you have a range of ideas or images which you associate with yourself or with your name? Are there things you could answer to the question: 'I am . . .'? Imagine a list of attributes or things which are true about yourself. What sort of feelings do you have in relation to the points you made? Do you feel positive or negative about yourself in general?

Why do people need a sense of distinctiveness, continuity and self-esteem?

Celia Kitzinger (1992) questions whether all people, in all cultures and societies, do need a sense of individuality or distinctiveness. She points out that people in agricultural, or pre-industrial, societies may regard themselves quite differently from people who live in Western technological societies. Western society requires individuals to perform in individualistic and often individually competitive

Modern high-technology jobs require individual performance

Agricultural workers at the turn of the century

ways. The existence of high-technology jobs requires, or is often designed to require, individual performance. For example, monitoring information on computer screens can involve a highly individual work focus. Kitzinger suggests that agricultural labour often requires a much more communal and co-operative approach to work. It may be that the Western focus on individuality has grown out of the political and social systems rooted in Protestant Christianity, capitalism and the industrial revolution. People who live in societies which have a different history may tend to develop different ways of understanding life.

Speculating about people in Britain around the turn of the last century suggests some different possibilities as to how they may have developed a sense of personal identity.

The group in the picture above may have relied on co-operation and collective working in order to earn their livelihood. They may have been born into a village society where they tended to know all the inhabitants. They may not have travelled much; they may not have talked to very many strangers outside their village life. Each person may have been born into a set of social expectations.

Years ago, people talked of their **social station** in life. A 'station' was a fixed role or position that a person undertook in society. A station indicated a permanent job or type of work, or a social role such as 'housewife'. A station identified an individual's position within the social hierarchy or class system. The point about a social station is that it stayed the same; it was static. All the people in the photograph may have described their identities in terms of duty to society, fixed expectations of life that they had learned from birth and fixed social relationships with others. It is very unlikely that these people would have used terms like identity, self-concept, self-esteem or even self-worth to understand themselves. Perhaps the term 'soul' would have provided a satisfactory alternative to individuality. A sense of 'soul' might sometimes have been used to describe their sense of duty, role and function in the community.

Breakwell (1986) quotes evidence which suggests that different cultures and societies do have different ways of understanding individual identity. She states, 'It has to be said that the very concept of an individual's identity may be a nonsense in certain cultures.' *(Page 184.)* Again, 'It would be arrant nonsense to assume that the model of identity principles here applies to anything more than Western industrialised countries.' *(Page 185.)* So there may be no natural, biological, reason why people should need a sense of individuality or an individual identity.

Eric Erikson made the notion of identity a centrepiece of his interpretation of post-Freudian theory, in his book *Childhood and Society*, first published in 1950. There is now a range of books and theories which concentrate on *self-concept* or *self-actualization*. The whole humanistic perspective within psychology focuses on individual self and its welfare. Glynis Breakwell surveyed a wealth of research in the field of social psychology before advancing her ideas on identity. Why is there so much attention to individual self, and individual distinctiveness, if it isn't something that every human being has always needed?

Perhaps current Western attention to individuality is not simply some kind of fashion which could change overnight, if someone thought of a better idea. It may be that the political, economic, social and technical history of Western culture has created an environment where survival is difficult without a sense of individuality and distinctiveness.

A child born into a culture where their social role and relationships can be predicted from birth may not need individuality. If culture is stable, then identity can become associated with stable group norms and roles. A person can live their life within the norms and roles that they grew up with. They may feel that it is better to die than to deny a fixed perception of themselves – and they may have no reason to deny it. They may be happy with the accepted norms.

However, Western culture is changing increasingly rapidly. The accepted knowledge or understanding about jobs, careers, sexual relationships, family roles, and so on, in the 1960s might now be seen as misguided. A set of assumptions about life doesn't necessarily last a lifetime any more. It may no longer be worth holding on to norms, roles or assumptions for more than a decade. Some people can find stability in their local culture and religion; but few people can avoid the changes to their life created by new technology and economic pressures.

Individuality or distinctiveness, continuity and self-esteem may be needed in order to navigate the range of problems, puzzles and stresses which a person is likely to experience in their constantly changing lives.

An individual's own personal sense of identity may provide the confidence to cope with an ever-changing world. Identity may motivate individuals to achieve. A strong sense of individual self might provide a person with the courage to cope with job interviews, exams and the stresses involved in achieving qualifications. A sense of personal identity may provide the confidence needed to explore sexual partnerships with others; where this is understood as an individual task. A weak sense of 'who you are', a lack of feeling 'special' or 'distinctive', a low opinion of your own worth might create problems with coping with modern life. Erikson (1963) wrote, 'In the social jungle of human existence, there is no feeling of being alive without a sense of ego identity.' *(Page 240.)* To Erikson, a confused or weak sense of identity suggested a great deal of emotional pain, and perhaps misery, for an individual. Satisfaction with life depends on a sense of knowing who you are!

Life in the late twentieth century can be confusing

THE DEVELOPMENT OF INDIVIDUAL IDENTITY

People are not born with an identity. A sense of self will develop, slowly learned from the social experiences that the child has undergone. Erikson (1963) believed that children would tend to have only fragmented or 'bits' of an understanding of themselves. Every child can remember things that have happened to them – friends that they like, outings with parents or carers that they have enjoyed, things that teachers have said to them. These bits of experience get remembered and form a basis for identity.

Learning processes

People probably learn their sense of self or identity in the same way as they learn other vitally important skills; for example crossing the road. A five-year-old can understand the idea of cars and traffic: they will know that they can be run-over and that it is important to check for traffic before trying to cross the road. But would you trust a five-year-old to cross a busy road safely? Most five-year-old children don't really understand; they can't really estimate the speed and braking distances required by vehicles. Few five-year-olds can be trusted to remember to stop, look and listen before attempting to cross the road. They know things about crossing roads, but they haven't put all this knowledge together so that they can be independent. This shouldn't matter because, hopefully, every five-year-old will be looked after by adults. When they need to cross busy roads, they will rely on others to guide them.

By 15 years of age, most people are expert at crossing roads. What has changed? Over ten years the child will have watched other people coping with roads. They will be able to imagine situations involving traffic, and work out what should be done. As well as watching other people, children will practise their skills nearly every day. Bit by bit, children learn to predict speeds and directions of vehicles; what started as knowing about roads and traffic becomes a personal skill. Most importantly of

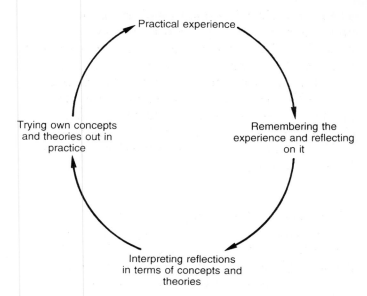

Figure 4.1 *The Kolb learning cycle*

all, the child learns all this because they need to: it's useful if you are going to cope with life!

The Kolb learning cycle (Kolb, 1979, see Figure 4.1, above) can be used to explain what is happening as the child learns. The cycle starts with the child having an experience. Perhaps the child is taken across the road; perhaps the child sees others taken across the road. At five years of age the experience will probably end there – after a while the child will forget it and nothing may be learned. If learning is going to take place, the child will need to use their imagination; they will need to think about what they have seen or what they usually do. Using imagination to re-think events is called 'reflection'. If the child reflects, then he or she may gradually build a series of memories in their mind which they can go back to when they need to cross the road. This is the theory stage of the cycle. If the child uses their memories of going across different roads, guessing the speed of cars and so on, then this is the experimenting (or 'testing out') stage of the cycle. Using ideas in practice should lead to new experiences of competence – success in getting across the road or perhaps helping others across. This next experience sets the whole cycle going round again. The more experience of thinking, remembering and doing the child gets, the more their skills develop.

The Kolb cycle is just one way of trying to understand learning experiences. Different psychological theories emphasise different aspects of learning. **Reinforcement theory** emphasises that people learn 'what works for them'. B.F. Skinner (1902–1990) believed that behaviour that led to pleasurable results would tend to be repeated. If the child feels pleased with their skills, and pleased with their performance – perhaps they will be motivated to keep practising.

Albert Bandura (1977) emphasised the role of imagination in his work on the social learning perspective of psychology. Bandura believed that people might learn as much, if not more, from watching other people than from experimenting with actions themselves. Bandura emphasised the idea that people learn by imitating or copying what others do. People mainly copy other people who they identify with. If someone seems similar to us, we are more likely to imitate them. We also copy people who seem successful, people who get *reinforced* (pleasurable outcomes) for their behaviour. Bandura believed that the main impact of reinforcement was in the person's imagination. If we see someone being successful and being praised, then we are likely to copy them. For example, we remember how someone else crossed a difficult road and then we try it in practice next time we have to cross the road.

It might take ten years or so to learn how to cope with traffic. It should be no surprise that learning to understand the social rules, customs and culture that surround us might take longer. A five-year-old will have a sense of themselves: they will see themselves as separate from other people; they will be interested in their own practical skills. However, Erikson (1963) believed that this sense of self did not become fully developed or fully operational until adolescence. Like the skills of coping with traffic, coping with society takes time to learn. The young child is protected from traffic by its carers. The young child doesn't have to cope with independent social roles, for example, with finding a job or with being a resourceful individual. Carers usually keep life simple, and explain social norms and culture bit by bit.

According to Erikson (1963), the need for an understanding of **personal identity** (or ego identity) becomes critical during adolescence. Before this time, the child can be dependent on parents or carers. With the onset of puberty the child develops sexual urges and needs. These provide a biological pressure to stop thinking of the self as a child, and to take on adult responsibilities. This move to adult status creates an **identity crisis**. Erikson called it a crisis because, to him, adolescence was a time of critical change. It was not a crisis in the sense of something being bad. The adolescent identity crisis was a period when a person finally has to make sense of themselves in order to cope in the adult world. Failure to build a working identity would result in *role confusion*. Role confusion might involve an unwillingness to grow up and take responsibility for self. Breakwell (1986) believes that the idea of a crisis is often too dramatic. For many people, learning to cope with adult social roles may come gradually and not be experienced as a period of critical change.

What a person learns about themselves during childhood will depend on their **social context**. Hedy Brown (1985) suggests that there are three levels to understanding social learning and social behaviour, these are:

- The *personal* level
- The *group* level
- The *society* level

At the *personal* level, we are interested in how people think and learn. At the *group* level, we are interested in how group membership influences and controls individual behaviour. At the level of *society*, we are interested in broad social factors and how these have an influence on the individual.

Socialisation

The child will begin to learn about their own identity through the process of socialisation. During early childhood we begin to develop language, we begin to learn assumptions about our environment, and we begin to learn the **norms** or rules of behaviour that our families or care groups expect of us. Socialisation is the process of learning the norms and belief systems of a social group, in order to become part of that group and to play roles within the group.

How are norms learned? It is possible to glimpse at the processes by watching children and their experiences.

Theory into practice

'Dev' is eight years old. He lives within walking distance of his school. He has been told to hurry back home after school, so that he can go shopping with his mother. Dev remembers this, but as he leaves school he meets three of his friends. Dev's friends suggest looking round the shops first; Dev wants to be 'in' with his friends and quickly forgets about the need to meet his mother. At eight years of age it seems right to go along with whatever is happening – Dev just goes with his friends without thinking. Dev gets home to find that his mother is very angry. At first Dev is puzzled: so he forgot – doesn't everyone make mistakes? But Dev is part of a family group where the parents, brothers and sisters have a set of norms about appointments. The norms (or rules) of this family group are: (1) if you agree to be on time you must keep your agreement; (2) you must not forget appointments – you must find a way to remember; (3) you must not let other members of the family down; (4) family arrangements are more important than arrangements with friends.

Dev will be criticised by all the family for failing to keep to the norms of his family group. Dev knows he has failed to live up to group expectations; he may feel guilty and try to do better next time. It's not the anger that he is worried about – it is the need to belong to, and be a respected member of, the family group.

Dev will come to learn the norms and values of his family group. He may come to believe that they are part of him – part of his identity as a member of the family. This is the process of *socialisation*. Because

the family group is often the first group to teach norms and values to an individual, this learning is often called **primary socialisation**.

On an *individual* level, Dev learns about keeping appointments because he thinks or reflects on what has happened. His brother gets praised for keeping appointments and so Dev tries to imitate or copy his brother's behaviour. When Dev is on time he gets praised – this is learning through reinforcement.

On a *group* level, Dev is expected to learn a whole range of norms and values. All social groups have expectations or norms as to how individuals should behave. Dev will have to share the beliefs or values of his family if he is to be accepted as 'good'.

On a *society* level, we could ask why Dev's family have the beliefs and norms that they do. Not all families behave or act this way. To understand Dev's family, it would be necessary to understand their social class and work norms. We may find that the family hold religious beliefs. We might be interested in the influence that local community or neighbourhood values had on the family, in addition to television and newspapers. Broad issues of politics and economics would eventually influence the social context that the family lives in.

So neither Dev, nor his family, are isolated. Dev lives in the context of his family and friends; but they all live in the social context of a broader society. As Dev grows older he will learn roles, norms and values associated with wider groups in society. This is sometimes referred to as **secondary socialisation**.

Task

Can you think of two very different people that you have met or worked with? Perhaps you could use yourself as one of the individuals to be studied? When you have identified two people you know, can you begin to imagine the social context they grew up in? What family or care network did they

grow up with? What friendship or social groups did they mix with? What norms, roles or values did they learn during their socialisation? How did the learning processes actually take place? Are there any stories like Dev's that illustrate social learning? You could begin to design a study using interview techniques (you might combine this work with Unit 8 interview work). If you do use interview techniques, be sure to check the ethics of your approach with tutors and supervisors (see Chapter 8, Research in Health and Social Care).

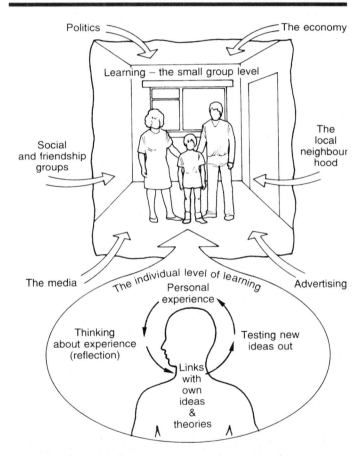

Figure 4.2 *The broad social context of learning*

The role of social factors

Socialisation may mark the early development of individual identity, but identity will continue to develop throughout a person's lifetime. Identity will continue to change and develop as individual life experiences continue to unfold. **Social factors** will continue to influence how a person might understand themselves as they grow older.

Social factors include both the group and society levels of influence. Indeed, it is possible to explain social influences in terms of the importance of different kinds of group membership for an individual person. We might expect personal identity to be most influenced by people that we meet face to face and mix with on a regular basis. Family, friends and work colleagues might provide us with *primary groups* or groups which have a primary (or first) influence on us. Each person will also see themselves in terms of various socially available categories.

For many people, these primary categories might include social roles such as 'mother', 'student', 'car driver'. The categories might also include some kind of concept of social class (although the person might not talk about 'class'). They are likely to include gender, race and religion. Sometimes, membership of a broad, general category (like female) may be called membership of a *secondary group*.

Some theories have described social influences in layers. This produces a kind of 'onion picture' of social influences. A person is seen as what history, general social context, secondary and primary groups have made them! (See Figure 4.3 below.)

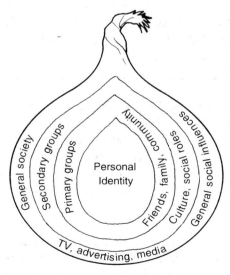

Figure 4.3 *The onion view of social influences: layers of influence on individual or personal identity*

Although this is one way of thinking about social influences, it may be confusing to take the onion idea too far. Each individual will have their own personal story to tell. Their own learning from personal experience will create different personal patterns. Kay Deaux (1992) recommends talking about personal and social identity. These are not two different kinds of identity but just terms to label the two ends of a continuum like two sides of a coin.

Personal identity becomes the person's own understanding of themselves; whilst **social identity** indicates the groups that a person belongs to (or identifies with). (See Figure 4.4 below.) Naturally, groups have an influence on the individual's own understanding of personal identity. There is no total separation between these areas. Deaux (1992) writes, 'The advantage of this approach is that it allows us to make a distinction between personal and social aspects of identity, while explicitly recognising their interconnectedness. Without personal meanings, categories of identity are hollow, designating a membership group without conveying what the membership means.' *(Page 25.)*

Knowing someone's race, religion, age, gender and social class, is enough to identify some of the risks

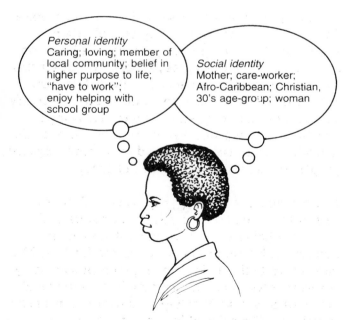

Figure 4.4 *Personal identity explains what the social identity categories mean for the individual*

of discrimination that that person may face (see Chapter 1). Knowing only these aspects of social identity will not be enough to understand the individual's needs (see Chapter 1). Social identity alone will not help a carer to ensure that they convey effective supportive skills (Chapter 2). To get to know a person, and to support their needs, some understanding of their own personal identity will need to be established.

The personal identity of a client is not always obvious. A care-worker should never assume that social roles or group membership creates the client's personal identity. Deaux (1992) writes, 'It is a mistake to assume that a social identity is necessarily claimed by all who fall in a defined category' *(Page 19)*. She goes on to quote a study which shows that 15 per cent of Hispanic students at university did not claim their Hispanic race as part of their personal identity. Deaux quotes two studies where gender was not part of personal identity for over 50 per cent of men and women. A further study showed that only 80 per cent of women and 50 per cent of men who had children owned the identity of parent. People do not necessarily use the social categories that they fall into as part of their identity. To assume that everyone's personal identity is dictated by their social group membership is perhaps an act of stereotyped thinking. Care must be taken to respect the individuality and choice of clients. Only the client can explain who they are. Assumptions about another person's personal identity may deny them respect, dignity and choice.

The power of groups

Tajfel (1971) (1978) defined social identity as being created from membership of social groups. Being a 30-year-old, being Afro-Caribbean, being a woman, might all be 'groups' or group classifications which form part of an individual's social identity. Tajfel argued that once people are classified, or once they classify themselves as members of a group, discrimination can occur. Tajfel believed that the development of a positive social identity required social comparisons between groups. People might get their own sense of identity clearer by working out who they identify with (people who are like me). If you can work out who you are similar to, then you can work out who is different (people who are not like me). Tajfel used the terms 'In-group' and 'Out-group' to describe these two classifications.

Theory into practice

How do in-groups and out-groups work in your own experience? Try to imagine the story of Janice. Janice is 15 years old. For as long as she can remember she has liked animals; she has a pet cat which she constantly makes a fuss of. Janice thinks of herself as loving, friendly, caring and kind. Quite a lot of Janice's friends at school do not eat meat. After hearing some of her friends describe meat-eating as cruel, Janice decided that she would become a vegetarian. At first, she had some arguments with her own family and other friends, but they quickly accepted her right to choose a vegetarian diet. But becoming a vegetarian didn't end there. Janice often talks with her other vegetarian friends about how healthy a vegetarian lifestyle is. She talks with her friends about how wrong it is to wear leather or to use any animal products. Janice feels that being a vegetarian is a way of life; it's an important part of her personal and social identity.

Whenever Janice and her friends talk about their chosen lifestyle they congratulate themselves on how kind, thoughtful and caring they are. It feels nice to have social support and to feel that you belong with your friends. But Janice's group also talk about what's wrong with people who eat meat. Meat-eaters get described as cruel, hard, fat, ugly, disgusting. Meat-eaters are stereotyped as wicked or stupid people. Vegetarians get stereotyped as kind, caring, attractive people. For Janice, being a vegetarian is now a matter of identifying with an 'in-group' (the people like me). Vegetarian is no longer just about what you eat – it's now about who you are. The others – the meat-eaters – are the 'out-group'. Janice has decided that she couldn't really be friends with a meat-eater, because 'You couldn't trust them'. The most important thing Janice wants to find out when she meets new people is, 'What do they eat?' This

Figure 4.5 *In-groups and out-groups: being against the out-group helps you to feel that you really belong to the in-group*

question enables her to judge how much to trust and like the new person.

Not everyone builds their social identity on a single 'in-group' membership like 'vegetarian'. Many people will have complex social identities based on membership of various groups. Social identity helps us to make sense of our social context. In-groups and out-groups may help some individuals to clarify and develop their own sense of identity. Being a member of an in-group also carries the risk that the individual might stereotype, and discriminate against, people seen as belonging to the out-group.

Just belonging to a group may be enough to lead a person to behave in ways that don't naturally fit their personality or past learning. A now-famous experiment by Philip Zimbardo, in the USA (1973), may illustrate this point. The experiment started by advertising for paid volunteer students who would take part in a kind of role-play simulation of prison experience. The original idea was to study the students' behaviour over a two-week period. All the volunteers who took part had passed a series of selection tests to check that they were emotionally stable, healthy and had no history of breaking the law. The volunteers were randomly put into 'prisoner' or 'guard' groups. Before the experiment started, the students had all generally preferred the idea of being a prisoner! Stanford University was used as a pretend jail.

The experiment had to be stopped after only six days. The group of students who were acting as guards had become aggressive, abusive and dehumanising in their behaviour. The prisoners attempted to revolt, but after this had been put down, some became apathetic, and others stressed or helpless in their reactions. Yet this was an 'acted' rather than a real-life 'situation'.

It may be that the guards' behaviour developed from just being a member of the guards' group – a group that developed its own norms and values. At the same time, the attitudes of the 'prisoners' may have again been the result of their immediate social context; rather than because of any past learning or personality issues. In other words, the 'guards' got nasty because this seemed to fit with their idea of being a 'guard'. The 'prisoners' became disturbed and helpless because this was the norm for their role. It started as an act, but it became real!

The way people treat other people may not always be due to attitudes, beliefs or past learning that has gone on. Kindness, cruelty and discrimination may often be a consequence of social identity. Some groups may establish norms that allow them to abuse other groups. Belonging to a group (like the guards' group above) may be enough to explain individual reactions to others.

Theory into practice

Reflect on any care settings you have worked in or experienced over the last six months. What social groups existed among the staff or among the clients? Who was friends with whom? What was the basis for the friendships? Did the staff treat the clients as if they belonged to an 'out-group'? Did the staff share 'power' with the clients (empowerment), or did the staff organise and control the clients all the time? Have you experienced in-group and out-group stereotyping within care work?

Groups like our families, friends, work colleagues, or other peer groups give us a basis for our social identity. But does belonging to an identified group always produce in-group and out-group labelling? Hedy Brown (1985) argues that discrimination against out-groups is not inevitable. She quotes studies from New Zealand which demonstrate that social identity among Polynesian children tends to be developed by generosity toward strangers rather than by discrimination against an 'out-group' *(page 116)*. It seems that broad cultural values, like competition or co-operation, may influence how membership of groups affects our behaviour. Hedy Brown suggests that the need to feel that our own social group is superior to others may be linked to cultural beliefs that people should compete with each other.

Task

Evidence indicators suggest the need to identify the development of individual identity for two contrasting individuals. Going back to the task on page 172 what social groups did the two people in your group belong to? What social roles have they played? Have you any evidence for in-group and out-group identification from what these people told you? List the main social influences that may have affected the people in your study.

· THE CONSTRUCTION OF IDENTITY ·

Being a member of a family, being a woman, being a client, being a vegetarian are some examples of group membership. Our social context and social group membership provide the basis for identity.

Culturally available concepts

Identity is also developed through learning experiences and may be influenced by **concepts** that are available to us in our everyday speech and listening. Concepts may influence the way we reflect, and the ideas and theories which we have to explain social experience.

To explore the way concepts work, use your imagination on the following four sets of descriptions:

- *Experience One*: You are walking forward over some ground. You can see all sorts of colours in front of you. There are light blues, wisps of white, slight mauve bits and golden yellow bits in the top half of what you can see. There is a sort of very complex line in the middle of your vision. Below the line there are colours of yellow, brown, grey, grey-black, and so on. In the distance it's green. Some bits of your view are brighter than others – there are a few tiny flecks of silver. These are very bright; they excite you, you feel good to be walking.

- *Experience Two*: You are walking in the countryside. It is a bright, hazy day. You are walking across a newly ploughed field; there are still a few small puddles from last night's rain. These look silver.

- *Experience Three*: You are walking in the countryside. It is a bright, hazy day. You are walking across a newly ploughed field. You look closely at the ground. What seem to be little yellow-brown stones are actually broken bits of pottery. Pottery bores you; you ignore it and concentrate on the little silver puddles – these look pretty.

- *Experience Four*: You are walking in the countryside. It is a bright, hazy day. You are walking across a newly ploughed field. You look closely at the ground. You recognise broken bits of pottery. You have studied history in the past. You realise that pottery might have come to the surface of the field due to the ploughing. You examine the fragments of the pottery and you realise that they could be ancient, perhaps Roman, remains. You feel excited; you contact your local archaeological society who come to investigate. Whilst investigating you find a pot full of gold coins. You and your group get on to the evening news. Not only that, but the gold coins are worth a lot of money.

These are the explanations of the descriptions:

- *Experience One*: This is an attempt to describe what it feels like to walk across a field – just experiencing the shapes and colours. Experience isn't being classified into concepts other than about colour and visual experience. Perhaps this is how the world feels to a very young child. We can't explain much, but who cares! The experience is very real; it might still feel exciting and good to be walking.

- *Experience Two*: General concepts like 'countryside', 'bright, hazy day', 'ploughed field', 'small puddles' are used to classify or label the person's experience. Perhaps a great deal of our lives are spent just experiencing things in categories. This person just experiences the categories: they don't really see the colours, they don't enjoy the walk. Experience is quite restricted and boring.

- *Experience Three*: Again the person just puts the experience into categories; the category of 'pottery' is used to classify the stone shapes, but the person isn't interested in 'pottery'. Pottery is an empty concept which classifies things which should then be ignored. At least this person enjoys the pretty silver puddles.

- *Experience Four*: This person has concepts which predict the future! This person doesn't just use concepts to label and to organise their experience of the world. This person can use the concept of pottery to predict the significance of what they have seen. Their knowledge of pottery enables them to respond and guess what to do next. They predict that there might be an important archaeological find nearby. The person's ability to use conceptual knowledge leads to social recognition, fame and fortune.

Sometimes, concepts just organise the world into categories, but concepts can enable prediction and control of the future.

We use concepts to simplify our understanding of the world

Ilona Roth (1986) claims that there are three key pressures which influence how concepts are developed and used by people. First, people are influenced by what they experience (*perceived world structure*). Secondly, people are influenced by the need to be able to explain as much as possible with the minimum of mental effort (*cognitive economy*). Thirdly, people are influenced by their culture and the need to be able to share ideas with other people – within their social context (the need for *shareability*).

What all this adds up to, is that **concepts** are not words that stand for real things or even real experiences. The concepts we use to think with, the concepts we use to predict our future, are inventions of our and other people's imagination! Many concepts are used because they are simplifications of experience – stereotypes save on mental effort. Other concepts are used because everyone else uses them – they are easy to share.

Should life be boring?

The first experience of walking across the field describes someone who is really open to their experience; someone who is really looking at what is there. Their disadvantage is that they can't share their experience with other people, and they can't make sense of their experience or predict anything. The fourth experience describes someone who can share their experience *and* can predict how to become rich and famous! The disadvantage of the fourth way of thinking is that it takes a great deal of time and effort to develop this kind of thinking system. Not only is this predictive thinking costly in time and effort, but fame and wealth rarely come as easily as in this example!

Many people will spend most of their thinking lives classifying the world – as described in experiences two and three. We simplify the world in order to make it easy to understand. Life is too complex really to explore everything. It is easier just to label much of our experience and leave it at that. A degree of ignorance (to ignore things) keeps life manageable! The cost of this option may be a boring life – if we ignore too much.

Think it over

Quickly jot down 20 things about yourself: concepts which describe what sort of person you are. Now think of a close friend and write 20 things about them. Think about the words you have used. Are these words completely accurate, are they 100 per cent true? What other words might you have used? Does your friend agree with your descriptions? To what extent are the words just convenient labels? Have you stereotyped yourself or your friend with any of the concepts you have used?

Self-concept

If *concepts* do not necessarily stand for real things, they are invented in order to simplify and to fit with our social context. It may follow that our **self-concept**, or idea of self, is also a construction or invention of our mind. This invention is not just a simple piece of imagination; it will have developed over the years, and it will be influenced by life experience and by the social context and culture that we live in.

Who needs to understand concepts of self?

Imagine working as a taxi driver or as a hairdresser. During the week you may meet hundreds of people. It will be important that you get on with them and that an appropriate social atmosphere is maintained. You would need to be able to guess things about your customers. Would they be likely to want to talk about holidays, or sport, or politics? Would they prefer you not to talk at all? What sort of opinions is it safe for you to offer?

Taxi drivers and hairdressers often get good at guessing or predicting what sort of conversation is appropriate. They can weigh their customers up and decide what they might like to hear. This 'weighing people up' may only require a few simple concepts or categories to understand people with. It's often possible to make a guess at a person's opinions from their age, gender, style of clothes, way of talking, etc. People often openly display clues as to their social identity. Detailed thoughts about *how* people have invented their own personal identity are not needed. For many people, life is straightforward; personal and work-based relationships are quite predictable – there is no need to explore how people think.

Care work involves listening to other people's worries, wishes and beliefs. Supportive relationship work, befriending and counselling require the professional to understand the problems that other people have. Understanding may develop into a deep awareness of other people's ways of thinking and feeling; this is called **empathy**. It is vital that careworkers do not label and stereotype clients by just using categories to 'weigh them up'. Skilled caring will involve spending time trying to understand the meaning and the feelings behind the words that clients use. Sometimes clients may have needs which are based on the way they think. The concepts which they use may be at the heart of their distress.

Theory into practice

Look again at the three studies at the beginning of this chapter.

The 17-year-old is saying that where they live their life is horrible. This may be more than a simple conclusion about life; it may be that this person's thinking is **pre-emptive**. The idea of pre-emptive thinking comes from George Kelly's theory of *personal constructs* (1955). Pre-emptive thinking is where a person has come to a fixed conclusion which is not open to further evaluation or reasoning. The 17-year-old has concluded that, 'There isn't much to life – no point in life really'. The 17-year-old's thought pattern might run like this:

Where I live = a horrible experience = life isn't worthwhile. (See Figure 4.6.)

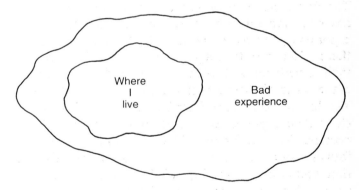

Figure 4.6 *A concept map*

The method of thinking is part of this person's dissatisfaction with life. No doubt life isn't good where they live, but fixed or pre-emptive thinking will mean that this person may now give up and perhaps could withdraw from trying to do anything about it.

The second person, the disabled adult, would prefer to be dead than to live their life with disability. Their thought pattern uses a network of concepts, see Figure 4.7.

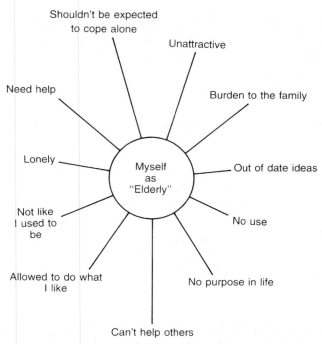

Figure 4.7 *A constellation of thoughts based on past assumptions about disability*

Figure 4.8 *A constellation of thoughts based on past assumptions about age*

This type of *concept map* was called **constellatory** by Kelly. It's a constellation because it makes a pattern like the constellations of stars in the sky. The idea of being disabled brings in a range of other concepts. In this map they are all negative and they have probably been learned from the discriminatory attitudes in this individual's past cultural experience. Now that this person is disabled they cannot accept the conclusions that follow. Once again, the person's method of thinking is part of the problem.

The third person, the elder, is also thinking in a constellatory way. They have lived in a culture that does not value older people. Because they have adopted the concepts available in their culture, they have stopped valuing themselves.

The concepts this person uses about themselves means that they stereotype and label themselves! The concept of 'elderly' causes a whole series of threatening concepts to be applied to their personal identity.

None of these three characters can be helped by advising them that they are thinking the wrong way!

Once we are fixed in our understanding and reasoning about identity, we will need time and fresh life experiences before we can be open to change. Kelly recommended role-play or new types of life experience in order to change these kinds of conclusions about self.

Kelly identified a third way of thinking called **propositional**. This is where our concepts or constructs are open to re-evaluation and to review in the light of new ideas. (Kelly used the term *constructs* because constructs are individually invented.) Thinking in an open way means that we are less likely to make false assumptions about ourselves and others. Naturally, it is best to be open to new experiences and ideas but it does cost mental time and energy. In a stressful life, not everyone can afford the effort that it takes to think in a propositional way. It's easier to label yourself and others, and risk a limited future. Life experience, education, culture and social context also have a lot to do with our way of thinking.

The age of a client and their mental powers, or *cognitive ability*, will also influence what type of thinking they can use. Propositional thinking about yourself is usually developed in adolescence and is often regarded as an adult way of thinking. It involves being able to reason and evaluate ideas. Propositional use of concepts may involve a degree of complexity and uncertainty in a person's understanding of themselves. Simple labels are so much easier!

If we are going to understand other people and develop empathy, it will be important to be able to imagine how others think. Yet we will have to imagine without labelling or judging others in terms of our own thought processes. The key issue is that personal identity may be influenced by our ways of thinking, as well as by past experience and cultural context.

Task

Following on from the task on page 176, how do concepts, labels and stereotyping influence the people you are studying? Can you think of any instances of self-labelling in your own life experience?

INTERACTION OF SOCIAL AND · PSYCHOLOGICAL FACTORS IN · PERSONAL EXPERIENCE

Personal identity forms through learning experiences from childhod on. Identity is strongly influenced by social context, membership of social groups, and by broad cultural factors. Concepts and thought processes will also influence the construction of personal identity. Glynis Breakwell (1986) also identifies the individual's own biology as a factor to be considered when trying to understand identity. Breakwell (1986) states, 'The development of identity structures has to be seen as a process occupying a person's entire life-span . . . During a lifetime (identity structures) consolidate around the basic material of the biological organism. Identity

structures are a product, initially of the interaction of the biological organism with its social context.' *(Page 11.)*

Biology implies all the physical and physiological systems and features that a person consists of. Biology should always be distinguished from genetics. 'Biology' means what we are born with – it does not imply that we have inherited these details from our parents.

Some theorists have supposed that when babies are born they come into the world without any trace of personality or individuality. These features are then supposed to develop during socialisation. There is now a reasonable body of evidence to challenge this view. The work of Thomas et al (1968) documented different temperamental characteristics in babies. 'Temperament' was used to refer to different behavioural styles which were readily observable in babies. Martin Herbert (1981) points out that not only do babies show major individual differences, but that the temperament of the baby has an influence on its mother. Babies exert an influence on their parents. Some are more rewarding and easier to care for than others. Herbert notes that over-activity in a child, 'is particularly tiring and sometimes disturbing, and leads to excessive attention-giving.' *(Page 63.)*

It is possible that that early behavioural styles or temperaments continue to influence a person's behaviour throughout life. Hans Eysenck (1965) formulated a theory of extroversion and introversion based on the notion of different biological temperaments. **Extroverts** were theorised to be people with a stimulus-hungry nervous system; whilst **introverts** were believed to possess nervous systems which would avoid excitment. Introverts might, therefore, be happy with repetitive and safe lifestyles; whilst extroverts would seek adventure and change. The exact expression of this need for stimulation would be different in different social contexts; but it was biological temperament which would fundamentally motivate the introvert's and the extrovert's behaviour.

A person's biology may fundamentally determine their sexuality and sexual orientation. Biology may determine a range of physical and cognitive attributes. An individual's profile of abilities and achievements may be influenced by the interaction of biology and social context. The physical appearance of an individual will be strongly biological in origin. It will then be evaluated by others in the individual's social context. The evaluation of an individual's physical appearance, abilities and achievements may have a strong impact on their identity.

Summary

In summary, **identity is a process**; it is being constantly built and developed during day-to-day experiences. Identity is influenced by:

- *Biology* – any biological or temperamental basis which affects your appearance, abilities and personality.
- *Personal learning* processes.
- Personal thinking styles and *cognitive abilities*.
- The *norms* and *values* you have learned during socialisation.
- Social categories or *social groups* (called social identity by Deaux, 1992).
- Broad influences in *society*, including economic and political influences.
- *Social comparisons*, comparing self with others or comparing social groups with other groups.

This list does not capture every detail or possible influence on identity; but it represents an overview of the factors which may interact to influence a person's understanding of themselves.

Task

Link the work you may have done for the tasks on pages 176 and 181. Thinking about life history so far, how would you finally describe the influences on your own or on another person's identity? Can you imagine how appearance, abilities or temperament might have interacted with society's values? What norms and values have been learned during socialisation? What social groups or

categories would you see as relevant? Are there any instances of self-labelling or stereotyping? What are the person's cognitive abilities like? How does the person compare themselves with other people or how do they evaluate themselves?

You will not have full details of all of these areas and even your memory will have its limitations. But can you use the theory in this section to begin to explain the influences which may lead a person to understand who they are?

What about people who can't describe an identity?

Erikson (1963) saw adolescence as a time of struggle to develop an identity. During adolescence, some individuals may be unsure of their own identity. Discussing personal identity may be an unsafe or threatening thing to do. Most clients of health and care services are in that position because they are vulnerable. Vulnerable people may not wish to share their life story with others. The only readily available area for study may be yourself!

Some people will not disclose or explain their own sense of self because they would not wish to: it's private! Others cannot explain their lives because they haven't the thinking skills to do it. Younger children will not be able to make social group comparisons or evaluate themselves in terms of their life experience. If you ask children to say things about themselves, they might tell you what they look like, their address, or who their carers are. These fragments may be part of their understanding of themselves. The children may not have a general idea of identity, or self, to guide them through.

A third group of people may not be able to describe a sense of self or a sense of social belonging – because they feel they *don't* belong! Breakwell (1986) describes a study where young people had suffered major disadvantages and probably discrimination. With little to look forward to in life, these people may not have believed that they had much control over their own future. No clear sense of identity could be described by the individuals.

It may be that some people do not evaluate their lives or themselves because of the low self-esteem this might create. It may be better to withdraw and ignore social and identity issues if you believe you have no control. Some people may find it *safer* not to think about their own lives.

The interaction of social and psychological factors in the process of identity: an example

Theory into practice

Ashra is 16 years old; she has just started a new course. She has never really thought about study or identity before. Going onto this course seemed like the best thing to do following her studies at GCSE. Ashra has learned to value education and achievement; this was one of the values she learned from her family during the process of socialisation. Norms of doing work at home have also been learned, as Ashra's parents are in professional occupations.

Ashra does not know what to expect on her course; her first feelings are that it is very difficult and she wonders whether she should have chosen to do something else. She is asked to work with a small group and produce a piece of work which counts as evidence. The other group members are a bit unsure what to do, but Ashra is able to think up some good ideas. Ashra is pleased with her own creative thinking. She has the thought: 'I could be good at this'. Two weeks later Ashra gives an assignment in. When it comes back the work is praised as being clever and creative. Ashra is pleased. Over coffee she asks her friends how they got on. Several of her friends say they found it very difficult. Ashra feels sorry for them, but the idea comes to her that: 'I am good at this, not just average – but good'.

The idea of being good at study takes on a special feeling. Ashra starts to imagine that she is clever and creative – she will be good at everything she does in her studies. Ashra starts to use her imagination. Sometimes, when she has a chance to daydream, she thinks about ideas for assignments – books that would help her to write sections of her work. Because she uses her imagination so effectively she starts to perform very well.

Ashra now sees herself as someone who is creative and clever – someone who is good at study. These ideas become part of her personal identity. When the next assignment comes back with the need for extra work, Ashra does not worry. She believes she is good: if a few things don't work it doesn't matter – she will get it right.

The idea of coping and controlling the workload is now built into Ashra's personal view of herself – her identity. Ashra now has the internal motivation to succeed.

This story provides a simplified view of the role of identity and self-evaluation. Ashra develops appropriate norms and values during socialisation to assist her study habits. She is given positive feedback from others to support her own reflective thoughts about being good at study. When Ashra compares herself to others, she seems to be doing well. There is a lot of evidence to support the idea that she is good at study: 'not just average, but good'! At this point, Ashra evaluates herself as someone who is good at *and* enjoys study. Once a person decides that they are something, the concepts they use to evaluate themselves may have a dramatic effect on their lives.

Ashra is now motivated to gain high grades and progress to further study. Ashra may believe that she is also intelligent, creative and skilled: she is someone who will succeed in any academic area.

This idea of 'learning that you are good at something' is called **self-efficacy**. Albert Bandura (1989) uses the term to cover a person's ability to understand their capabilities, motivation, thought patterns and emotional reactions. Self-efficacy is how you estimate your abilities; what you believe about yourself. Self-efficacy is learned. It is learned from past experiences, watching and thinking about what happens to others, copying others and from the feedback we get from other people. High self-efficacy means believing you will succeed at a task. Low self-efficacy means believing you may fail.

Once a person believes they are good at something, this belief will motivate them to keep building on their success. Of course, the opposite is also true. If you believe you are no good, then you will probably withdraw from the activity and avoid it.

Breakwell (1992) believes that self-efficacy may become a general feature of a person's identity. Some people may learn to think of themselves as capable individuals, who will be able to cope with the puzzles and problems that life holds. Others may fail to develop this view of themselves. Some people may go through life without believing they can influence what happens to them. These people may experience their lives as a series of events which just 'happen to them'. An evaluation of self as a capable decision-maker may be needed before an individual can be assertive and before they can take responsibility for their own lives. An identity which includes a belief in the self's own capability may be needed in order to navigate social and career chaos in life.

· THREATS TO THE MAINTENANCE OF IDENTITY ·

There is a saying, associated with Buddhism, that the only certain thing in the world is that there will always be change and something which changes.

Change can be exciting and desirable. Life would become boring and stressful if you had to spend every day doing exactly what you had done the day before. Just a change in the weather – the first snow of winter, perhaps – can create a feeling of excitement. However, whilst some change makes life interesting, too much change can create stress. Throughout life we have to cope with changes in our social relationships, our social context and in society as a whole.

There is a range of life events which create a need for personal change which affect many individuals. In children and adolescents the list might include:

- Coping with the arrival of a new brother or sister.
- Coping with changes in family structure – new step-parents.
- Starting at a new school.
- Coping with moving house.
- Making friends.
- Changing friends.
- Coping with new coursework and exams.
- Choosing a career.
- Making relationships; breaking up and changing relationships.

These changes may be experienced as exciting, or as things that just happen. These changes might also be experienced as upsetting, disabilising changes which destroy the individual's sense of security, understanding of themselves and their social role. **Change** can threaten identity.

Think it over

Think over the list below. Can you remember feeling threatened by any of the above events? How did you cope? How did the experience influence your understanding of yourself at the time?

Many of the changes described above involve a *loss* or a letting go of some attachments. We may have liked our friends and the life at our first school. Moving to a new school takes all that away from us. Gradually losing touch with old friends; having to find new friends may involve a loss. Sometimes it may feel as if a part of ourselves is lost – the loss can cause a threat to identity.

Elders who receive social care support are often very vulnerable to the threats associated with loss. Some of the life-event threats which face elders include:

- Loss of partner (bereavement).
- Loss of a socially valued role – not being needed by children or work colleagues.
- Loss of health – restricting activities, illness and loss of enjoyment of life.
- Loss of hearing and vision, restricting satisfaction with life.
- Loss of mobility – restricting social contact and satisfaction with life.
- Loss of body image – self-labelling as unattractive.
- Fear of loneliness.
- Fear of pain.
- Fear of loss of control over own lifestyle and decision-making.
- Fear of dying.

These life-event threats are not simply unpleasant or unwanted events. For some people, these events may remove any sense of capability or of being a person who can cope.

Loss as a life-event threat: an example

Consider the example of Mrs Kershaw – 84 years old, white, husband died two years ago. Mrs Kershaw feels that she no longer has a meaningful social role. Her children do not visit her very often and do not seem to need her. She often feels that she is just a burden, both to her children and to her neighbours who collect her shopping. Mrs Kershaw has a heart condition which means that she cannot get out easily. Because she cannot walk far, she feels that she is unable to visit her friends who live several streets away. Mrs Kershaw has cataracts on both eyes which mean that reading is becoming increasingly difficult. She can no longer enjoy her books. Despite the fact that Mrs Kershaw could have an operation, she feels that everything is coming to an end. She used to have an estimation of herself as competent and capable (we could call this high 'self-efficacy'). Mrs Kershaw feels that her life has changed; she can no longer guess or understand

what she is capable of and feels threatened. She no longer feels that 'she is the person she used to be'. Mrs Kershaw's concept of age means that 'being elderly' is a threat to her identity.

A combination of events may cause elders to become threatened, or a single event may be the focus for disruption. Eric Erikson (1963) saw the main challenge for older people as being the need to keep a sense of meaning to life. In Erikson's terms, this was called **ego-integrity**, keeping a sense of self together. If this challenge was lost then a sense of despair and a lack of purpose in life might follow.

Holmes and Rahe (1967) set out to try and catalogue just how much change different life events involved. They came up with an index of how much readjustment different life events might involve. Barrie Hopson (1986) states that this general index was found to be consistent across European countries and with the cultures of Japan, Hawaii, central America and Peru. Naturally, the amount of work needed to readjust to a life event differs for each individual. Each person has particular vulnerabilities, strengths and weaknesses in their lifestyles and in their construction of identity. The Holmes-Rahe scale is no more than a general overview originally researched in the USA in the 1960s. The value scale suggests that on average the death of a partner involves ten times the change, and perhaps the threat, that being caught for speeding does. Changing to a new school is half as stressful (on average) as a new sibling being added to the family.

The Holmes-Rahe scale (see Figure 4.9) may be a useful list of life-event threats. But it is important to remember that few people are 'average'. In your own personal life you may rate some issues as far more or less stressful than the list overleaf suggests.

Think it over

If the average person (in the 1960s) found being dismissed at work (sacked) half as stressful as the death of a partner, what sort of variation might exist between individuals? Could some individuals find the loss of a partner less stressful than the loss of their job? What are statistical averages or means? (See Chapter 10.)

Life Event	Value
Death of partner	100
Divorce	73
Marital separation	65
Going to prison	63
Death of a close family member	63
Personal injury or illness	53
Marriage	50
Being dismissed at work	47
Marital reconciliation	45
Retirement	45
Change in health of family member	44
Pregnancy	40
Sexual difficulties	39
Gaining a new family member	39
Business or work adjustment	39
Change in financial state	38
Death of a close friend	37
Change to different line of work	36
Change in number of arguments with partner	35
Mortgage larger than one year's net salary	31
Foreclosure of mortgage or loan	30
Change in responsibilities at work	29
Son or daughter leaving home	29
Trouble with in-laws	29
Outstanding personal achievement	28
Partner begins or stops work	26
Begin or end school	26
Change in living conditions	25
Revision of personal habits	24
Trouble with boss	23
Change in work hours or conditions	20
Change in residence	20
Change in schools	20
Change in recreation	19
Change in religious activities	19
Change in social activities	18
Mortgage or loan less than one year's net salary	17
Change in sleeping habits	16
Change in number of family get-togethers	15
Change in eating habits	15
Holiday	13
Major festival, e.g. Christmas	12
Minor violations of the law	11

Figure 4.9 *Holmes-Rahe Life Event Scale*

What is threat?

As we grow and develop, our learning, socialisation, group and social experiences enable us to construct a personal or individual identity. In a perfect life, change would only happen at our own pace and just the right kind of change to keep us from boredom.

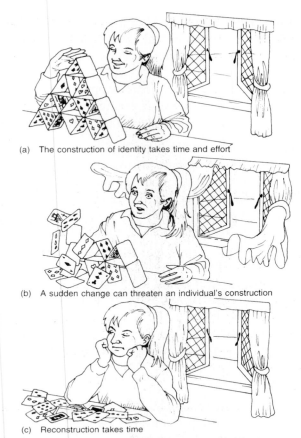

(a) The construction of identity takes time and effort

(b) A sudden change can threaten an individual's construction

(c) Reconstruction takes time

Figure 4.10 *The construction of identity may be like constructing a card house*

As change happened we would make minor adjustments to our sense of who we were.

This construction of a personal identity may be like constructing a 'house of cards'. You need a level surface with enough friction to stop the cards from falling. Bit by bit you can build your structure. If a small piece falls – that's OK, you can catch it before it does too much damage to the rest of the structure. You can start again. But suppose a breeze blows through the window, or someone knocks the table, the whole structure may collapse. It will take a bit of time to rebuild now.

Identity may be like a house of cards, in that it is vulnerable to sudden unwelcome changes. If it has to be rebuilt, it will be a painful and emotionally costly task. A house of cards is just a pastime. Trying to cope without an effective idea of who you are might mean that life isn't worth living.

Breakwell (1986) argues that threats can affect the continuity, the distinctiveness or the self-esteem components of identity (page 48).

Theory into practice

Nick is a student; he has studied for three years, perhaps on a professional or degree level course. He has adapted his identity to include the idea that he was going to become a professional – he was going to be successful. Then he received news that he has failed a vital exam. He will not get to pass; he will not get to become a professional. The news of failure will threaten the way Nick understands himself. The main threat might be to continuity. Nick had thought of himself as a successful professional, but now this is all shattered. The line of career development and progression is broken. There is a break in continuity. The house of cards has (in part) fallen down.

Nick goes to interviews to see if he can get a job based on his previous qualifications. Each interviewer tells him, 'Oh everyone's got that qualification'. Nick feels he is just one of a vast group of people with little hope of employment. Feeling that he is 'the same' as everyone else is a threat to the distinctiveness of Nick's identity.

Finally, Nick gets employment. When he talks to his boss about his past years of study and his interests, he is told, 'Well, you can forget all that rubbish, that won't get you anywhere'. Being told that your efforts and past life are rubbish by someone with power and authority acts as a threat to self-esteem.

Theory into practice

Mrs Kershaw (see page 185) has been admitted into a residential home as a short-stay resident and the staff are not sensitive to her needs. The simple act of going into care might be a threat to the continuity of her identity. She used to be able to cope; she used to be in control of her life but now she is a resident. In her mind she is a resident in an 'old people's home' – so she is now old! But Mrs Kershaw had never thought of herself as 'old' before – this could be a threat to continuity.

Mrs Kershaw is told that there are set meals, set times to go to bed, set routines, set activities, and that everyone is treated the same. This could be enough to threaten her sense of distinctiveness.

Mrs Kershaw overhears two staff members talking. One says, 'No, I don't like working here – all these old people. It's dreadful being old isn't it, hope I never get like it!' This fits all of Mrs Kershaw's worries and seriously threatens any sense of self-esteem she may have had.

Theory into practice

Joy came to England from the Caribbean in the early 1960s. She had been socialised to regard her identity as British. When she first looked for employment she was shocked to be discriminated against and regarded as a 'foreigner'. The discrimination threatened her sense of continuity. Joy was also put down by well-meaning white people who thought all non-whites were the same. She was often assumed to be from Africa or even Asia! This threatened her distinctiveness. Joy came to realise that there was a high degree of racism in the area where she lived and that being black meant you were considered of lower status than someone with white skin. This threatened Joy's self-esteem.

Discrimination may cause much of its damage in terms of what it can do to an individual's identity. The ability to develop a sense of high 'self-efficacy', or an independent and coping idea of self, may be threatened by **discrimination** within your social context. Joy is threatened by racial discrimination, whilst Mrs Kershaw is threatened by ageist attitudes.

Nick is not necessarily a victim of discrimination. Not all threats to personal identity come about because of prejudice or discrimination.

What can these three people do about the threats they face? On a practical level, there is the possibility that they can confront the systems or the individuals that are causing the threat. Persistent attempts to confront prejudice usually require social support and resources. When people believe they are alone this can be difficult. (See Chapter 1, Equal Opportunities and Client Rights.)

An alternative reaction to threat may be to withdraw, or even to adopt a helpless act where the threats appear to be ignored. Mentally, a person can use 'defences' to try and cope with threats to their identity.

Coping with change

The Holmes-Rahe Scale places loss of partner at the top of the table of life-event threats. The process of *bereavement* may provide a good starting point for examining psychological readjustment following a serious threat to identity. Bereavement is described as a process, because it involves making sense of the loss and reconstructing a new identity. Bereavement is not just a matter of feeling sad because someone has died.

When two people have been partners for some time and one dies, what will the surviving partner have lost? Naturally, the surviving person has lost someone they were attached to, someone they loved. They will grieve for this person. There may be a whole list of other losses as well. The surviving partner will have also perhaps lost:

- The main person they talked to.
- The main person who gave them advice.
- Their sexual partner.
- The person who shared life tasks with them.
- The person who made social events work well.
- A person to go out with.
- The main person who provided emotional support.
- The focus of domestic life.

- A source of protection.
- A source of income.

Loss of a loved one might seriously upset a person's life and lifestyle. Grief is not just about missing a person, it may also be about having to reorganise personal identity.

Bowlby (1969) believed that humans, and indeed many animals, would form close emotional attachments during their lives. When an attachment is broken, the first reaction is the pain of separation and a desperate desire to find the lost person again. When a partner (or close family member) dies, the first phase of grief will focus on the desire somehow to find the dead person again. During this first phase, the individual's identity may be threatened but the individual is unable to change. A person has to let go of their past assumptions and expectations which are focused on the lost partner before change is possible.

In the second phase of grief, the bereaved person will experience anger and despair. This phase involves developing a degree of detachment from the dead partner. During this phase a grieving person's identity may become disorganised.

In the third and final phase, the grieving person reorganises their sense of self and their expectations and habits. This is the stage when an individual starts to rebuild their lives and their identity. This rebuilding or reconstruction is, perhaps, like reconstructing the house of cards after it has fallen down.

Going through a bereavement involves coping with a massive amount of unwelcome change. At first, the individual cannot let go of the attachment to the lost loved one. Letting go involves coping with new ways of understanding self and lifestyle. The journey through a process of grieving ends when an individual is able to reconstruct their identity.

Colin Murry Parkes (1975) explained grief as a life crisis or a major time of transition and change for an individual. Going through a change involves a need for psychological work and this takes times and effort. Parkes wrote, 'As the old assumptions about the world prove ineffective and a fresh set of assumptions is built up, so the old identity dissolves and is replaced by a new and different one' (1975, *page 129*). Much of the pain and sorrow associated with loss may really be connected with our tendency to resist change. Again, Parkes wrote, 'Resistance to change, the reluctance to give up possessions, people, status, expectations – this I believe, is the basis of grief' (1975, *page 25*).

Murry Parkes (1975) described a process of grieving based on his observations and studies of grief.

Naturally, each person experiences the struggle of grief differently; but there may be some general components of coping with change, that can be identified.

Initially, many people experience *shock* and numbness when they are first confronted with loss. This phase may involve an inability to accept the reality of the loss, let alone trying to change.

A reaction of *searching* for the lost person may follow (sometimes, literally, searching faces in a crowd). Perhaps the mind can cope with news of the loss, but not with its meaning. A feeling that, 'Yes, I know that they are dead, but that won't stop me from meeting them again.' Emotions of anger and guilt may actually help someone to begin to become detached from the lost love. A phase of experimenting with defences, of beginning to try to cope with change, may occur before it is possible to gain a new identity. Parkes referred to the 'beginning to cope' phase as *mitigation*. The final phase of developing a new identity is called *reconstruction*.

Identity defences

Defences are reactions which have the purpose of defending the identity or providing a measure of self-protection. Defences are a way of enabling an individual to cope with an otherwise intolerable situation. The idea of defence mechanisms originates in **Freudian** or **psychodynamic theory**. In psychodynamic theory, defences are unconscious and are used to protect the conscious self, or *ego*, from the full implications of reality. Some well-known defences discussed by Freud are denial, repression, displacement, sublimation and projection.

Denial

Threatening situations are simply not accepted or believed. For example, if a person hears that they have failed a test, they assume the information must be a mistake. On hearing that someone has died, their partner might say 'No that's not true, I know they will be all right'.

Repression

This involves forcing an idea out of conscious awareness and into the unconscious. Memories of having failed an exam or test might be repressed so they don't trouble your self-perception as a competent person. Sexual thoughts about others were often repressed in the culture that Freud worked in. That is, individuals were able to stay consciously unaware of sexual needs that were not socially approved of.

Displacement

Displacement involves finding a different outlet for feelings, such as focusing feelings of anger on an 'out-group' rather than on the members of your own family who have made you angry.

Sublimation

Sublimation involves a change of state in the way mental energy is directed. For example, strong sexual urges are converted into artistic work or into study. The sexual energy is transformed into a totally different activity which provides an outlet.

Projection

Projecting your own thoughts and feelings onto others. What we see in others is really our own imagination. So, if we have feelings of hatred, we project them onto another person and suggest that they hate us. This saves us having to own up to our real feelings.

The thought systems described by these defences are ways of distorting reality so that an individual may feel safer. In a sense, they are *mind games* which might enable a person to cope with emotionally threatening situations – at least for a while.

Glynis Breakwell (1986) identifies mental coping strategies for protecting a threatened identity. She identifies three basic types of strategy: (1) strategies which *deflect* a threat and resist change; (2) strategies which aim to minimise the amount or speed of change, called *acceptance* strategies; and (3) strategies which enable a person to make new sense of their identity, called *re-evaluation* strategies.

Deflection strategies include denial, depersonalisation and fantasy. *Denial* is a way of buying time. To begin with, it is possible to deny that anything has happened. In grief, it is possible to deny that a loved one has died: 'No, they will come home – the information is wrong'. Then it is possible to deny that there will be any serious consequences: 'I know that they are dead but I still love them, I still sense them here'. The need to change can be denied: 'I'll still lay the table for them – I know they're gone but I do it in remembrance'. The emotional pressures can be denied: 'I know I'll have to change my life – but I'll cope'!

Depersonalisation can involve the feeling that you are not really there, that you are somehow watching yourself or observing yourself. Your life is going on but you are now just an observer. Things that happen or things you do may not really be real.

Fantasy involves using imagination to escape from an unpleasant reality. Imagination is needed to enable an individual to work through a grief. During the early stages of threat, imagination can be used to create protective day-dreams which provide escape from the need to change.

Deflection strategies enable a person to continue with their life even though their understanding of themselves and their social situation is no longer real. A person might deny that it mattered that they had lost a partner, or they might fantasise that they were back with their partner again. These mental techniques might protect the individual for a while. They will defend a person against the pain of changing their understanding of themselves.

Acceptance strategies, as explained by Breakwell (1986), are used to bring about some identity change with the minimum amount of damage to self-esteem,

continuity or distinctiveness. Once again, the objective is to defend an individual's identity whilst allowing some development and modification of personal understanding. Acceptance means not denying the need for change. A person who is grieving might accept that their partner has died, that they are now alone. But 'being alone' can be made safe by the thoughts that the individual uses: 'I know I'm on my own, and I never wanted this – but this will give me more time to make new friends. I'm still good at my job – I can get extra status there. I'll make myself more attractive – buy some new clothes, alter the style of clothes I wear – I'll become a bit different.' The person here is making change 'safer'!

Finally, there are **re-evaluation strategies**. This is where past roles or beliefs about self are re-interpreted. Simple examples might be where a grieving person thinks: 'I'm better off now I'm alone, being single is better than having to live with someone. At least I'm my own person again now – being with someone else was a mistake.' Or, again, they might think: 'As one door closes, another opens – I used to live as part of a couple, now I have the opportunity to do some serious work with this voluntary organisation. That's really what I've always wanted, that's really me. I used to believe that what mattered was being together, now I see life differently. I'm now worth something because of my voluntary work!'

Defences, or coping strategies, are ways of thinking that enable individuals to come to terms with change and with threat. Without defences, life would be unbearable. Everyone will surely use some sort of self-protective thinking during their lives.

Theory into practice

Jack had been married for 22 years when his partner unexpectedly died of a heart attack. They had been very close. When Jack was first told about the death he made little reaction. Friends had to persuade Jack not to go into work the next day. Jack had said that it would give hime something to do, take his mind off things. Later, at the funeral,

Jack said that he felt frozen inside and that he did not want to eat. It was some weeks later that Jack said he felt better because he could talk to his partner, sitting in a chair late at night. Jack admitted that he never saw his partner, he just felt their presence.

As time went on, Jack said that he felt he could have done more to prevent the heart attack: if only he had noticed some signs, if only they hadn't smoked. Jack felt angry with their local doctor. His partner had seen the doctor only two months before. Surely, if the doctor was any good, they should have noticed something! On occasions, Jack just became very angry and bitter about how badly everything had gone; perhaps he was to blame?

Months later, Jack explained that he had sorted his life out a bit. Whereas his partner had used to organise things, he had now learned to cope alone. He explained that he spent time with a close friend, 'a shoulder to cry on' as he put it.

After a year and a half, Jack still misses his partner but he now says that the experience has made him stronger: 'It's as if I understand more about life now. I feel – if I could cope with this loss – well, there isn't much I can't cope with'. Jack has now become involved with the local voluntary support group for people who are bereaved. He says that helping others has helped him: 'It has given me new meaning and purpose in life. I think everything in life has a purpose – things are meant to happen to you. I had a good life before and now I've got a new life to lead.' Jack says that, 'life feels OK now'.

Theory into practice

Explore this brief story. What defences or coping strategies could you identify here?

Discussion: Jack's first reactions might suggest that he couldn't take the full implications of the loss. He relied on 'deflection' or denial defences to cope. The

sense of his partner could be a real thing or it could be a protective fantasy. The anger and the guilt could be a sign that Jack is struggling to come to terms with the loss. He is mentally involved in trying to make sense of himself and accept some change. Jack's 'sorting out' might indicate that he has accepted the reality of the loss. Jack is now using acceptance strategies and making changes to some areas of his life and self-perception. Finally, Jack has resolved the loss and re-evaluated his identity. A new sense of self now gives Jack some fulfilment in life. Jack has reconstructed his identity. Jack still misses his partner, but can lead a fulfilled life despite those feelings.

You may have thought of other ideas: it is possible to see many different things in a real-life situation. What is important is to recognise that bereavement and identity change is a **process**. A person has to find their own way through it at their own pace. There are no forms of advice or special skills which can 'cure' people or 'solve' their problems.

A general way of understanding change

Bereavement is just one example of change which may create threats to identity. Holmes and Rahe identified 43 other changes which might require some mental effort and some coping strategies. Positive life experiences, such as promotion at work, moving house or pregnancy, are included in the Holmes-Rahe scale because even positive life events require mental work and coping strategies. Just because something is welcome and exciting, it doesn't mean that there is no social readjustment. Coping with any transition or change may involve some stress. Barrie Hopson (1986) identifies a general way of understanding 'transitions' or change in life.

Hopson proposes that there are seven phases that people often go through when facing identity change. Hopson believes that these phases apply equally to situations involving a sudden shock or where there is a slow growing awareness that change is inevitable. Whenever people are threatened, it may be possible to identify phases of immobilisation, minimisation, depression, letting go, testing, searching for meaning and internalisation.

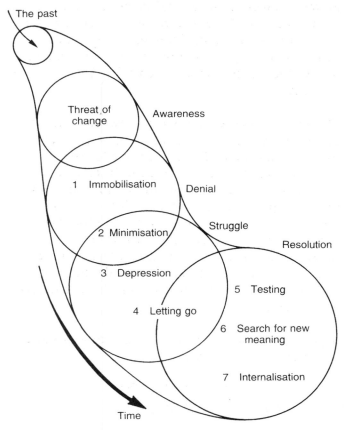

Figure 4.11 *Coping with personal change (transitions): a 7-stage model from Barrie Hopson (1981)*

Immobilisation This first phase involves being unable to cope, so failure to respond may result. Immobilisation can include a denial that change will happen. The individual may feel 'frozen up'.

Minimisation This involves denial and deflection defences. One way of trying to cope with change is to trivialise it or pretend that it won't matter.

Depression When people become aware of the full need for change, depression may set in. Anger, frustration and helplessness may also occur at this time. Self-esteem may be threatened as people take the full implications of change on board.

Letting go Letting go involves accepting the need to change, accepting a new reality. Optimism may become possible.

Testing This stage of self-testing may involve trying out new behaviours and experimenting with new

lifestyles. Hopson claims that this stage may involve a tendency to see life in stereotyped ways.

Search for meaning This sixth stage involves understanding the whole process of transition and change.

Internalisation The seventh stage involves the final reconstruction of expectations, ways of behaving and ways of understanding self.

Hopson sees the morale of people going through transition as at its lowest point during the third stage (depression). So, going through a transition involves the feeling that things are getting worse until the light at the end of the tunnel is seen during stage four (letting go).

Task

Think of a life-event threat which may be experienced by clients you work with or you have met. Research books and articles which may explain some of the stresses and threats to identity involved in this process of transition. List some of the events and some of the defences or coping strategies which people might use to protect and develop their identity.

Abuse

Not all threats to identity are caused by change. Abuses like discrimination, racism, sexism and ageism, are targeted on people's self-esteem, continuity and distinctiveness. Discrimination can threaten the development or the maintenance of a person's identity (as illustrated in the short stories about Joy and Mrs Kershaw, page 187).

Abuse includes behaviour which is intended to exploit, dominate and/or damage another person. It may involve the deprivation of human and/or legal rights. Abuse can be catalogued into many different types; but an overview would include:

- *Physical* abuse: hitting, pulling, pushing or causing physical pain to another person.
- *Emotional* abuse: sometimes called psychological abuse. This might be humiliation and intimidation or undermining another person's identity.
- *Financial* abuse: exploiting or using another person's financial resources.
- *Sexual* abuse: exploiting another person for sexual gratification (sexual pleasure).
- *Neglect*: sometimes called passive abuse. Neglect involves ignoring a person's needs to the point where health or emotional well-being are affected.

Where a person is receiving health or care services they will often be vulnerable to pain, to isolation or to life-event threats which may threaten their identity. Discrimination or abuse will add an additional level of threat.

In some situations, clients might be deliberately abused because they are seen as members of an 'out-group'. In such a situation of direct discrimination clients might be neglected, emotionally threatened or even physically mistreated. This may happen because they are despised as old or as belonging to the wrong racial group. Where such behaviour is detected it should always be reported and disciplinary or legal action taken.

Abuse is not always caused because of straightforward desires to exploit or dominate other people. Li McDerment (1988) raises the issue of abuse that 'just happens' in care settings. This abuse is not caused because of hatred or anger, or because of a desire to 'use' people. This abuse comes about because of the way some 'care' settings work. The *system* causes abuse, not the individual staff. McDerment identifies three factors which may lead to abuse in care settings. These are: (1) dependent clients; (2) stressed staff; and (3) power belonging to the staff alone.

Dependency is where children, people with learning disability or elders rely on staff for general support in daily living. Elders, in particular, may be vulnerable to threatened identities.

Stress occurs when staff are short of time; when they feel that they can't deliver care effectively because of the demands made on them.

Power involves the staff making all the decisions, feeling that they have to control the routine of the home or day centre; staff feeling that they know best. Power being centred on the staff means that they will not bother to ask clients for their thoughts or wishes.

McDerment believes that when these three things occur together then abuse is likely to result. The staff of a home may feel responsible for the residents, yet they have no time to listen to them. They have no time to show respect and value for residents' past lives and beliefs. There is no time to offer choice, and no time to find out about the residents' social or 'personal' identity so that discrimination can be prevented. A lack of time could even lead to breaches of confidentiality if records and notes are not maintained and reqeusts are not respected.

McDerment calls this situation 'the abuse triangle' (see Figure 4.12, below).

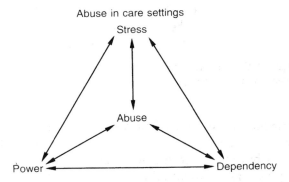

Figure 4.12 *The abuse triangle (adapted from Li McDerment, 1988)*

All of the 'O' unit values (see page 5) can be violated and not used. Residents' basic rights and needs may not be met. As staff become more stressed they may seek more power to control the residents. As residents become more controlled, so they become more dependent. As residents become more dependent, their identities become more threatened. Residents will, in extreme cases, be driven into withdrawal or into isolating themselves from others. Expression of identity may be denied if the residents end up conforming to a strict routine aimed at reducing the stress for staff.

Both physical and emotional abuse are likely to result from the kind of situation described above. A lack of care values will result in unintentional threats to clients' identities. It may become important to always hurry residents. Physical abuse can result if staff have to struggle with 'difficult' people. When staff are exhausted, neglect becomes an ever-more tempting possibility; yet the staff may not intend any of this abuse. Indeed, accusing the staff of abuse may threaten the self-esteem and continuity of the staff's identities! The system creates the abuse and the threat, not the personalities of the people involved.

Effects of abuse

The effects of abuse on clients may include fear, initial aggressive behaviour, withdrawal, depression, loss of self-confidence, loss of self-esteem, loss of control and doubt about their own abilities (loss of a sense of self-efficacy). Abuse may also cause loss of identity, attention seeking, imitation of abusive behaviour, increased dependency, stress and possibly mental illness, or even death from a combination of helplessness, frailty and despair.

Emotional abuse is often likely to result where caring values (as defined in the NVQ standards – the 'O' Unit) are not used in health and social care practice. Part of the function of the value base is to reduce the threat experienced by clients.

Answers to the abuse triangle should centre on: (1) providing care which is *empowering* – this is where residents are encouraged to keep their own routines and make their own choices; (2) working within a care value base which promotes anti-discrimination and respect for individual identity; (3) reducing pressures and stresses on staff.

. PROTECTING AND SUPPORTING . THREATENED INDIVIDUALS

The most important issue to keep in mind is that identity is individually constructed, even if it relies on the local 'building materials' available in social context and culture. When identity has to be *reconstructed*, the task has to be undertaken by the individual concerned. Support from other people is often useful, but other people cannot always put things right. Theory may help us to understand what is happening. Theory may help us to understand how to be sensitive and caring. Theory will not provide care-workers with the answers to each client's needs. Theory should never be used as a way of labelling or stereotyping clients. Each individual will have their own personal needs and their own unique identity.

Health care, social care and social workers who work with threatened individuals can help to support and protect a person's identity by working within the guidelines of the care value base. This value base requires that professionals develop skills in working and practising in an anti-discriminatory way. Professionals must maintain *confidentiality* with their clients in order to avoid threat. Professionals must promote individual *rights* and *choice*, as this enables people to express their identity. Professionals must acknowledge their clients' personal beliefs and *identity*. An amount of listening and conversational skill will usually be needed in order to develop an understanding of a client's identity. Finally, clients must be supported through effective *communication*. The basic principles of understanding, warmth and sincerity will often be useful at this stage.

As well as working within a professional value base, social workers may be able to design a care plan based on an assessment of the client's needs. The assessment of need may often include an understanding of the client's self-awareness and identity needs (see Chapter 7). Care-workers will need to monitor and update care plans in order to meet identity needs.

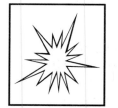

Theory into practice

An elder in care may enjoy discussing their past life and interests in a reminiscence group, where people share their memories. This activity might help the elder to maintain their self-esteem, continuity and distinctiveness. If pictures or slides were used to get the session going, it would be very important that the pictures and slides linked with the past lives of all the elders in the reminiscence group. If people lived some of their lives in other countries, then reminiscence material would need to value this. Care activities and care plans would need to be designed to support client identity.

Where people suffer high degrees of stress, or where abuse is a risk, social workers may be able to intervene in order to remove the abuser, or to design a care plan which offers some relief from stress. Voluntary services provide services such as women's refuges, which provide an escape for victims of stress and abuse.

Where individuals have suffered abuse or threat to their identity, counselling or befriending services may be a source of protection and support for people. Counsellors sometimes specialise in specific areas of need such as stress or grief. Counsellors will sometimes work from different theoretical bases but most counselling will focus on the need to assist the client to clarify their own difficulties. The counselling process will not tell the client what they need to do, rather it will aim to enable the client to work their own solution out.

Many individuals will get the help and support they need from social support groups. These include groups like Cruse, a bereavement care group which provides counselling, advice and opportunities for social contact for all bereaved people. Many individuals can undertake the mental work needed for coping with change more easily if they have other people to talk things out with. Friendships, or social groups, may often be needed in order to work out our own understandings of life. We may not always know what we think until we hear what we say!

The National Council for Voluntary Agencies publishes the *Voluntary Agencies Directory*, which provides an up-to-date catalogue of local and national groups who provide support services. Books, health education guidance notes, information leaflets on where to go for help, can also provide a starting point for someone who feels they need to

find a new group or individual to support them in identity maintenance work.

Task

Explore the 'Voluntary Agencies Directory' for organisations which provide support for people who may be experiencing 'life-event threats'. Work out what kind of support might be appropriate for individuals experiencing the life-event threat chosen in your previous task (page 192). Combine this work with the previous task.

· STRESS ·

When engineers design a bridge or a building they have to work out how much pressure it will be able to take. The parts of the structure are under stress or under load pressure. The idea of stress in people is similar. Being stressed means being under pressure. But where does the 'pressure' come from when we talk about people being stressed?

Hans Selye (1946) explained stress in terms of a three-stage reaction process. In the first stage, a threatened individual experiences shock, followed by a physiological adaptation to the shock – the stress response. In the second phase the individual attempts to meet the demands made by the situation; energy is used to try and cope with stress. If the threat cannot be dealt with, then the third stage is eventual exhaustion. Physical energy is exhausted and attempts to adapt may collapse. Illness may result from this collapse.

In Selye's model, the body tries to cope with excess demands. If coping is successful then everything is fine. Stress results from prolonged resistance or struggle with a threatening situation. If the threat cannot be dealt with then eventually the body will be unable to cope any longer.

As an example, imagine that you are crossing the road. You suddenly realise that there is a van travelling at high speed toward you – it will not stop in time. Your mind warns you that you face death or injury, you feel threatened. The threat will trigger your own **stress response**. Bob Whitmore (1987) describes this response as automatic, immediate and powerful. The stress response is *automatic* because it is automatically triggered by threat. Once you believe you may be injured, no further mental work is necessary – the stress response goes into action. The survival value of the stress response is that it helps you to fight or run away ('fight or flight'). If you are going to escape the van, the response has to happen very quickly – and it is *immediate*. The stress

response is *powerful* – you are physically changed. The outcomes of the physiological changes which happen when the stress response is triggered are summarised by Peter Hanson (1986) and displayed in Figure 4.13 below.

The physical changes which come into operation with the stress response produce outcomes which appear to offer special survival advantages:

- The senses become more acute. If you are in physical danger, sharp eyesight, hearing, sense of touch, taste and smell, may help you to detect a threat in time. Clear thinking is vital if you are to react quickly.

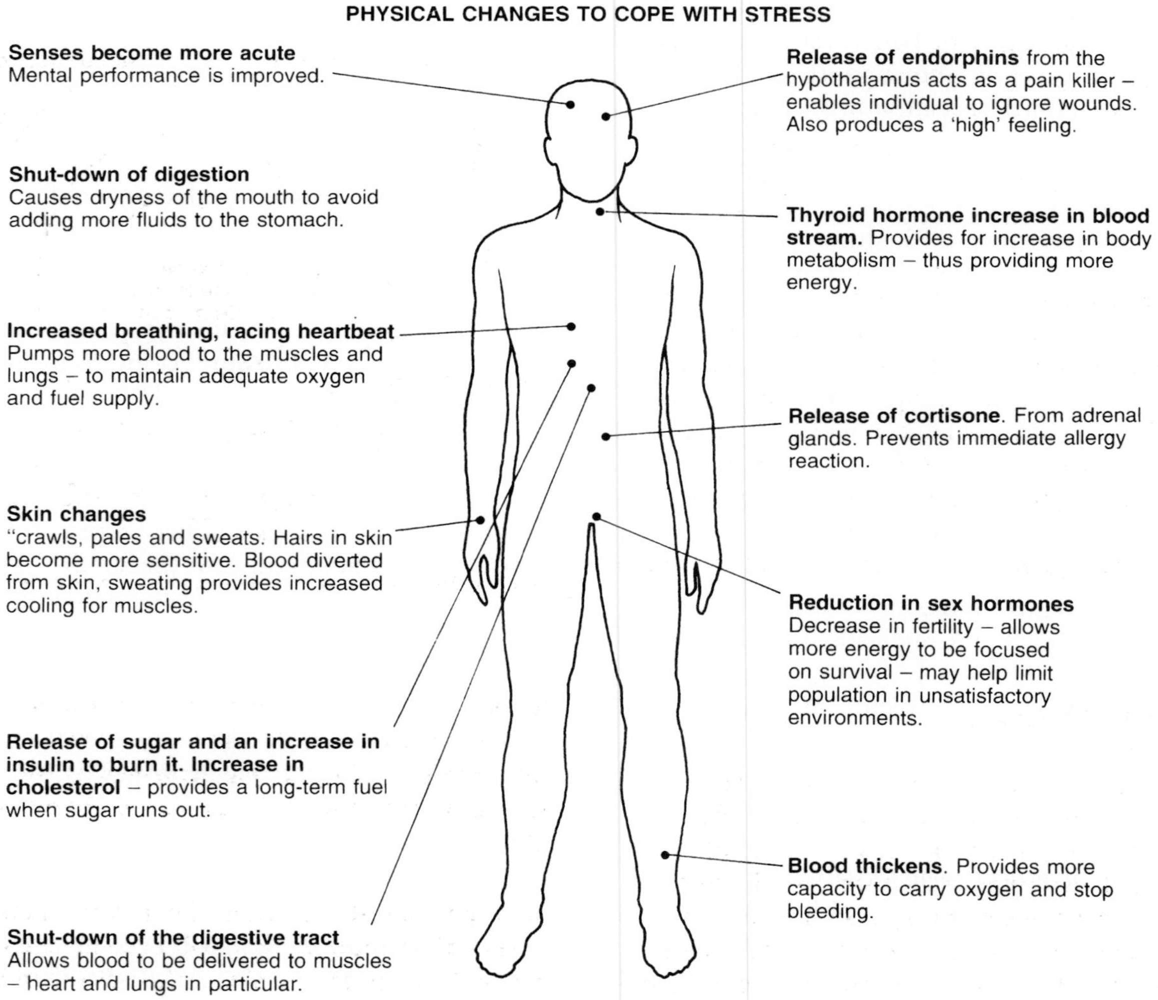

PHYSICAL CHANGES TO COPE WITH STRESS

Senses become more acute
Mental performance is improved.

Shut-down of digestion
Causes dryness of the mouth to avoid adding more fluids to the stomach.

Increased breathing, racing heartbeat
Pumps more blood to the muscles and lungs – to maintain adequate oxygen and fuel supply.

Skin changes
"crawls, pales and sweats. Hairs in skin become more sensitive. Blood diverted from skin, sweating provides increased cooling for muscles.

Release of sugar and an increase in insulin to burn it. Increase in cholesterol – provides a long-term fuel when sugar runs out.

Shut-down of the digestive tract
Allows blood to be delivered to muscles – heart and lungs in particular.

Release of endorphins from the hypothalamus acts as a pain killer – enables individual to ignore wounds. Also produces a 'high' feeling.

Thyroid hormone increase in blood stream. Provides for increase in body metabolism – thus providing more energy.

Release of cortisone. From adrenal glands. Prevents immediate allergy reaction.

Reduction in sex hormones
Decrease in fertility – allows more energy to be focused on survival – may help limit population in unsatisfactory environments.

Blood thickens. Provides more capacity to carry oxygen and stop bleeding.

Figure 4.13 *The stress response*

- Digestion shuts down. The body needs to prioritise blood supply to provide oxygen and fuel to the muscles. There is no need to digest food if you're about to die!
- Increased breathing and heartbeat. This is needed to get more oxygen to the muscles.
- Skin becomes more sensitive. This may have the benefit of increasing sensory awareness. We may pick up movement in air currents, and so on.
- Sugar, insulin and cholesterol are increased – useful fuel to keep the muscles going if you have to run or fight for a long time.
- Endorphins – reduce awareness of pain, provide for a coping response if you are injured; may help you to keep running or fighting when you are trying to escape.
- Thyroid hormone – helps provide for the body's energy requirements.
- Cortisone – prevents allergy reactions. Hanson points out that you don't want to start having a sneezing attack if you are fighting for your life.
- Thicker blood – helps if you are wounded.
- Reduction in sex hormones – if you are running for your life, it's not the best time to get interested in reproduction!

So if you are about to be run over by a van, the stress response is designed to help you to escape. Your senses become crystal clear, your muscles enable you suddenly to spring out of the way – you survive. Your mind lets you know all is well; after a brief 'wobble' you will feel OK. Your body adapted to the situation; you survived. You have experienced just a few seconds of stress and now the body's stress response system can be turned off. (See Figure 4.14.)

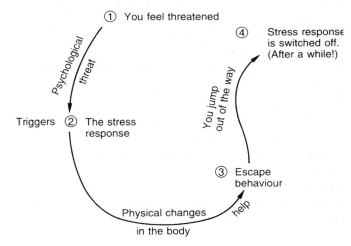

Figure 4.14 *The stress response working effectively*

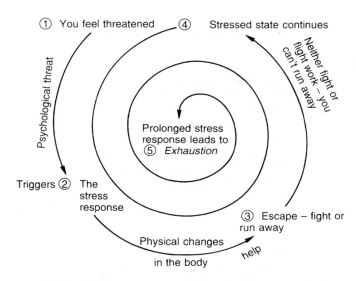

Figure 4.15 *The stress response activated by threats to identity*

The effects of stress

However, not all stresses are this simple. Take bereavement, for example. The loss of a close relationship may threaten a person's sense of themselves. Bereavement may threaten identity and this may trigger the stress response. But in this example there is no escape – loss can't be fought or run away from. If the stress response is constantly trying to help us to adapt to threat, it will fail. The threat is in our own psychology, not in the outside world. Putting extra cortisone, sugar and insulin into the blood will not help us to cope. Instead, the stress response will increase our problems as we cannot take physical action to escape. (See Figure 4.15 above.)

With prolonged activation the grieving person feels 'stressed', eventually they will become exhausted. The risks of stress on physical health then become noticeable. Peter Hanson (1986) summarises the risks as shown in Figure 4.16.

THE DANGER OF PROLONGED STRESS

Prolonged muscle tension
leads to pain – particularly in neck, shoulders and back.

Senses become more acute
"It seems that the senses 'burn out' after unrelenting stress, and become less efficient. The person becomes less observant of details around him or her, pays little attention to tastes or smells, tunes out whole conversations, and ignores touch."
(Peter Hanson, 1986)

Increased breathing, racing heartbeat
Possible risk of increased blood-pressure. If high blood-pressure becomes a permanent condition then heart attack is possible.

Release of sugar and insulin
"Diabetes can be aggravated, or even started, by excessive demands on the pancreas for insulin"
(Peter Hanson, 1986)

Increase in cholesterol
May tend to deposit in the blood vessels. May cause 'hardening of the arteries' and can be associated with heart attacks.

Shut-down of digestive tract
Lack of moisture impairs speech. A range of stomach disorders may result from forcing food into a system which has 'closed down'.

Release of endorphins
Chronic stress can deplete levels of endorphin available. This may aggravate migraines, backache and pain in general.

Thyroid hormone
In excess may cause exhaustion, "burn-out', insomnia, weight loss (where food intake unaltered), jumpiness, intolerance to heat.

Release of cortisone
"If chronically elevated, cortisone destroys the body's resistance to cancer, infection, surgery and illness – the immune response weakens. The ability to fight off even minor colds is greatly impaired".
(Peter Hanson, 1986)
Ulcers may be caused by cortisone.

Reduction in sex hormones
Often causes increased stress within relationships. Sexual anxieties not always understood as stress related.

Blood thickens
Encourages the possibility of strokes or heart attacks.

Skin changes
Signal stress – sweating response may not be socially acceptable; may make skin more susceptible to rashes and other problems.

Figure 4.16   *Dangers resulting from constant activation of the stress response*

Becoming exhausted through stress is likely to result in increased aches and pains, including migraines, headaches, back pains. Insomnia (inability to sleep and rest appropriately), emotionality and tension reactions are likely. Heart disease and strokes have long been a central illness associated with stress. Other physical illness associated with/or aggravated by stress include diabetes, digestive system problems and skin problems, including eczema, and rashes. The role of cortisone in suppressing the immune system may be partly behind the increased amount of infectious illness experienced by people who are stressed. People may become more vulnerable to colds, flu or other illnesses when exhausted with stress.

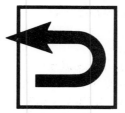

Think it over

Think of a time when you were under pressure or stressed by a long-term problem. What outcomes did stress have on your health?

As well as affecting physical health, prolonged stress can cause or can increase problems associated with depression, anxiety and phobias (irrational fears). It is also possible that stress may have a role to play in more serious psychiatric illnesses.

Tension levels

Bob Whitmore (1987) explains how general tension levels can lead to anxiety and panic attacks. Many people's experience of anxiety may not be caused by a single life-event threat or a single problem. Stress-related anxiety and tension may often be caused by a series of events which lead to a final loss of control.

Take, for example, the story of Samira. Samira is 28 years old and works in a care home for elders. Samira is liked by both staff and residents and is regarded as a good worker. Two months ago, Samira began to have arguments with her partner. Week by week the arguments got worse, although she was careful not to let these affect her professional work practice. The arguments meant that there was a general increase in *life strain* (Whitmore 1987). Life strain relates to the general amount of tension we experience as we go through life. We all need some tension, otherwise we may not be motivated and can get very bored with life. Many people find the right level of tension in their daily work.

Samira used to work at the right level of tension for her, but now the problems at home have made this worse. The graphs in Figure 4.17 (a), (b) and (c) (opposite) record Samira's tension levels over a period of time. (See Figure 4.17(a).)

Because Samira's 'life strain' has increased, she will show signs of tiredness and irritability; but she will still be supportive in her conversation work with residents. (See Figure 4.17(b).)

Because Samira is tired, she has a minor accident whilst driving. She feels she has no-one who she can talk to. Although it was only 'something that could happen to anyone', Samira feels very upset about the accident. She feels 'everything is going wrong'. Samira begins to see the accident as a threat to her self-esteem. Her tension levels are increased.

There is a lot of sickness and shortage of staff at the home where Samira works. The head of the home asks Samira to do some extra work. Samira doesn't really want to do the work, but she feels that she

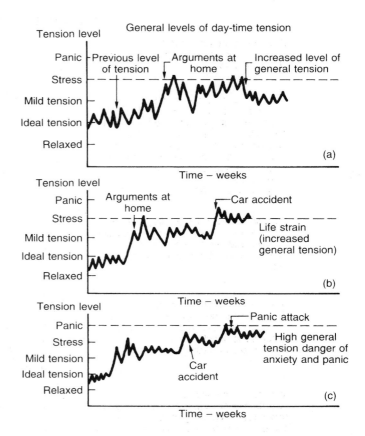

Figure 4.17 *Graphs to show Samira's tension levels*

can't let the others down. This increases the life strain even further.

Finally, Samira goes for a routine dental appointment. She has no fear at all of the dentist, and has never had any real pain during treatment. Whilst waiting in reception Samira worries about her work; she feels tense and on edge, anyway, and when she thinks about the dental fillings she feels her heart pounding. She becomes very hot, soaked in perspiration and dizzy. Samira almost faints, she desperately wants to get out of the room. She feels afraid, foolish and can't make sense of what happened. She fears she is seriously ill.

Samira's level of tension is now disabling; she is now open to repeated panic attacks. Because she cannot understand what is happening she is likely to believe she is ill. The belief that she is ill is a threat to her self-esteem. (See Figure 4.17(c).)

With so much tension, and even panic, inside her Samira begins to ignore clients in need. Other staff notice this and comment that something is wrong. The idea that something is wrong further threatens Samira's identity. Without help, Samira now faces a dangerous situation where she may withdraw, become depressed or suffer a crisis in terms of her own self-confidence.

Theory into practice

If you had to continue this story and get things to turn out well, what sort of help would you want Samira to receive?

Anxiety may often be the result of a number of small events. These life events may interact so that, in the end, the person collapses from exhaustion: they can no longer adapt and cope. Increased tension levels or life strain may also explain some of the reasons people develop rigid habits, obsessions and phobias. Anything which provides relief from tension may become a habit or an obsession. The need to withdraw from feared situations may help to create fear in individuals with high general tension levels.

Tension or life strain needs to be understood properly. If Samira could understand what was happening, this might remove some of the threat to identity. Relaxation skills and new places to go, or people to see, in order to unwind the tension, would need to be an important part of Samira's lifestyle. Finally, having the economic and social resources to cope, might assist Samira to avoid life strain. Self-help groups and voluntary groups might be a possibility if Samira does not have adequate social support. Professional advice or counselling might assist her to understand everyday stress if there was no other source of support.

Stress and behaviour

Tension levels may often be outside our control. However, some people may learn to behave in tense and stressed ways. Meyer Friedman (1975) identified the idea of 'Type A' behaviours. Type A behaviour is described by Hanson (1986) as 'hurry sickness': competitive drive, aggression and hostility if threatened. 'Type A' people try to achieve as much as possible in a short time; they tend to be too busy to bother listening to others and often try to do two or three things at the same time. People with Type A behaviour may be insecure; they may spend a lot of time trying to gain approval from their employer or the public. Type A's may feel guilty when relaxing; they may be selfish, impatient, easily bored. They may be highly competitive – treating life as a game to win.

'Type B' behaviour contrasts with Type A. Type B behaviour means being easygoing, putting just the right amount of effort into a task. 'Type B' people are not rushed: they listen, they relax, they are not competitive. Friedman believed that Type A behaviour might link with the risk of heart attack. 'Type A' people may have learned to stress themselves up in order to get on in their careers or in order to cope with life pressures. 'Type A' people create their own anxiety and risks to health.

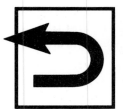

Think it over

Do you know any people who behave in a Type A way? How much pressure do you see in care settings: do any of the staff use 'Type A' behaviour in an effort to cope?

· COPING WITH LIFE-EVENT THREATS ·

Mildred Blaxter (1990) published the results of a national survey into health and lifestyles. She reported that, 'self-perceived stress was strongly associated with poorer health of every kind' *(page 104)*. She notes, 'Social loss or social isolation are particular forms of stress which have been shown to be particularly dangerous to health. 'Life-events' such as widowhood or other bereavement, divorce, job changes, unemployment, migration, even moving from one home to another, are all associated with increased risk of morbidity (disease) or mortality (death).' *(Page 103.)* One key factor, which appears to be vital in protecting people from the effects of stress, is having close social support networks. Friends, family, partners and community links, all seem to act as a buffer against stress. Michael Argyle (1987) writes, 'Many studies . . . have found that distress is caused by stress. This effect is, however, greatly reduced or minimised if there are supportive relationships. This is known as 'buffering'. *(Page 25.)*

So friends and supportive relationships may protect an individual against stress. They may be vital to maintain self-esteem and, perhaps, the continuity and distinctiveness of identity when these are threatened. Relationships may be critical when our identity is threatened. According to Argyle, a key issue is the quality of support. Some people have many friends but still feel lonely. Argyle writes, 'It has recently been discovered that lonely people do not have sufficiently intimate conversations with their friends, do not make enough self-disclosure. Talking for hours about sport is not enough.' *(Pages 28–29.)* It may be that we need friends with whom we can talk about our own feelings. Being able to discuss our own beliefs, to share ideas about what we think is important in our lives, may be a critical need if we feel stressed or threatened. Argyle noted that both males and females found conversations with females to be 'pleasanter, more intimate – to involve more self-disclosure' and to be more 'meaningful' than conversations with men, when this was researched in the early 1980s. This may be an interesting and important aspect of gender role socialisation.

Blaxter (1990) reported that, 'Family relationships and close bonds have been shown to be strongly protective, perhaps through effects on self-esteem and feelings of control . . . Certainly, the relationship between social networks and health has been found to be so strong that it can be used predictively in relation to mortality.' So it seems that people with poor social support may be at more risk of dying from an illness than those with close relationships. Argyle quotes a study of 7,000 people in California during the 1970s (Berkman and Syme, 1979). Those with supportive social networks had a much lower death rate even after initial health, health practices, obesity, smoking, drinking and social class had been taken into account. In terms of type of support, marriage produced the strongest protection; with friends and relatives then offering more protection than belonging to churches or other organisations.

A study reported by Wojtas (*Times Higher Education Supplement*, October 22, 1993) found that, 'coronary patients with a wide network of friends were more likely to survive a heart attack, and that car ownership, which indicates a higher income and more likelihood of socialising, also raised the chances of survival.' This study, by staff at Nottingham University, looked at 1,300 suspected heart-attack patients between 25 and 84 years of age. Those who were socially isolated (poor contact with family and friends, not members of any club or religious group) were '49 per cent more likely to die following recovery from a heart attack than those with social support'. In addition, 86 per cent of car owners survived compared with 74 per cent of those without a car.' The study suggests that moderate affluence (wealth) and good social support are important aspects of preventative health.

But how do relationships make a difference to a person's physical health? Argyle (1987) writes:

> One way in which stress is bad for health is that it impairs the immune system, the natural defence against disease . . . Social support could restore the immune system, by its power to replace negative emotions like anxiety and depression, and their accompanying bodily states, by positive emotions. A second way in which relationships may affect health is through the adoption of better health practices . . . Those who have good relationships are able to cope with stress by seeking help and social support. Those without are more likely to use other means of coping, like smoking and drinking. *(Page 184.)*

Blaxter's study (1990) provides evidence that there is a positive relationship between marriage, or living with a partner, as compared to being single. This relationship was particularly significant for men and, indeed, older men. For men especially, living alone was associated with more illness and poorer psychological and social well-being. The number of social roles a person had (roles like parent, worker, regular worshipper) also related to measures of good health. Although these general findings from a survey cannot be used to make predictions for individual health and happiness, it does appear that partners, friends, family and community social links help protect people from stress. People with close supportive relationships may have useful resources to fall back on when they encounter life-event threats. Socially isolated people may lack a buffer to protect themselves against the anxiety, life strain and threat that life events may cause.

Task

Following on from your work to explore support for people who may experience life-event threats (page 195), work out how stress may affect threatened individuals. What stress-related illnesses might the people in your study be at risk of? How might social support networks assist individuals in coping with life-event threats?

Health, wealth and life-event threats

Wealth refers to the value of things we own: such as a car, home, pension rights, savings, investments or other property. *Income* relates to the money we receive from work or investments, usually on a monthly or weekly basis. *Economic resources* include our total wealth, capital assets (such as house, saving investments) and income. *Expenditure* refers to what is spent by individuals.

Wealth is very unevenly distributed or shared in Britain. Pat Young (1985) writes, 'In 1981, 23 per cent of the country's wealth was owned by 1 per cent of the population, 60 per cent was owned by 10 per cent of the population. The least wealthy 50 per cent owned only 6 per cent of the wealth.' (See Figure 4.18 opposite.)

An article by Robert Chote and Patricia Wynn Davis in *The Independent* (9 February 1994)

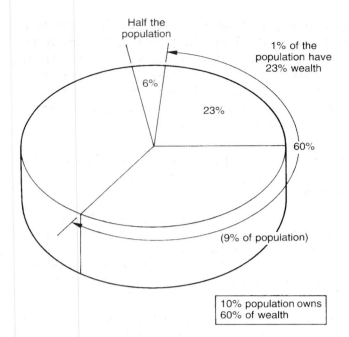

Figure 4.18 *The wealth cake in Britain*

suggested that 'tax changes announced since 1985 made the richest 10 per cent of the population better off by an average of £30 a week, whilst the poorest 10 per cent has lost nearly £3 a week', according to a report by the Institute for Fiscal Studies. Another *Independent* report by David Nicholson-Lord on 27 January 1994, summarised data from *Social Trends* (1994, HMSO). The top 20 per cent of earners in the country saw their income grow (after housing costs) from 35 per cent to 43 per cent of total income for the country. By contrast, the bottom 20 per cent of earners saw their income drop from 10 per cent of the country's total to 6 per cent. This means that 80 per cent of people in Britain increased their real income during the 1980s, but the bottom 20 per cent have suffered a loss. People in the poorest fifth of the country's population spend half of their income on food and housing, compared with only 32 per cent (less than one-third) for the other 80 per cent of people.

A second report from Nicholson-Lord (*The Independent*, 1 February 1994) quotes Mintel's 'British Lifestyles' report for 1994. The report suggested that the wealth gap will go on widening for the next five years. Mintel's head of research is quoted as saying, 'In simple terms, the well-off are getting wealthier; the poor, poorer.' He is reported to have explained that the growing polarisation had important implications for business markets. 'On the one hand there is an increasing demand for luxury goods and services, while on the other, a growing proportion of households only have sufficient income for simple products and necessities.'

The Independent report, based on the Mintel study, goes on to explore the 'strong link' between wealth and diet:

> The affluent are more likely to eat fresh fruit and vegetables regularly, to have a varied diet, and to say they try to eat healthily than those on a lower income. People who are dependent on state benefits have the least varied diet and are least concerned about healthy eating, maybe because they can't afford to be.

Poorer people were also reported to consume more snacks like crisps and sweets than higher earners.

A National Children's Home study was reported by Mary Braid (*The Independent*, 9 November 1993). The study focused on 120 young people, aged 16 to 25 years, who had left care. One in three of this group said they had only had one or else no meals in the last 24 hours. The diet of nearly all this group was reported as nutritionally very poor. Most of this group were living alone and said they were depressed, worried or anxious. The main worries were money and health.

It would be very unusual for wealth and power to be distributed evenly in any society. The concept of social stratification is used to divide society into different layers (or strata) of wealth and power. In Britain, these layers or social strata are usually referred to in terms of the class system. Traditionally, there has been an upper class, a middle class and a working class. Occupation is used as the basis for the Registrar-General's social classification, which is widely used in research into social issues. (See Figure 4.19 opposite.)

The occupations given as examples for each class are chosen because they are linked to more than a level of income. They are ranked according to the general standing of the occupations within the community, which means that people in these occupations have a

	Social class	Examples of occupation in each class
Middle class	**Class 1** *Professional people*	Doctor, lawyer, accountant, architect
	Class 2 *Managerial and technical people*	Manager, teacher, librarian, farmer, airline pilot
	Class 3A *(non-manual)* *Clerical and minor supervisory people*	Clerk, sales representative, office worker, policeman
Working class	**Class 3B** *(manual)* *Skilled people*	Electrician, tailor, cook, butcher, bricklayer
	Class 4 *Semi-skilled people*	Farm worker, postman, packer, bus conductor
	Class 5 *Unskilled people*	Porter, labourer, window cleaner, messenger, cleaner

Figure 4.19 *The Registrar-General's social classification*

particular place or status in society and the behaviour and lifestyle associated with it.

This is illustrated by the way that Class 3 is divided into two, with 'non-manual' placed above 'manual' in the ranking of occupations. Although a skilled manual worker's income may be higher than a clerk's, he or she is still regarded as being in the working class. Non-manual (or 'white collar') workers are seen as tending towards the middle class and are expected to have many of the values and norms of behaviour associated with middle-class culture.

There are clearly great differences between people in the case of both wealth and income. Those in the poorest categories may be at risk of poorer health. Two pieces of evidence mentioned above point to poorer people also having poorer diets. But there is also substantial evidence that lack of wealth may link with lack of health.

Jones and Moon (1987) quote evidence from the Registrar-General in 1978, showing that death rates for people are closely related to social class. In the case of still births (babies born dead) and infants, children and adults, there is far more premature death (mortality) amongst people in Social Class 5 than in Social Classes 1 and 2. In the case of infants less than one-year-old, there is more than double the amount of mortality in Social Class 5 (unskilled) than there is in Social Class 1 (professional).

Data from the *General Household Survey* 1976, reported by Jones and Moon (1987), shows that the amount of chronic (persistent) illness, and chronic and limiting illness, is again more than double for the unskilled class as compared with the professional class. Not only this, but there is an increase in illness for each class as you go down the scale (at least for men). Social Class 2 has more illness than Class 1, but Social Class 3 (non-manual) has more illness than Class 2. Social Class 3 (manual) has more illness than Class 3 (non-manual), and so on.

In 1980 Sir Douglas Black chaired a report on inequalities in health. The Black report identified strong class-related differences in mortality rates, very marked differences in deaths from accidents, poisonings and violence and differences in deaths from infective and respiratory disease. Once again, the upper and middle classes experienced less 'premature' death than the lower classes. The same pattern was found with respect to various kinds of diseases. The Black report data has been updated by Margaret Whitehead (1988) in her work on *The Health Divide*. She confirmed that more recent statistics still show the pattern originally evidenced by the Black report. In addition, Whitehead notes,

Other indirect measures of affluence and poverty, such as household-based classifications and employment status, also highlight inequalities in health. Owner-occupiers continue to have lower rates of illness and death than private tenants, who in turn have lower rates than local authority tenants. It is well known, and confirmed in recent studies, that the unemployed have much poorer health than those with jobs. *(p. 263)*

Argyle (1987) states, 'The lower social classes are affected by most illness more often, take more days off from work, and die a little sooner because of them (the illnesses). This is partly due to inequalities in the conditions of life – smaller homes, less

heating, larger families, less good food, and so on.' *(Page 189.)* Argyle goes on to argue that middle-class people make more use of preventative health services such as antenatal clinics, vaccination programmes and cervical screening, than do working-class people. 'Doctors spend more time with middle-class patients and there is evidence that National Health Service expenditure on middle-class people is 40 per cent higher than on those in Classes 4 and 5 – because Classes 1 and 2 know how to make better use of the system' *(page 190)*. Argyle suggests that middle-class people may have responded to health education campaigns more effectively than working-class people in the past. In particular, there is evidence that middle-class people smoked less, were thinner and took more exercise than working-class people in the past.

Task

If upper- and middle-class people had less chronic illness, and less risk of death, than working-class people in the past, what could be the main causes? How far might having a positive identity, feeling socially valued, having listening and assertion skills play a part? How far is education important? How far does housing and money help? Make a list of the differences which might characterise middle-class and working-class lifestyles. What advantages and disadvantages can you identify? It is unlikely that all the advantages will be in favour of middle-class people, although many of them might be.

Mildred Blaxter's study (1990) throws some interesting light on the class issue. Her work finds a very strong relationship between low income and disease, disability, illness and poor psychological and social (psycho-social) health. But it seems that it is poverty which is associated with ill health, rather than the case that health gets better the richer you are! Her studies show that there might be just slightly more illness and disease for the very rich than for the more moderately well-off. Money itself doesn't seem to create health; but a lack of money may be strongly associated with disease and illness. Blaxter writes, 'The apparently strong association of social class and health is primarily an association of income and health.' *(Page 72.)* Blaxter's study found that self-perceived stress was strongly associated with poorer health of every kind, but, 'It is notable that the relationship was particularly strong for men in manual classes, at all ages.' *(Page 104.)*

Poverty and stress

Poverty creates problems for an individual in terms of managing their daily living requirements. Poverty may remove many of the small daily satisfactions of life, such as buying small presents for friends, going out and giving yourself 'treats'. Poverty or low income may also provide a source of stress for individuals. This stress may be linked to the self-esteem and identity of people who may not be able to keep up with the consumer values which are promoted by advertising and which are a big part of current society. If you have lost the consumer race, you may be inclined to evaluate yourself as a 'loser'. This alone could create stress.

When a person feels 'stressed', anything which creates an easing of tension will be very desirable. A National Children's Home study, 1994, found that, 'two-thirds of children interviewed said they smoked to "escape" their problems, while one in three said they drank, and one in six took [illegal] drugs'. Sarah Hirsh of the charity, 'Quit', an anti-smoking charity, is reported in *The Independent* on the 9 March 1994, as saying, 'As smoking rates increased in line with poverty, it was not surprising that women found it more difficult to stop. Women who are in the lower social groups may be stuck at home with no luxuries. Many tell us on the helpline that smoking is all they have got.'

It appears that people choose to smoke or drink, to be lazy and not exercise, or to eat a poor diet. But it may be that many individuals feel compelled to drink excessively or to smoke because this activity helps to relieve day-to-day stress. People may smoke to cope! Eating snacks, crisps and chocolate may be a little treat in a life that feels empty. Eating fruit or carrots doesn't have the same rewarding feel.

People may trade-off aspects of a healthy lifestyle in order to cope with other pressures. An overworked business person may ignore exercise in order to spend more time with their work. In this way the person can maintain their identity as a successful individual and make money. Health is traded for identity needs.

Blaxter reported that only 15 per cent of people in her sample had completely healthy habits in the areas of diet, smoking, exercise and drinking. Only 5 per cent had totally 'unhealthy' lives. What was striking was that people knew the risks they were running but may have chosen to trade risks to their health in an attempt to control personal stress and threats to identity.

Blaxter (1990) writes,

> The Health and Lifestyle Survey adds to much existing evidence that beliefs are not very good predictors of behaviour. It seems from the interviews here that the public have, in general, learned very well the lessons of health education . . . it is those who indulge in unhealthy lifestyle habits who are most conscious of the links between behaviour and disease . . . substantial proportions of the population did not see health as the most important thing in life – and these were more likely to be people with more, rather than less, education *(pages 240–241)*

As a general conclusion, people appear to have believed in health and understood health; but other pressures meant that they did not necessarily act on their beliefs.

Poverty and low social class appear to be very closely linked with ill health. A lack of income may directly cause problems with the purchase of a satisfactory diet, and so on. But it may be that lack of income also causes people to ignore health as a priority. Why worry about diet, exercise, immunisation, hygiene and health information if there are other threats and stresses which take priority? Argyle quotes studies which show that lower-class people made less use of preventative and other health maintenance services. It may not be because of any restriction or lack of entitlement, but rather an issue to do with how they saw life's priorities.

Coping with life-event threats may include coping with poverty, coping with unemployment and coping with being devalued, as well as coping with issues like grief.

It would appear that poverty or low income may provide a source of stress and compound other stresses which an individual may face. Blaxter notes, 'People with very low incomes, the unemployed, single-handed parents, the divorced and separated, elderly widowed men living alone – all these fared badly on measures of stress and on measures of social isolation.' *(Page 222.)* Blaxter's study found that for people over 40 years of age, lack of income seemed to relate more to ill health than lack of social support. Less illness was experienced by people with high income but low social support, than by those with effective social support networks but low income. Whilst income and social support are always important, the health of men under 40 years of age appeared to be vulnerable to a lack of support rather than a lack of income.

Task

Continuing your work on support for people who experience life-event threats, work out how economic resources (wealth) might influence coping. What evidence can you quote to show that income or wealth could have an influence on the health of stressed or distressed people? What evidence can you quote to demonstrate that there may be a relationship between income, expenditure and health?

Think it over

Try playing the Stress Game, on the following page.

Self-assessment test

1 Which of the following is likely to have a major effect on the early development of an individual's identity?
   a Childhood illnesses.
   b Continuity.
   c Primary socialisation.
   d Learning through reinforcement.

2 Why is it useful to develop a sense of identity or self?
   a In order to cope with life-event threats.
   b Because society requires us to have an identity.
   c To avoid stereotyping others.
   d In order to cope with the complexity of life in Western society.

3 Breakwell's theory suggests that identity can be threatened by threats to self-esteem, threats to distinctiveness, threats to continuity.
   If a person's identity involved the idea of being caring, which of the following statements might threaten
   a Self-esteem?
   b Continuity?
   c Distinctiveness?
   1 'You only care about yourself.'
   2 'Oh, but everyone cares about people nowadays'.
   3 'Caring people are useless – they're just weaklings.'

4 Self-efficacy is where:
   a A person is very efficient.
   b A person uses defence mechanisms to cope with stress.
   c A person believes they can accurately predict their own abilities.
   d A person is influenced by their social context.

5 Care-workers should avoid sterotyping clients because:
   a Stereotypes may limit and prevent the carer understanding the client's identity.
   b Stereotypes simplify our thinking.
   c Stereotypes save time and effort when trying to make sense of things.
   d Stereotypes always result in discrimination.

The Stress Game

6 Social context is important in the development of individual identity because:
   a It forms the basis of a person's temperament.
   b It describes the setting for group and social influences on individual learning.
   c Social context creates a person's identity.
   d It is influenced by culture.

7 Which of the following might be a life-event threat?
   a Culturally available concepts.
   b Unemployment.
   c Socialisation.
   d Perceived world structure.

8 Temperament refers to:
   a Behavioural styles based on biological influences.
   b A person's personality.
   c Childhood learning.
   d Genetic differences between people.

9 How might physical abuse threaten identity?
   a Cause stress.
   b Cause lower self-esteem.
   c Create fear.
   d Interfere with learning.

10 How might culturally available concepts influence the development of an individual's identity?

11 How do norms influence the way a person understands themselves?

12 Which of the following is not a defence mechanism?
   a Shareability
   b Displacement
   c Projection
   d Repression

13 Which of the following might describe a successful process for coping with transitions in life?
   a Denial, projection, acceptance, testing, immobilisation, letting go, internalisation.
   b Immobilisation, search, denial, deflection, acceptance, re-evaluation, depression.
   c Immobilisation, depression, search for meaning, internalisation, testing, letting go, minimisation.

   d Immobilisation, minimisation, depression, letting go, testing, search for meaning, internalisation.

14 Which of the following illnesses is unlikely to be directly caused or directly influenced by stress-related exhaustion?
   a Coronary heart disease
   b Osteoporosis
   c Insomnia
   d Diabetes

15 The stress response is:
   a An automatic physical reaction which adapts the body for fighting or escape behaviours.
   b A powerful depressive reaction which occurs in response to life-event threats.
   c A culturally defined process which explains transitions in relation to life-event threats.
   d The result of life strain and its impact on physical heath.

16 Which of the following might be appropriate methods for supporting individuals whose identity is threatened by life events?
   a Counselling.
   b Reflective listening within a supportive relationship.
   c Residential care.
   d Citizens' Advice Bureau.

17 Why do close, supportive relationships help to protect people from illness?

18 Why might a lack of income or wealth be associated with ill-health and mortality?

19 'Type A' behaviour is:
   a Being assertive.
   b Any behaviour which creates stress.
   c A learned pattern of behaviour which may be associated with heart disease.
   d Anxious behaviour caused by life-event threats.

20 What factors can you think of which might promote a content, coping and healthy lifestyle in Britain in the 1990s?

Fast Facts

Abuse   Behaviour which exploits, intimidates, humiliates or damages another person. Abuse is often catalogued into examples of physical, emotional, financial and sexual abuse. Neglect is also classified as a kind of passive abuse. Abuse of clients can be caused by systems.

Bereavement and loss   A process of transition or coping with change following a loss. Loss of a loved person is usually called bereavement; but the process may be similar in any loss, such as loss of a limb. The process may involve phases of shock, searching, using defences, anger and guilt, before final reconstruction of identity is possible.

Concepts   Linguistic or language terms used to classify, predict and explain physical and social reality. They are probably dependent on experience of events, usefulness in terms of simplifying experience and ability to be shared with others.

Construction   Construction means to build or develop. Beliefs about self and others are often built or 'constructed' from our experience within a social context. Identity is a construction – it is built or invented from our experience.

Constructs   Individual concepts which don't have to be shareable. Constructs are private ways of evaluating ourselves, others or things. They can be used in patterns to create pre-emptive, constellatory or propositional evaluations.

Continuity   Continuing on without a break. A sense of continuity – being the same person – is an outcome of identity in Breakwell's theory (1986). Continuity can be threatened by events which contradict assumptions about oneself.

Coping strategies   A term used by Breakwell (1986) to describe attempts to cope with threats to identity. Three major types of coping strategy are: deflective strategies, acceptance strategies and re-evaluation strategies. These strategies may function in a similar way to the idea of defences in Freudian theory.

Culture   The collection of values and norms that are associated with large and identifiable groups. Culture will include status and role definitions for individuals. Culture will describe the features of a group that make it distinct from other groups.

Defences   Ways of protecting a threatened sense of self (described as *ego* in Freudian theory). Defences distort a person's perception of reality and social meaning in order to help the individual to cope on a temporary basis.

Discrimination   The basic meaning is to be able to distinguish between things. Discrimination in this sense is necessary in order to use concepts. 'Discrimination' in health and care contexts is used to mean not only distinguishing between groups of people, but going on to deny one group the same quality of opportunity or service that a different group receives. For example, discrimination would happen where people from one racial group were offered opportunities denied to members of other racial groups.

Distinctiveness   The feeling that you are special, distinctive and individual. An outcome of identity in Glynis Breakwell's theory of identity (1986). Distinctiveness may be threatened by events which suggest that you are just like everyone else, just part of a group, nothing more.

Health   The World Health Organisation's definition of health is, 'A state of complete physical, mental and social well-being, and not the absence of disease or infirmity'.

Holmes-Rahe Scale   A scale of 'life events' which may put pressure on individuals to make a social readjustment. The scale was researched in the USA in the 1960s by Holmes and Rahe. The scale may be a useful starting point for cataloguing life-event threats.

Identity   Put simply, a person's identity is how they understand themselves and make sense of their life in relation to other people and society. Breakwell (1986) defines identity as, 'a dynamic social product, residing in psychological processes, which cannot be understood except in relation to its social context and historical perspective' (p. 9). Deaux (1992) distinguishes between personal identity – how the individual understands themselves – and social identity – the social group memberships which might influence personal identity.

Income Money that an individual or household gets from work, from investments or other sources. Income is usually thought of as income per week or income per month. For statistical purposes, income per year may be recorded.

In-groups and Out-groups The idea that people develop and support their identity in relation to their membership of social groups. Once a person has identified with (or become a member of) a group, they may support their own identity by seeing other groups (the out-groups) negatively. A great deal of prejudice and discrimination may be understandable in terms of in-group/out-group psychology.

Kolb-learning cycle One way of describing the process of learning. In this theory, learning starts with experience. This experience is reflected on and then developed into the individual's own theories about life. The theories are then put to the test by experimenting or trying them out in practice. This process repeats itself throughout life. Learning is never complete. Learning is seen as very different from remembering.

Life-event threats Major changes or transitions which threaten an individual's identity or sense of self. Life-event threats include issues like bereavement and unemployment, and perhaps many of the higher valued events in the Holmes-Rahe scale.

Life strain A term used by Bob Whitmore to describe the strain created by prolonged operation of the stress response. The term may also relate to the stage of resisting threat, identified by Hans Selye. Life strain involves increased tension levels. Life strain may make individuals vulnerable to anxiety, panic and obsessional behaviour. Life strain may be a factor which explains why some people ignore health advice.

Norms Rules of behaviour which are followed by members of groups. Norms apply to members of the group only, and are usually different from norms of other groups.

NVQ – value base The defined value system for competent practice in caring. The value system underpins effective support work with threatened individuals. It includes anti-discriminatory practice, the maintenance of confidentiality, maintaining clients' rights and choice, respecting identity and beliefs, and valuing clients with appropriate conversation.

Self-concept The use of many concepts to describe, understand and perhaps predict what we are like. Understanding of self.

Self-efficacy An individual's ability to understand and perhaps predict their own abilities in relation to any task or challenge. High self-efficacy involves the belief that you will succeed at a given task. Self-efficacy may become a general feature of a person's identity.

Self-esteem How you evaluate your sense of self, the value you place on aspects of identity. Self-esteem may be threatened by events which devalue your identity or ideas about yourself.

Social class A social group who share a common degree of power or wealth in society. Class membership is linked to occupation, income, wealth, beliefs and lifestyle.

Social context The setting for group and social influences on individual learning.

Social role The behaviour adopted by individuals when they are in social situations. Group norms and individual status help to define a role.

Social stratification The outcome of dividing the population up into layers or strata. Society can be stratified on the basis of class, income, race, age, or any other characteristic by which people can be separated into groups.

Social support networks Partners, friends, family and relatives, membership of community groups which provide a source of support for own identity. Support may often be provided in the context of conversation which permits self-disclosure (or talking about oneself).

Socialisation The process of learning and accepting the norms and values of a group, and developing your own role within it. Through socialisation, people become part of a group or culture.

Stress The result of the activation of the stress response. The stress response enables an individual to fight or run away more effectively than normally. The stress response works effectively as a reaction to physical threat but may create problems when activated in response to threats to identity. Prolonged activation may lead to life strain.

Stress-related illnesses Many illnesses may be made worse by stress. Illnesses particularly associated with stress are heart disease, strokes, diabetes, digestive disorders, skin problems and extra vulnerability to colds and flu. Migraines, headaches, aches and pains, anxiety, insomnia and obsessional behaviour may all be caused or made worse by stress.

Temperament The behaviour style or styles that an individual develops as a result of biological influences. Behaviour patterns in babies and infants are thought to influence their care-givers. As well as early reactions, traits like introversion and extroversion have been theorised to be due to temperament.

Transitions Changes in a person's life which may require a process of readjustment. Transition is a wide term which can include changes in work patterns and work culture, as well as issues like life-event threats.

'Type A' behaviour A stress-inducing behaviour pattern which people may learn. 'Type A' behaviour is associated with heart disease. Key features of 'Type A' behaviour include being hurried, competitive, aggressive, selfish, impatient and easily bored.

Wealth Covers economic resources such as property, houses, cars, investments and pension rights.

Values Values are learned principles or thought systems which enable individuals to choose between alternatives and make decisions. Values guide behaviour in relation to what is judged to be 'valuable' or appropriate. Values will be learned in a cultural context and will develop from the beliefs and norms which exist within a cultural group.

References

*Recommended further reading

*Argyle, M. (1987) *The Psychology of Happiness* Methuen

Bandura, A. (1977) *Social Learning Theory* Prentice Hall

Bandura, A. (1989) 'Perceived Self-Efficacy in the Exercise of Personal Agency. In *The Psychologist* 2 (10), 411–24

Black, D. et al (1980) The Black Report. In Townsend, P. et al (1988)

*Blaxter, M. (1990) *Health and Lifestyles* Routledge

Bowlby, J. (1969) *Attachment and Loss Vol. 1* Hogarth Press

Breakwell, G. (1986) *Coping with Threatened Identities* Methuen

Breakwell, G. (ed.), (1992) *Social Psychology of Identity and the Self Concept* Surrey University Press

Breakwell, G. (1992) Processes of Self-Evaluation: Efficacy and Estrangement. In Breakwell, G. (ed.) (1992)

*Brown, H. (1985) *People, Groups and Society* Open University Press

Deaux, K. (1992) Personalizing Identity and Socializing Self. In Breakwell, G. (ed.) (1992)

Erikson, E. (1963) *Childhood and Society* Norton

Eysenck, H. (1965) *Fact and Fiction in Psychology* Pelican

Friedman, M. and Roseman, R. (1975) *Type A Behaviour and Your Heart* Wildwood House

*Hanson, P. (1986) *The Joy of Stress*, Pan Books

Herbert, M. (1981) *Behavioural Treatment of Problem Children* Academic Press

*Herbert, M. (Second edition, 1986) *Psychology for Social Workers* The British Psychological Society and Macmillan

Holmes, T.H. and Rahe, R.H. (1967) The Social Readjustment Rating Scale. In *Journal of Psychosomatic Research* 11, 213–218

Hopson, B. (1986) Transition: Understanding and Managing Personal Change. In Herbert, M. (ed.) (1986)

Jones, K. and Moon, G. (1987) *Health, Disease and Society* Routledge

Kelly, G.A. (1955), *A Theory of Personality* Norton (Norton Edition, 1963)

Kitzinger, C. (1992) The Individual Self Concept. In Breakwell, G. (ed.) (1992)

Kolb, D., Rubin, I. and McIntyre (Third edition, 1979) *Organizational Psychology – an Experimental Approach* Prentice Hall

McDerment, L. (1988) *Stress Care* London, Social Care Association

*Murry Parkes, C. (1975) *Bereavement* Penguin

*National Council for Voluntary Agencies (Twelfth edition, 1991) *The Voluntary Agencies Directory* Bedford Square Press

Roth, I. (1986) *Perception and Representation*, Open University Press

Selye, H. (1946) The General Adaptation Syndrome and the Diseases of Adaptation. In *Journal of Clinical Endocrinology* 6, 117

Tajfel, H. (ed.) (1978) *Differentiation Between Social Groups: Studies in the Social Psychology of Intergroup Relations* Academic Press

Tajfel, H. Billig, M.G. and Bundy, R.P. (1971) Social Categorization and Intergroup Behaviour. *European Journal of Social Psychology, Vol.1 No.2* pages 149–78

Thomas, A., Chess, S. and Birch, H.G. (1968) *Temperament and Behaviour Disorders in Children* University of London Press

Townsend, P. et al (1988) '*Inequalities in Health*' Penguin

Whitehead, M. (1988) The Health Divide. In Townsend, P. et al (1988)

*Whitmore, B. (1987) *Living with Stress and Anxiety* Manchester University Press

Young, P. (ed) (1985) *Mastering Social Welfare* Macmillan

Zimbardo, P.G. et al (1973) A Pirandellian Prison: The Mind is a Formidable Jailor. In *New York Times Magazine* 8 April, 38–60

5 HEALTH PROMOTION

This chapter aims to explore the idea of health and the factors that affect health. Chapter five also looks at risks to health – including substance abuse, smoking, alcohol, sexual practices and sexually transmitted diseases as well as risks to personal safety.

Health has been at the fore of the news in recent years with the government producing documents such as the 'Health of the Nation' (1992) in an attempt to set targets for the nation's health and initiate ways to implement these targets and monitor their success. The chapter will look at how to promote health: how to put across health messages to different audiences, including planning, materials and the equipment that can be used, and how to evaluate the success of a programme.

However, first, it may be useful to look at what being 'healthy' means, and the factors that affect an individual's health. This will help the health promoter structure messages more effectively.

· WHAT IS HEALTH? ·

Being 'healthy' means different things to different people. It is very much a personal issue. An individual may be very well aware of the risks to health connected to a habit such as smoking, but may still do it; for example, a doctor or nurse who smoke.

Some habits are *addictive* – the individual has an abnormal physical dependency on them which is hard to break. Dependency can prevent an individual breaking a habit despite being aware of the risks to health.

Think it over

Write down what being healthy means to you. Discuss your ideas with a partner or small group. Report your findings back to the main group.

Comment on how the ideas are similar or differ.

The World Health Organisation defines health as, 'a state of complete physical, mental and social well-being, and not merely the absence of disease or infirmity'.

Physical health covers the normal functioning of the body. *Mental* health covers the health of the mind, being able to think clearly and carry out intellectual processes. It can also include being able to express emotions appropriately and cope with mental demands such as stress and worry. *Social* health covers being able to form and keep relationships, both on a personal and professional level. As much of modern life involves contact with others, this is an important aspect of health and it is often said that loneliness can be a major contributor to ill health.

The World Health Organisation gives a starting point for looking at the idea of being healthy. It could be suggested that this definition is somewhat unrealistic, as complete physical, mental and social well-being is hard to achieve, but the definition does emphasise the holistic view of health. It highlights the idea that being healthy is not only a physical thing: for example, an individual who has suffered a bereavement may be physically healthy but, for a while at least, may not be mentally healthy. Also, it is important to remember that each of the 'categories' often links with the others. A physical illness can also have an effect on the mental health of an individual. For example, a pregnant woman whose pregnancy is in danger due to high blood-pressure might spend a considerable time in hospital; she may become depressed because she cannot do much and is away from her family. So each area of health cannot be seen in isolation of each other – any health promotion programme should reflect this.

Think it over

Go back to your ideas on what being healthy involves. How do your ideas fit within the categories of physical, mental and social well-being?

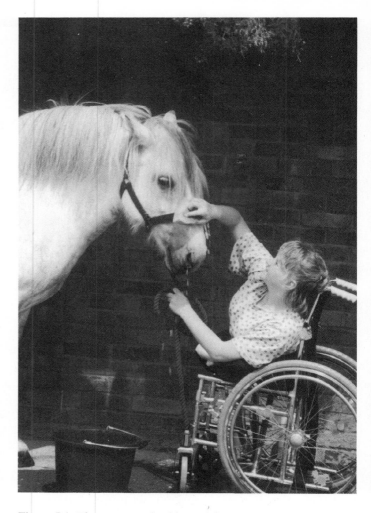

Figure 5.1 *This person is healthy and fit. (Winged Fellowship Trust 'Images of Caring' Competition by Agnes W. Leith.)*

The state of people's health can have an effect on everything else that they do. Health can affect a person's ability to work and, consequently, their earning potential which in turn has an effect on lifestyle.

Health is also something that changes, more often for some people than others. An individual who suffers from migraines may have days when they are not 'healthy' and cannot function as normal, but there will be other days when they can. Alternatively an individual with progressive AIDS may be physically ill all of the time, compared with someone who does not have the illness, but may have some days which are better than others and which the individual may consider as times of health.

The definition of health can change depending on what you compare it to – someone with a chronic (or persistent) illness may always be seen as physically ill in some people's eyes but, in their own view, they may live to their potential. A person becomes 'ill' only when they are unable to function to their own standards.

In short, the definition of 'health' is not easy or clearcut. It covers many facets of the individual, varies according to their circumstances and may constantly change.

What factors affect health?

It is difficult to look at the question, 'what is health?' without considering the factors that affect an individual's health. These are complex and broader than many people think. It is probably useful to look at these factors on three levels – the individual level, the group or family level and the society/environment level (see diagram below).

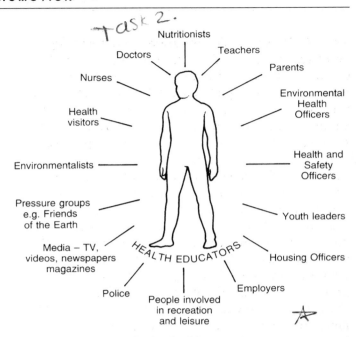

Figure 5.3   *People involved in health promotion*

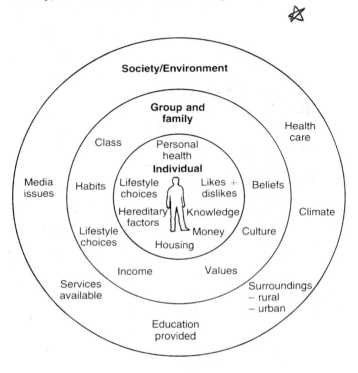

Figure 5.2   *Factors that affect health*

Again, each of these levels interlink and have an effect on each other. A middle-aged man may want to change a habit which is proving to be a risk to health, such as eating a high-fat, high-sugar diet when he is obese and running the risk of a heart attack. However, he needs the support of his family to do this: many middle-aged men rely on their partners to shop and cook food. If this man's partner does not appreciate the need to change, he will not succeed in eating a healthier diet. Equally, he may need his workplace to support him by providing healthier food at working lunches. Both of these situations have a direct effect on his ability to change but he may have little control over them.

· WHAT IS HEALTH PROMOTION? ·

Health promotion aims to make people aware of things that affect health, to give information on ways to improve health and essentially empower people to make informed decisions about the choices they make in their life which affect their health. It *can* involve habit changing but this is not always its main aim. The diagram above shows some of the people and agencies who are involved in health promotion.

There are also a number of ways in which employers can promote health just through the policies they make. These might include:

a No smoking on the premises, or providing a designated smoking area.
b Regular health checks for staff.
c A well-exited building with a clear system for escape from fire which is regularly practised.
d Regular maintenance and safety checks of premises and equipment.

Levels of health promotion

Health promotion occurs on different levels. Ewles and Simmett (1992) suggested three:

a *Primary health promotion* (prevention)
Health promotion aimed at informing different groups about health-related issues with the aim of prevention. For example, telling children about the risks related to smoking in the hope that they will not take up the habit.
b *Secondary health promotion* (curative)
Health promotion advice which encourages people to change the habits they already have. This may be a result of symptoms and/or illnesses connected with a habit, and trying to prevent it getting worse. For example, an overweight individual may have health promotion advice on healthy eating, weight loss and how to eat a healthy diet. The aim of this advice is to prevent the person becoming obese and so suffering the symptoms that often go with it; such as heart attacks, varicose veins and breathlessness when doing anything that requires exertion.
c *Tertiary health promotion* (adjustment)
This involves educating the individual to get the most out of life despite an irreversible or chronic illness or condition. For example, rehabilitating an individual who has had a heart by-pass operation and advising them on the changes in lifestyle that may be needed (e.g. diet and exercise).

Areas of health promotion advice

Health promotion advice can be given on a range of topics from personal health to personal safety – including how the individual can ensure a quality of life through lifestyle choices and how Environmental Health departments might monitor food outlets and educate food handlers with the aim of reducing food poisoning. However, before any advice can be given, the subject matter has to be thoroughly understood. The next section of this chapter will look at a range of risks to health, which can be used as a basis on which to plan a health promotion package.

· SEXUAL PRACTICES ·

Sex is a natural part of life. It offers a way for people to express their feelings for one another and it is also the way humanity reproduces itself. However, being sexually active does carry risks, such as unwanted pregnancy and sexually transmitted diseases including HIV and AIDS. The current advice is to practise 'safer sex' to minimise risks.

Contraception

Unless they wish to conceive a child, contraception is an extremely important issue for any sexually active couple. However, contraceptive methods can also have a secondary function of preventing the spread of sexually transmitted diseases – including HIV. It is important, therefore, that contraception is seen as a joint responsibility and *not* just that of the female.

Contraception aims to prevent conception. Therefore a review of the male and female reproductive systems, including how conception occurs, will enable a better understanding of how each method of contraception is designed to work. An understanding of the reproductive system may also assist in understanding how the spread of STDs may be prevented (these are discussed later in the chapter). A knowledge of contraception is also important in the light of the 'Health of the Nation' document (1992) where two of the aims are connected to contraception and sexual health. These are:

a To reduce the incidence of gonorrhoea (see chapter 3) by 20%
b To reduce the number of conceptions in the under-16 age group by at least 50 per cent by the year 2000.

Reproductive systems

From the age of puberty, girls become fertile; this is marked by the start of monthly periods (menstruation). Each ovary produces an egg alternately on a monthly basis. The egg, once released, travels down the fallopian tubes to the womb (uterus). In the first part of the monthly cycle

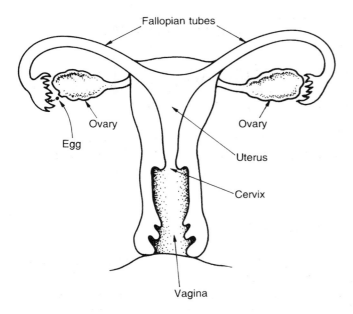

Figure 5.4 *Female reproductive system*

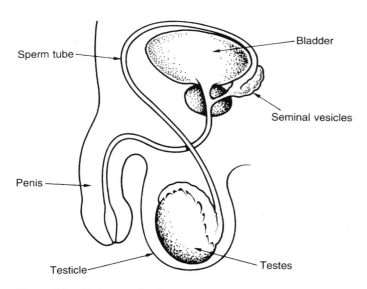

Figure 5.5 *Male reproductive system*

the womb lining builds up to be receptive to the development of an embryo – should the egg be fertilised. If this happens, a pregnancy has begun. If not, the womb lining breaks down and the blood is lost as a period.

The male testes produce sperm. When sexually excited, the penis fills with blood and becomes erect. The sperm mixes with seminal fluid to become semen and is ejaculated. (It is thought that each ejaculation contains at least 300 million sperm.)

Nature has designed the male and female reproductive systems to complement each other for the purposes of reproduction. During sexual intercourse, the penis enters the vagina and sperm can then be ejaculated closer to the area where fertilisation takes place. The sperm is able to 'swim' its way from where it is ejaculated, through the cervix and into the fallopian tubes to fertilise the egg. The fertilised egg will then move down from the tube to embed itself in the wall of the uterus where its development will begin. Each method of contraception aims to interfere with this process in one or more ways. The table on the following page shows the different methods of contraception and explains how they work.

Each of the different methods of contraception has its own disadvantages and advantages, and individuals need to decide what is best for them according to their circumstances. For example, a couple in a long-standing relationship may not be so concerned about the risk of contracting a sexually transmitted disease and therefore do not want a barrier method; whereas an adolescent, in a relatively new relationship, may feel that a barrier method of contraception, such as a condom, is best to reduce the additional risk of contracting HIV.

The other table on the following page shows some of the advantages and disadvantages of different methods.

Sexually transmitted diseases

Sexually transmitted diseases (STDs) can be passed from one individual to another whether they are having sexual intercourse as part of a casual or long-term steady relationship. STDs are termed **genito-urinary** diseases, or GUs, by doctors as they tend to affect the urinary system as well as the genital area. It should be appreciated that anyone can contract an infection – men and women, heterosexuals and homosexuals. Getting an infection is not dependent on having lots of sexual partners; although the more partners an individual has, the greater the risk of

Method	How it works
Combined pill (Progesterone and oestrogen)	Works in three ways: a. Increases mucus in the cervix – prevents sperm entering womb b. Prevents womb lining building up so it is unreceptive to the fertilised egg c. Prevents ovulation Highly reliable
Mini pill	Thickens mucus in neck of womb which acts as a barrier to sperm
Male condom	Covers the penis and collects the semen in the tip, so preventing it from entering the vagina
Female condom	Lines the vagina to prevent the sperm reaching the egg
IUD (Intrauterine device)	A copper wire inserted into the uterus which makes the environment unsuitable for embryo development
Cap/diaphragm	Soft rubber cap with metal ring which fits over the cervix and prevents the sperm reaching the uterus. Must always be used with a spermicide and left for six hours after intercourse
Spermicide	Foam, cream, jelly or foaming tablet inserted high into the vagina before intercourse. They destroy sperm but also act as a barrier. Should always be used with a condom/cap
Sterilisation: Male Female	Should be seen as irreversible Cuts and ties are made in the tubes which carry the sperm from the scrotum to prevent sperm being mixed with semen Cuts or ties are made in the fallopian tubes to prevent the egg reaching the uterus or sperm passing up the tubes to the egg
Injection (Depo-Provera)	Similar to combined pill (injectable every three months)
Withdrawal (coitus interruptus)	Man removes penis before ejaculation occurs. Very unreliable as sperm can be released during love-making before full ejaculation
Rhythm method	Relies on estimating the time during the woman's monthly cycle when she is likely to conceive and avoiding intercourse then. Very unreliable as the time of ovulation is not easily predictable

Method	Advantages	Disadvantages
Combined pill	Most reliable form of contraception. Reduces blood loss during menstruation. Relieves period pain. Easy to take. Does not interrupt the act of sexual intercourse.	Carries risks such as thrombosis and high blood-pressure. Not suitable for women who smoke heavily due to this.
Mini pill	Does not interrupt the act of sexual intercourse. Can be used whilst breast feeding	Must take at very regular intervals to be reliable. Periods can be irregular
Condom	Suitable for anyone, including those having unplanned or irregular sex. Helps protect individual from contracting sexually transmitted diseases. Protects from the HIV virus	Interrupts the sexual act as it must be put on. Relies on an individual carrying one. Can dull the sensation for the male. Some people find them embarrassing to buy. Can be expensive
IUD	Does not interfere with the sexual act	Can cause heavy, irregular and painful periods. Can cause fertilisation of the egg in the fallopian tubes
Cap	Correct size needed for greatest reliability	
Injectable methods	Very reliable. Do not have to think about taking them	Menstrual cycle may be disturbed
Spermicide		Not very reliable if used alone
Withdrawal method	Does not require anything to use it	Not very reliable. Can be frustrating for the couple
Rhythm method	May suit those who, for religious reasons, do not believe in contraceptives, e.g. some Catholic Christians	Not very reliable
Sterilisation	Very reliable. Suitable for couples who know they do not want any more children	Considered irreversible; so little opportunity to change your mind although reversal operations are possible

contracting or passing on an STD. Sometimes, an infection can lay dormant in one of the partners and then reactivate itself to infect the carrier and their partner.

It is therefore important to know how to minimise the risks of infection. Barrier methods of contraception as described earlier, particularly the condom, are effective ways of minimising the risk of contracting STDs.

There are many different types of sexually transmitted diseases. They are often caused by bacteria or viruses which are explained in Chapter 3. The table opposite gives a summary of different STDs – their causes, symptoms and treatment.

HIV and AIDS

One of the most publicised sexually transmitted diseases of recent years is infection by HIV – Human Immuno deficiency Virus. This virus attacks and damages the body's defence mechanisms, preventing it from effectively fighting certain infections or illnesses. It lives in body fluids – blood, semen and vaginal secretions particularly.

AIDS – Acquired Immune Deficiency Syndrome is the end stage of a chronic infection by HIV. (A syndrome is a collection of illnesses.) An individual cannot 'catch' AIDS, only HIV. AIDS is said to be present if an HIV positive individual (i.e. after laboratory tests, an individual found to have HIV antibodies in the bloodstream) develops a particular infection or specific cancer with no apparent cause. AIDS first appeared in the 1970s but was not recognised until 1981. There is no cure for HIV or AIDS yet. The virus attacks and destroys certain types of white blood cells known as lymphocytes (T-helper cells). It enters an uninfected individual through a break in the skin or pink lining tissue (mucosa).

Mode of transmission

Although the virus is known to occur in saliva, tears, breast milk and urine, the 'normal' routes by which it spreads are via blood, genital tract secretions or

STD	Cause	Symptoms	Treatment
Gonorrhoea	Bacteria which live in warm moist internal linings of the body	– discharge from vagina or penis – irritation or discharge from anus – pain in lower abdomen in women – pain on passing urine	antibiotics
Thrush	Yeast called 'Candida albicans'	– thick white discharge from vagina – itching around genitals – soreness and pain on passing urine	pessaries and/or cream
Genital warts	Virus	warts of varying sizes around genitals	ointment
Genital herpes	Herpes simplex virus	– small painful blisters in genital region – tingling or itching in genital area – flu-like symptoms (headache, backache) – pain or tingling on passing urine	
Pubic lice	Small lice living in pubic hair	itching and small eggs on pubic hair	special lotion
Hepatitis B	Virus in blood and bodily fluids, resulting in liver inflammation	Two stages: 1 Two to six months after contact with infection: flu-like symptoms including sore throat and cough. Feeling of fatigue, loss of appetite and joint pain. 2 Jaundice stage: skin and eyes take on yellowish tinge. Stools become grey and urine brown. Abdomen is sore	Bed rest and healthy food. Vaccinations are available for people in certain risk situations

from mother to baby via the placenta. Main ways of spreading are therefore:

1 Sexual transmission – because semen and vaginal fluid carry the virus. The greatest risks are male homosexual and heterosexual anal and vaginal intercourse, especially if there are ulcerations or erosions present. According to the World Health Organisation, nearly half of all newly infected adults are women. Anyone can contract HIV from unsafe sex (intercourse without the protection against sexual fluids of a partner).

2 From mother to foetus before birth, at delivery or soon after through breast feeding. At present 20 per cent of babies born to infected mothers will have the virus. As more women become infected so will the number of babies born with HIV rise.

3 By the sharing of equipment between injecting drug users – particularly syringes and needles. This is because they might receive contaminated blood or blood products from the equipment. The government, through the 'Health of the Nation' document (1993) has set targets for reducing the numbers of drug users who report sharing injecting equipment within the previous few weeks by at least 50 per cent by 1997 and by at least a further 50 per cent by the year 2000. This would give a maximum of 5 per cent of drug users who practise this habit.

In the UK blood and blood products have been screened for HIV since October 1985, so both receiving and donating blood in this country are safe. All equipment for this purpose is sterilised.

Most developed countries in the world share these safe practices but this may not apply to all countries. [Advice can be obtained from the Medical Advisory Service for Travellers Abroad 071-631-4408.]

In the early years of the disease, many haemophiliacs contracted HIV and AIDS because their blood transfusions were not screened for the virus as they are now.

The virus is fragile and cannot live outside the body for long. It is also inactivated by disinfectants such as alcohol, bleach, peroxide etc. This means that the virus cannot be passed on by:

- eating food prepared by an HIV infected individual
- being in the same room as or by coughs and sneezes from an infected person
- swimming in the same water
- mosquito or other insect bites
- casual contact such as touching, kissing, hugging
- using the same cutlery or crockery as an infected individual
- giving first aid treatment providing safe hygienic practices are carried out e.g. disposable gloves, disinfecting body fluids etc.

How do HIV and AIDS affect the body?

Many people infected with HIV are not aware they have the virus and carry on a normal working life, feeling healthy and well.

There is no evidence that rest, exercise or sensible nutrition stops transmission or progression of the infection.

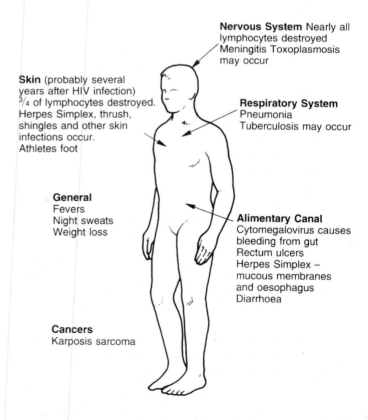

Nervous System Nearly all lymphocytes destroyed Meningitis Toxoplasmosis may occur

Skin (probably several years after HIV infection) ³/₄ of lymphocytes destroyed. Herpes Simplex, thrush, shingles and other skin infections occur. Athletes foot

Respiratory System Pneumonia Tuberculosis may occur

General Fevers Night sweats Weight loss

Alimentary Canal Cytomegalovirus causes bleeding from gut Rectum ulcers Herpes Simplex – mucous membranes and oesophagus Diarrhoea

Cancers Karposis sarcoma

Figure 5.6 *AIDS-related illnesses and approximate times of onset*

One of the longest studies so far carried out suggests that about half the number of HIV positive individuals will develop AIDS within 10 years, and eventually 99 per cent will contract it. How long it takes to develop depends on the individual. When AIDS develops, some people die, but others can stay well for a long time if they have good care. Even if an individual becomes seriously ill they can often be nursed back to better health for a while. After several years during which the virus gradually destroys the lymphocytes, the body's defence system is unable to cope with certain infections and these are responsible for 90 per cent of the deaths from AIDS.

Strategies for control

At present time there is no current treatment or vaccination to prevent HIV infection but the disease could be controlled by behavioural changes.

1 Screening of blood – already implemented:
   a high risk individuals excluded from blood donations
   b blood donors screened for antibodies against HIV
   c manufacturing processes for blood products incorporate heat treatment to inactivate HIV.
2 Education programmes in schools, colleges and for the general public have raised awareness about the need for changing behaviour in homosexual, and heterosexual males and females and intravenous drug users.
3 Safer sex recommendations include:
   a limiting the number of sexual partners
   b use of (kitemarked/British Standard) condoms to create barrier between body fluids
   c encouraging non-penetrative sexual acts between partners such as kissing, touching etc.
4 Providing support and counselling to intravenous drug abusers to end practice but to take advantage of syringe exchange schemes if they persist.
5 Treatment of other sexually transmitted diseases.
6 Safe hygienic practices associated with any procedures involving body fluids.

Government has set up a programme of anonymous surveys to seek up to date information on HIV and AIDS.

Figures apply up to March 1992 in England	HIV infection	AIDS
Number of reported cases	15 133	5 366
Number of deaths		3 336

Location of surveys	Incidence rate
Antenatal clinics (London)	1 in 500 infected
Genito-urinary medical clinics for: • Homosexual and bisexually orientated males	1 in 5 infected
• Heterosexually orientated males and females	1 in 100 infected

Important points to note about the above tables are:

1 The figures give *reported* cases and many people are unaware that they are infected with HIV virus.
   a Blood tests for HIV antibodies are unreliable until at least three months after the date of infection. The body takes a few months to produce antibodies for HIV.
   The actual figures will be very much higher.
2 Experts agree that new HIV infection and AIDS cases among gay men will probably peak in 1993 or 1994. This is providing safe sex behaviour continues to be practised. There is some concern that this may not be the case with the younger generation of gay men.
3 Each year until 1997, nearly a hundred HIV positive haemophiliac cases will develop AIDS.
4 Heterosexual cases of HIV are steadily increasing – this is the fastest growing section of the community. Around 25 per cent of current HIV infections arise from heterosexual contact:
   a 73 per cent from exposure overseas
   b 13 per cent from high risk partners.
   Now the virus is in the heterosexual community the infection will accelerate. About 7 000 men and women in Britain have become infected by HIV through heterosexual intercourse (excluding drug users). It is thought by some researchers that as many as 80 per cent of the infected heterosexuals have no idea that they may carry the virus.

If you think you may have contracted the virus, it can take at least three months or longer to be sure because the blood has to be checked for HIV-antibodies. The body can take a few months to produce these.

Therefore people who contract HIV and AIDS and their families need a lot of support. Carers need to understand fully the nature of AIDS to be able to do this effectively.

To protect yourself from the risk of HIV and AIDS you should:

- always practise safer sex
- limit the number of sexual partners you have
- always use disposable gloves when dealing with any body fluids
- always use disposable gloves when dealing with other people's wounds, no matter how small
- wipe surfaces with a disinfectant immediately after dealing with any body fluids or blood.

Think it over

What precautions should be taken by staff who work in care homes in order to protect themselves from hepatitis and HIV?

· SUBSTANCE ABUSE ·

Substance abuse is a broad term used to cover **alcohol**, **drugs** (including smoking) and **solvent abuse**. All three have socially acceptable uses. *Abuse* involves using substances in a way which is not socially acceptable and which can present a risk to health. Sometimes individuals make a conscious choice to take risks; sometimes people put themselves at risk because they are not fully aware of the consequences for their health. In this section, the risks related to alcohol, smoking, drugs and solvent abuse are explored.

Alcohol

Alcohol is very much a socially accepted drug in Britain. It is an important part of many celebrations and festivities, such as weddings, Christmas, good news or a success. Alcohol is, however, a chemical substance and a drug – although it is not often seen in this way.

Some medical evidence seems to suggest that drinking alcohol in moderation may have a beneficial effect on health. It is suggested that red wine can help to reduce cholesterol in the blood, and cholesterol may be associated with heart attacks.

It is suggested that individuals do not exceed the recommended weekly intakes of alcohol which are a maximum of 14 units for women and 21 units for men. A unit is roughly equivalent to one glass of wine, one measure of spirit or half a pint of lager or beer. A person who frequently exceeds these recommendations is thought to be placing their physical and mental health at risk.

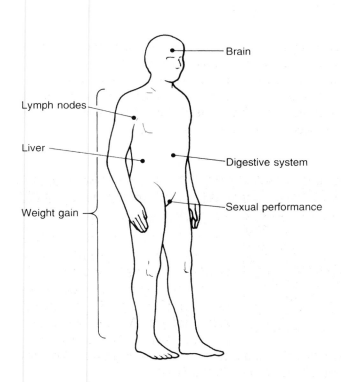

Figure 5.7 *Where alcohol may attack the body*

The initial effect of drinking alcohol can be to make you feel happy. However, alcohol affects the speed with which the brain can make judgements. This might cause individuals to misjudge situations and distances when driving which could lead to accidents. This is why even a moderate intake of alcohol is connected with so many road accidents where people 'drink and drive'. If *excess alcohol* is consumed by women in early pregnancy it can damage the development of the foetus, causing permanent harm to the baby. Excess alcohol is responsible for many lost working days due to sickness following a 'heavy session'.

Why do people drink?

Drinking often starts during socialisation. Drinking may be linked with eating and celebrations, and having an enjoyable time. Children have often experienced their first alcoholic drink long before the age of 16 (Portman group leaflet). Sometimes *peer pressure* plays an important role in the amount of alcohol consumed – whatever age you are. In some social contexts people can be ridiculed if they refuse a drink and feel uncomfortable doing so.

Some people also drink as a way to reduce stress or anxiety, or to forget any worries they may have. However, alcohol, in this context, works as a tranquilliser: it does not do anything to help the situation which has caused the drinking (and which may become worse because of it).

Task

Choose a client group and design a questionnaire or survey to find out their perception of alcohol and its place in society. Assess their understanding of the health risks associated with drinking. Collate your findings. What conclusions can you draw? Compare your results with those of another client group. How are they similar or do they differ?

Smoking

Smoking is another habit which has been part of western society for many years. It is the only retail product which when used as the manufacturer recommends – even in moderation – kills the consumer. It is the most significant cause of preventable disease and early death in Britain today. Approximately 111,000 people die each year because of smoking-related causes: 26,000 from lung cancer and the rest from other diseases caused by tobacco (Health Education Authority, 1991). Figures have shown that around 29 per cent of women and 31 per cent of men smoke; and that approximately 25 per cent of children smoke regularly by the age of 15, despite the widely publicised relationship between smoking and health risks (Health Education Authority, 1991). It is believed that some smokers, whilst aware of the risks, take the attitude 'It won't happen to me'.

The acceptability of smoking, has, it could be suggested, declined in recent years. There has been an increase in the number of smoke-free areas, especially in public places, as a response to raised awareness of the dangers of passive smoking. Increasingly, non-smokers are refusing to accept a cigarette-polluted atmosphere.

The adverse effects of smoking

Cigarettes contain harmful substances such as tar, nicotine and carbon monoxide – as can be seen in the diagram below.

Nicotine is the part of the cigarette that creates dependence on smoking. It is absorbed into the

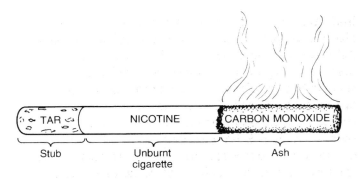

Figure 5.8   What a cigarette contains

bloodstream and has numerous effects on the body including increasing the heart-rate, blood-pressure and hormone production. This explains why smokers are more at risk from heart attacks. If smokers have narrowing of the arteries, an increase in heart-rate and blood-pressure, this may increase the chances of heart attacks. Nicotine is also thought to thicken the blood and is therefore connected to an increased possibility of blood clots forming in the arteries, ultimately this could result in amputation of limbs.

Carbon monoxide is the poisonous gas found in cigarette smoke. It readily combines with *haemoglobin*, the part of the blood which carries oxygen, thus reducing the blood's oxygen-carrying capacity. As oxygen is essential for the functioning of tissues and organs in the body, a reduction in supply can affect growth, repair and nutrient absorption. The body tries to compensate for this by producing more haemoglobin, in order to increase oxygen-carrying capacity, but this increases the risk of blood clots or *thrombosis* – which ultimately could lead to limb amputation. It is also believed that carbon monoxide is connected to *atherosclerosis*, the depositing of fatty substances on artery walls. This contributes to a narrowing of the arteries, which in turn is connected with coronary diseases.

About 70 per cent of **tar** from cigarettes is deposited in the lungs. It is this tar which is particularly related to cancer: 81 per cent of people who died from lung cancer were smokers in 1991. Tar is also known to cause a narrowing of the bronchioles (small tubes in the lungs), along with increased coughing and bronchiole mucus. Tar damage affects the small hairs which line the lungs and help protect the lungs against dirt and infection. In this way the smoker can become more susceptible to chest infections, including *bronchitis* (an inflammation of the mucus membranes) and *emphysema* (emphysema involves the destruction of the walls of the air sacs in the lungs, reducing the surface area for gaseous exchange – see Chapter 3 – and consequently the ability to breathe).

Smoking in pregnancy causes additional adverse effects. The reduction in the ability of the blood to carry oxygen has an effect on the amount of oxygen which is able to cross the placenta to the foetus.

Therefore, smokers often give birth to smaller, lighter babies, who are weaker and more prone to infections. There is also an increased risk of miscarriage or spontaneous abortion as well as perinatal mortality (death around time of birth). The risk of illness is increased if parents or carers continue to smoke around the baby after birth. The child is effectively a passive smoker who, unlike many adults, has no choice over the matter.

Passive smoking occurs where a non-smoker breathes in the cigarette smoke of others: either in the form of the smoke the smoker has already exhaled (*mainstream smoke*) or the smoke from the tip of the cigarette (*sidestream smoke*). Passively smoking smoke from the tip of the cigarette is often worse than smoking itself as the smoke is not being filtered in any way. Recent research has shown that there is a 10 to 30 per cent increased risk of lung cancer in non-smokers as a result of passive smoking (Health Education Authority, 1991). However, despite these figures, the government appears reluctant to legislate to prevent passive smoking and prefers that smoking is reduced through a voluntary approach. The view taken is that legislation may only be considered if voluntary pressure does not work (Brown and Goodwin, 1994).

If employers fail to provide a safe working environment, they can be prosecuted by employees who believe that their health has suffered as a result. With a compensation case successfully being brought against employers by employees who have become ill due to passive smoking in the workplace, many employers will now be under strong pressure to ban smoking. (Clement and Hall, 1994)

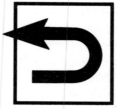

Think it over

Should smokers be allowed to smoke in public places and work situations? Whose responsibility is it to provide us all with a healthy environment?

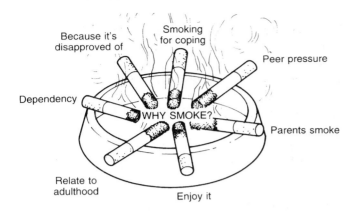

Figure 5.9 *Why smoke?*

Reducing the risks of smoking

Risk-reduction should be considered for both the smoker and the non-smoker.

1 Give up smoking completely. After giving up smoking, an ex-smoker's risk of getting lung cancer falls to being only slightly greater than that of a non-smoker after 15 years.
2 Smoke lower tar cigarettes. But it should be remembered that just because a cigarette is low in tar, it does not automatically follow that it is low in other substances such as carbon monoxide or nicotine.
3 Try using nicotine substitutes, such as the nicotine patch, to help lose the dependency on nicotine. (These substitutes can be expensive as they are not currently available on the National Health Service.)
4 Try smoking only in certain places, as this will cut down the opportunity to smoke and, therefore, the amount smoked.
5 Cut down the amount smoked generally.
6 Increase your intake of vitamin C through fresh fruit and vegetables, and fruit juices, as this is believed to help the body get rid of nicotine.

Think it over

How could society in general help to cut down risks from smoking? Should there be policies on smoking in public places?

Generally, society could also contribute to reducing risks from tobacco by:

- having policies that ban smoking in *all* enclosed public places and public transport, unless separate ventilated areas can be provided for smokers
- banning advertising of tobacco in any form, including promotional advertising such as at motor races.
- tougher monitoring and prosecution of those who sell tobacco to the under-16 age-group
- offering more practical advice and support through the NHS to those who wish to give up
- developing a high profile health education programme, particularly ensuring that all education centres deliver health education programmes appropriate to their clients
- using media such as TV, radio and magazines to put over the message that it is every adult's responsibility to protect children from breathing in smoke, and to dissuade children from smoking.

Task

Choose a client group and develop a plan to help them stop smoking. Include in the package a way to promote the message that smoking is not healthy. Ensure that your plan promotes accurate evidence on the effects of smoking whilst acknowledging individual rights and choice.

Other drugs

As we have seen, both alcohol and nicotine are drugs – but socially acceptable ones if used within limits. Other drugs, such as those included under the heading of substance abuse, are less acceptable. These may be found in cases of **drug abuse**, i.e. where they are not socially acceptable; or in cases of **drug misuse**, where a drug is socially acceptable (for example, used for medicine like tranquillisers), but is used in a socially unacceptable way.

Figure 5.10 *Drugs and drug equipment. (Health at Work Photo Library.)*

The prolonged use of any drug is dangerous to health. But the level of risk varies according to the way the drug is taken; for example, injecting a drug into the bloodstream is more dangerous than smoking a drug. It should also be understood that different people vary in their reactions to the same drug, depending on factors such as their body size, state of health, tolerance of the body to the drug and so on. This is why the same 'dose' of one drug can kill one person and not another. For analysis of some common drugs see table on the following page.

Why take drugs?

There are many reasons why people might take drugs:

- dependence – both mind and body can become dependent on drugs.
- escapism – some people see drugs as a temporary way to escape difficulties in life, such as personal problems, financial worries or work-related dilemmas.
- boredom – drugs can be seen as a way to escape boredom.
- lack of confidence – some people who are shy and lack self-confidence may find that drugs can help them overcome their inhibitions.

- image – drugs are seen by some people as being daring and exciting, partly due to the associated risks.
- peer pressure – there may be pressure from friends to try drugs.
- opportunity – some people just take drugs because they are available.

Reducing the risk from drugs

The only way to reduce the risk from drugs is not to take them at all. However, the way this message is put across is crucial: straight education, merely providing the facts does not always work.

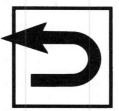

Think it over

Why do you think that simply informing people about the dangers of drugs does not always succeed in preventing them from trying drugs?

When talking to people about drugs, the following points are recommended (Boice and Gamble). It is important to keep an open mind and:

1 to be sure you are clear about the facts concerning drugs and their use.
2 develop good communication with the group/individual concerned. They need to value your opinion in order to take it on board.
3 try not to act hastily but consider how to approach problems. Acting on the spur of the moment without fully thinking through the consequences of an action may well have an adverse affect.
4 develop positive values in other things. Encourage a strong self-image in the group/individual so they do not feel they have to use drugs to prove themselves and they are able to resist peer pressure.

Solvents

Solvents are often classified in the same grouping as drugs. The term *solvents* covers a range of products,

Type of drug	Form	Use	Effects	Health risks
Cannabis (pot/hash)	Resin in form of solid brown mass	Smoked – usually crumbled and mixed with tobacco	• Relaxation & talkativeness • Appear 'high' or drunk • Possible hallucinations • Unable to function logically. Heavy doses – distorted judgements of space, slow reactions, drowsiness and poor concentration	• Psychological dependency for enjoyment/coping with life • Bronchitis, lung cancer • Heart disorders • Might lead to use of stronger drugs within some social contexts
Ecstasy ('E')	Tablet or capsule – white, brown, pink or yellow	Swallowed – effects begin in 20 minutes	• Calmness with raised awareness of colour and sound • Loss of coordination • High doses result in anxiety and confusion	• Prolonged use can reduce sleep • Those with high blood-pressure, heart conditions, epilepsy or mental illness at risk due to stimulant effects • Possible death
Amphetamines and cocaine (coke) (*stimulants*)	White powder	Usually sniffed, but can be injected	• Stimulates nervous system which can result in over-excitedness and sleeplessness. Also linked to aggressiveness • Breathing and heart-rate increases, pupils dilate • Feel alert, energetic, cheerful and confident • Reduces tiredness for a time • Reduces appetite	• Poor sleep, loss of appetite, bodily itching leading to scratching and anxiety • Lower resistance to disease • Damaged blood vessels and heart failure • Damage to nose membranes • Depression and suicidal tendencies
LSD ('acid') (*hallucinogens*)	Impregnated into small sheets, like blotting paper	Dissolved on tongue	• Affects perception – can be visions of joy and beauty or nightmares • Confusion and disorientation. Distorts colour, space and time • Gives user unrealistic perceptions of their ability, (e.g. think they can fly)	• Accidents due to confusion and perceptions of reality • Can be a damaging experience to those with mental illness
Heroin	White or brown powder	Sniffed, smoked or injected	• First alertness, then drowsiness. Detached feeling of relaxation • Overdose results in unconsciousness and death.	• Dependency on heroin. • Poor health due to inadequate diet • Risk of AIDS if needles are shared
Magic mushrooms	A range of fungi	Tablets	Toxic effects, hallucinations, sleep disturbances and nervousness	• Injury/death due to accidents whilst confused

Analysis of some common drugs

including household products which give off gases or fumes such as glue, lighter fluid, aerosol sprays, petrol and correction fluid.

Solvents are either sniffed through the nose and mouth, usually from bags (*huffing*), or sprayed directly into the mouth. Some solvents, such as thinner, may be sniffed from a cloth or coat sleeve in a similar way to how nasal decongestant is used for a cold. Because solvents are portable, sniffing can occur anywhere but often people go to remote or isolated places to abuse solvents.

What are the effects of abusing solvents?

The effects of glue sniffing are very similar to the effects of alcohol but the 'drunkenness' occurs more quickly. This is because the vapour is inhaled into the bloodstream through the lungs and not through the stomach, which delays the effect (depending on what else is present). As the vapour is inhaled through the lungs, the effects also wear off quickly and so a sniffer has to keep sniffing to maintain the effects. People who sniff may also experience hallucinations; unconsciousness is also possible.

What are the risks from abusing solvents

Possibly the greatest risk from solvent abuse is from what happens when the person who sniffs is 'intoxicated'. The substance abuser may not be realistic or 'aware' and may take risks they would not take under normal circumstances. In the same way abusers may be unable to react to danger. Accidents as a result of this represent risk.

Sniffing solvents also has an effect on the heart and any physical exertion or fright following sniffing can result in death. If the solvent is sprayed directly into the mouth, this has been shown to cause a swelling of the throat tissues which can result in suffocation. It has also been shown that people who sniff can die from choking on their own vomit. As they often go to isolated places to sniff solvents, there is not always someone around who can help them in this situation.

Most of these risks are immediate and are directly connected to the sniffing of the solvent or the short-term intoxicating effect.

Why do people sniff solvents?

Solvent abuse is portrayed as a young person's habit. However, only about one in ten secondary pupils try sniffing and many do not keep the habit for very long (Ives, 1992). As with the other 'drugs', people partake for various reasons, including the following:

- as an alternative to other drugs
- because solvents are cheap and easily available. Although the law makes it an offence (under the Substance Supply Act 1985) to sell a young person under 18 a substance if they believe it will be used 'to achieve intoxication', this is very difficult to prove, and consequently there have been few prosecutions under this Act
- it can be exciting; and some people like the hallucinations that go with it
- because it might shock those seen as authority figures, such as parents and teachers
- because they enjoy it
- to avoid or blot out problems.

· RISKS TO PERSONAL SAFETY ·

Electrical safety

Electricity is a utility used by everyone and is therefore, perhaps, not considered as a risk to personal safety. However, it is often overlooked as a significant cause of fire in the home. Figures from the Home Office (1991) state that approximately 28,000 domestic fires each year are caused by electrical faults, accidents or misuse of electrical equipment, and over 2,500 people are killed in these fires.

The electric source comes into a building through the meter. The home has a wiring circuit which then takes the electricity to various points in the building. The wiring should be checked regularly to ensure it is safe. Signs of dangerous wiring include:

- hot plugs, sockets and switches
- fuses blowing for no reason
- lights flickering
- scorch marks on sockets and plugs.

The contact between the electrical current and the applicance is made by the plug. It is essential that a plug is wired correctly; all flexes are colour-coded to help.

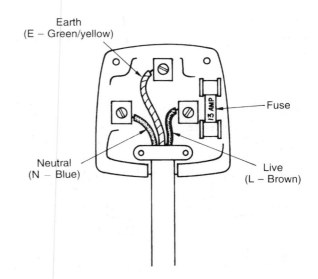

Figure 5.11 *A plug and fuse*

It is also essential that the correct fuse is fitted as this could prevent a fire: if there is a surge of electricity, the fuse melts and breaks the circuit. An RCD (Residual Current Device) can also be used with electrical equipment. This will detect incorrect functioning in electrical cables or other faults in the system and will cut off the current in a millisecond, thus giving added protection against electrocution and electrical fires.

When purchasing a plug, it is always best to buy the three-pinned plug which conforms to British Standards. This carries the BS kitemark – the sign that it has been checked for safety.

When buying electrical equipment, always look for the BEAB Mark of Safety. This means the appliance has been checked by the British Electrotechnical Approvals Board. Some electrical equipment is now being sold with moulded plugs already attached and, unless absolutely necessary, these should not be removed.

Some types of electrical equipment are designed to be left on all of the time; others should be switched off at the mains and unplugged after use. Always check the manufacturer's instructions if unsure. Plugs should always be removed carefully and not by pulling the flex.

Sockets should not be overloaded with plugs/adaptors. If using an adaptor, ensure the correct fuse is used.

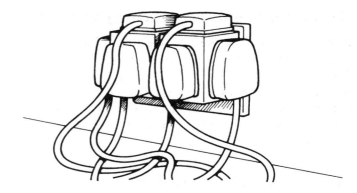

Figure 5.13 *Overloaded plug socket*

Electric shock

Electric shocks can occur on different levels. A minor electric shock may make you jump but not do any real damage. More severe electric shocks may cause burns, where the current enters and leaves the body; shocks can also cause muscle spasms. The electric current may affect the rhythm of the heart and possibly make it stop. It can also affect the brain and the way it controls the body's breathing. **Electricity can kill**.

If you suspect someone has had an electric shock, *do not touch them* unless you are sure that the current

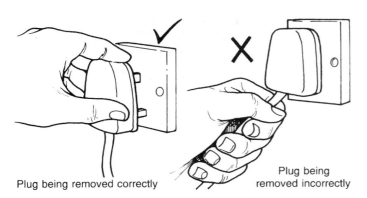

Plug being removed correctly

Plug being removed incorrectly

Figure 5.12 *Removing a plug from the wall*

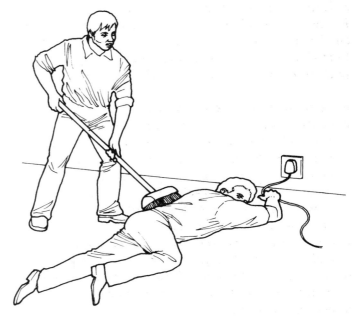

Figure 5.14 *Moving an electric shock victim*

has been switched off – as the current can pass to you and you then become part of the accident. If the electricity cannot be turned off, you could use a **non-metal** item, such as a wooden broom handle, chair or walking stick, to push or pull them away from the electrical source.

Once the casualty is free of the electrical source, treat as for severe bleeding or shock as necessary (see below). Call an ambulance if the accident appears serious or if you are in any doubt.

Shock

This is a serious condition caused by the body tissues and organs not getting their normal supply of oxygen. It is often described as 'circulatory collapse'. Causes of shock include burns and bleeding, which can both result from an electric shock, and it can lead to death.

Stages of shock

The different stages of shock – including symptoms and signs – are as outlined in Figure 5.15.

Care procedure for shock

1 Get help quickly but keep calm. Do not alarm the patient as anxiety will deepen the shock.

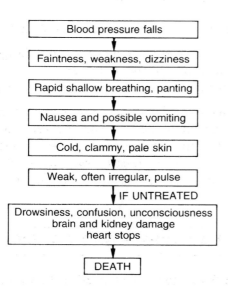

Figure 5.15 *Stages and symptoms of shock*

2 Take action to stop any bleeding – see below.
3 Lie the casualty on a coat or blanket with the head lower than the trunk and the feet raised. This helps raise the blood pressure slightly and encourages blood drainage to the vital organs. It means the heart has less work to do. (Do not use a pillow.)
4 Loosen any tight clothing, especially around the neck, chest and waist which may restrict breathing and blood circulation.
5 Do not give anything to eat or drink in case an anaesthetic is needed. If the casualty is thirsty, moisten the lips only.
6 Keep the casualty warm with blankets or coats. But do *not* overheat as this can cause the blood to be diverted away from the brain, heart and lungs, or cause more fluid loss due to sweating.
7 Check and record vital signs every 10 minutes.
8 If consciousness is lost, place casualty in the *recovery position*.
9 If breathing stops, begin resuscitation immediately and continue until medical help arrives.

Think it over

What is the recovery position?

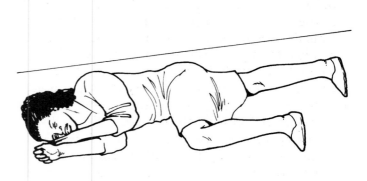

Figure 5.16 *The recovery position*

Care procedure for bleeding

If the casualty shows signs of bleeding as a result of the accident you should always call for an

---

THE RECOVERY POSITION

Experts agree that if more people knew how to put an unconscious person in the correct position, many lives would be saved.

There is really no subsitute for a trained person demonstrating the technique to you, who then watches you practise several times. You should try to do this with all first aid procedures, so if necessary join a local first aid class. Your local library will be able to tell you where.

The **recovery position** is a steady position which keeps the airway open, allows fluid (particularly vomit) to drain out of the mouth so that it does not enter the lungs. It also prevents the tongue from falling back and blocking the back of the throat.

Putting a casualty in the recovery position

The procedure is the same for a woman or a man

1. Open the airway.
2. Kneel alongside the casualty and straighten her legs.
3. Place the arm nearest to you at right angles to her body with the elbow bent and the palm facing skyward. (Some people like to tuck the nearest arm under the casualty's bottom.)
4. Take the other arm across her chest and tuck this hand palm downwards under her cheek to cushion her head. You will probably need to hold it there.
5. Cross the further ankle over the nearer one.
6. Grasping her hip, waistband and shoulder, turn her smoothly over to rest against your knees. Support her head as she rolls.
7. Adjust her head to lie on the hand so that it remains tilted backwards and the other bent arm gives stability (if you tucked the arm under the bottom, pull behind now to stop her rolling backwards – the two positions of the lower arm are equally acceptable, but slightly different).
8. Adjust the upper leg so that both hip and then knee are bent at right angles.

REMEMBER: IT IS BEST NOT TO LEAVE THE CASUALTY ALONE. IF YOU HAVE TO GO AND GET HELP, THEN RETURN AS SOON AS POSSIBLE.

---

ambulance unless the wound is very minor. Whilst waiting for help you may also:

1 *Raise* the bleeding part above the level of the casualty's heart if possible.

2 Apply direct *pressure* to the wound for long enough to allow the body's own system for closing off wounds to operate (about 10 to 15 minutes). If a wound is large, it may be necessary to hold the wound edges together with both hands. If it is not possible to apply direct pressure because of the wound, then apply indirect pressure at the nearest pressure point – where the artery crosses a bone.

3 After 10 to 15 minutes, you should remove the pressure and observe the wound. If the wound has stopped bleeding, you may dress it lightly. Watch the dressing and, if blood continues to seep through, apply further dressings on top. Do not try to remove the old dressing as this may disturb any clot that is forming.

With internal bleeding, the symptoms of shock appear and blood may flow from a body orifice, such as the mouth. Treat for shock and wait for the ambulance.

Safe equipment

Besides ensuring that the electricity supply is safe and that the plug is wired correctly, equipment also needs to be checked regularly to ensure it is safe for use and not a safety hazard. Many tasks in the home and workplace involve the use of equipment which can make jobs both easier and quicker. Such equipment includes machines, tools and plant.

The Provision and Use of Work Equipment Regulations were introduced in1992 to ensure that working equipment is safe and used properly to minimise risks (Institute of Environmental Health Officers, 1993). Employers have a duty to provide and maintain suitable and safe equipment. Employers also have to ensure that anyone using the equipment has been appropriately trained. There are five main types of danger from machines as can be seen from Figure 5.17.

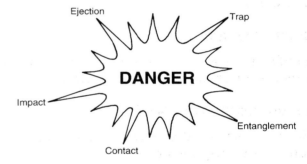

Figure 5.17 *Danger from machinery*

Safer use of equipment can be ensured through:

- safer design to remove any potential dangers
- safe positioning in the workplace
- appropriate guards to cover dangerous parts

Many workplaces have their equipment checked regularly, usually once per year. However, a piece of equipment is only as safe as the person using it. Figure 5.18 overleaf, suggests ways in which the individual can aim to increase safety at work.

· HAZARDOUS SUBSTANCES ·

The term 'hazardous substances' includes a range of substances, from those which are very *toxic* to those

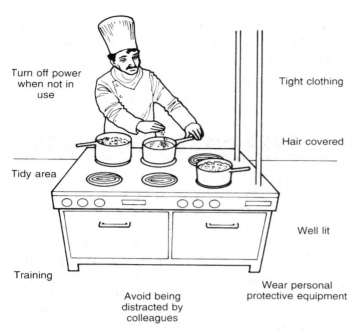

Figure 5.18 *Ways to improve safety when using equipment*

which are irritants. They can be liquids, powders, solids, dusts or gases. They cause damage in a number of ways.

COSHH regulations

COSHH stands for the 'Control Of Substances Hazardous to Health'. The COSHH regulations require employers to complete a risk assessment of all hazardous substances used in the workplace. This must be recorded for inspection if necessary (Institute of Environmental Health Officers, 1993). In a care establishment this will range from the correction fluid used in the administration department to the disinfectant used for cleaning and sterilisation. Steps must then be taken to protect employees exposed to the substance through risk assessment.

Hazard = anything with the potential to cause harm.
Risk = how likely it is that the hazard will cause harm.

The stages of **risk assessment** are as follows:

1. Identify any hazardous substance that is used in the workplace.
2. Identify who is at risk by assessing who uses or comes into contact with the substance.
3. Evaluate the risk by assessing how it might cause damage to health. Potential accidents should be assessed in terms of how likely they are to happen and how serious they might be.
4. Decide on a control measure. This might entail changing the substance for another which does the same job but is less hazardous, if that is possible, or introducing strict controls for use.
5. The assessment must be *recorded*.
6. The assessment should be *reviewed* regularly and, additionally, every time there is a change in the circumstances such as new staff or equipment.

All employees must be informed of any substance which may be hazardous to their health and receive appropriate training in their usage. Some substances may be hazardous but the risk that a hazard may occur may be small on assessment; therefore the establishment may be prepared to take the risk with guidelines.

Theory into practice

Think of a situation in a care setting which may present a hazard. Design a flow chart to show the stages of risk assessment which the establishment should go through.

There are various common signs which inform the users of hazardous substances how they might present a danger to health. See Figure 5.19.

Health and Safety at Work Act 1974

This act brought together a range of legislation covering health and safety since the first act was introduced in 1802. It covers almost everyone in a work situation, except the armed forces and domestic employment. Although the act emphasises how important it is that everyone plays a part in health

Figure 5.19 *Signs of hazardous substances (Reproduced by kind permission of the Royal Society for the Prevention of Accidents)*

- serve a *prohibition notice*, which immediately stops the unsafe piece of equipment/practice being used until it is made safe.

Employers can be prosecuted under the Health and Safety at Work Act and may be fined or imprisoned.

Task

Choose an appropriate group and produce a resource pack which could be given to them which identifies the different risks to health, their potential effects on health and how the risks could be minimized. Justify your choice of information, and the approach you have chosen to use, in the light of the needs and level of advice required for your target audience.

and safety, it places most of the responsibility on the employer – including the provision of somebody with responsibility for health and safety.

The HaSaW Act is enforced by two main bodies:

a **Environmental Health Officers** dealing with health and safety in smaller areas such as nursing homes, shops, restaurants etc.
b **Health and Safety Executive** whose inspectors deal with health and safety in other settings such as factories, hospitals, etc.

Representatives from these two bodies are able to enter premises at any reasonable time to carry out an inspection of the workplace and activities. They could take photographs as evidence of what they see, take samples or even remove equipment. They can ask to see documents such as evidence of risk assessments made under COSHH. If unhappy about arrangements they could:

- provide *advice* to help improve safety
- serve an *improvement notice*, which gives a time limit within which any requirement for improving health and safety must be made

· HEALTH PROMOTION PROGRAMMES ·

Having looked at various aspects of health promotion, this chapter will now explore *how to promote* the health messages in the most appropriate way. This not only involves having a clear understanding of the issues involved in the area of health to be promoted, but also being able to decide on the equipment and resources to be used to put the message across. Essentially, all health promotion programmes have similar aims. These include:

- self-empowerment – giving the individual the knowledge and understanding to be able to make an informed choice about something
- change of behaviour/attitude – the aim might be to bring about change in some way
- providing knowledge – increasing the understanding of a group on a topic
- raising awareness – this might not involve a behaviour change as such, but attempt to increase someone's perception of a topic. An example of this would be AIDS education, where health professionals aim to inform people who are working in situations where they may be

potentially at risk from contracting the HIV virus how they can protect themselves.

Whatever the intended outcome, however, initially you need to consider the target group (e.g. children, adolescents or adults), as this can affect the approach and level of information provided. It is important to remember that all groups may need to be educated in a particular health area but their stage of development and their needs will vary. Consequently the resources you use will vary. For example, health promotion messages on smoking may vary according to the client group concerned.

Think it over

Choose one of the target groups (children, adolescents or adults) and suggest factors you might consider when planning a health promotion programme for them.
Consider: the level of information; the way the programme might be run; and the materials/ resources used.

The different levels of health promotion might occur in any of the target groups, depending on their age/ stage of development and their level of understanding. In each of the target groups, there will be wide variations on the types and level of information required; but there are several similar aspects which the health promoter needs to address before planning a programme. These will include:

1 Level of understanding of the target audience.
2 What do they already know? What is the starting point?
3 What do they need to know about the topic?
4 What is reasonable to expect them to remember in the time allocated? Remember that the average person remembers about four to five points from any one session.
5 How can you involve the audience in the session? It is believed that people remember more if actively involved. However, you need to be quite confident and well organised to develop audience participation to its fullest.

6 How do you keep the concentration of the audience? This has a direct effect on maximising learning – a lot of talking can turn an audience off, so you need to include a variety of different methods within the presentation.
7 Always ensure the information you are giving is relevant to the topic.
8 Take account of cultural issues, as these can affect choices and can help to ensure you value the cultural identity of individuals in your audience. For example, it would be inappropriate to suggest that Asian women should spend more time sunbathing to increase Vitamin D levels if their culture does not include habits like sunbathing. Therefore other recommendations and possibilities should be thought through.
9 Communication skills – you should speak slowly and clearly. Do not try to pack so much information into the presentation that you lose the interest of the audience.

. PLANNING A HEALTH PROMOTION . PROGRAMME

There are several stages to work through, no matter what sort of programme you intend to develop or the time over which you intend to run the programme. Following these stages will help to order the development of the programme and ensure that all aspects are covered.

The stages are the same for an hour's presentation or a month-long campaign. However, you are likely to need to evaluate progress during a longer programme as well as at the end of it, to ensure you are meeting needs successfully. Adaptions can then be made to the process as seems appropriate in order to ensure that time, money and effort are not wasted.

The planning stages can be set out as a flow diagram, as can be seen on the next page.

Needs

Needs have to be identified. The person to do this might be:

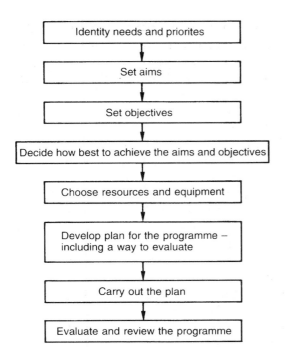

Figure 5.20 *Stages in developing a health promotion programme*

- the health educator, who will decide what they feel the target group might need to know on a subject
- the group/individual who might themselves perceive a need to be informed about a topic and therefore identify what they want or need to know

These needs might be broad, for example, 'more on smoking and health', or more specific, such as, 'the effect smoking has on the lungs'. The needs identified may be so many that it is impossible to cover them all in the time allocated. It might be necessary to *prioritise* against certain criteria, thus producing *needs* and *priorities*. These needs and priorities will naturally flow into *aims*.

Aims

These are broad statements about what you are hoping to achieve from a programme or session. They often begin with a verb, for example:

- To explore the issue of smoking on health.
- To appreciate the role of diet in coronary heart disease.

There may be one or several aims to a programme and this might cover an hour's work or a year's campaign. Aims are broken down into objectives.

Objectives

These develop from the aims and the two are therefore linked together. Objectives are more specific and are often measurable. They may also state *how* you intend to achieve the aim they are connected to. They should be attainable and, if possible, measurable. For example:

- To develop a questionnaire for adolescents to assess their perception of the effects of smoking on health.
- To discover the percentage of people who smoke.
- To carry out food analysis for saturated fat content.
- To devise a list of foods most likely to contribute to coronary heart disease.
- To provide the audience with information on the effect that fat has on the arteries.

Deciding how to achieve the aims and objectives set

You may have decided on some ways to achieve the aims when writing your objectives – e.g. questionnaires – or you may have left it more open, for example, to provide information . . . Now you need to decide how to provide that information, whether through video progammes, leaflets, a lecture, slides and so on.

Think it over

List factors which might affect the resources you choose to use in a programme.

Often there can be a range of ways to achieve the same aim/objective. But the way you choose to go about it may depend on a number of factors such as:

- cost – if money is a problem, you are not likely to buy expensive leaflets to cover a point but may use an overhead projector (OHP).
- time available – if a session lasts an hour, you are not likely to show a 45-minute video as there will be little time left for anything else.
- appropriateness for the target audience – many health promotion topics are appropriate for lots of different audiences, but the way the message is put over varies.
- ease of use.
- familiarity to the health educator – it is very unwise to use material you are not familiar with when presenting a programme to a group. You can end up looking very silly!
- facilities available.
- size of group – for an audience of 50, group work may not be appropriate, whereas it may work very well for smaller numbers.

Theory into practice

Think of one area of health promotion and discuss how the message is adapted – in the way it is presented – to meet the needs of a range of target audiences.

Develop a package of advice, covering the same message for three different target groups.

Resources and equipment for health promotion

Resources and equipment often go hand in hand so it is difficult to divorce one from the other. For example if you wish to show a video on Sexually Transmitted Diseases (*resource*), you will need a video recorder and monitor (*equipment*). When using any resource or equipment, it is important to consider the points which help to ensure a professional approach and avoid mishaps which can throw a presenter off track. So make sure that:

1 the equipment/resource is available before the start of the presentation
2 the equipment/resource is positioned suitably

3 the equipment is working, or that all the parts of the resource are there
4 you know how to work the equipment or use the resource, so you can give a verbal explanation if needed

This may mean that you need to arrive at a venue a little earlier but will ensure a smooth start and a more polished performance.

The table on the following page sets out some of the pros and cons for different resources that can be used in health promotion.

Planning the programme

Once you have identified the resources to use, it is important to plan the programme with estimated timings – especially if you have a designated time to fill. You will not want to find that you have too much material and therefore have to rush through it. This can cause the audience to get confused. If you have too little material you might end up finishing with half an hour left and nothing to do!

Figure 5.21 *Poor planning may lead to time on your hands!*

A presentation should have clear sections: rather like a sandwich with the bread being the introduction and the evaluation and the filling being the middle sections.

Resource	Advantages	Disadvantages
Leaflets	• Audience can use at own pace • Self-teaching • Reduce need to take notes • Easy to produce • Can be free	• Not always read • Cannot check if they are understood • May be biased/used as means of advertising (especially if produced by a company)
Handouts	• Easy to produce • Reduce need to take notes • Can allow audience to recap at own pace later • Can be self-teaching • Could expand points raised in session	• Not always read – could be regarded as producing waste material • Not all will fully understand content and there is no opportunity to clarify • Need to be trialled to ensure that text is appropriate before fuller use
Posters	• Useful for raising awareness • Can attract attention if in prominent place	• Aimed at small audience • Not always read
Videos	• Most suitable for small- to medium-size audiences • Can show reality • Can use as trigger for discussion • Can have a lot of movement which keeps attention • Can be self-teaching	• Must be checked for relevance • Need to ensure it will keep attention • Length of video playing time must be checked
Display	• Can attract attention and raise awareness	• Must be eye-catching to be successful
Games	• Good way to check and confirm knowledge • Probably best used with groups which know each other reasonably well	• Some people do not like games (fear of looking ignorant)
Role-play	• Encourages audience to put themselves in the situation	• Some people may feel self-conscious or threatened • Audience may spend more time thinking about their 'performance' than the topic
Slides	• Easy to use • Can help explain/clarify points	• Lacks movement, which can keep attention • Dark room and screen needed
Overhead Projector transparencies	• Cheap and easy to produce • Illustrates point of talk • Can be used to show main point for audience and as reminder for speaker	• Presentation is important • Too many can be confusing. • Too much information can lead the audience to look at the Overhead Projector rather than concentrate on the talk

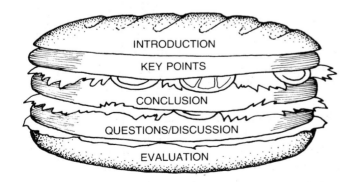

Figure 5.22 *The presentation sandwich*

You should produce a timed action plan for the programme. This could be as detailed as the planning you do for assignments (as discussed in the introductory chapter). This planning will allow you to show how the advice is based on the needs of the audience, and that you have considered which materials/resources you will need. Your main plan might be supported by a more basic plan which is used to ensure you have adequate material to fill the time and as a memory jogger for you. Such a plan may look something like the one on the following page for a session on healthy eating.

Time	Action	Special points
9.00 am	Introduction Outline what aim to cover in session.	
9.05 am	Brief outline of the current dietary goals being produced and background behind them.	Use OHP (Overhead Projector)
9.15 am	Video on health risks connected to not following dietary goals.	Make sure video and TV work
9.30 am	Group work – each group with different goal to suggest how it could be incorporated into the diet	Need large paper, marker pens and flip chart
9.40 am	Group feedback and discussion.	
9.55 am	Coffee	
10.10 am	Practical demonstration of how to incorporate dietary goals into meals.	Remember to involve audience
10.40 am	Tasting food samples and discussion	
10.50 am	Conclusion. Opportunity for further questions.	
11.00 am	Evaluation and close.	

Planning the parts of a presentation

- **Introduction** – setting out what you intend to cover. It is often suggested that the introduction should contain a startling fact/joke/action to gain the attention of the audience.
- **Key points** – areas which you intend to discuss and expand on. These key words/points could be given on a OHP (Overlead Projector) slide as a prompt for you and a guide for the audience. Unless you are particularly confident, you will need to make notes on cards for yourself to remind you of the issues to be raised – it is easy for your mind to go 'blank' when in front of an audience. As a guide, you might plan to use approximately 110 words per minute. This section should also include plans for any active group work. Again you will need to give very clear instructions and ensure you have all the necessary materials.
- **Conclusion** – an opportunity to sum up the main points of the programme and perhaps those you hope the audience will take away and remember.
- **Question/discussion time** – this part is extremely important and allows the audience to seek

clarification if needed. It is useful to tell the audience at the beginning that there will be an opportunity to ask questions and discuss any points raised, so they can note down anything they want to say as it is raised during the session. This will hopefully help to avoid silence when this time occurs. If you do meet silence, you may need to initiate the discussion by asking the audience a question, so be prepared for this – discussion does not always happen naturally.

If a discussion is slow to start, it may be wise to use another tactic such as some group work requiring feedback. People are often more prone to talk and offer ideas in smaller numbers. You can always ask the group to allocate each of themselves with a number, for example from one to four, if four in the group, and then allocate each number with a specific role. So: one is the leader; two is the writer; and three and four are people to feedback to the main group. This way everyone is involved. Within this approach you might use other ways to help a discussion to get started. Ideas include using trigger materials such as photographs, statements or just a question for the group to work with. Alternatively, you could try one large brainstorming session with the whole group. The main thing is to be prepared and not to be caught out. It is far better to have excess material than not enough.

- **Evaluation** – a very important section which allows you to analyse the programme and its value to the target audience.

Remember that throughout a programme you might be presenting ideas to an audience which could be in conflict with their current practices. Audience members may choose to challenge you. For example, in a session on the effects of smoking on health, someone may well quote the case of their Gran who smoked 30 a day and lived until she was 90. Any feedback you give on any comments made should always be constructive and non-judgemental. It is important that you do not bring your own personal values and feelings into the discussion or the discussion may become personal rather than of value to the audience or group. Never get involved in an argument – you must simply present the facts as you have them. As said before, individuals have to make the choice themselves; you can only empower them to make an informed choice by offering clear and balanced information.

Evaluation

Evaluation is a vital skill which allows you to review and assess the methods and approach used. It allows you to see what worked and what didn't, and to make changes to a similar programme in the future. It may take the form of a questionnaire or a rating or ranking exercise. It is worth stressing to the audience the importance of their comments to you. Remember when devising the evaluation that questionnaires requiring a free response need more audience time. These questionnaires may result in limited responses which tell you little. Therefore it may be wise to include a range of question styles to elicit the information you require. Some examples are:

- **Free response** What have you enjoyed the most about the session?
- **Ranking** Rank in order of preference the aspects you most enjoyed about the session (1 = high; 3 = low): video ( ) role-play ( ) lecture ( )
- **Rating** Indicate the statement which most reflects your thoughts about the video: very useful ( ) useful ( ) not useful ( ).

If using the sheet with children, you may like to use faces to depict their feelings, for example:

If the questions for the rating/ranking are carefully constructed, you can gain a useful range of information. Evaluations should cover all aspects of the programme and not only involve the 'consumers' – you should look critically at your own performance. Include:

a planning
b methods used
c materials/resources used

d conclusions
e venue/eating arrangements, if appropriate

The evaluation should relate to the original aims of the programme to assess whether they have been achieved. A sample evaluation sheet is given below in Figure 5.23.

Evaluation of session on HIV and AIDS

Session: *Date:*

The time spent on this session was:
  about right
  too short
  too long
Did the session cover all you expected? Yes/No
Comments:

On a ranking of 1 to 5 (1 = low; 5 = high), how do you rank the learning potential of the session:
1 2 3 4 5
Which method did you find most and least enjoyable? (tick)
                    most   *least*
  lecture
  role-play
  group work

On a ranking of 1 to 5, how relevant and useful were the key sections for your job (1 = high; 5 = low)
  Information on transmission
  Information on development of the virus
  Information on hygiene practices
Any other comments you wish to make.

Figure 5.23 *Sample evaluation sheet*

Following an evaluation, it is important to collate the results and draw conclusions – and then to use them! It is important to see comments as part of a learning process and not as criticism. It is a way to ensure your 'consumers' are satisfied with your product. It is also useful to pass on comments to your colleagues who may be doing similar work, as this can be a valuable learning experience for them.

Evaluation tips

1 Keep it short.
2 Keep it clear.
3 Use yes/no or multiple choice answers as these speed up the process for the user.
4 Be clear about how the collection of the evaluation questionnaire or evaluation sheet is to be organised.
5 Emphasise the importance of the evaluation sheets to you – this will make the audience more likely to do it.

Task

Choose one main risk to health and plan a health promotion session aimed at one of the target audiences (children, adolescents or adults). Produce one original health promotion resource to use in the session.

You may like to follow these stages for your health promotion session.

1 Choose risk and target group.
2 Produce overall plan for achieving the task.
3 Research the topic.
4 Decide on approach for presentation, showing consideration of the different materials and equipment you could use.
5 Choose resources and equipment to use. Justify your choice.
6 Plan session, remembering to produce the time plan.
7 Prepare any materials/resources needed.
8 Prepare audience evaluation sheet.
9 Present session and carry out audience evaluation.
10 Complete an overall personal evaluation of the task.

Self-assessment test

1 The regulations which require employers to make an assessment of any hazardous substances in the workplace are:

a COSHH
b Health and Safety Regulations 1991
c Health and Safety at Work Act 1974
d Environmental Health Regulations

Many of the lifestyle choices that people make can lead to risks to health. These might include:
a cirrhosis of the liver
b emphysema
c HIV
d atherosclerosis

2 Which is connected to excess alcohol?

3 Which might be related to unsafe sexual practices?

4 Which is connected to smoking?

5 Glue, lighter fluid and petrol all belong to the group of substances known as
a drugs
b solvents
c tranquillisers
c amphetamines

6 Drug misuse is the term used to describe the:
a use of socially accepted drugs in an unacceptable way
b use of socially unaccepted drugs
c use of many different drugs at the same time by one person
d injection of drugs into the bloodstream

7 An example of a drug classified as a stimulant is:
a LSD
b Ecstasy
c Valium
d Cocaine

8 For health reasons, doctors recommend a maximum unit intake of alcohol for males and females each week. These are:
a 10, females; 14, males
b 14, males; 21, females
c 21, males; 14, females
d 10, females; 20, males

9 When pregnant, you should not drink alcohol because:
a it increases the chance of high blood-pressure
b it crosses the plancenta in the blood to the foetus and may influence its development

c it causes the foetus to put on body fat

d it always leads to miscarriage

10 One way that HIV is passed from an infected person to a non-infected person is through:

a kissing

b drinking from the same cup when it has not been washed

c sharing hypodermic needles

d swimming in the same water

There are many different contraceptives available today. Each suits differing needs. They include:

a condom

b combined pill

c IUD

d spermicide gel

Of these four, which would be best in the following circumstances?

11 Offering the highest protection rate against pregnancy.

12 Protection against contracting an STD.

13 Most reliable for a woman with a regular partner who has had children but is unable to take the pill because she is a heavy smoker.

A good health promotion plan has the following elements:

a introduction

b key points

c conclusion

d evaluation

14 Which offers the target audience the opportunity to assess the success of the programme in meeting their needs?

15 Which gives the target audience an outline of the content of the programme?

16 Which involves the presenter in summing up the main messages from the programme?

17 An example of a piece of audio-visual equipment is:

a an OHP (Overhead Projector)

b video and monitor

c tape-recorder

d dictaphone

18 Give the advantages and disadvantages of using a leaflet in a health promotion programme.

19 Explain the difference between aims and objectives when planning a health promotion programme.

20 One way that an audience can be given the opportunity to seek clarification is to:

a complete an evaluation

b have a question/discussion session

c ensure the speaker sums up the main points

d have a display available on the topic

Fast Facts

AIDS Acquired Immune Deficiency Syndrome – the illness that HIV develops into.

Aims Broad statements which outline goals people are hoping to achieve. Linked to *objectives*.

Alcohol A drug; a colourless, flammable liquid which causes the intoxicating effect of alcoholic drinks. It is initially produced by fermenting sugars.

Bronchitis Inflammation of the bronchial tubes caused by bacteria, virus or irritation of the respiratory tract, e.g. by smoking.

Carbon monoxide A poisonous gas found in cigarette smoke which combines with haemoglobin and reduces the amount of oxygen the blood can carry.

Conclusion A summing up of the main facts.

COSHH Control of Substances Hazardous to Health: regulations which require that all employers carry out a risk assessment of any substance which might be considered hazardous to their employees' health and to minimise that risk.

Contraception Ways to reduce the risk of fertilisation of the female egg by the male sperm, leading to pregnancy, as a result of sexual intercourse.

Dependency Relying on something for physical or mental functioning.

Disease   Any reduction in the normal physiological functioning, affecting all or part of the body.

Drug abuse   The use of socially unaccepted drugs in a socially unacceptable way.

Drug misuse   The use of socially accepted drugs, such as tranquillisers, in a socially unacceptable way.

Emphysema   A condition where the air sacs of the lungs are enlarged, causing breathlessness and wheezing. Caused by smoking.

Equipment and resources   Necessary materials or items of support which might be used in a health promotion programme, e.g. OHPs, leaflets.

Evaluation   A way to review the success of something, such as a health promotion programme or materials used. It is used to assess successful aspects as well as the less successful ones, and is used as a tool for improving future performance.

Feedback   Information which is given back in response to an enquiry, whether as a question or statement.

Free response   Question which allows the respondent to answer how they wish.

Fuse   Protective device which safeguards electrical circuits. A fuse will break the circuit if it becomes overloaded with electricity and therefore a fire risk.

Genito-urinary infections (GUs)   Infections which affect both the sexual organs/reproductive system and the urinary system.

Hazard   Anything that has the potential to cause harm to someone in some way.

Health   The state of being physically and mentally free from disease; the general condition of the body and mind.

Health and Safety at Work Act 1974   An amalgamation of a number of acts which covers most work situations. It places responsibility on the employer to ensure a safe environment.

Health promotion   To further or encourage health.

Human Immunodeficiency Virus (HIV)   The virus which causes AIDS.

Introduction   The start of something, such as a talk or book. It should set out briefly what is going to happen; a way of setting the scene.

Key points   The main areas that a health promotion presentation is covering; the main issues the presenter is hoping to focus on.

Mental health   The health of the mind; the ability to think clearly and carry out intellectual processes.

Objectives   Linked to *aims*, but are more specific and measurable. Statements saying what an individual is hoping to achieve and possibly how they intend to do it.

Passive smoking   A non-smoker breathing in the cigarette smoke of others, which is either from the end of the cigarette as it burns or the smoke the smoker has exhaled.

Physical health   The health of the body and its organs.

Planning   A detailed scheme or method for achieving an *objective*; may have a timescale.

Primary health promotion   The process of informing different groups about aspects of health care before they risk health, with the aim of preventing this happening.

Prioritise   A way of ranking a number of issues/ tasks according to importance, to allow some but not all to be covered if time is limited.

Residual current device (RCD)   Device used with electrical equipment. It can detect damage to electrical cables or other faults and will cut off the electric current extremely quickly, thus protecting against electrical accidents.

Recovery position   The recommended way to position a person who is unconscious. It keeps the airways open and allows fluid to drain from the mouth, thus reducing the risk of choking.

Risk   A measurement of how likely a potential hazard is to cause harm.

Secondary health promotion   Health advice which aims to encourage people to change existing habits, which have the potential of being health risks, to healthier ones.

Shock   A condition of bodily collapse or near collapse. May occur as a result of circulatory failure or lowering of the blood-pressure from severe bleeding, burns or fright.

Social health   Being able to form and keep relationships going with other people both on a personal and professional level.

Sexually transmitted diseases (STDs)   Diseases which are passed from one individual to another through sexual contact.

Tar   Substance in cigarettes which causes narrowing of the bronchioles and damage to the small hairs which line the lung. This makes the lungs less efficient and more prone to infections.

Target audience   The potential audience you are aming your health promotion material at. The type of audience will determine the material and approach used.

Tertiary health promotion   The re-education of the individual to get the most from life when they have an irreversible or chronic illness.

Unit   The way alcohol is measured and individual's consumption is assessed.

References

[Discussion documents]

World Health Organisation, 1984, *Health Provision*
Ewles and Simmett, 1992, *Promoting Health: A practical guide*, Scutari Press
Institute of Environmental Health Officers, 1993, *Basic Health and Safety at Work*, Environmental Health Training
Dept. of Health, 1992, *Health of the Nation*, HMSO

Newspaper articles

McKie, 1993, 'Aids Vaccine hits ethical hurdle', The Observer
Brown & Goodwin, 28.1.94, 'Passive smoking laws are rejected by Bottomley', The Independent
Clement & Hall, 28.1.94, 'Passive smoking victory may lead to smoking ban', The Independent

Leaflets

Portman Group, 'Talking to your children about drinking. A guide for parents', Portman group
HEA, 1992, 'That's the limit', Health Education Authority
HEA, 1991, 'Smoking – the facts', Health Education Authority
Boice & Gamble, 'You don't need to be an expert', Health Education Authority
Ives, 1992, 'Solvents: a parents guide', Department of Health
Home Office, 1991, 'Electrical safety leads to fire safety', Home Office

chapter 6 STRUCTURE AND PRACTICES IN HEALTH AND SOCIAL CARE

The two main services which organise the provision of health and social care in Britain are the National Health Service and the Local Authority social services. Further services are provided by voluntary organisations and by private health and care services. This chapter starts by looking at the organisation of health and social care services as they are today. This information is put into context by a review of the historical background to these services. The chapter then goes on to explain the roles of health and care workers, access to care and its provision, and priorities and strategies for delivery of services.

· THE STRUCTURE OF THE NHS ·

The National Health Service is one of the largest employers in the country. The provision of health services can be seen as dividing into three main strands:

1 **Primary** services, such as general practitioners (GPs).
2 **Secondary** care such as hospital care.
3 **Community** services.

Primary care means the first (or primary) contact with health services. Primary care involves the services offered by Family Health Services. These services involve GPs, dentists and practice nurses. **Secondary** care is secondary because it often follows referral from primary care. Secondary care focuses on hospital care, day surgeries and out-patient treatment. More specialist care is sometimes referred

to as *tertiary* care and may be provided in specialised units. **Community** services include district nurses, health visitors, domiciliary midwives, and some services offered by physiotherapists, chiropodists, occupational and speech therapists.

Primary health services

Primary health services are provided by professional people who are often the first line of call if there is a problem. General practitioners (GPs), dentists, opticians and pharmacists are the most obvious examples. This provision is overseen in an area by the Family Practitioners' Committee, which keeps a register of services and monitors the complaints of service users.

The GP's surgery is usually the first place to go if you feel unwell. The GP will, if necessary, refer you to the other services you need. For this reason, the staff at the surgery are often known as the **primary health care team**. The 'team' consists of the GP, the district nurse, the health visitor, local practice nurse and the community psychiatric nurse. Sometimes a social worker is included. They are all based full-time or part-time at the local surgery.

Each member of the team has a specific role, and each one complements the others to provide overall care. Nowadays a GP's surgery offers a wide range of services, including 'well man' and 'well woman' clinics and possibly some minor surgical treatments. The primary health care team is interested in preventing illness as well as curing it.

Figure 6.1 *A GP offers primary care*

Everyone can be registered with a particular GP to get treatment, although someone can register as a temporary patient if visiting another area.

The GP contract

General practitioners, or GPs, are not directly employed by the National Health Service. GPs are independent contractors who have a contract with the local Family Health Services Authority to provide general medical services. GPs can advertise and employ their own staff to assist them.

The GP's contract requires them to do the following:

- Publish a directory of services, an annual report on their facilities and give fuller details of themselves.
- Specify minimum standards of care.
- Meet specified targets for various preventive measures like vaccination and screening.
- Be available 26 hours each week over five days and accept 24-hour responsibility for patients.
- Provide more services for the over 75s (including the offer of annual check-ups and home visits) and a more regular assessment of the development of young children.
    'NHS Made Easy' (Department of Health)

Large GP practices may hold their own budgets, and are called GP fund holders.

Secondary care in the National Health Service

While primary care can meet around 90 per cent of the needs for health care, more intensive diagnosis and treatment is sometimes needed.

Hospitals

Hospitals are providers of secondary care. Access to them is made through a referral from primary care (except in the case of emergency or through direct referral to clinics such as those for sexually transmitted diseases).

In the past, hospitals have tended to be of two main types: those providing for short-term care (*acute care* – out-patients, accident and emergency, general surgery etc.) or long-term care (for the mentally-ill, elders and so on.) In the future, hospitals may care almost entirely for the acutely ill on a short-term basis.

Hospitals might be grouped either as NHS Trusts or Directly Managed Units (DMUs).

NHS Trusts are self-governing units within the National Health Service. They are run by boards of directors and are accountable directly to the centre. Major acute hospitals are the obvious candidates for this status but trusts can cover a range of services including community services, services for patient groups such as people with mental illness, and ambulance services.

By being a trust these organisations can:

- Determine their own management structures.
- Employ their own staff using their own terms and conditions of service.
- Acquire, own and sell their assets.
- Retain surpluses and borrow money (subject to annual limits).

Each trust has a board of directors with complete responsibility for managing the trust's affairs. Each year they prepare a business plan, setting out proposals for service developments and capital investment. At the end of the year they prepare and publish an annual report and accounts.

Directly managed units (DMUs) are controlled by District Health Authorities. Although not having the freedoms available to trusts, DMUs have a much greater responsibility for the management of their services than hospitals had previously.

Adapted from 'NHS Made Easy'
(Department of Health)

Community services

Community nursing staff

Community nurses play a vital role in the delivery of community care. Under the NHS and Community Care Act, emphasis is placed on maintaining more dependent people in the community for longer periods; community nurses have a key role to play. These nurses will assess nursing care needs. Both health visitors and district nurses have a knowledge of and contact with local community networks, and so may play a valuable role in mobilising resources to meet individual needs.

Community therapy services

With more dependent people living in the community, there is an increasing demand on therapy services, e.g. occupational therapy, physiotherapy, speech therapy, psychology, chiropody and therapists for visual or hearing impairment. These community therapists have the skills to enable people to be more independent in the community.

The dental service

There are about 23 000 dentists practising in the UK – the majority (about 80 per cent) are contracted to carry out some work for the NHS. This is mainly care of children's teeth and care of patients who have been registered for some time. In many parts of the UK it is now quite difficult for new clients to register as NHS patients and they must consult a dentist privately.

As with GPs, a contract has been introduced. The dentist must not only leave the patient 'dentally fit', but is also required to offer care and treatment to secure and maintain the patient's oral health.

The contract between dentists and the Family Health Services Authority (FHSA) allows NHS patients the freedom to choose and change dentists as they wish. The dentist can also choose to accept or refuse any NHS patient.

Mental health services

In 'Health of the Nation', one of the objectives is to develop comprehensive locally-based services. In January 1993, the Mental Health Task Force was established to help ensure the substantial completion of the transfer of services away from large hospitals to a balanced range of locally-based services, including community-based beds.

The Department of Health is targeting three main areas in mental health:

1 Elderly mentally ill people.
2 Child and adolescent mental health services.
3 Mentally disordered offenders.

In August 1993, the Secretary of State for Health announced a ten-point plan to reinforce community care for mentally ill people covering a series of initiatives designed to improve their health and social opportunities. The proposals include the introduction of a new power of supervised discharge for the small number of mentally ill people who need special support when they leave hospital. A new Code of Practice on the Mental Health Act (1983) has been published.

Think it over

Can you think of any services that have been developed in your area for people with mental health problems?

Child health services

This service has been the subject of a review in 1993/4 by the Community and Acute Services Steering Group. This is reviewing services specifically to look at ways to shift services from acute settings to primary and community settings.

As part of the shift of emphasis from acute care to primary and community care, many District Health Authorities are commissioning Home Care Paediatric Teams, who work with the medical needs of children. District Health Authorities may also have Adolescent Health Clinics, which may highlight the needs of children with learning and physical disabilities, Child and Adolescent Mental Health Services and School Health Services.

· THE MARKET FOR CARE ·

The government has been concerned to create a market system for the delivery of health care. A market place is where people sell things to customers. In health and social care the sellers are called 'providers' and the buyers of services are called 'purchasers'. So, in order to create a market for health care provision, the National Health Service is divided into a system of purchasers and providers. Providers offer the direct care a person receives when they attend a doctor's surgery or hospital. 'Purchasers' organise and plan what types and levels of care provision are needed.

In a market place, providers set out their stall, whilst purchasers work out what they need to buy. Market places often encourage cheaper prices for things like fruit and vegetables. There might be competition between providers – more than one stall selling fruit. Providers have to work hard and try to provide good quality at the most competitive prices if they are to attract purchasers and stay in business. The government has transferred this idea of a market place into both health and social care provision.

Supporters of the market idea argue that it will lead to good quality care for patients. Patients will be treated more like customers; they will be seen as vital for the maintenance of staff jobs. Supporters of the market idea also argue that competition will lead to greater efficiency and that services will improve at no extra cost to the tax payer.

Not everyone supports the market idea for health care. One argument against it is that a complex service like medicine will not respond to the simple ideas which work when selling fruit and vegetables. Some opponents of the market idea claim that certain individuals may be disadvantaged because 'their purchasers' are not in such a powerful position as other purchasers. Some opponents of the market system believe that the market will eventually lead to a privatisation of services. This would mean that certain types of care will only be available to individuals who can afford to pay privately. These issues are open to political debate.

Task

The system for financing health care is outlined below. Find out about the system in greater detail. Will the internal market of purchasers and providers work to create a better deal for clients or can you see any areas for concern? You could organise a debate or discussion with your group on the advantages or disadvantages of the new NHS financing arrangements. You will be able to use this for evidence towards core skills in communication.

GP fund holders are both providers of primary care and purchasers of secondary care. Some people argue that patients registered with fund holders who need secondary services are at an advantage compared to patients of non-fund holding GPs. The fund holder can buy services direct from a range of providers but the ordinary GP has to place patients on a waiting list for District Health Authority funded services. Some individuals have claimed that this creates a two-tier system; however, both fund holders and non-fund holders are working within limited budgets.

Theory into practice

How aware are people of the distinction between fund holding and non-fund holding GPs? What opinions do people in your placement or college have with respect to this issue? Devise a simple interview approach or questionnaire and research this issue.

You may be able to gather evidence for research as well as for this unit.

Purchasers of health services

Primary care services, such as doctors' surgeries, are organised and paid for by the Family Health Services Authorities (FHSAs) which act as purchasers of primary care. There are 90 FHSAs in England. They are responsible for assessing the health care needs of the population and they manage the services (such as those provided by GPs) to meet those needs.

Secondary care services, such as hospital provision, are organised and 'bought' by District Health Authorities (DHAs) or by GP fund holders. There are 186 DHAs in England. As provision for secondary care moves to independent NHS Trusts and to more autonomous Directly Managed Units (DMUs), the DHAs will be able to concentrate on assessing the population's need for secondary health care and purchasing services to meet those needs.

In 1994, Family Health Services Authorities and District Health Authorities were accountable to Regional Health Authorities. However, it is likely that the current fourteen Regional Health Authorities will slim down to just eight National Health Service Executive Agencies in the future. The term 'Regional Health Authority' will therefore disappear. This may mean that the English system becomes more like the Welsh Health Service which consists of nine District Health Authorities but has no Regional Health Authorities.

Currently, in England, Regional Health Authorities provide a framework in which the purchaser and provider market functions.

The purchaser/provider mechanism

The Regional Health Authority (RHA) is given a block of money by the government. This money is mainly gained from tax and National Insurance payments. The money is calculated to be appropriate

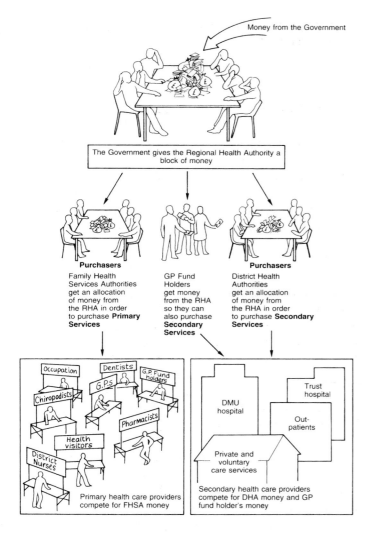

Figure 6.2 *The internal NHS market*

Purchasers of primary care: Family Health Services Authorities

FHSAs are responsible for:

- The administration of the new contracts for GPs, dentists, pharmacists and opticians.
- Identifying primary health needs of the population.
- Developing services to meet those needs.
- Managing funds for GP practice team development and premises improvement.
- Making services responsive to consumers' wishes.

'NHS Made Easy' (Department of Health)

Purchasers of secondary care: District Health Authorities

DHAs are responsible for:

- Assessing the population's needs for health care.
- Evaluating the effectiveness of services.
- Drawing up service specifications.
- Negotiating contracts with providers.
- Building in quality standards.
- Monitoring contract performance.

'NHS Made Easy' (Department of Health)

---

for the population of the region. The calculation takes account of local variations in things like the age of the population and cost of services.

The RHA then divides the block and allocates money to its Family Health Services Authorities for primary care and District Health Authorities for secondary care. These bodies then look at the health needs of their population and use their allocation to purchase the services to meet those needs.

A GP fund holder is also a purchaser. Larger GP practices can elect to have their own budget to purchase secondary care.

District Health Authorities have become 'Purchasers of Care' services. The purchasing intentions of each DHA have been guided and influenced by the Government's White Paper, 'Health of the Nation', published in July 1992. The White Paper outlines a strategy for health in England and it achieved two objectives:

1 It focused attention on the importance and benefits of maintaining good health and preventing ill health.
2 It set in motion an initiative to improve health.

The 'Health of the Nation' White Paper sets targets for improvements in health: it identifies areas for action and people who need to be involved. A health theme of the White Paper is working together to improve health.

Five key areas were identified in the 'Health of the Nation' as being particularly in need of targeting:

1 Coronary heart disease and stroke.
2 Cancers.
3 Mental illness.
4 HIV/AIDS and sexual health.
5 Accidents.

Purchasers of health care services need to pay special attention to services that address these five key areas. Purchasers also need to look at the needs of local people and purchase health care for those in its district through contracts with providers. Different areas can have different needs: there may be a high number of elders who perhaps need special physiotherapy and arthritis clinics; many young children under five who need vaccination programmes; or there may be widespread poverty and the risk of TB.

GP fund holders

Although they will still remain in contract with their local FHSA for the provision of general medical services, any GP practice with more than 9,000 to 11,000 registered patients can apply to become a fund holder in its own right. If successful they will be allocated a budget to purchase a range of diagnostic tests, in-patient and day care treatments and out-patient services through contracts with the providers of these services. This is in addition to funding prescribing costs and the costs of their staff and premises.

'NHS Made Easy' (Department of Health)

Regional Health Authorities

In 1994 the role of Regional Health Authorities was to plan, allocate resources and monitor the performance of District Health Authorities and Family Health Services Authorities. They also advised on the introduction of National Health Service trusts, the development of new funding systems, the design and development of contracts in the purchaser/provider market and monitoring the performance of District Health Authorities and Family Health Services Authorities.

Special Health Authorities

There are a number of health authorities outside of the structure described above. They are called the Special Health Authorities (SHAs) and they report directly to either the Department of Health in London, or the NHS Management Executive. There are three types:

1 Non-hospital SHAs: these provide a service for the whole NHS which needs some co-ordination at national level. Examples are the NHS Supplies Authority and the Health Education Authority.
2 Hospital SHAs: a number of specialist post-graduate teaching and research hospitals in London have SHA status. Examples are the Hammersmith, the National Heart and Chest Hospitals and the Royal Marsden.
2 Special Hospitals: Special Hospitals are those dealing with the care of seriously disturbed offenders (Rampton, Ashworth and Broadmoor are the English Special Hospitals). They form an SHA in their own right – but not all SHAs are Special Hospitals.

'NHS Made Easy' (Department of Health)

Think it over

Where is the nearest Special Hospital to you?

The cost of health

Health services are available to all. However, this doesn't mean that everyone has access to all services whenever they like.

Some services are available free to all, such as seeing a doctor or obtaining family planning. Some services (e.g. dental work, prescriptions) are only available free to particular groups. Sometimes services are mixed – for example, you can see a doctor without

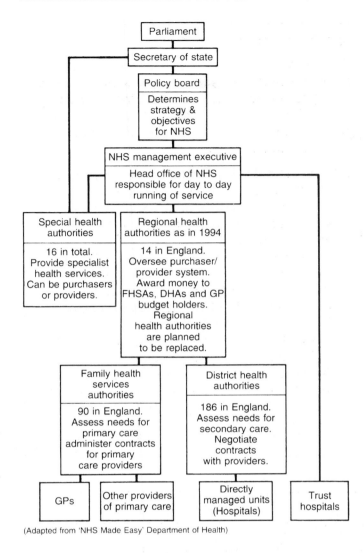

(Adapted from 'NHS Made Easy' Department of Health)

Figure 6.3 *The management structure of the National Health Service in England*

charge but may have to pay for medicines your doctor prescribes for you.

Some people choose to 'go private', which means they opt out of the service provided by the government and pay for a service. This private service may in fact be provided by the same person who does the work for the National Health Service, but it might mean that the individual is seen sooner.

The statutory and private provisions may be mixed. For example, you could see your GP with a problem and be recommended to see a specialist (a 'consultant'). If the consultant has a long waiting list of NHS patients, you could opt to go private (i.e. pay) at this point and be seen earlier.

Many people now take out health insurance which they can call upon when they need treatment that the NHS cannot provide quickly.

· MIXED ECONOMY OF CARE ·

Many areas operate what is called a 'mixed economy of care'. This means that the major agencies work together to satisfy the needs of the individual.

The government has a policy of promoting care in the community, which means that people should be cared for in their own homes or an establishment in the community whenever this is possible. Under the NHS and Community Care Act, responsibility for services in the community lies with Local Authority social services departments. Each social services department appoints care managers who are responsible for purchasing services from the full range of statutory, voluntary and private providers.

In order to ensure the delivery of cost-effective health and care services of quality, the organisations responsible for the services need to work together. Community care, on one level, involves a partnership between the District Health Authority, social services department and Family Health Services Authority (representing GPs). On another level it involves the practitioners who provide the care – the social workers, community nurses, support workers and informal workers.

The partnership between the District Health Authority, social services department and Family Health Services Authority is at a senior (or strategic) level. These three organisations work together to produce a plan for the district they cover. Publication of a yearly *plan* is required by law under the NHS and Community Care Act. The 'strategic plan' provides a strategy or plan of action for the area. The three organisations take an overview of the district's situation in relation to the health and care needs of people living in the area and the services needed to meet these needs.

Funding the NHS

The NHS is funded mainly from receipts from taxation and National Insurance contributions. Although many of the services appear to be free, we all pay for them in an indirect way. Public services are funded by local and national taxes – income tax, Value Added Tax (VAT) and National Insurance contributions (by individuals and organisations).

Benefits

An individual's health and care problems may be linked to his or her social and financial situation.

With the exception of housing benefit (which is dealt with by the Local Authority), financial matters are dealt with by the Department of Social Security (DSS) via the Benefits Agency. The latter works for the Department of Social Security. The DSS produces a number of leaflets which set out people's rights and entitlements.

Benefits can be the same for everyone (such as child benefit) or they may be *means tested*, that is, account is taken of any income or saving before a benefit is awarded. Sometimes no benefit is given because the person applying has too many savings. A reduced benefit is sometimes given when people have some savings or income. Some benefits are only payable if the individual has paid contributions to National

Insurance. These include unemployment benefit, sick pay, maternity pay and pensions.

Task

Collect the range of leaflets available from your local DSS office. You could use the information to start a project on the type of financial help available to a client group of particular interest to you.

. STRUCTURE OF SOCIAL CARE . PROVISION

The Secretary of State for Health is responsible for the *provision* of social services, however it is the Local Authorities that administer them. Local Authority social service departments have responsibility for the coordination of all forms of social care in the community.

Each Local Authority has a Social Services Committee which has responsibility for the social services within its area. It must appoint a Director of Social Services. The director is in charge of the department which administers the services. Social Service Departments are often organised into area offices from which the services for that area are operated.

Organisational structures within the local authority Social Services Departments have changed considerably in the past couple of years to enable the departments to carry out their new roles, as required by current legislation and, in particular, the National Health Service and Community Care Act 1990 (see below). Many Social Services Departments have new sections within them, such as Inspection and Monitoring Sections (these sections often also have the responsibility for dealing with complaints procedures). Planning and Development Sections have taken on increased importance now that the authorities are required to work more closely with

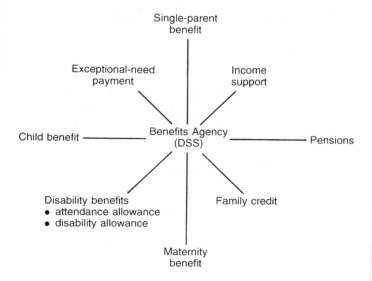

Figure 6.4 *The Benefits Agency*

Health Service planning colleagues, as well as with the private and voluntary sector. Additionally, some local authorities have sections which are specifically responsible for contracting with service providers. Many Social Services Departments have also re-organised their staffing arrangements in order to reflect a clear division of the purchasing and providing responsibilities. (See Figure 6.5.)

County Councils run Local Authority social services in England and Wales, as do Metropolitan Councils and the London Boroughs.

In Northern Ireland there are four Boards set up to administer social and health services. This unified structure is outside political control. In Scotland, Regional Local Authorities control social work departments.

Social services should not be confused with the Department of Social Security (DSS), which administers benefits and pays out money. (See previous page) Apart from an occasional small sum in an emergency, the social services do not hand out money. Their main function is to offer advice, to provide access to services and to provide a number of services themselves. They provide access to

community and residential services for all client groups, such as children, people with mental health problems, people with mental or physical disabilities and older people.

Task

Visit your local Social Services Department and find out the organisational structure. Make a diagram of the structure.

· THE LEGAL CONTEXT OF CARE ·

Care services operate within a legal framework. The powers and duties of the services, in particular the social services, are set out in various Acts of Parliament. The difference between powers and duties is quite straightforward. Where the law imposes a *duty* on someone, or on an organisation,

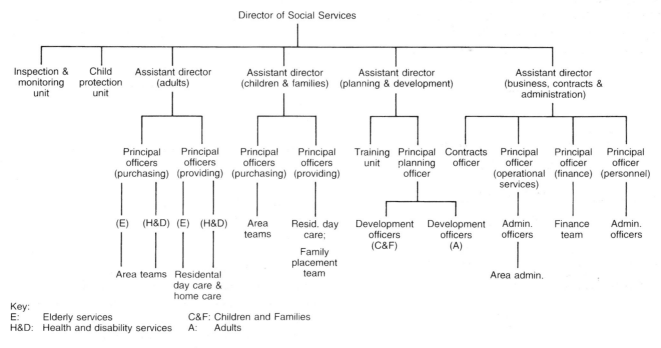

Figure 6.5 *Example of a social services department structure*

then they have to carry out that duty; they have no choice. Where the law gives someone or an organisation the *power* to do something, then they may choose to exercise that power; but they are not obliged to do so.

The principal Acts referred to in this chapter are:

- The National Assistance Act 1948
- The Health Services and Public Health Act 1968
- The Local Authority Social Services Act 1970
- The Chronically Sick and Disabled Persons Act 1970
- The Mental Health Act 1983
- The Disabled Persons (Consultation and Representation) Act 1986
- The Children Act 1989
- The National Health Service and Community Care Act 1990

Historical background

The 'Poor Law' was the beginning of the concept that there should be legislation in order to provide a basic 'safety net' that would prevent people from literally finding themselves in the gutter. At that time it was considered that people were totally responsible for their own misfortune and therefore they were only given very basic relief, and they had to work for it (i.e. in 'work-houses'). Initially, it was the responsibility of the local parish council to administer the 'Poor Law'. The job was then taken over by the national government in order to ensure a uniform national level of subsistence benefit. Social Services functions are derived from the original role of the parish council. Additionally, the drive for public health, through the supply of adequate water supplies and drainage, led to the development of a Public Health Service. The *1946 National Health Act* set up a national system for health care in its widest sense.

The National Assistance Act 1948

The National Assistance Act was designed to replace the old Poor Law, which had given an outdated and punitive form of poverty relief. It was designed to complement the National Assistance Acts of 1946, providing financial assistance to people in need.

Part three of the Act empowered local authorities to provide many services designed to improve the quality of lives for people who were disabled. It imposed on local authorities the duty to provide homes and hostels for older people and people with disabilities, who were unable to care for themselves and who had no-one to look after them. Local authorities were also empowered to charge residents according to their means, leaving some part of their pension for personal expenses.

The Act made it a duty for local authorities to inspect and to register the private residential establishments for older people and people with disabilities. Section 29 of the Act gave the power to local authorities to promote the welfare of all people with disabilities, such as those with a mental disability. Use of these powers varied greatly from authority to authority.

The Health Services and Public Health Act 1968

Section 45 of the Health Services and Public Health Act provided local authorities with the general power to promote the welfare of older people. Subsequently the provision of meals on wheels, home care, day care (including transport to day centres), adaptations to property and the provision of warden-controlled property (with Housing departments usually having responsibility for this), have been developed. However, local authorities do not have a duty to provide any of these services.

The Local Authority Social Services Act 1970

Following the Seebohm Report and the subsequent Local Authority Social Services Act 1970, Social Services departments developed into the way that we know them today. This Act requires local authorities to set up Social Services Committees to administer all of the functions carried out by the Social Services departments. The Act sets out the framework for social services provision, however it is not specific about the way in which this is to be organised.

The Chronically Sick and Disabled Persons Act 1970

This Act makes further provision for the welfare of people with disabilities. It gives local authorities a positive duty to provide amenities and services recommended under the Act; legislation with regard to access to buildings was passed for the first time under this Act.

Some of the services referred to in the Act include:

- Home helps
- Meals on wheels
- Aids to daily living
- Adaptations to homes
- Telephones
- Occupation at home and at centres
- Outings
- Provision of transport to places of occupation, entertainment and education

Figure 6.6 *Access for disabled people*

This Act is also very important for older people, since people over the age of 60 comprise approximately 60 per cent of the disabled population as a whole.

The Mental Health Act 1983

This Act provides professionals with the power to make decisions about a person's welfare when that person, due to a mental disorder, is not able to make decisions regarding their own welfare. The Act is supported by the Code of Practice, which is a guide to good practice in the interpretation of the Act. It lays down procedures that try to ensure that abuse of power does not occur, while necessary treatment and containment is still provided. It aims to find a balance between maintaining the basic civil liberies of the individual and the need to impose interventions. However, section 131 of the Act makes it clear that, for anyone over the age of 16, capable of expressing his or her own wishes, then an informal admission to hospital should be the norm 'and should be used whenever a patient is not unwilling to be admitted and can be treated without the use of compulsory powers'.

Admission to hospital can be made under the Act in various ways:

- *Section 1 – Compulsory Admission*
  Applications for admission under this section can be made either by an Approved Social Worker or by the person's nearest relative.
- *Section 2 – Admission for Assessment*
  Applications must be founded on the recommendations of two medical practitioners and allows the person to be detained for a limited period of up to 23 days.
- *Section 3 – Admission for Treatment*
  This allows for admission to hospital and also involves the power to give treatment to the person without their consent.
- *Section 4 – Emergency Admission*
  This allows for admission for assessment on the grounds that admission is urgently required and that compliance with all the procedural formalities under section 2 would cause undesirable delay.

The definition of the term 'mental disorder' is central to the functioning of the Act. Section 12 refers to four specific forms of mental disorder: mental illness; arrested or incomplete development of mind; psychopathic disorder; and 'any other disorder or disability of mind'. This definition means that people with learning difficulties may come within some sections of the Mental Health Act. Sexual deviancy or dependence on drugs or alcohol do not constitute a mental disorder and do not come within the scope of this Act.

The Disabled Persons (Consultation and Representation) Act 1986

The Act requires local authorities to provide information not only about their own services, but also about those services provided by other statutory and voluntary agencies concerned with people with disabilities. The Act also requires that the needs of carers be taken into consideration when the need for services is being assessed. (See Chapter 7.) Sections 1 to 3 of the Act provide for the appointment of advocates, or representatives, to be appointed, to speak on behalf of those clients who are unable to express themselves directly. Section 3 also requires the local authority to provide a written statement setting out the assessment of need.

The welfare of the child is paramount. (Winged Fellowship Trust 'Images of Caring' Competition by Bob McCallion.)

Task

*Make a list of the services that local authorities have a **duty** to provide for people with disabilities.*

The Children Act 1989

The Children Act 1989 is a major piece of legislation in that it supersedes many previous existing pieces of legislation that had built up in a piecemeal fashion over the years. The aim of the Act is to clarify the law relating to children. However it also introduces new duties and responsibilities for courts, Social Services departments and, to a certain degree, parents. Three main principles guide the Act:

i   the welfare principle
ii   the non-delay principle
iii the non-intervention principle

The *welfare principle* requires the courts to treat the welfare of the child as paramount. Although the courts still have to balance the rights of the child and the rights of the parents, ultimately they must do what they consider as being in the best interest of the child.

The *non-delay principle* is a response to the recognition that delays in settling issues are not usually in the best interest of the child. For many reasons there are often delays within the legal system. The section of the Act relating to this principle requires that in any proceedings involving children courts must: (i) draw up a timetable for the proceedings; (ii) give directions so that the timetable is adhered to.

The *non-intervention principle* states that the court should not make an order unless it considers, 'that doing so would be better for the child than making no order at all'.

Duties of the local authority

The Act outlines the duties of the local authority in relation to children, such as responsibilities relating to child protection (section 47), and general safeguarding and welfare of children (section 27). Additionally, section 17 itemises a comprehensive list of powers and duties, which includes:

- Identification of children in need and the provision of information
- Maintenance of a register of disabled children
- Assessment of children's needs
- Prevention of neglect and abuse
- Provision of accommodation in order to protect a child
- Provision for disabled children
- Provision to reduce the need for care proceedings
- Provision for children living with their families (e.g. family aides)
- Family centres (to provide guidance for children and their parents)
- Maintenance of the family home (to enable children to continue to live with their family, or to maintain contact with them)
- Duty to consider racial groups to which children in need belong. (This has implications when selecting day centres, foster parents etc. for a child.)

Theory into practice

What are the implications for the provision of meals, the kind of toys, story books and pictures, in a day centre for children from different cultural and racial backgrounds? Visit a local nursery, family centre or 'early years centre' and make a list of any ways in which children from different cultural and racial backgrounds are catered for. How does this compare with your list?

Orders that can be made under the Children Act include:

i Care Order (section 33)
The main function of a care order is to give the local authority parental responsibility, it makes the local authority the child's 'parent'.

ii Interim Care Order (section 37)
Most interim orders are made in the situation where, for one reason or another, the full hearing cannot take place.

iii Supervision Order (section 34)
A supervision order is an alternative to a care order. In the Act there is no guidance given as to when a supervision order should be made rather than a care order.

iv Interim Supervision Order (section 38)
Just as there are specific provisions for interim care orders, so there are provisions for interim supervision orders.

v Child Assessment Order (section 46)
This provision allows the compulsory assessment of the state of the child's health and development, if need be by the removal of the child from the home.

vi Emergency Protection Order (section 44)
This is a new order that is designed to remove the criticisms of the former place of safety order. It is a short-term order that removes the child from the home, for a period of an initial seven days, extendable to fifteen days for medical reports.

vii Removal by Police to Accommodation (section 46)
The police, in the course of their duties, may come across children at risk who need protection. As there may be the need for immediate action, they are given the powers, under the Children Act, to take them into police protection.

There were four new orders under section 8:

a Residence Order
This is an order 'settling the arrangements to be made as to the person with whom the child is to live'.

b Contact Order
This order requires the person with whom the child is to live to allow the child to have contact with specified others. Contacts may be by letter, phone or visits, which may be supervised. It may provide contact with any other person e.g. parent, sibling, grandparent, friend.

c Prohibited Steps Order
This is an order that would be used where it is necessary for the court to play a continuing role. The court may specify matters which have to be referred back to the court e.g. it could prohibit a child's removal from the UK.

d Specific Issues Order
These may be made on their own or in conjunction with residence or contact orders.

Children at risk

The legal framework suggests three possibilities for action when a child is considered to be at risk:

- leaving the child at home and providing support
- removing the child from the home on a temporary basis
- removing the child on a permanent basis

There are five ways in which a child may be removed from the home on a temporary basis:

i by obtaining a child assessment order (section 43)

ii by obtaining an emergency protection order (EPO) (section 44)

iii by the police removing the child to suitable accommodation (section 46)

iv by obtaining an interim care order (section 38)

v by obtaining a care order (section 33)

When a child is removed from home on a temporary basis, they may be 'accommodated' by being placed with a relative or other suitable person (such as a foster parent), or by placing them in a children's home or in secure accommodation.

In order for a child to be removed from home on a permanent basis a care order must be obtained. However the Act envisages that this step should only be taken as a last resort. Unless a care order is discharged (or ended) earlier, it remains in force until the child is 18.

Supervision orders

Additionally, as an alternative to a care order, the court can make a supervision order (section 34). The duties of the supervisor include:

a to advise, assist and befriend the supervised child

b to take such steps as are reasonably necessary to ensure that the order is carried out

c to request variations to, or discharge of, the order when it is not complied with, or when it is no longer necessary.

Adoption

In certain circumstances it is clear that some children will never be able to return to their parents or any other family member. In these cases the local authority must seek an alternative permanent substitute family. (Exceptions can be made if the child would benefit from remaining in some form of children's home.) Adoption is governed by the Adoption Act 1976, but has been modified by the Children Act. Section 12 of the Adoption Act defines 'adoption'. The main effect of the new Children Act on existing legislation is that, following adoption, the child now has the right to retain contact with its family of origin whereas, previously, all ties were severed.

Parental responsibility

The Children Act uses the concept of 'parental responsibility' to replace the notion of 'parental rights and duties', which was used in earlier legislation. The phrase emphasises the fact that, legally, parenthood is a matter of responsibility rather than rights. The extent of the responsibilities varies according to the age of the child. For example, parents are required to sign forms consenting to medical treatment for a child until the child reaches the age of 16.

The National Health Service and Community Care Act 1990

The NHS and Community Care Act received Royal Assent on 29 June 1990. It incorporates the proposals set out in the Government White Papers 'Working for Patients' (on reforming the NHS) and 'Caring for People' (on community care).

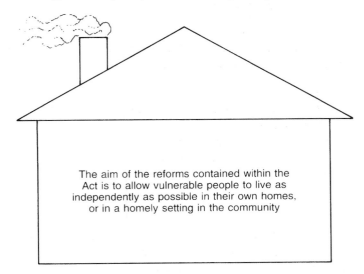

The aim of the reforms contained within the Act is to allow vulnerable people to live as independently as possible in their own homes, or in a homely setting in the community

There are six key objectives:

- to promote the development of home care, day care and short-stays in residential units, to enable people to stay in their own homes for as long as possible.
- to ensure that the needs of the carers are also taken into consideration by service providers.
- to make full assessments of the needs of the individual and to promote good case management to ensure a high quality of care.
- to encourage the development of the independent sector alongside good quality public provision.
- to clarify the responsibilities of both the social services and health authorities and to hold them accountable for their performance.
- to secure better value for taxpayers' money by introducing a new funding structure for social care.

The reforms were introduced in various phases:

- In July 1990 the Regional Health Authorities were reconstituted and new consultants' contracts introduced.
- In September 1990 District Health Authorities were reconstituted.
- By December 1990 the first NHS Trusts were approved.
- In April 1991 the system for contractual funding was introduced, with District Health Authorities and GP Fund Holders as the purchasers of health care.
- In April 1991, local authority complaints procedures and inspection units were set up. Specific grants were made available for mental illness, drug and alcohol services. Work on the purchaser/provider split continued.
- In April 1992 the first joint local authority and health authority community care plans were published. Development of assessment and care management procedures was being carried out.
- From April 1993, DSS funds were transferred to local authorities and new funding arrangements for people seeking public support for residential and nursing home care came into effect. Also, local authorities became responsible for assessing the needs of individuals and for arranging appropriate care.

The Government expects local authorities to secure the delivery of services by developing a purchasing and contracting role, rather than simply acting as direct providers themselves. Local authorities will now be able to enter into contracts with the voluntary and private sectors in order to ensure the provision of services; they are, in fact, encouraged by the government to do this.

Two new terms are permeating the provision of care services: a 'mixed economy of care' and a 'market-place culture'. A *mixed economy of care* means that local authorities will not only be able to provide services themselves, but will also be able to purchase services from other service providers. These might include a private residential home or day centre, or a day centre managed by an organisation such as Age Concern. A *market-place culture* refers to the fact that authorities will be negotiating the cost of services with the service providers in order to ensure that they use the funds available to them in the most effective way. In contracting with other service providers, much emphasis will be placed on quality control and quality assurance. In order for a service provider to obtain a contract with the authority, they will have to comply with certain terms and conditions set out in service specifications contained within the contract. (See Chapter 7.)

Similarly health authorities are responsible for ensuring that the health needs of the population in their area are met. District Health Authorities have taken on the role of assessing health needs and, together with GP fund holders, have responsibility for purchasing the health care to meet those needs. NHS Trusts, hospitals and other services have taken on the management of their own units, and are service providers.

As well as carrying out their new duties under the NHS and Community Care Act, authorities will continue to be required by section 4 of the Disabled Persons' Act 1986 to decide whether they need to provide certain welfare services (i.e. home care and day care) for people who are disabled under section 2(1) of the Chronically Sick and Disabled Persons Act.

The services that an authority may provide, or is required to provide, are principally set out in:

- Part three of the National Assistance Act 1948
- Section 45 of the Health Services and Public Health Act 1948 (welfare services for older people)
- Section 2 of the Chronically Sick and Disabled Persons' Act 1970 (welfare services for people with disabilities)
- Section 117 of the Mental Health Act 1983

(See above.)

Task

Visit your local Social Services Department and obtain a copy of their Community Care Plan. Make a list of the services that are currently available and those that are being planned for the future.

THE ROLES OF HEALTH AND CARE WORKERS

Health and care services are delivered by a wide range of professional and voluntary workers.

Health care workers

Hospital specialists

These are senior hospital doctors (consultants) who specialise in the treatment of a particular condition or disease. Your GP will refer you to a named consultant should you require a specialist diagnosis or treatment. You may ask to be referred to a consultant if you want to get a second opinion about either your GP's diagnosis or treatment of your condition. Hospital specialists may include:

- Geriatrician – specialist in diseases of older people
- Neurologist – specialist in diseases of the brain and nervous system
- Orthopaedic surgeon – specialist in problems caused by disease or injury to bones
- Paediatrician – specialist in care of children and childhood diseases
- Psychiatrist – specialist in mental illness

- Rheumatologist – specialist in diseases related to rheumatism

There are many more! Consultants are supported by a number of other professionals, including junior doctors.

Nurses

Nurses constitute the biggest workforce of professionals in a hospital. As a result of a new system of training for nurses, called Project 2000, learner nurses undertake most of their training in higher education colleges or universities.

In a general hospital (i.e. one that does not specialise in a particular branch of medicine) ward sisters are usually Registered General Nurses (RGNs) and may have additional qualifications. Training for the Enrolled Nurse (EN) has gradually been phased out; but a course for conversion from EN to RGN is available. Essential non-nursing care, such as general hygiene and helping older people with daily living skills, is now undertaken by health care assistants, many of whom will eventually hold NVQS.

Nurses who work in specialist hospitals and units normally hold a qualification relevant to the nursing area in which they practise.

An increasing number of nurses are qualified to degree level and the profession is now attracting many more men than it once did.

GPs

General practitioners (GPs), or 'family doctors', work from their own premises or from health centres. The role of the GP is to provide consultation and physical examination, as appropriate, in order to prevent, identify or treat illness, disease or injury. Providing immunisation and vaccination against infectious diseases such as measles, mumps and rubella (German measles) and polio, as well as more unusual diseases which can be contracted whilst travelling abroad, are also part of the doctor's role. When necessary, the GP can refer patients to other service providers such as hospital consultants, social workers, community nurses and midwives, and to providers in the private and voluntary sectors.

Practice nurses

Practice nurses are employed by GPs to carry out a range of nursing functions, usually in the doctor's premises or 'practice'. Practice nurses give routine injections and screen elders to prevent, or identify at the earliest stage, those medical conditions that are treatable. Practice nurses also take part in health promotion.

Practice nurses are qualified Registered General Nurses (RGNs) or Enrolled Nurses (ENs). Some may have additional qualifications.

Task

Visit a GP's practice and find out what the role of the practice nurse is within the practice. Also find out details of any health promotions that are taking place in the area.

District nurses

District nurses, sometimes called 'community nurses', provide the full range of nursing care in people's own homes. District Nursing Sisters are RGNs (Registered General Nurses), with an additional qualification, who may head a small team of ENs (Enrolled Nurses) and health support care workers. Support workers may have an NVQ in Care. District nurses are usually based at GPs' premises or at health centres.

District nurses may be able to arrange some of the following equipment: bed rails or a raised bed; special mattresses; sheepskin underblankets; hoists of various kinds; bath seats and boards; incontinence pads or sheets; access to bathing services; and access to a night nurse. However, this might depend on what is available locally.

Midwives

Today most babies are born in hospital, although some are born at home. Midwives provide ante-natal and post-natal care as well as delivering babies. Community midwives, who work with GPs and hospital doctors, may be based in clinics, doctors' surgeries and health centres; or they may work from home. Hospital midwives work within a hospital setting.

All midwives, regardless of whether they work in the community or in a hospital, hold the same midwifery qualification of Registered Midwife (RM).

Health visitors

The health visitor has multiple qualifications: health visitors are RGNs, holders of an obstetric nurse's or midwifery qualification and a health visitor's certificate. Health visitors work from clinics or health centre and visit people in their own homes.

The health visitor also teaches health education in schools and a variety of other settings. The role of the health visitor is to provide advice and guidance on health matters. The bulk of the work is related to babies and children under the age of 5. The promotion of good health and the prevention of ill-health is the health visitor's main function.

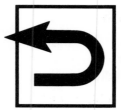

Think it over

What are the main differences between the role of the District Nurse and the Health Visitor?

Occupational therapists

Occupational therapists (OTs) may work in the community, in hospitals or in private establishments. Those working in the community will usually be employed by the local authority and be based in the social services department.

The role of the OT is to work with people who have a disability; to promote independent living skills, such as dressing, washing, toileting. They ensure that capabilities are maximised and disability minimised. OTs use therapeutic activities including craft work.

OTs can also advise on what equipment or home adaptations might help the individual, and they may help to arrange for the provision of these. Equipment for everyday living may include: washing aids; dressing aids; a commode; chairs with high seats; adapted cutlery; play equipment; and adaptations including widening doors, installing stairlifts etc.

Physiotherapists

Physiotherapists help to relieve pain and provide treatment for, and advice on, restoring and maintaining mobility through the use of physical activity and exercise. They may be based in hospitals, in the community, in voluntary organisations or might be in private practice.

Some physiotherapists specialise in certain areas of treatment, for example, in sports injuries. Community physiotherapists will visit people in their own homes to give advice and treatment in relation to mobility and fitness. They can use various kinds of therapies; for example, play therapy with a child who has a physical or mental disability. Physiotherapists may also be able to arrange for the provision of some equipment, such as: walking aids

The role of the health visitor is to promote good health and prevent ill-health

e.g. a walking stick or zimmer frame; or a wheelchair.

Speech therapists

Speech therapists can help adults or children who have speech difficulties. Speech problems may arise as a result of disability, an illness such as a stroke, or through damage such as a head injury caused by a road traffic accident. Speech therapists may also be able to assist where a person has swallowing difficulties.

Speech therapists can be based in schools, clinics, health centres or in hospitals. They may sometimes visit people in their own homes.

Chiropodists

Chiropodists are qualified professionals who specialise in foot care. This can be essential for older people, or people with a disability, in helping them to remain mobile. However they provide a service for people of all ages. Even a minor foot injury or condition, such as a corn, can lead to difficulty in walking.

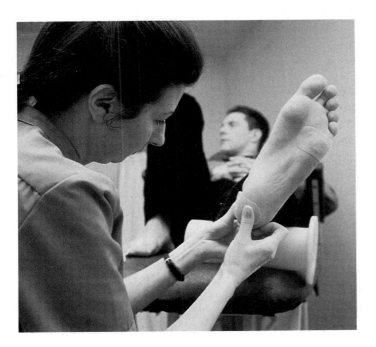

Chiropodists hold surgeries in hospitals, health centres and clinics; some are self-employed and work from private practices. Community chiropodists visit people in their own homes; however, in some areas this service is very limited. GPs can arrange an appointment with a chiropodist or individuals may refer themselves for a private appointment.

Dentists

The role of the dentist is concerned with promoting dental health and hygiene, as well as identifying and treating conditions of the teeth and gums. Many are contracted to the National Health Service through Family Health Service Authorities. Other dentists are in private practice, or offer a combination of these services. Some dentists will visit people in their own homes.

People preferring private dental care will have to meet the costs in full, or through dental care insurance. Those receiving a service through the NHS will also be expected to contribute towards the cost of treatment unless they qualify for free treatment. (See DSS Leaflet – *NHS Dental Treatment* No. D11.)

Opticians

Opticians usually work in dispensaries (opticians shops) or clinics, although some will visit people in their own homes. Many people are required to meet the full cost of eye tests and the cost of glasses or contact lenses. Other people, including children under sixteen years of age, may qualify for either free eye tests or vouchers towards the cost of glasses. (See DSS Leaflet – *NHS Vouchers for glasses* No. G11.)

Continence advisers

Some Health Authority Trusts employ continence advisers. Their job is to assess continence problems, treat incontinence where possible and give practical advice on the management of continence problems. They also advise on aids and equipment, such as incontinence pads, pants or sheets.

Task

Contact your local District Nursing service and find out if there is a Continence Adviser in your area. Visit the Adviser and obtain information on aids and equipment.

- Meals on wheels
- Laundry services
- Equipment for daily living
- Adaptations to the home
- Day care facilities for adults and older people
- Residential homes for short-stays or permanent care for adults and older people
- Nursing home placements
- Nursery or play group placements
- Short or long-term fostering placements
- Short or long-term residential care for children

These services may be directly provided by the local authority, or may be commissioned by them from the independent sector (i.e. private or voluntary agencies).

Paramedics

'Paramedic' is a collective term used for any health worker other than a doctor, nurse or dentist, who supports the work of those professionals. Examples include physiotherapists, radiographers, laboratory assistants and ambulance workers.

Social care workers

Social workers

Social workers, who are usually organised in teams, aim to provide a coordinated service to families and individuals with a wide range of social problems, including personal, practical and financial difficulties. Some social workers specialise in child care, others in working with people with mental illness, learning difficulties, physical disability or with elders.

Many 'field' social workers (the name given to those who work in the community) hold the Certificate of Qualification in Social Work (CQSW) or the Diploma in Social Work (DipSW). Most field social workers are based in area offices. However some may be based in hospitals, although they remain employed by the Social Services Department. Occasionally social workers may be attached to general practices or health clinics. They can act as a useful link between health and social services.

A social worker may be the 'gatekeeper' to many service provisions, such as:

- Home care services
- Night care services

Residential and day care staff

Some social care staff provide physical and emotional care on a daily basis for the full range of clients in either day care or residential care settings – including, for example, older people in residential homes and day centres.

An increasing number of residential and day care staff (at management levels) hold CQSW, DipSW or CSS (Certificate in Social Services) qualifications. Other staff are gaining NVQs in Care, Preliminary Certificate in Social Care (PCSC) or In-service Course in Social Care (ICSC) certificates.

Home care workers

Home care staff go by different names in different parts of the country. They may be called 'home carers', 'home helps', 'domiciliary care workers' or 'community care aides or assistants'. They provide support in a number of ways according to the individual needs of the service user. Most home care staff work with elders, although they can work with any client group. Home carers may be holders of NVQs in care or PCSC or ICSC certificates.

Home carers can provide physical care, including help with personal hygiene and everyday activities, as well as domestic chores, such as housework, cooking and shopping, which may be provided as part of a package of care. (See Chapter 7.) A home carer may be the only contact an elder enjoys with the outside world – so it is a very important role.

· SOCIAL CARE SERVICE PROVISION ·

Children

Child protection

The social services are required to keep an 'at risk' register of all children who they feel to be in danger from psychological, physical or sexual abuse. They will monitor everyone on the list and must be ready to take action if necessary, such as obtaining a court order to remove the child from danger pending investigation. (See the 'Children Act' legislation briefly described above.)

Family support

Social Services aim to support families as far as is possible. A range of help and support could be offered, with the aim of keeping a family together in their own home in their local area. Such help might include a 'family aide' – a person who offers practical help in the home while a parent is ill; or a 'family caseworker' – to work with the family as a whole, trying to improve the quality of family life that a child is experiencing.

Some areas offer 'family centres' where parents and children can go each week for support. Centre

activities may include working with the parent and child to improve communication and understanding, or working just with the parents on the skills of parenting – whilst children are looked after by other qualified staff. There is a move away from the traditional *nursery* provision, towards family centres. Nurseries generally only provided day care for children under school age and provided limited opportunities for working with the parents or family as a whole.

Fostering and adoption

This is now sometimes referred to as 'family placements'. Sometimes children need to be looked after temporarily while they are away from their parents. There could be a number of reasons for this, such as illness, bereavement or being at risk. It is usually a short-term measure. The social services take on the role of organising a foster family which will suit the needs of the child. They also monitor the child in the placement.

Social workers have a crucial role to play in the adoption of a child. They assess the suitability of those who wish to adopt the child and match them with a suitable child. They may also prepare reports for the courts who make the adoption order.

Residential care

Children sometimes require accommodation in residential care homes. Reasons for this may include the illness or absence of parents or parents having difficulties in providing the necessary care or control of the child. Children's homes are usually run by social services staff; they aim to provide a stable background for the children, as close to home life as possible. Residential care also provides homes for children with special needs. Each child is usually offered a 'key worker' who takes a special interest in them.

People with physical disabilities

Day care

Some day care for people with physical disabilities focuses purely on the personal development of the

individual and programmes will focus on the needs of the individual. Many offer social activities and some may be able to provide access to various kinds of therapy, including physiotherapy or occupational therapy.

Residential care

Short-term care may be available in specially adapted and staffed residential units. These can provide opportunities for people with disabilities to enhance their life skills, such as personal hygiene, cooking etc., as well as providing social events and contacts. It also means a rest for the carer. Long-term care may be offered in group homes rather than the more traditional hostel-type accommodation.

Home adaptations

Social services departments may be able to help with various adaptations to the home, such as putting in ramps, the installation of a shower unit or stairlift, or widening doorways. This could enable the person to remain in their own home.

Equipment for daily living

Local authorities will be able to provide a range of equipment to assist the individual to live and cope more easily within their own homes. Although local authorities may differ in exactly what they offer, equipment for daily living might include hand rails in the bathroom, along passage ways or up stairways, and equipment to assist with washing, dressing, eating, getting in and out of bed and so on.

People with learning difficulties

People with learning difficulties may also have physical disabilities and so may require some of the services offered above.

Day centres

Day care services can differ greatly from one local authority to another. Some are still termed 'adult training centres', although in more recent years many have been called 'social education centres'. Both these type of centres have tended to be large institutions which have offered clients employment in limited ways, as well as teaching life skills with the aim of encouraging independent living. However, more recently there has been a move away from these large, multi-functional buildings towards providing a range of innovative daytime activities in smaller units, or in community-based facilities, such as adult education classes within colleges of further education. Other daytime activities may include such projects as drop-in centres or clubs for social activities; small business enterprises; and community service ventures.

Residential accommodation

In the same way, there has been a move away from the provision of large hostel-type accommodation towards living together in smaller units in group homes. The amount of staffing for these homes will vary, depending on the abilities of the residents. For example, in some homes there may be twenty-four hour staff cover, whilst in others a group home's officer may only call in a few times each week or when there are particular problems.

Task

Visit your local social services department and find out what services have been available to people with learning difficulties over the past ten years. Also find out what services are being planned for the future, and how they are to be managed and funded.

People with mental health problems

In line with provision for other clients with 'special needs', such as those described above, day care and residential care provision for people with mental health problems is likely to be provided in much smaller units in the future. However, whereas the local authority has the lead role in provision of services for other client groups, it is the health service who now, under the NHS and Community Care Act 1990, will take the lead role in respect of services for people with mental illness. (See above.)

Services for elders

Home care

Home care for elders has also changed radically in the past few years. The days of the domestic home help have passed and a new type of 'home carer' has come into existence. The home carer's main role is now focused on the personal care of the client, assisting them to get up, wash, bathe, toilet, dress and undress, and get back to bed, as well as preparing meals. Social services may no longer provide a housework-only service; although helping people with these domestic tasks may be provided as part of a care package. (See Chapter 7.)

Many social services are also providing, either directly themselves or through the independent sector, specialist home care services such as 'home from hospital' teams, specialist bathing services or home carers specially trained to work with people

with dementia, physical disabilities or learning difficulties. Other specialist services may include peripatetic night carers (peripatetic means moving from one setting to another). These carers provide a drop-in service throughout the night to people who need assistance with toileting, or people who need help with turning in bed or people who may, due to confusion, be prone to wander at night. Some authorities provide night-sitting schemes, although these tend to be rare. Many of these services may also be available to a wider variety of client groups.

Meals on wheels

Some people are unable to prepare a meal for themselves and have no carer who is able to do so for them. In these situations the local authority may be able to arrange for the provision of meals. This can be done in a variety of ways. The meal may be prepared, cooked and then delivered hot to the client, in specially heated containers. Alternatively, frozen pre-cooked meals, which just need reheating at home, may be provided. These meals would normally be delivered at regular intervals i.e. twice weekly, once a week or even fortnightly. Meals services may be staffed by local authority employees or volunteers or may be provided by voluntary organisations or the independent sector.

Laundry service

This service is provided for older people with particular problems, such as incontinence, where bed linen will need frequent changing. In such cases, social services can sometimes arrange for a home carer to take care of personal laundry for the client.

Day care

Social services often provide day care for people with mobility difficulties which prevent them from getting out and meeting others. The centres may offer social activities and various therapeutic activities, such as exercise classes to maintain or enhance mobility; there may also be reminiscence groups and exercises to help people who may be becoming disorientated.

The management of centres for older, more active people is increasingly being handed over to the voluntary sector, including organisations such as Age

Concern, with local authority provision focusing on the needs of elderly frail people and people with dementia.

Sheltered housing

Sheltered housing is sometimes viewed as a mid-way solution between going into residential care and remaining at home. Sheltered housing consists of individual self-contained living units, either in bungalows or flats, with some communal facilities such as a lounge and laundry. The units are usually unfurnished so that the person can have some of their own things around them. The person is able to live independently but have the support of a warden.

Sheltered accommodation enables a person to live independently but have the support of a warden

Sheltered accommodation may be run by the social services department or the housing department of the local authority. However, there is an increasing number of sheltered housing schemes available in the private sector.

Residential care

Residential accommodation provides twenty-four hour care for those people who have been assessed as requiring this level of support. (See Chapter 7.)

The introduction of 'Home Life Standards' (see Chapter 1), has resulted in a move away from communal living in large, multi-bedded units, to what is called 'unit living'. This aims to provide

homely accommodation for small groups of people (often between five and ten), who have their own lounge, dining, kitchen and bathroom facilities. Many more people are now able to have a single bedroom. However, where people do still have a bedroom, consideration must be given to how their privacy and dignity can be maintained.

Nursing homes

Nursing homes are similar in many ways to residential homes, however they are able to provide twenty-four hour nursing care for those people requiring it. Since April 1993, local authority social services departments have been responsible for the funding of nursing home placements for those people needing financial assistance. (See the 'NHS and Community Care Act' legislation and section on funding above). Social services will, therefore, be responsible for assessing the need for nursing home care, although assessments will often be undertaken with the help of, or by, health service staff.

Task

Consider the differences in circumstances of two older people who are known to you. What services do they receive from health and social services? List any additional services which you think they would benefit from and explain why.

. ACCESS TO HEALTH AND SOCIAL . CARE

Access to health and care services can be achieved in one of three ways: through self-referral; by referral by a 'third party' such as a relative, friend, neighbour etc.; or by being referred by a GP, health visitor, social worker or any other professional.

GPs, social workers and hospital consultants act as 'gate-keepers' to other services. GPs are the 'gate-keepers' to all other medical and nursing services.

Social workers can provide access to social care services, and may also be able to give information about the availability of services in the private and voluntary sector. Other people, such as health visitors, district nurses, occupational therapists and community psychiatric nurses, can often help gain access to various services. Voluntary, private and self-help organisations also accept self-referrals.

Think it over

Imagine that you had permanent mobility problems following a road traffic accident. How would you gain access to health and social care services? What services do you think you might require?

· PRIORITIES AND STRATEGIES ·

Health service

The legal responsibilities for health authorities/boards to provide and promote health care in the community are unchanged by the NHS and Community Care Act 1990. Health authorities/boards are expected to play their part in assessing community care needs and responding to those needs.

Improving health through the strategy set out in 'Health of the Nation' was identified as a top objective for the NHS in 1993/94. All regions produced 'Health of the Nation' implementation plans in January 1993. These set out how regions propose to take forward the strategy locally. The plans set regional goals in addition to the national ones. These goals take account of local needs and variations in health, and place emphasis on health promotion alongside treatment and rehabilitation.

Local authorities

Local Authorities have been given the lead responsibility in relation to community care. For the first time, under the NHS and Community Care Act 1990, legislation places a formal duty on Local Authorities to bring apparent health care needs to the attention of the appropriate health authority/board. Similarly, health professionals are expected to identify social care needs and advise patients appropriately. Community care plans should spell out how the two agencies will put this into effect.

In England and Wales Local Authorities will have to engage with both District Health Authorities and Family Health Services Authorities as the purchasing authorities. There may also be direct negotiation between Local Authorities and provider units, such as NHS trusts, where these offer social care facilities.

Strategies for delivering services

National and regional issues continue to contribute and shape priorities for both health care and social care. Amongst the most significant is the '**Health of the Nation**'. This is a strategy for achieving better health and is a core part of all strategies aimed at prioritising areas of health. Local strategies will be produced by a partnership of District Health Authorities, Family Health Services Authorities, Local Authorities, voluntary organisations and others. (See pages 249–50.)

The Patients' Charter

The Charter offers measurable standards for services, which can be communicated to people using services

and on which they can offer feedback on the effectiveness of local achievements. The areas which can be measured are many but include length of time on waiting lists for in-patient treatment.

Mental health strategy

With the closing of large psychiatric hospitals, and the reprovision of care into the community, major changes have occurred and are occurring in mental health. Moving into the community from an institution requires consultation with users, carers and a range of voluntary and statutory organisations and professionals. This ensures the creation of comprehensive, flexible community-based services that meet the needs of people who often have only known the institutional model of care.

The NHS and Community Care Act

This is the legislation which ensures that community care plans are developed between Local Authorities, Health Authorities and the voluntary and independent sectors. These plans are necessary to meet the individual needs of older people and people with mental health problems, learning disabilities, physical disabilities and the needs of those who care for them.

There is now an emphasis on improving the health of local people, and health care being delivered as near to people's own homes as possible. This necessitates the effective commissioning (or setting up) of primary health care teams. From a base of good primary health care teams, care may be provided effectively in people's own homes.

Strategies are being set in place which will shift the balance of resources from secondary to primary health care. This shift in resources aims to improve people's physical and social function and improves on their role limitations, both emotional and physical. The shift may also show improvements in mental health.

Task

Find out how standards suggested in the Patients' Charter are being measured in your area.

HEALTH CARE SERVICES: STRATEGIES FOR INTERVENTION

There are various models of intervention used within the health services in delivering care or treatment to those people requiring help. Basically there are five main models:

1 Preventative
2 Medical
3 Multi-disciplinary
4 Holistic
5 Remedial

(1) **Preventative** care sets out to encourage people to be more aware of how they can maintain unnecessary onslaught of ill health. The government set out their strategies for preventative campaigns in various White Papers. A recent example of this sort of campaign is HIV and AIDS awareness, which included advertising on national television.

(2) **Medical** models of intervention include drug therapy (e.g. chemotherapy in respect of cancer), surgery and radiotherapy. Drug therapy is very widely used for both physical and mental illnesses and is probably the type of intervention that the majority of people are most familiar with.

Alternative medicine, such as osteopathy (manipulation of bones and muscles by an osteopath), acupuncture and herbal remedies, are not widely used by the health service. It has received varying degrees of support from the medical profession.

(3) **Multi-disciplinary** approaches combine the skills of other professionals, such as occupational therapists and physiotherapists, as well as the more conventional medical models. The aim of this is to use all these forms of therapy in order to restore or maintain levels of ability and health.

(4) **Holistic** approaches go one step further, by taking the person's whole lifestyle into account when treating them. So diet, leisure activities and emotional responses, as well as physical and medical needs, will be considered together. Well-women and well-men clinics are an example of the services that have been developed which use a holistic approach to health care.

(5) **Remedial** approaches do not involve direct chemical or surgical intervention. They concentrate on re-training or providing remedies for a condition. Physiotherapists and occupational therapists will often provide remedial treatments for patients, by providing a series of exercises or activities which may assist recovery from an illness.

All the above strategies involve therapy or therapeutic activities. Sometimes activities such as group work and psychotherapy are considered as separate from other forms of therapeutic intervention. These techniques can be combined in multi-disciplinary approaches, but may sometimes be considered as a sixth strategy.

Self-assessment test

1 Name the three main strands of health care provision.
2 Name the three main purchasing organisations for health care.
3 What are the main sources of funding for the NHS?
4 Name three services that are included in Family Health Services.
5 Name three services that are included in Community Health Services.
6 The provision of health and social services has always been based on a purchaser/provider system. True or false?

7 List two problems that might limit the effectiveness of care services when delivering health or social care.
8 Trust status enables provider units (hospitals) to become independent. Name two areas of independence which might be influenced by trust status.
9 In Northern Ireland, what organisations carry responsibility for providing health and social care?
10 Name two priority areas in 'Health of the Nation'.
11 What powers did the National Assistance Act give to local authorities?
12 Name two Acts of Parliament which have particular significance for older people. Explain why.
13 What are the aims and objectives of the NHS and Community Care Act?
14 How does the Mental Health Act define 'mental disorder'?
15 Name six pieces of equipment for daily living that might assist people with physical disabilities.
16 What is the role of a Continence Adviser?
17 Name the qualifications that a residential care worker might hold.
18 Name two types of worker that might be involved in offering support to children and their families.
19 How are the services for people with learning difficulties changing?
20 Name some specialist home care services that might be available to older people living in their own homes.

Fast Facts

Advocacy Speaking for another person and representing their interests on their behalf.

Children Act An Act of Parliament passed in 1989 which supersedes many previous Acts relating to the welfare and protection of children.

Choice The right of clients to be able to make choices about the care that they receive.

Chronically Sick and Disabled Persons' Act An Act of Parliament which makes provision for people with disabilities. The Act was passed in 1970.

Client Children and their families, adolescents, people with a physical disability or learning disability, people with mental illness and elders make up the main categories of clients or service users.

Community Health Councils These monitor the services commissioned by District Health Authorities (DHAs). They represent the views of health service clients (service users.)

Contracts Formal legal agreements to ensure delivery of services.

Department of Health A central government body which administers health and social care.

Department of Social Security A central government body which provides benefits such as income support and child benefit, and is responsible for social security. The DSS is responsible for the work of the Benefits Agency, which covers one section of social security work.

Disabled Persons (Consultation and Representation) Act An Act of Parliament (1986) which requires local authorities to provide information about the services that are available and requires them to assess the needs of people requesting services.

District Health Authorities Purchasers of health care.

Family Health Service Authorities Family Health Service Authorities employ the services of GPs, dentists, opticians and pharmacists. They share the same geographical boundaries as District Health Authorities (DHAs) and have strong links with them.

Local Authority social services Local Authority social service departments are responsible for ensuring that clients' social care needs are met in the community.

Local Authority Social Services Act An Act of Parliament which sets out the framework for social services provision. The Act was passed in 1970.

National Assistance Act An Act of Parliament (1948) which replaced the Poor Law and gave local authorities the duty to provide accommodation for elders and people with disabilities who were in need.

National Health Service In England, the Secretary of State for Health has the overall responsibility for the National Health Service. The organisation of the NHS in England includes the Department of Health and Health Authorities. In Northern Ireland, Scotland and Wales the organisation is different.

National Health Service and Community Care Act An Act of Parliament passed in 1990 which aims to allow vulnerable people to live as independently as possible, within their own homes or in a homely setting in the community.

Need A need is an essential requirement which must be met in order to ensure that an individual reaches a state of health and social well-being.

Primary Health Care Team A local team of professional health workers, including GPs, district nurses, health visitors, practice nurses and community psychiatric nurses.

Private services These provide an alternative form of care for which there is a charge. Private organisations are run as businesses and are profit making.

Provider An organisation that sells services to a purchaser.

Purchaser An organisation that buys in necessary services.

Service specifications Statements describing the nature of the services that the purchaser expects to buy.

Statutory organisations Health and care services are provided by statutory, voluntary and private organisations. Statutory organisations must be set up by law (statute) to provide a service or range of services. The National Health Service and Local Authority social services departments form two main branches of the health and social care industry.

Voluntary organisations   Voluntary organisations provide a vast network of services to bridge gaps in statutory provision. Their services are often provided free of charge. Voluntary organisations are non-profit making.

Recommended further reading

Stephen Moore (1993) *Social Welfare Alive* Stanley Thornes Ltd.

References

Brayne and Martin (1990) *Law for Social Workers* Blackstone Press Ltd

Kohner, Nancy (1988) *Caring at Home* King's Fund

McDonald and Taylor (1993) *Elders and the Law* PEPAR

Care Management and Assessment: The Managers' Guide (HMSO 1991)

Purchase of Service (HMSO 1991)

'Caring for People – Community Care in the Next Decade and beyond' (White Paper, HMSO 1989)

'Caring for People – Information Pack for the Voluntary and Private Sectors' (Department of Health Community Care Information, February 1993)

'Contracting in the Social Services: Caring for People' (No. 10, 1992)

'NHS Made Easy' (1993, Department of Health, NHS Management Executive, Staff Development Unit)

'Health of the Nation' (1992, Department of Health, HMSO)

'Community Care Changes in April 1993' (1993, Department of Health Community Care Information)

Appendix 1 '**Health of the Nation**' **TARGETS IN FULL (1992)**

Coronary heart disease (CHD) and stroke

To reduce death rates for both CHD and stroke in people under 65 by at least 40% by the year 2000 (from 58 per 100,000 population in 1990 to no more than 35 per 100,000 for CHD and from 12.5 per 100,000 population in 1990 to no more than 7.5 per 100,000 for stroke.)

To reduce the death rate for CHD in people aged 65–74 by at least 30% by the year 2000 (from 899 per 100,000 population in 1990 to no more than 629 per 100,000).

To reduce the death rate for stroke in people aged 65–74 by at least 40% by the year 2000 (from 265 per 100,000 population in 1990 to no more than 159 per 100,000).

To reduce the prevalence of cigarette smoking in men and women aged 16 and over to no more than 20% by the year 2000 (a reduction of at least 35% in men and 29% in women, from a prevalence in 1990 of 31% and 28% respectively).

To reduce mean systolic blood pressure in the adult population by at least 5mm Hg by 2005.

To reduce the percentages of men and women aged 16–64 who are obese, by at least 25% for men and at least 33% for women by 2005 (from 8% for men and 12% for women in 1986/87 to no more than 6% and 8% respectively).

To reduce the average percentage of food energy derived by the population from saturated fatty acids by least 35% by 2005 (from 17% in 1990 to no more than 11%).

To reduce the average percentage of food energy derived by the population from total fat by at least 12% by 2005 (from about 40% in 1990 to no more than 35%).

To reduce the proportion of men drinking more than 21 units of alcohol per week from 28% in 1990 to 18% by 2005 and the proportion of women drinking more than 14 units of alcohol per week from 11% in 1990 to 7% by 2005.

Cancers

To reduce the death rate for breast cancer in the population invited for screening by at least 25% by the year 2000 (from 95.1 per 100,000 population in 1990 to no more than 71.3 per 100,000).

To reduce the incidence of invasive cervical cancer by at least 20% by the year 2000 (from 15 per 100,000 population in 1986 to no more than 12 per 100,000).

To halt the year-on-year increase in the incidence of skin cancer by 2005.

To reduce the death rate for lung cancer by at least 30% in men under 75 and 15% in women under 75 by 2010 (from 60 per 100,000 for men and 24.1 per 100,000 for women in 1990 to no more than 42 and 20.5 respectively).

To reduce the prevalence of cigarette smoking in men and women aged 16 and over to no more than 20% by the year 2000 (a reduction of at least 35% in men and 29% in women, from a prevalence in 1990 of 31% and 28% respectively).

In addition to the overall reduction in prevalence, at least a third of women smokers to stop smoking at the start of their pregnancy by the year 2000.

To reduce the consumption of cigarettes by at least 40% by the year 2000 (from 98 billion manufactured cigarettes per year in 1990 to 59 bn).

To reduce the smoking prevalence among 11–15 year olds by at least 33% by 1994 (from about 8% in 1988 to less than 6%).

Mental illness

To improve significantly the health and social functioning of mentally ill people.

To reduce the overall suicide rate by at least 15% by the year 2000 (from 11.1 per 100,000 population in 1990 to no more than 9.4).

To reduce the suicide rate of severely mentally ill people by at least 33% by the year 2000 (from the estimate of 15% in 1990 to no more than 10%).

Accidents

To reduce the death rate for accidents among children aged under 15 by at least 33% by 2005 (from 6.7 per 100,000 population in 1990 to no more than 4.5 per 100,000).

To reduce the death rate for accidents among young people aged 15–24 by at least 25% by 2005 (from 23.2 per 100,000 population in 1990 to no more than 17.4 per 100,000).

To reduce the death rate for accidents among people aged 65 and over by at least 33% by 2005 (from 56.7 per 100,000 population in 1990 to no more than 38 per 100,000).

HIV/AIDS and sexual health

To reduce the incidence of gonorrhoea among men and women aged 15–64 by at least 20% by 1995 (from 61 new cases per 100,000 population in 1990 to no more than 49 new cases per 100,000).

To reduce the percentage of injecting drug misusers who report sharing injecting equipment in the previous four weeks by at least 50% by 1997, and by at least a further 50% by the year 2000 (from 20% in 1990 to no more than 10% by 1997 and no more than 5% by the year 2000).

To reduce the rate of conceptions amongst the under 16s by at least 50% by the year 2000 (from 9.5 per 1,000 girls aged 13–15 in 1989 to no more than 4.8).

· WHAT IS A CARE PLAN? ·

A **care plan** is a written document which outlines how the needs of an individual are to be met. It states what the needs are and sets out how these are to be met. There are two forms of care plan:

- The **macro care plan** is the overall identification of needs and lists all the agencies who will be involved in providing services.

- The **micro care plan** is the plan which the individual service provider will use to describe the action plan within their own agency.

For example, below are the care plans for Mrs Banerjee:

Macro care plan

Needs	Action	Provider
Help with personal hygiene	(i) daily wash (ii) weekly bath	Home Care Bath Service

Micro care plan (home care)

Needs	Action	By whom
(i) daily wash	● assist to bathroom ● wash face, neck, hands, arms ● assist to dress after drying	Home Carer

Micro care plan (Bath service)

Needs	Action	By whom
(ii) weekly bath	Wednesday a.m. ● seated bath ● hair wash ● nails cut	Bath attendant

What is the purpose of care planning?

Care planning is a tool which provides direction for all those working to meet the clients' needs. It:

- ensures continuity/responsibility/commitment
- should be realistic/practical/workable
- recognises client's choice/carer's needs
- gives consistency – linking all appropriate services
- has flexibility

Who is it for?

A care plan is a clearly defined document of *needs*, designed for the client, bringing together all the agencies involved in providing services.

Part of an assessment and care management process

Care planning is part of the **Assessment and Care Management** process. This process of identifying and arranging care underpins all other elements of community care. It is relevant to a large number of people, in all care agencies, whether in local authorities, in health authorities or boards, or in the independent sector.

Read Case-study A below.

Case-study A

Mr Andrews is 68 years old. He is currently in hospital following a serious chest infection which caused him to become extremely confused. He has recovered from the chest infection, but has other problems related to multiple sclerosis which he has suffered from for the last ten years. He has become less mobile and is finding it difficult to walk, even using sticks.

Mr and Mrs Andrews are a white couple who have been married for thirty years and live in council accommodation. They have no children.

Mrs Andrews is happy to care for her husband, but this has put her under great emotional and physical strain. Mrs Andrews weighs only eight stone; her husband weighs sixteen stone. Mrs Andrews needs support and time for herself. She would like to be able to go out shopping without having to worry about her husband. She would also like to be able to visit a friend who lives many miles away, once or twice a year.

Mr Andrews has reluctantly agreed that he needs to use a wheelchair. This means that some adaptations are needed to their home. The bedroom has currently had to be moved downstairs, to be on the same level as the toilet and kitchen; but it would be difficult to get a wheelchair into the toilet. Mr Andrews enjoys the company of other people and likes to play cards occasionally.

Mr Andrews is keen to get home. His wife is also keen for him to leave hospital, but is anxious about how the care package will work out. In the past she has only had contact with the District Nurse, and more recently has had some support from Age Concern. Neither are sure what help could be available to them.

Theory into practice

Who is the client? How would a care plan help Mr and Mrs Andrews? What are the main concerns of Mr Andrews? Mrs Andrews?

ASSESSMENT AND CARE MANAGEMENT

Assessment and care management constitute one integrated process for identifying and addressing the needs of individuals, recognising that those needs are unique to the individuals concerned. *Care management* is the process of tailoring services to individual needs. *Assessment* is an integral part of care management, but it is only one of the seven core tasks that make up the whole process.

The process of care management is outlined in Figure 7.1 below. As the diagram shows, care management is a cyclical process.

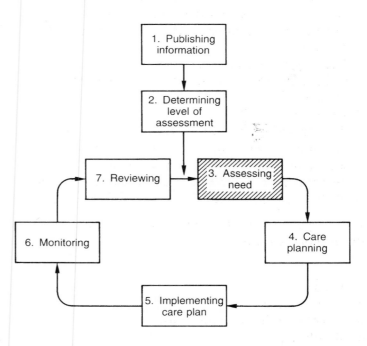

Figure 7.1 *The process of care management*

Core tasks

The seven core tasks of the Assessment and Care Management process are:

1 *Publishing information*
Clients and their carers are given information about the needs for which care agencies accept responsibility and the range of services available.

2 *Determining the level of assessment*
An enquirer requests more than just information, sufficient details are obtained in order to determine the type of assessment that is required, e.g. a simple assessment or a complex assessment.

3 *Assessing need*
The needs of the individual are assessed in a way that recognises their strengths and aspirations, as well as those of their carers. The purpose of the assessment is to define the individual's needs in the context of local policies.

4 *Care planning*
The role of the assessor is to assist the client in making choices from statutory, private or community sources that best meet their needs.

5 *Implementing care plans*
This means securing the necessary finance or other resources. It may involve negotiating with a variety of service providers and ensuring that services are co-ordinated with one another.

6 *Monitoring*
Because circumstances change, the care plan has to be monitored continuously and adjustments made where necessary.

7 *Reviewing*
At specified intervals, the progress of the care plan has to be reviewed with the client, carers and service providers to ensure that the service remains relevant to needs, and to evaluate services as part of the continuing quest for service improvement.

For the purpose of this chapter we are concentrating on the core tasks of:

- Assessment
- Care planning
- Implementation of care plans
- Monitoring
- Reviewing

· HOW ASSESSMENT WORKS ·

Under the NHS and Community Care Act 1990, all assessments must be focused on the actual *needs* of the client and of their carer, irrespective of what resources are available. A *needs-led* assessment fits resources to people – not people into services.

What is 'need'?

The term *need* is used as shorthand for: the requirements of individuals to enable them to achieve, maintain or restore an acceptable level of social independence or quality of life.

Individuals may perceive their needs in different ways, therefore the assessor must understand the viewpoint of the client and what is important to them. This will determine the scope of the assessment and the degree of detail required in order to complete the assessment. Needs may be categorised in different ways:

- personal and social care
- physical health
- mental health
- cultural and religious needs
- accommodation
- transport/access
- finance
- education/employment/leisure
- needs of carer

The assessor, who could be a social worker, occupational therapist, home-care manager, community psychiatric nurse, district nurse etc., carries out the assessment through discussion with the client and their carer. The assessment takes into account the whole range of needs and wishes. The assessment may involve further meetings and discussions with others (with the permission of the client), including other professionals and possible service providers. However, only in a minority of cases will there be any kind of formal panel meeting or conference. (See Figure 7.2, on the next page.)

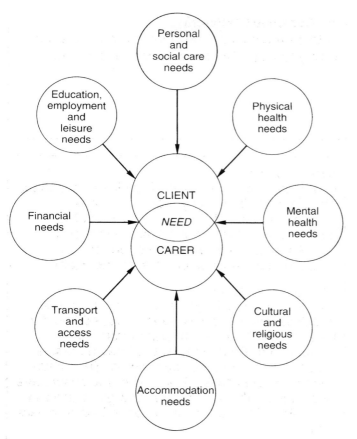

Figure 7.2 *Determining 'need'*

Macro care plan assessment

Assessment of need checklist

It is suggested that this checklist is not printed as a form as such, but as a set of headings and pointers with spaces, so that people can use it as a note pad or aid to memory, etc. The intention is to gain information for the care management and assessment process, so as to enter appropriate needs information on the care planning and assessment form. It is important to avoid collecting too much information or intruding on clients' privacy.

1 Environment and housing

1.1 (Any problems with the heating or the person's ability to control it? Any problems with access or issues for providing services? Can the person use telephone, hear/answer front door?

What about handles, switches, taps etc.??) Emergency contact?

1.2 Is the housing suitable? Problems? Type of housing (owner occupier, council, private, rented, sheltered, shared, house, flat etc. if relevant)

1.3 Access to transport?

2 Communication

Do we have a problem in communicating – i.e. do we need to supply an interpreter? Does the person have any problems with sight, hearing, speech that cause difficulty? Equipment used/needed?

3 Personal care

Dressing/undressing – difficulty? help needed?
Washing –
Continence –
Mobility (indoors and out), transfers (chair, bed, toilet)

4 Housework

Prepare meals? Feed selves? Equipment/help?
Shopping
Laundry
Cleaning

5 Physical and emotional health

Any concerns about the person's health?
Any disability? Relevant doctor's diagnosis?
Been contacted?
How does this affect daily living?
Any problems with e.g. forgetfulness, sense of direction etc.?
Bereavement, loss, other major changes?
Sleep pattern?
Can the person manage medication (what is it if relevant)?

6 Abilities, aptitudes, social life

What does the person enjoy, do well, want to do?
Any difficulties in their doing it?
Who do they like to be with/ditto
Live alone? With whom?

7 Employment, educational needs/wishes

8 Financial information

Is income sufficient for needs? Are they receiving a benefit?

9 Other agencies

Are other agencies involved? What help are they giving? Any problems around this? Any key people?

10 Carer/care network

Is there a carer/care network? Who is able and willing to help? Stresses? Gaps? Long term?

Case-study B

Mrs Bradshaw suffers from Alzheimer's Disease. The illness is in its early stages and was diagnosed about six months ago. She also suffers from arthritis and takes medication for this. There is some evidence of an alcohol problem, but details about this are not clear.

Family background
Mrs Bradshaw is 71 years old. She is married and lives with her husband in a ground-floor flat. Mr and Mrs Bradshaw migrated from the Caribbean to England in 1955. They have four children, who live away from home. They have seven grandchildren. Mr and Mrs Bradshaw have close links with their children and grandchildren. Both Mr and Mrs Bradshaw have retired from paid work.

Services involved and current situation
Mrs Bradshaw attends an Afro-Caribbean lunch club one day a week to give her husband a break. Staff there say she often seems worried and agitated on arrival, but is in a better state by the time she leaves.

Mr Bradshaw has contacted you (a social worker at the local Social Services office) through the staff at the lunch club. He would like a longer break from his wife and wonders if something residential could be arranged, so that he could visit relatives on his own. He says that he is finding his wife's behaviour hard to handle. She doesn't sleep well, is often up during the night, and her memory is deteriorating. For example, she often decides to do something, like go to the kitchen, and when she gets there, she can't remember why she's gone. She likes to drink and, now that her memory is so bad, he worries that she is drinking too much, because she can't remember if she's had one already. She is becoming difficult with him when she mislays things and accuses him of hiding things from her.

Theory into practice

Who is the client?
What are Mr Bradshaw's main areas of concern?
What do you think are the key needs of: Mrs Bradshaw? Mr Bradshaw?
How would you begin to assess the needs of Mr and Mrs Bradshaw?

The assessment process

Referrals come into the agency and are allocated to the appropriate client group. For example, in Social Services – Physical Disabilities, Learning Disability, Mental Illness, Children and Families, or Elderly Services; in Health Settings – acute or community services. After allocation a person will be identified to assess the client's needs, but they must also take into account the needs of the client's carer.

The assessment of need should broadly follow this sequence:

- negotiate scope of the assessment
- choose setting for assessment
- clarify expectations with clients
- promote participation with clients
- establish relationship of trust between yourself and clients
- assess need
- set priorities
- agree objectives with clients
- record the assessment

See Figure 7.3 in the next column.

1 *Negotiating the scope of assessment*
Simple needs will require less investigation than complex ones. The assessment should be as simple, speedy and as informal as possible.

Procedures for assessment should be based on the principle of what is the *least* that it is necessary to know. It follows therefore that the assessor must be trained to use their discretion and to target the

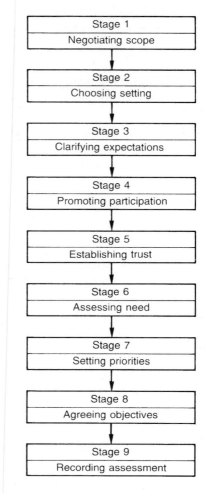

Figure 7.3 *9 stage assessment process*

relevant areas of need. The scope of the assessment has to be individually negotiated.

Assessment is a two-way process between the assessor and the client. However, it may be necessary to involve other people and other agencies in the process. This will generally be in the more complex assessment and must be subject to the consent of the client. The minority of clients will have complex needs. (See Figure 7.4 on the next page.)

2 *Agreeing the setting*
The assessor carries out the assessment through discussion with the client (and carer where appropriate), at a prearranged place and time. In order for the client and carer to participate as fully as possible it is often better to use an informal place

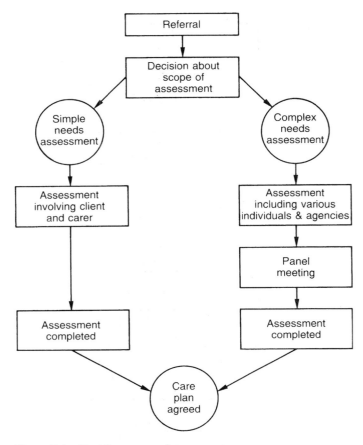

Figure 7.4 *Deciding scope of assessment*

for the interview, such as the client's home, rather than the formal setting of an office. This will encourage the client to relax and thus give a fuller picture of their needs and wishes.

If the client is considering admission to a residential or nursing home, involving the irreversible loss of their home, they should always be given the opportunity of experiencing that setting before making their final decision.

It may be necessary for some part of the assessment to be undertaken away from their home, for example at a day centre or residential care setting, which enables the assessor to work more closely with the client and for longer periods. It is therefore important to look flexibly at what setting is to be used when completing the assessment. However, care must be taken to avoid unnecessary disruption to the client.

3 *Clarifying expectations*
The assessor must ensure that the client understands:

– what is involved in the assessment
– the likely timescale for completing the assessment
– the possible outcomes
– their entitlement to information, participation and representation
– their right to withdraw from the process at any time

4 *Promoting participation*
The assessor must judge how the client and/or their carer can actively be involved in the process. Some clients will have a clear understanding of their own needs. Some clients will confuse 'wants' with 'needs'. For example, a person who feels isolated due to lack of mobility, and difficulties in getting up and down stairs, may *want* alternative accommodation. What they *need* may be an adaptation to the home, such as moving the bedroom downstairs or the installation of a stairlift. Others will need the support of representatives (or advocates) in order to be able to make their needs known. Where clients and carers are unable, for any reason, to be able to speak for themselves, it is important that they are given information regarding any advocacy schemes funded by the local authority or run locally. For example, the local branch of Age Concern may have volunteers who will work with individuals by helping them express their views in discussions with others.

If the assessor can focus on the clients' strengths at the beginning of the assessment process, then this will encourage the client to contribute to the whole assessment procedure.

An assessment should help both the assessor and the client to balance both the positives and negatives in a given situation. In so doing, clients are helped to feel that they are being regarded as whole persons. The assessor will be enabled to place the client's needs in perspective. Clients and carers should receive every help to speak and act for themselves by ensuring that:

● staff have, wherever possible, the appropriate communication skills (e.g. language, cultural understanding or technical skills, including signing).

- clients and carers have ready access to communication equipment and to interpreters or communicators, where assessment staff do not possess such skills
- the use of interpreters or communicators in no way disadvantages clients and carers from also having an independent representative, if that is what they wish.

5 *Establishing a relationship of trust*

The assessor has to establish a relationship of trust with the client and their carer. Listening, observing and understanding are of paramount importance. Assessment involves considerable skills in **interpersonal relations**. Assessors should be aware of their limitations and know when to involve others with more specialist expertise or cultural understanding.

If clients are dissatisfied by either the process or the outcome of the assessment, they should be supported in making representation under the Complaints Procedures. This will encourage trust.

6 *Assessing need*

The assessor has to define as precisely as possible the cause of any difficulty; for example, someone with learning disabilities may be under-functioning through lack of knowledge, loss of confidence or depression, or as a consequence of some breakdown in relationships. The proper identification of the cause is the basis for the selection of the appropriate service response. Everybody involved in the assessment process is likely to perceive the need in a different way. The assessor must aim for a degree of consensus; however, wherever the client is competent, and capable of expressing their wishes, their view must carry most weight. Where differences between the views of the client and the assessor are irreconcilable, these views should be acknowledged and recorded as this may help in the understanding of the client's needs over time. The assessment process must ultimately define the *client's* need.

7 *Setting priorities*

The assessor and client must now agree on their relative priorities. It will be comparatively easy to distinguish between:

- immediate needs e.g. health crisis or breakdown of care

- acute short-term needs, e.g. home care following a fractured hip
- chronic long-term needs, e.g. continuing support for personal care

However, the assessor will first wish to identify:

- those needs that most concern the client
- those needs that most concern the carer
- those needs that the client/carer is most motivated to address
- those needs on which intervention is acceptable to the client/carer

8 *Agreeing objectives*

The final stage of the assessment of need consists of agreeing the objectives to be met for each of the prioritised needs. As far as care agencies are concerned, objectives fall into four main categories:

- promoting or restoring independent functioning
- maintaining care for the client
- providing substitute care
- arranging support for carers

To have any value, objectives must be capable of being measured. This is easy when it relates to quantitative goals, like the speed or frequency of completing self-care tasks; but it can be more difficult for qualitative goals where, for example, social well-being may have to be measured by indicators such as contact time with friends.

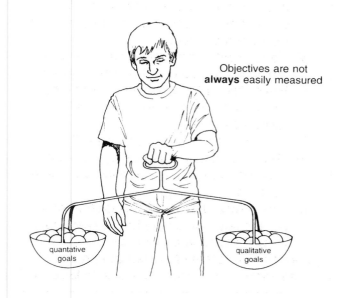

Objectives are not **always** easily measured

quantative goals

qualitative goals

9 *Recording the assessment*

All assessments must be recorded and most agencies will have some type of proforma. This is a pre-designed form which can be used with each client. In many instances the Local Authority and Health Authority will use a form that has been designed jointly.

Although it is the assessor's responsibility to ensure that the form is completed appropriately, there is no reason why the client (or their carer) should not complete part, or all, of their own assessment form. Again this encourages full participation in the assessment process. Assessment forms should therefore be easily understandable and in clear language. It must distinguish between fact and opinion, 'wants' and 'needs'.

The client, their carer, any representative of the client and all the people who are to provide a service to the client, including other agencies, should receive a copy of the assessment form. This record will normally be accompanied by a written care plan (the next stage of the care management process). The care plan will set out how the needs of the client and their carer are to be addressed.

Task

Think about either Case-study A or B, then write out possible answers to the checklist questions above. Or think about a real person you have worked with and answer the checklist questions.

· DEVELOPMENT OF A CARE PLAN ·

At the start of this chapter care plans were defined. To recap, a care plan is a specific plan of action with clearly defined aims and objectives. It should include and allow for regular monitoring and evaluation. It should include all aspects of a person's ability to function in daily living.

It is the role of the assessor (purchaser) to develop a care plan. A care plan is a clearly defined document of needs designed for the client, bringing together all the agencies involved and indicating what services are provided and by whom. The assessor is also called a *care manager*. An assessor may be a social worker, occupational therapist or home care purchasing officer.

The care manager carries out the assessment though discussion with the client (and carer if appropriate) at a prearranged place and time. The assessment takes account of the whole range of needs and wishes.

As assessment is a purchasing function it is important that the care manager has an

---

Assessment checklist

Assessors can use this list to check that they have covered all the key points.

1) Has the assessment been negotiated with the client and their carer?
2) Has the appropriate setting been chosen?
3) Has the client (and their carer) understood how the assessment will be done, what this will involve and how long it will take?
4) Has the client (and carer) been involved in making the assessment? Have their ethnic, cultural and communication needs been taken into account?
5) Have clients and carers had access to advocacy support where appropriate?
6) Have different perceptions of need been reconciled? If not, have they been recorded?
7) Have the needs been prioritised?
8) Have the objectives been agreed and the way that they are to be measured been decided?
9) Has a record of the assessment been shared with the client, their carer and relevant service providers?

(Adapted from *Care Management and Assessment – Practitioners' Guide* HMSO, 1991) understanding of the financial resources available and is able to discuss these and the client's own financial situation with the client and carer if appropriate. This is an integrated assessment of need and financial situation, rather than a specific assessment for a particular service.

The outcome of the assessment will normally be a clear statement of needs and realistic options for meeting them.

A needs-led assessment must:

- share and agree information and inter-agency assessments of needs
- define clients'/carers' needs
- agree and plan options for packages of care.

The plan agreed after this process is the Macro Care Plan.

Care planning

Definition of 'care plan'

A definition could be as follows. 'To identify the most appropriate ways of achieving the objectives identified by the assessment of need and incorporate them into an individual care plan.'

Process

First, the assessor should, having identified the needs, link into the appropriate resource to meet those needs. Care planning is then a series of linked activities: determining the type of plan; set priorities, and so on.

Determining the type of plan

Care plans will vary according to the complexity of need. If it is a simple need which can be met by a single service, the care planning will be swiftly accomplished. All people who receive a service should have a care plan which defines the user's needs and the objectives to be met by any services from a number of different agencies. For example, see Case-study A of Mr Andrews and the Care Plan on page 276.

Set priorities

The assessment should have prioritised the client's needs so they should be tackled in priority order. Care planning should be flexible and able to adjust priorities as the needs of the client change. For example, Mr Andrews may need more residential respite care as his condition changes.

Complete definition of service requirements

Once the client's needs are defined, and the services identified to meet those needs, the macro care plan must be precise as to how the service will meet those needs. For example, times of the day that care will be needed.

Explore the resources of clients and carers

For the majority of clients the aim will be to promote their independence and care planning should enable clients and carers to make the most of their own resources and abilities, i.e. the things that they can do well.

Review existing services

Existing services should be reviewed in the light of the needs-led assessment and new services introduced appropriately.

Consider alternatives

In taking a fresh look at users' needs, it is essential that practitioners have a comprehensive knowledge of services available across the statutory and independent sector. Care planning is an opportunity to be creative and innovative in designing packages of care to meet the users' needs.

Discuss options

Once identified, these options should be fully discussed with the client and relevant carers only.

Establish preferences

Wherever possible clients should be offered a choice of service options appropriate to their ethnic and cultural background. For example, Mr Bradshaw (page 279) attends Afro/Caribbean club.

Cost care plan

It is vital that the care plan be costed. Clients should always know the estimated cost to themselves of any options under active consideration.

Assess financial means

If charges are to be levied in respect of any services, care planning will involve an assessment of the clients' financial means and ability to pay. Clients should not agree a care plan before they have been advised in writing of any charges involved.

Reconcile preferences and resources

Having established the wishes of the client, and the cost of the selected options, these may have to be checked against the available resources. This may be done by the care manager alone, if they hold delegated budgets, or in conjunction with other relevant management.

Agree service objectives

Having confirmed the service options that can be resourced, the next stage is to finalise the agreements with all the agencies and individuals who are to contribute to care plans. This will include the contribution of the clients and carers themselves. The objectives of their inputs should be made clear to all contributors. These should be consistent with the objectives agreed with the client during the initial assessment stage. There should also be a common understanding of how these objectives will be measured.

Co-ordinate plan

Care managers and other workers must integrate the parts of a care plan into a coherent whole that makes sense to the client and their carers. All contributors to a care plan should be aware of the overall objectives of the plan and be mutually supportive to one another. A care plan must be flexible.

Fix review

The client should be told the name of the worker (or key worker) who will be responsible for the implementation, monitoring and review of the care

plan. A date should be set for the first review of the care plan. The key worker (a named person with special responsibilities toward the client) should undertake an earlier review should circumstances require this.

Identify unmet need

Having completed the care plan, the worker should identify any assessed need which it has not been possible to address and identify for what reason. This information should be fed back for service planning and quality assurance.

Record the care plan

Care plans should be set out in concise written form linked with the assessment of need. A care plan should be a blueprint for action.

Task

Using Case-study A or B, or a real-life situation, check if the care plan contains the components suggested in the checklist (see next page).

Care planning: checklist

Practitioners can use this list to check that key points are covered:

1 Is the care plan based on the needs, priorities and objectives identified at the assessment stage?
2 Does it have a clear overall objective with specific objectives for all contributors, including the means of measuring their performance?
3 Does it set out the services to be supplied?
4 Does it make maximum use of the client's and carers' own resources?
5 Was the user offered a genuine choice of options?
6 Does it make co-ordinated and cost-effective use of the resources available to the client and agencies across the statutory and independent sectors?
7 Has it been costed?
8 Does it identify any unmet need?
9 Does it record any points of difference?
10 Have the practitioner(s) responsible for implementation, monitoring and review been decided?
11 Has a date for the first review been set?
12 Has a copy been given to the client and other contributors?

(Adapted from *Care Management and Assessment – Practitioners' Guide* HMSO, 1991)

. IMPLEMENTING THE MACRO CARE . PLAN

The guiding principle of implementation should be to achieve the stated objectives of the care plan with the minimum of intervention necessary. It should therefore seek to minimise the number of service-providers involved.

Process of implementation

The person responsible for devising the care plan should carry the responsibility for its implementation.

The tasks of implementation will include the following:

- determine the client/carer participation
- agree pace of implementation
- confirm budget
- check service availability
- renegotiate existing services
- contract new services
- test options
- revise care plan and costing
- establish monitoring arrangements

Determine the client/carer participation

The starting point for implementation should be the clients and their carers, because all other inputs should be geared to supporting their contribution. Clients and carers should be encouraged to play as active a part in the implementation of their care plan as their abilities and motivation allow. Clients may require considerable reassurance and persuasion to accept help, as may carers who feel threatened by such intrusion. All clients should be included in the decision-making associated with the implementation of their care plans.

Agree pace of implementation

Work on implementation should commence as soon as the care plan has been finalised, but the pace at which it is implemented should be carefully negotiated with the clients and their carers.

Assessment by Care Manager (Health and Social Services)

DATE
CUSTOMER - Mr Andrews
CARE MANAGER
KEY WORKER
REVIEW DATE

Needs	How needs are met	Action by
1) Personal care to assist Mr Andrews to get up, go to bed and use toilet. 2) Regular breaks/respite, so that Mr and Mrs Andrews have more personal space.	1a) Personal care service daily, morning and evening as part of care package. 2a) Mr Andrews to have day care 4 times a week, and to have a bath while there. b) Mr Andrews to have short stays in residential respite care for 2 weeks twice a year. c) Mrs Andrews to attend carers' group – once every fortnight. d) Person to sit with Mr Andrews while Mrs Andrews goes to carers' group. e) Transport needed to enable these breaks/respite to occur.	1a) Care Manager to negotiate Home Care Service. 2a) Care Manager to negotiate with Day Centre/Key Worker. b) Care Manager to negotiate with Residential Home. c) Care Manager to negotiate with Age Concern. d) Care Manager to negotiate with Cross Roads. e) Care Manager to negotiate with Day Centre/Key Worker.
3) Emotional needs – both Mr and Mrs Andrews need somebody to talk through their situation.	3a) Mr Andrews needs to be met by Day Centre Worker – Key worker. b) Mrs Andrews will attend carers group.	3a) Care Manager to negotiate with Day Centre/Key Worker. b) Care Manager to negotiate with Age Concern.
4) Mr Andrews feels he needs broader interests and hobbies. 5) Mrs Andrews wants to know more about her husband's condition and how she can help as a carer.	4a) Day Centre Worker – Key Worker – to discuss and pursue with Mr Andrews. 5a) Support for Mrs Andrews through carers' group. b) Care Manager will ask GP to discuss with Mrs Andrews.	4a) Care Manager to negotiate with Day Centre/Key Worker. 5a) Care Manager to set up. Key worker to link with chair of carers' group. b) Care Manager to activate.
6) Continuing assessment of Mr Andrews' ability to perform tasks in his home. 7) Adaptation of home to ease access problems.	6a) Occupational Therapy assessment to be updated once has moved home. 7a) Door to be widened if possible. b) Possibility of lift to be considered.	6a) Care Manager to negotiate with Occupational Therapist. 7a) Care Manager to request and liaise with Occupational Therapist and Housing Department.

Figure 7.5 *Example of a care plan – see Case-study A (page 276)*

Assessment by Care Manager (Health and Social Services)

Needs	How needs are met	Action by
1) Mrs Bradshaw needs assessors who respect cultural background.	1a) Contact Afro/Caribbean agency and request person from same cultural background.	1a) Care Manager
2) Mrs Bradshaw needs to be able to continue with friends/sports/other activities.	2a) Involving her children, grandchildren and friends in her care whenever possible.	2a) Care Manager
3) Mrs Bradshaw needs to be able to express fears re. her condition/change of role.	3a) Weekly meetings with Community Psychiatric Nurse.	3a) Care Manager
4) Mrs Bradshaw needs to be able to sustain relationships with family.	4a) Encouraging family visits and outings	4a) Care Manager
5) Mrs Bradshaw needs to establish a regular sleep pattern.	5a) Involve GP.	5a) Care Manager
6) Mrs Bradshaw needs to keep as much in touch with reality as possible.	6a) Lifestyle needs to be reality/orientation-centred.	6a) Specialist Home Carer for dementia
7) Mrs Bradshaw needs system to monitor her alcohol.	7a) Set up a system of diarying alcohol intake.	7a) Home Carer and husband
8) Mr Bradshaw needs a break regularly.	8a) Arrange regular short-stay breaks for Mrs Bradshaw.	8a) Care Manager
9) Mr Bradshaw needs to be able to sustain relationships with family	9a) Point 8 would assist Mr Bradshaw to do this.	9a) Care Manager
10) Mr Bradshaw needs to understand diagnosis and prognosis.	10a) Regular meetings with Community Psychiatric Nurse and Carers' Support Group.	10a) Care Manager
11) Mr Bradshaw needs to be able to talk about his fears and frustrations.	11a) Regular meetings with Community Psychiatric Nurse and Carers Support Group.	11a) Care Manager
12) The whole family need to be facilitated to meet to problem solve.	12a) Regular meetings of family with Care Manager.	12a) Care Manager

Figure 7.6 *Example of a care plan – see Case-study B (page 279)*

Confirm budget

It is essential to confirm that relevant finance is available.

Check service availability

The practitioners must check on the availability of preferred services and confirm with the client whether they are prepared to wait for a particular service or settle for another option. If services are unavailable it is essential that the service planning system is informed.

Renegotiate existing services

It may be that the existing pattern of services may have to be re-negotiated, either to accommodate changing needs or simply to achieve the desired objectives more effectively.

Contract new services

In accessing new services practitioners will have to adjust to the contracting arrangements that authorities and agencies are developing as part of the community care changes. Practitioners will have to acquire skills in devising service specifications and quality standards, and in negotiating and monitoring contracts. The aim is to produce a quality service as cost effectively as possible within the agreed timescale.

Establish monitoring arrangements

It is essential to establish monitoring arrangements to ensure that the care plan remains on course.

Task

Using Case-Studies A or B check whether the key points are covered from the 'Implementing the care plan: checklist' (see below).

Implementing the care plan: checklist

Practitioners can use this list to check that key points are covered:

1 Has the client been involved to the limit of their capacity in the implementation process?
2 Have the inputs of clients and carers been maximised and have formal service inputs been geared to their support?
3 Has the pace of implementation been agreed with the client?
4 Has the budget for implementation been clearly defined, together with the responsibility for allocating that budget?
5 Have deficiencies in service availability and quality been notified to service planning and quality assurance/inspection respectively?
6 Have existing services been renegotiated to meet the care plan objectives more effectively?
7 Has the care plan been delivered to time and to quality?
8 Have resources been co-ordinated in a cost-effective way?
9 Have the reasons for any departure from the original care plan been recorded?
10 Have arrangements been established to monitor the ongoing implementation?

(Adapted from *Care Management and Assessment – Practitioners' Guide* HMSO, 1991)

Case-study C

Mr Collins has a severe physical disability. He is 47 years of age. Following a road traffic accident at age 15, he is a wheelchair user with legs extended in spasms and he cannot raise his arms above shoulder level. His speech is very slurred. Cognitively he is very alert.

Referral
Mr Collins lived with his father who is 84 years old and his main carer. Following a dispute which neither wished to resolve, Mr Collins decided he wished to live independently in the community.

Outcome
Mr Collins was admitted to an assessment centre to take part in the independence Training Programme to acquire new skills in

independence. He submitted an application form for a purpose-built flat. A multi-disciplinary assessment was undertaken to identify his needs. He applied to the Independent Living Fund (prior to April 1993) and was awarded £465.00 per week towards purchasing the care and assistance he needed.

A multi-Disciplinary Assessment Panel was held and Mr Collins' needs were identified as: 1) personal care; 2) domestic; 3) equipment; 4) transport; 5) accommodation. A Social Worker was allocated as his Care Manager, to work jointly with an Occupational Therapist.

Mr Collins was allocated a purpose-built flat by a Housing Association. Mr Collins assisted in the design of the package of care he felt he required. He employed 4 private carers, through contacts made by staff at the local assessment centre and private agencies and other customers in a similar situation to himself. Independently, he: 1) worked out a rota for his private carers, carefully timetabling the support he required; 2) decided how much the hourly rate of pay would be by seeking advice from the Disability Action Group; 3) found out about paying his carers' tax and National Insurance through an information pack obtained from the Inland Revenue and further advice from a Disability Action Group.

Through advice from his social worker, Mr Collins selected the appropriate household contents, personal accident and professional liability insurances.

Conclusion
Mr Collins will be living independently in the community with the support of a care package he assisted in designing. Mr Collins has been able to organise his own care, although physically unable to care for himself. He applied to the DSS Social Fund for a Community Care Grant, which he used to furnish and equip his own flat.

This, along with his Independent Living Fund Award, support from Social Services Staff (Social Worker, OT, Assessment Centre Staff) and local Disability Action Group, has: 1) enabled him to achieve his aims to live independently in the community; and 2) empowered him to mobilise community resources to meet his needs.

See the following page for the macro and micro care plans for Mr Collins

---

CLIENT RESPONSE TO FIELDWORK ASSESSMENT

Mr Collins is in agreement with the assessment shown and is very keen to achieve independent living in the community.

Client: _____

Assessing Social Worker: _____

Team Manager
Physical Disabilities Team _____

Date _____

Figure 7.7 *Example of Client Agreement Form*

· CLIENTS' RIGHTS ·

Clients come from all sections of the community and will differ in many aspects from one another, such as age, ethnic and cultural background, gender, disability/ability. Their needs will be different and their preferences as to how these needs are to be met will be different. Whatever the personal characteristics and needs of the individual are, *everyone* has the same rights as a client. Equality of care is a central value to all the caring professions and is written into codes of practice, and in the government's *Patients' Charter*. There are also laws designed to protect vulnerable groups from discrimination in employment, education and other areas of life. (See also Chapters 1 and 6.)

Clients have a right to expect certain standards, or codes of practice, to be followed by those assessing their needs, and those providing a service to meet the needs. These rights include:

Macro Care Plan – Mr Collins REVIEW DATE 2 months after moving date

Needs	How needs are met	Action by
1a) Assistance with personal tasks e.g. dressing and undressing, bathing, hair washing and care of feet.	1a) Personal care service to be arranged.	1a) Social worker to liaise with providers.
b) A suitable toilet facility.	b) Closomat toilet to be installed in new property.	b) Social Worker and Occupational Therapist
c) Assistance with transferring on and off bed, toilet, and in and out of wheelchair.	c) Rails to be fitted and personal carer to assist with transfers.	c) Social Worker and Occupational Therapist
2a) Assistance with all domestic tasks, some food preparation shopping, bed making and ironing.	2a) Domestic service and home carer to assist.	2a) Social Worker to liaise with providers.
3a) To be able to summon help quickly in an emergency situation, to open front door, to operate TV and switch on lights.	3a) Environmental Control unit at previous address to be reassessed to accommodate all these functions.	3a) Occupational Therapist.
b) To have access to a telephone and assistance with handset and speaking on the phone.	b) British Telecom to be approached.	b) Occupational Therapist.
4a) Various items of furniture household equipment and furnishings. Where possible materials should be fire resistant.	4a) To be purchased with Community Care grant *when* obtained from DSS Social Fund	4a) Mr. Collins.
5a) Certain domestic appliances and work should be height adjusted.	5a) Kitchen units in new property are adjustable and work surfaces at wheelchair height.	5a) Occupational Therapist.
b) Items of equipment such as grabrail shower chair, cutlery, non slip mats and other kitchen equipment.	b) OT Assessment.	b) Occupational Therapist.
6a) Assistance with collecting benefits and paying bills.	6a) To collect benefits with escort and pay bills by standing order.	6a) Mr Collins to organise standing orders and pay bills.
7a) To go shopping weekly.	7a) To be escorted.	7a) Social Worker to liaise with possible provider and/or volunteers.
b) To be able to visit his father.	b) To be escorted.	b) Social Worker to liaise with possible provider and/or volunteers.
8a) Assistance with booking dial-a-ride and taxi's	8a) To plan ahead and make booking with help from Local Assessment Unit.	8a) Assessment Unit.
9a) Regular support to be able to live independently in the community.	9a) Regular pattern of respite care at local respite facility.	9a) Social Worker to liaise with local respite facility.
10a) To be able to accommodate a large outdoor electric wheelchair.	10a) New property has space under stairs with power point for battery to be recharged.	10a) Provision exists in new property.
b) To be able to charge wheelchair battery overnight.	b) Carer would need to plug in.	b) Social Worker to liaise with provider.

Micro Care Plan – Mr Collins
The micro care plan for Mr Collins contains the detail needed to ensure Mr Collins is able to live independently.

Needs	Needs
1 **Personal care** The care manager, who is a social worker, arranges for a home carer to visit every morning and every evening to assist Mr Collins to dress and undress. The home carer will also assist Mr Collins with personal hygiene. The care manager arranges a bathing service to visit twice weekly, and a chiropodist to visit weekly.	4 **Visits to his father** The care manager will arrange for a volunteer to accompany Mr Collins when visiting his father.
2 **Domestic tasks** Care manager to liaise with domestic services and home carer. The care manager will ensure that help is available three times a day for the preparation and cooking of food, plus time set aside daily to complete other household tasks. The home carer will accompany Mr Collins on shopping trips twice weekly.	5 **Respite care** The care manager will book this on a regular basis with the local assessment centre.
3 **Collecting benefits** Care manager will arrange an escort to accompany Mr Collins when he needs to collect his benefits.	6 **Charging wheelchair battery** The care manager would arrange for the home carer to plug in the charger every evening.

The staff involved with Mr Collins will need to monitor the effectiveness of the micro care plan and suggest alterations to his care plan as time goes on.

- Freedom from discrimination
- Confidentiality of information
- Independence – as far as possible
- Power of choice
- Dignity in the care received

Freedom from discrimination

All people have a right to expect to be treated equally. People should not be treated differently for any reason; for example, because of age, gender, ethnic, racial, cultural or religious backgrounds, disability or sexual orientation.

Discrimination may take many different forms. It ranges from physical and verbal abuse to judgements made about people based on stereotypes with which they have been labelled. (See Chapter 4.)

Discrimination may also appear in other ways, such as information regarding what services are available, or how an assessment and care plan is to be carried out, not being accessible to everyone. Information may not be available in appropriate languages, or in braille, or on tapes for those who cannot see. Interpreters, including signers, may not be available either at the assessment stage, or through service delivery. Another example of discrimination could be that a day centre, or residential establishment, may not take account of the dietary needs required by the

religion and culture of some clients. Managers need to make sure that all groups are equally catered for.

Confidentiality

Clients have the right to know that information about themselves will not be repeated to others. When any information is to be shared with another person or agency, the worker should explain to the client why this needs to be done. For example, there may be times when the worker needs to share information with another professional in order to get the care that the person needs. Confidentiality ensures that clients continue to trust the worker and will talk to them freely about their situation and their needs.

Independence

Clients have the right to remain as independent as possible whilst receiving care. There is a danger of clients losing their independence because of the care they receive. For example, an older person may find that they have all their personal care, such as dressing, done for them, instead of the worker encouraging the client to find alternative ways of coping and allowing the client to take their own time to do things. In a care situation, where the client is reliant on others for assistance, the client is vulnerable to loss of independence. Clients must be helped to do as much for themselves as they possibly can.

Choice

In order to be and to feel independent, it is important that the client is able to maintain choice. Traditionally, services have offered clients little choice and clients have not been aware of what choices are open to them. It is important that clients have as much information as possible regarding what services are available to them, and that assessors and care-workers fully involve the client in any decision-making.

Dignity

All clients should be treated with respect, and their feelings and wishes given due consideration. All clients should expect assessors and care-workers to treat them with courtesy and to pay due regard to their dignity. Some people, such as those requiring help with personal tasks, e.g. bathing, are particularly vulnerable. The effect of not respecting or taking account of a clients feelings will be to lower their self-esteem. (See Chapter 4.) Maintaining the dignity of a client, in situations where people are very dependent on others, is a skill that care-workers must develop in order for clients to have their dignity respected.

Figure 7.8 *Care-workers must ensure that the client's dignity is preserved (Winged Fellowship Trust 'Images of Caring' Competition by Ian Tatton.)*

Think it over

Think about clients' rights. Write down five ways (i.e. one for each of the rights listed) that clients could have their rights violated.

· MONITORING ·

What is the purpose of monitoring?

The purpose of monitoring is to:

- monitor the care plan objectives
- co-ordinate all services
- ensure that services are delivered according to laid-down specifications
- oversee the quality of care
- manage the budget
- support users, carers and service providers
- fine-tune the care plan and contribute to the review

1 Care plan objectives

The first purpose of monitoring is to ensure that the objectives set out in the care plan are being achieved. The person monitoring the care plan has to check that each agency providing a service is on-track in terms of delivering their specific objectives.

2 Co-ordinating services

The more contributors there are to the care plan, then the more important becomes the role of co-ordination. The person with the responsibility for monitoring must ensure that the services complement each other and that all necessary information is shared. They must also play a key role in managing any changes that are made in the way in which services are delivered, so that continuity of care is maintained.

3 Service delivery

The contributions of all the people and agencies participating in the care plan, including the contributions of the client and their carer, must be written into the original care plan. It is important that all contributors continue to fulfil their commitments to the care plan, or all of the care arrangements could be jeopardised. It should be remembered that unpaid carers, such as a husband, wife, partner, other relation, neighbour or friend, may also be contributing to the care plan. For example: a neighbour may be providing the client with a light meal each weekday evening; a relation may be providing personal care and meals at the weekend.

4 Overseeing the quality of care

Each of the service providers, and participants in the care plan, has a responsibility for the quality for their own contribution. However, the standards for the quality of each service should be specified in contracts between the monitoring worker (*purchaser*) and the service provider. These agreements are called *service specifications*.

Quality lies in the attention to detail that matters to each individual. The care manager or monitoring worker, therefore, has a responsbility to ensure that contributors take account of the personal requirements of the client. For example, the way a person with a disability likes to be lifted.

5 Managing the budget

The monitoring worker may have responsibility for the budget and may be required to oversee the budget. This will become more important where financial responsibilities are devolved from senior managers to individual care managers.

6 Support to clients, carers and service providers

Support to clients, carers and service providers may take different forms:

– counselling
– progress-chasing
– resolving conflicts

7 Fine-tuning the care plan

Changes in the needs of the client and carer need to be taken into account in the care plan; therefore as the needs change so the care plan must be adjusted in order to reflect those needs. However, adjustment to the care plan will only take into account minor changes in need. Any major changes in need will be sanctioned (agreed) by a *Review*.

Reviews will normally be held at regular intervals, however they can also be triggered should anyone involved in the provision of care perceive any difficulties. Where a client's capabilities are diminishing, monitoring has to identify when a review is required so that the increased needs of the individual can be reassessed.

The monitoring process

Wherever possible, the person responsible for assessment, care planning and implementation should continue to hold the responsibility for monitoring. This person will co-ordinate the monitoring process, although various other people should be involved in it. For example:

- clients, carers – as contributors as well as service-users
- service providers – as monitors of their own service
- managers – to oversee the quality of services
- purchasing agents – as monitors of contracts
- inspection units – as monitors of quality standards in residential care

Approaches to monitoring

Care management stresses the importance of monitoring in ensuring that objectives are being met and in adapting the care plan to the changing needs of the clients. Monitoring can be achieved in a variety of ways, depending on the complexity of the care plan. For example:

– home visits
– telephone calls
– letters
– questionnaires
– observation

Monitoring questionnaire for a bathing service

1 Are all referrals assessed within 5 working days?
2 Has feedback been given to the referrer regarding the outcome of the referral?
3 Has a key-worker (person with special responsibility for the client) been identified?
4 Have joint assessments and visits been undertaken where appropriate?
5 Is training provided to all staff on an ongoing basis?
6 Have systems been introduced to assess client satisfaction?
7 Is there a clear complaints procedure in place?
8 Has a Care Plan been devised for each client?
9 Does each client have a copy of their Care Plan?
10 Are Service Specifications being met?
11 Is the service being delivered within budget?
12 Are procedures in place so that Reviews can be called if necessary?

Figure 7.9 *A sample questionnaire*

Monitoring checklist

Monitoring Workers can use this list to check that they have covered all the key points.
1 Is the type of monitoring appropriate to the care plan?
2 Are clients and carers actively involved?
3 Is the monitoring of objectives regularly undertaken?
4 Does the Monitoring Worker continue to co-ordinate all the contributions to the care plan?
5 Are services regularly checked against Service Specifications?
6 Is the care plan being delivered within the budget?
7 How regular is the support to clients, carers and service providers?
8 Are the reasons for minor changes recorded?
9 Is monitoring systematically recorded?
10 Are all contributors aware of the procedures for calling a Review?

(Adapted from *Care Management and Assessment – Practitioners' Guide* (HMSO, 1991)

Task

Using Case-Study C, write out how you would monitor the care plan, using the checklist above as a guide.

Draft a simple questionnaire to be used for testing client satisfaction. (This task might link with work for Unit 8.)

· REVIEWING ·

What is the purpose of a review?

A review fulfils a variety of different purposes. It might be needed to:

- review to see if care plan objectives have been achieved
- evaluate reasons for failure or success
- evaluate quality and cost of care provided
- reassess current needs
- revise objectives of the care plan
- revise services that are required
- reassess cost
- note any unmet need
- record results of review
- set date of next review

1 Reviewing care plan objectives

It is important that each review should first consider the views of the client and carer as to what progress has been made in achieving the care plan objectives. The views of the service providers should also be obtained. The realism of the original objectives and their continuing relevance can then be determined.

2 Reasons for failure or success

An evaluation of why objectives may – or may not – have been met, should help to determine any future action and future care plans.

3 Quality and cost of care

By using the evidence gained through the monitoring process, the review will be able to check that services have maintained the required standards of quality and are being provided within the budget limits. A judgement regarding the cost-effectiveness of the care package, to date, should be taken into account when adjustments or changes are made to the care plan.

4 Reassessing current need

A review should not repeat the original assessment. It should pick up any needs that were previously not identified and any new needs that have developed since the previous review. It should also take into account any changes in the preferences of the client and their carer for how the needs are to be met.

5 Revising care objectives

The original care objectives should be reviewed and adjusted to meet changing needs. The short-term objectives of each provider should also be reviewed and new targets should build on past achievements.

6 Revising service requirements

Changes to the care plan may result in the renegotiation of services contracts, including the level of service and/or the way in which the services are to be provided.

7 Recalculating cost

Changes in service levels may result in a financial change – how much the package will cost. A new budget for the package may have to be agreed.

8 Unmet needs

Either the required quality of service, or ways to meet identified needs, may not be available. Any shortcomings should be noted and this information should be passed to those responsible for planning services.

9 Record results of review

The findings of the review should be recorded and a copy given to the client and all other contributors to the review. The recording of the review should include:

– evaluation of achievement of objectives, with reasons for success or failure
– evaluation of the quality and cost of services provided
– reassessment of current needs
– revision of care plan objectives
– note of changes required in service provision
– revision of cost of care package
– identification of any unmet need
– date of next review; name of person who is to carry out the monitoring until next review; name of person who is to co-ordinate the next review.

10 Date of next review

Agencies should set a minimum frequency for reviews. However, intervals between each review should reflect the complexity of the care package

REVIEW FORM

NAME OF CLIENT: REVIEW HELD ON:

FIRST\SECOND\THIRD REVIEW (delete)   AT:

	Action	By
PRESENT		
APOLOGIES		
REVIEW OF DECISIONS MADE AT PREVIOUS REVIEW	Action	By
VIEW OF CLIENT RE: CARE PLAN		
VIEW OF CARER RE CARE PLAN		
VIEW OF KEY-WORKER		
VIEW OF SERVICE PROVIDER		
REASONS FOR SUCCESS/FAILURE OF CARE PLAN		
REVISED SERVICE REQUIREMENTS		
REVISED COST OF CARE PACKAGE		
UNMET NEEDS		

DATE OF NEXT REVIEW: CO-ORDINATOR:

Figure 7.10 *A sample review form*

and/or the anticipated pace of change in the needs of the client. For example, where a client has a rapidly deteriorating illness, then it may be necessary to review the situation every eight weeks. Additionally, it must be possible to hold reviews sooner than the specified date should the need arise.

The review process

Scope

As with *Assessment*, the scope of the Review will depend on the complexity of need and the frequency as to how quickly the needs are subject to change. Also, like Assessment, reviewing should be **needs-led**. Not everyone contributing to service provision is required to attend every review. However, all those involved in the original care plan, or previous review, should be consulted either by telephone, letter or direct meetings.

Venue

The venue should be decided by what is judged to be the most effective way of involving the client and their carer. It may therefore be appropriate to hold at least part of the review in the client's home, or at any venue where they receive some of the services, for example at a day centre.

Review Worker

In order to maintain continuity both in the processes and in understanding the client's needs over a period of time, there are advantages in the Assessment, Monitoring and Reviewing processes being the responsibility of one person.

Think it over

Using Case-Study C, think about who you would ask to make contributions to a Review. Consider how frequently a Review for a client might need to take place.

Review checklist

Reviewing Workers can use this list to check that they have covered all the key points.

1 Is the review taking place on the scheduled date?
2 Is the review centred on the needs and preferences of the client?
3 Are all the service providers involved?
4 Has the client (and their carer) been able to participate and have their wishes been taken into account?
5 Has the review addressed both the positive and negative aspects of the care plan?
6 Has the evaluation taken into account both the quality and cost of services?
7 Have all changes in the services to be provided, and any changes in how they are to be provided, been noted?
8 Has the review been recorded and the date of the next review set?

(Adapted from *Care Management and Assessment – Practitioner's Guide* HMSO, 1991)

· MAINTAINING CLIENTS' RIGHTS ·

Various research studies have shown that clients hold the following views:

1 Most people prefer to stay in their own homes.
2 Most people want to have control over what happens to them.
3 Most people want choice and flexibility in the services that are offered to them.
4 Most people want to be assured of the level and quality of services that they receive.

Freedom from discrimination

Discrimination on the basis of race or gender is against the law. (See Chapter 6.) Nevertheless, people are sometimes discriminated against on these or other grounds within our society. (No doubt many of you are aware of the 'does he take sugar' syndrome.) It is essential that all care-workers look

at their own attitudes and behaviour in order to ensure that no individual or group of people are treated less well than others.

Care-workers should be aware of what is happening when they make assumptions about a person based on preconceived stereotypes. (See Chapters 1 and 4.) For example, making an assumption about a person because of their appearance.

Discrimination may also occur within systems. For example: residential, day care and meals-on-wheels services may not cater for preferred or special diets; or buildings may be inaccessible to people with a physical disability, thus preventing the individual from using the services offered within. Provision of service delivery should take account of the needs of potential clients in all aspects of planning. Failure to do so is a form of discrimination against those who are excluded.

Each agency and workplace should have its own local policy on how to deal with acts of discrimination. The policy should assist care-workers to promote anti-discriminatory practice. Challenging discrimination can sometimes be very difficult; however, if left unchallenged, discrimination is likely to continue. A knowledge of the local policies may indicate what actions may be appropriate.

Confidentiality

Health and caring agencies need to keep detailed information about clients in respect of their needs and to ensure their care and well-being. However, only certain people should have access to this information and workers should only have access on a 'need to know' basis. Systems through which information about a client is handled should allow appropriate access, but must also maintain confidentiality. (See Chapter 00).

Care-workers will be given information about a client which will help the worker to provide the care that is required; however, this information should not be passed on to others unless it is necessary to do so in order to maintain that care. A client may choose to give the care-worker additional information, but in these cases it is also important that the worker keeps this to themselves. Breaches in confidentiality could result a care-worker being disciplined.

Situations may arise when the care worker feels they need to pass on confidential information given to them by the client. For example, if a client is depressed and has indicated that they are contemplating suicide. When a client starts to tell a care-worker something they think that they might need to pass on, it is important that the worker stop the client and tell them that they may need to pass the information on, if they hear more. However if the client does not want their comments to go further, then their wishes should be respected wherever possible. The care-worker may need to discuss the particular situation with their line manager, when they are in doubt as to what action, if any, should be taken.

Independence

Promoting independence can be achieved by involving the client in their own care as much as possible; i.e. doing things *with* the client where possible, not *for* them. Clients and their carers should be involved in the decision-making processes regarding the care to be provided. People need to be *empowered* to take control of their lives – and encouraged to do so.

It is important to find out what people can do for themselves. Even if it could be quicker for the carer or worker to do it for them, the client should be encouraged to do things for themselves. Clients should be allowed time to find out how to help with their own care. It may be that the only contribution they can make is in discussing the issue of how their care is to be carried out, but this may also increase their feelings of independence and self-esteem. (See chapter 4.)

Figure 7.11 *By being encouraged to do things for themself, the client is being empowered to take control of their life*

Clients can be further empowered by ensuring that they have the necessary equipment to help them. They should be helped to make the best use of the equipment that is available to them so that their independence is improved.

Choice

In many cases the needs of the client will dictate the type of care that they receive, and so the amount of choice that the individual has may be limited. However, if clients are made aware of this, and are informed about the alternatives that are available,

they will be able to contribute to the decision-making process.

Working practices should promote as much client choice as possible. For example, in a residential unit, there should be a certain amount of flexibility in mealtimes; there should be a choice of menu and residents should be able to retire to bed at a time that is suitable to them. Residents should also be encouraged to personalise their rooms and be offered some choice in the arrangement of the environment.

Some clients may have difficulty in expressing their wishes, either because of a disability or because their past experience of care has discouraged them from doing so. Care-workers can help by assisting people to speak for themselves: this is called *self-advocacy*. Helping people to understand their rights, and helping them to develop skills to express their wishes, are the principles on which self-advocacy is based.

Programmes aiming to promote self-advocacy may be built into a care plan. Increasing the person's ability to express their feelings and wishes will result in increasing their participation in decision-making.

In some instances, the client may not be able to develop skills in self-advocacy, for example where the client has advanced dementia. It will then be necessary for another person to take on the role of advocate, such as the carer, care-worker or some other independent person. Advocacy for others requires sensitivity and care, in order to ensure that the actual feelings and wishes of the client are being accurately related.

Dignity

People must be treated with a great deal of respect in order for their dignity to be maintained, especially in situations where the person's needs include high levels of personal care. It is easy to destroy a person's dignity if they feel that their feelings are not being taken into account when personal care tasks are being carried out. Systems and care-workers must operate in a way that helps to preserve the dignity of clients. For example, when a client is being assisted to a bath they should be helped to undress in the bathroom, not undressed in another room and then transferred to the bathroom. They should only have one care-worker with them in the bathroom. If need be, appropriate equipment, such as a hoist, should be used. People can feel at their most vulnerable when they are undressed. People should always be given as much privacy as possible.

Other ways in which a person may feel that their dignity has been disregarded may include: a care-worker conveying feelings of disapproval when carrying out unpleasant tasks, such as dealing with the effects of incontinence; impatience or lack of interest when a client has difficulty in expressing themselves; and carrying on with a conversation with a third-party as if the client were not there.

Clients should feel comfortable with the care that they receive and must never be made to feel that they are causing problems because of their needs.

Task

Imagine that you are manager of a Home Care Bathing Service and write a guide entitled 'Maintaining Clients' Rights' for new workers. Use the following headings: Freedom from Discrimination; Confidentiality; Independence; Choice and Dignity.

Self-assessment test

1 What is a care plan?
2 Name the general process of which care planning is a part.
3 What are the seven core tasks of Assessment and Care Management?
4 What factors should a needs-led assessment include?
5 Name any five activities which should be part of the care plan process.
6 Why is it important to record the care plan?

7 'The guiding principle when implementing a care plan is to achieve the stated objectives of the care plan with the minimum intervention necessary.' Is this statement true or false?
8 Name five of the headings in the Care Management and Assessment checklist.
9 Why does Care Management stress the importance of monitoring?
10 Name three ways in which monitoring can be achieved.
11 What is the purpose of reviewing?
12 Which of the following are, aspects of the Review process?
   a Scope
   b Questionnaires
   c Venue
   d Review worker
13 Which of the following are areas of client rights?
   a Freedom from discrimination
   b Co-ordination of the care plan
   c Confidentiality
   d Independence
   e Service specification
   f Dignity
14 Why is confidentiality one of the main rights of clients?
15 'The role of an assessor is to collect information in order to be able to assess the care needs of an individual and their carer.' Is this statement true or false?
16 What is the function of the Key Worker?
17 'A service specification is a set of minimum requirements relating to a service to be supplied.' Is this statement true or false?
18 What is a purchaser?
19 What is a macro care plan?
20 What is a micro care plan?

Fast Facts

Advocacy   Speaking for another person and representing their interests on their behalf.

Assessment and Care Management   The process of assessing, co-ordinating and implementing services to meet an individual's needs.

Assessor The person undertaking the assessment of need of an individual. (It may be the same person as the Care Manager.)

Care Manager The person undertaking the care management process in order to address the needs of the individual.

Care Package A combination of services designed to meet the assessed needs of a person requiring care.

Care Plan (Macro) A care plan is a written document which outlines how the needs on an individual are to be met. It lists all the agencies who will be involved.

Care Plan (Micro) The plan which the individual service provider will use to describe the action plan for a client within their own care setting.

Care Planning The process of negotiation between assessor, client, carers and other agencies on the most appropriate ways of meeting assessed needs, within available resources and incorporating them into an individual's care plan.

Choice The right of clients to be able to make choices about the care they receive.

Client Rights The rights of clients to particular standards of treatment.

Confidentiality The right of clients to have private information about themselves kept secret.

Dignity Being worthy of respect and possessing pride and self-esteem.

Discrimination To treat some people less well than others.

Independence The right of clients to be free of control by others, and to be able to help attend to their own needs.

Inspection The process of external examination intended to establish whether a service is managed and provided to stated quality standards.

Key Worker The service-providing practitioner who has most contact with the client. (May undertake similar co-ordinating function as Care Manager.)

Monitoring The process by which the implementation of the Care Plan is evaluated. It also supports clients, carers and service providers in delivering quality services.

Monitoring Worker The person who undertakes the Monitoring process. (It may be the same person as the Assessor and Care Manager.)

Need A need is an essential requirement which must be satisfied to ensure that an individual reaches a state of health and social well-being.

Provider Any person, group of persons or organisation that sells a community care service to a purchaser.

Purchaser An organisation that holds the budget to buy in necessary services.

Review A formal meeting attached by the client, their carer and service providers in order to reassess the needs of the individual and revise the care plan as necessary.

Reviewing The process by which the needs of the individual are reassessed with a view to revising the care plan. Reviewing is undertaken at specified intervals.

Service Specification Set of minimum requirements relating to a service to be supplied.

References

Social Services Inspectorate (1991) *Care Management and Assessement – Practitioners' Guide* HMSO

Beardshaw, V. and Towell, D. (March 1990) 'Assessment and Case Management' in Briefing Paper No. 10. King's Fund.

British Association of Social Workers (1990) *Managing Care* BASW

chapter 8 RESEARCH IN HEALTH AND SOCIAL CARE

· INTRODUCING RESEARCH ·

What is research?

Whatever field of work they are involved in people need knowledge and information. Whether we are interested in physics, economics or social science, we must be able to find things out. The process of finding things out in an organised and thoughtful way is called research. Research can take a variety of forms, and use different methods, depending on the subject being studied. As carers our field of study is people, and this chapter deals with research in health and social care.

Why is research important?

Until the sixteenth century it was generally believed that the earth was the centre of the universe, and that the sun and planets all revolved around it. Research done by the astronomers Copernicus and Galileo showed, eventually, that this was wrong – and that the solar system has the sun at its centre. This knowledge sparked off a revolution in thinking that helped the development of modern astronomy to take place.

How is this relevant to research in health and social care? Because it illustrates dramatically how assumptions about the world can be taken for granted until careful research gives a more accurate understanding. Assumptions about social issues are all around us. They are often stated in the media

and crop up in conversations as 'common knowledge'. Statements like, 'people are only poor if they are lazy', or 'most women don't really want a career' may provoke you to confront these statements and give your own opinion; but without research it is just argument and opinion.

This does not mean that social research is a straightforward matter, and that you simply have to do research to find out the truth. Finding out about people is often extremely difficult, and convincing others that your research is accurate and useful means thinking carefully about what you are doing every step of the way. Galileo was eventually imprisoned for his discoveries and beliefs. You are unlikely to encounter such stiff opposition to your findings, but the need to convince others must be kept in mind.

But I think my research produced good results!

302

Asking questions and collecting data

Social scientists are interested in just about all aspects of people's lives. This is a vast field of study, and the range of research methods that have been developed reflect this.

All research begins with an area of interest. This may be discrimination, health and lifestyle, religious beliefs or any other area relevant to health and social care. From an area of interest specific questions emerge, and research can be planned to answer these questions.

Questions may be about the situations people are in, such as, 'What percentage of households live on low incomes?' or, 'What is the ratio of male to female students on a GNVQ Health and Social Care course?'. Questions might be focused on people's behaviour, such as, 'How many people watch football on television?' or, 'What percentage of students on your course smoke cigarettes?'. Or questions may be about beliefs and opinions, such as, 'Do people think that the National Health Service is improving?' or, 'Do young people believe that sex before marriage is morally wrong?'. The type of question you are interested in, and the people it applies to, will have a great influence on the methods of research that may be used. A structured research project that seeks information on social issues is referred to as a *survey*.

Quantitative and qualitative data

Whatever the question, your research will involve finding things out – and the information that is collected is called *data*. Data can take different forms. Some data is numerical, for example, the number of people attending a day centre for elders. Other data may be more descriptive and personal, for example people's feelings about attending the day centre.

Data which is numerical, and can be analysed using statistical methods, is known as *quantitative data*. The number of single parent families in an area, or the number of people giving the same answer to a particular question, are examples of quantitative

data. Quantitative results can be displayed using graphs, charts and tables.

Data which concerns attitudes, opinions and values is often unable to be expressed in numerical form. It may include comments people have made about a subject, or accounts of their feelings about it, or reactions to it. This information is known as *qualitative data*. Qualitative data cannot be analysed and reported on using statistical methods.

It is important to understand that both quantitative and qualitative data can provide important and useful results. One is not better or more scientific than the other. The important thing is to choose the right type of data and collection technique for the questions you are interested in. Most really good research includes both types of data. This is the best way to provide background and balance in social investigations.

Think it over

Choose an area of health and social care that you are interested in. Think about the types of questions you could ask about it. List the questions you have thought of and decide which would give quantitative data and which qualitative data.

Sources of data

There are basically two ways of getting information. You can find out yourself by carrying out your own research project, or you can look at work that has been done already by other people. Carrying out your own research project is called **primary research**, and most of the chapter is about how to do this. Looking at the work of others is called **secondary research**, and it is a very sensible starting point for any investigation.

· SECONDARY RESEARCH ·

Carrying out secondary research, or collecting secondary data, means looking at existing sources that contain information useful to your research. There are good reasons for looking at secondary sources at an early stage. First, you may pick up useful ideas and concepts about the subject you are interested in. Secondly, you may get ideas for methods you could use for your own primary research. Also you may discover that others have already carried out basically the same research project that you are interested in! This last point shouldn't put you off. It can be very interesting to compare the results of your own carefully conducted research with other published results. It is often through repeating the work of others that new insights arise, and differences may point to interesting new areas of investigation.

The places you look for secondary data will depend upon the subject you are interested in. Information of all sorts is published in books, government publications, newspapers, journals and in a variety of other places. Whatever you are researching, it is likely that useful information exists somewhere. Finding out where to look may be your first problem. Other problems crop up when you have found the material. All secondary sources need to be treated with some caution, and there are several points to bear in mind when using them.

First, it is important that you *understand* the information you have found. Sometimes data appears in forms which are difficult to follow unless you are familiar with the field. Secondly you must assess how *relevant* the information is to your work. The people who collected and published the data will have had their own purposes in mind. Thirdly, there is the crucial question of the *quality* of other people's research work. Published data is by no means guaranteed to be accurate! Errors and distortions can result from careless or misguided research work. They can also occur because of deliberate bias on the part of the researcher. Unfortunately the quality of research behind secondary sources is often hard to judge.

It's certainly weighty – but is it light on quality of research?

Official statistics

National and local government organisations produce a wide variety of official statistics. Official bodies need facts and figures of all sorts to assist in planning and decision making.

The government carries out a *census* of the British population every ten years. The last one was in 1991. The census requires every household in Britain to fill in a questionnaire which asks about such topics as families, housing, education and work. Many other surveys and research projects are also carried out by government departments. These are not as comprehensive as the census, and usually concern specific topics such as transport or trade.

There is a variety of books available which contain official statistics; all of these are available in local reference libraries. The census results are also published in book form. They contain both national and regional information on a variety of topics. However, remember that some census results take several years to be published.

The *Annual Abstract of Statistics* contains important government statistics. *Social Trends* is similar to the *Annual Abstract of Statistics* but may be more useful as it includes some discussion. It also looks at changes over time, and is published annually. *Regional Trends* is similar to *Social Trends* but contains information for particular regions. *Key*

Data is an annual publication and covers important social and economic statistics. If you talk to the librarian you should be able to find these and other books in your local reference library.

Official statistics are often straightforward and understandable. Most appear in the form of tables. You must make sure that you have read and understood the headings, and what the figures represent. There is such a wide range of statistics available that you are likely to come across some data that is relevant to your work. The danger may be that you find a lot of interesting data and try to include too much of it in your final research report. Remember to use secondary sources as a guide to carrying out your own research project. Quote secondary data *only* when it adds useful background to your work, or when it provides interesting comparisons with your own results.

Very large-scale official surveys, like the census, are carried out extremely carefully. Methods of data collection and analysis used by the government's statistical staff have helped to define good practice. The results which emerge are likely to give a pretty accurate picture of things like housing, income or family composition in British households. Unfortunately, however, the quality of all official statistics cannot be taken for granted. Although scrupulous care may be used in data collection and analysis, some official figures may not represent the true picture. For example, figures on crime may seem straightforward to collect. Crimes known to the police are recorded, and totals for different types of crime can be presented as results. But figures can shift if the police decide to 'crack down' on particular areas. A sudden apparent increase in cases of fraud, for example, may be the result of increased police activity in fraud detection. Also campaigns in the media can result in increased reporting of certain crimes by the public.

Think it over

Official data may suffer from problems of distortion. Statistics on unemployment seem apparently easy to collect, but may not reflect the situation accurately. For instance the definition of unemployment may vary from time to time.

Think about ways in which unemployment statistics may be affected by official policy and public behaviour.

Books

Whatever field of research you are interested in, there are probably books that can help you in libraries you have access to. Books could include textbooks, reference books or the published work of social researchers. Any of these may provide useful background, and introduce you to concepts and definitions relevant to your research. You may also find published results that you can compare with your own work. If you make good use of library filing systems, and the advice of staff, you should find plenty of material.

However, there are also pitfalls when using books. The published research of social scientists is sometimes difficult to understand, and lengthy to read. It is often better to look at textbooks containing brief, condensed accounts of their work. Another problem is that data in textbooks and reference books may be out of date. Even recent works will have taken time to write and publish. Always try to check the age of any statistics quoted.

The accuracy of data from books is usually extremely difficult to gauge. Research methods may not be explained, or they may be hard to understand and evaluate. Also it is possible that the researcher's own bias has influenced the results. You can certainly refer to the data produced by others, but *don't* assume that it is correct.

Newspapers, magazines and journals

Newspapers and magazines print information of all types. Apart from quoting data produced by official sources, they sometimes print the results of their own 'polls'. Articles are likely to be easy to understand,

Newspapers can be biased one way or another

but the big problem is with quality. Newspapers tailor their content to suit the politics and expectations of their owners and readers. Stories can easily be slanted in the direction the editor wishes. Statistics quoted may have been carefully chosen so as to project a particular point of view. The problem of bias can make it difficult to rely on information found in newspapers and magazines.

Journals and professional publications may print more reliable information than newspapers. This is because they are aimed at people who are specialists in a particular field, so they report seriously on professional research results. The problem is that *because* they are aimed at specialists some articles may be written in technical language. Also there is still no guarantee that the research reported has produced accurate results that are free from bias.

Publications by other groups

Many groups and organisations produce information. Some are funded by government, like the Commission for Racial Equality. Some, such as Amnesty International or the RSPCA, are funded by donations from the public. Others, like the Trades Union Congress or the Confederation of British Industry, are paid for by members whose interests they represent. Political parties also sponsor and publish research.

These organisations are usually happy to send you any data that they have if you write and ask for it. The major drawback is that information from pressure groups is likely to be heavily subject to bias, since the group is keen to get their message across. This may not be such a problem with some officially sponsored organisations, but data produced by privately funded pressure groups should be treated with considerable caution.

Using secondary sources

Secondary sources have an important role to play in helping you to prepare your research project, and in providing material for background and comparison. Despite the reservations expressed above it is always a good idea to consult the work of others when planning your own investigation. When referring to secondary sources it helps to follow some basic guidelines.

Remember to be *critical* in your approach to secondary data. Taking other people's results as proven fact is not good practice. Only quote material that is really *relevant* to your research topic, or that adds useful background information. Don't pack your work with lengthy sections of irrelevant, second-hand data. Finally remember to keep a list of *sources* you have looked at, even if you don't use them in your final report. Showing that you have read around a topic helps to establish the credibility of your own research work.

· PRIMARY RESEARCH ·

Collecting your own data is known as primary research. Good primary research needs careful planning, and decisions on key issues must be made at an early stage.

What information are you looking for? Is the data likely to be quantitative or qualitative? Or do you want to collect data of both types?

Populations and samples

Who could you collect the data from? The term *population* is used to describe the total number of people that your research is interested in. For example, if you are researching the attitudes of students towards smoking then your population would include all students. Unless the population is particularly small only vast projects, like the government's census, can survey all or most of their population. This means that a smaller group, a *sample*, must be selected for questioning. Sampling methods have been developed to help make the sample as representative of the whole population as possible.

When you have some idea of who your population includes, and of the type of data you intend to collect from them, you can decide which techniques of data collection are best suited to your research.

· TECHNIQUES OF DATA COLLECTION ·

Questionnaires

One way of getting data is by asking questions; and a questionnaire is simply a list of questions. Questionnaires can be given, or posted, to members of the selected sample who fill them in without the researcher being present. This part of the chapter is about questionnaires that are administered in this way. Alternatively, the questions can be read out to respondents and the answers filled in by an interviewer. This method is known as **structured interviewing** and is dealt with in the section below.

Questionnaires are used extensively in social research, and they can have several advantages. First, they give you the chance to collect information from a large sample of your population. It is fairly cheap to reproduce and distribute large numbers of questionnaires. Secondly there is no danger that the behaviour or appearance of an interviewer could affect the results. This problem occurs in all research which involves interaction between the researcher and the subjects. Distributing questionnaires is one way to avoid it. Thirdly, respondents have time to

consider their answers and consult others if necessary. For example: if you stop somebody in the street and ask them how much their household spends on food per week they are likely to respond with, 'Don't know', or make a guess. To get an accurate answer it is probably better to give respondents time to think, and to ask other family members. Finally, postal questionnaires may be the only practical way of contacting members of some populations. Postal questionnaires can be sent to people who are very far away and who otherwise would be impossible to interview. Also some people, such as doctors or other professionals, may be more willing to fill in a brief questionnaire than give up time for an interview.

Postal questionnaires can be sent to a large number of people

Most questionnaires are designed to collect quantitative information. This means that results can be compared between respondents and analysed statistically. This can be seen as another advantage. Remember, however, that good-looking statistics may mask sloppy research work. Well-presented results are not necessarily good results.

When the information required is comparatively straightforward a questionnaire can be a very effective research instrument. However, there are problems associated with questionnaires that can sometimes outweigh the advantages.

Problems with questionnaires

A major problem is that questionnaires often attract a very low response rate. Those who do respond cannot be taken as representative of the whole population, however carefully you selected your original sample. Statistical analysis of the data collected has little value in this situation. A poor response rate may be due to bad questionnaire design. Long or confusing questionnaires usually end up in the bin. Another possibility is that questions are asked which people are reluctant to answer, perhaps because the subjects are too personal or sensitive. The only answer to a low response rate is to make the subject and content of your questionnaire sufficiently interesting to members of your sample that they are motivated to complete and return them.

A related problem is that the responses that you do receive are likely to be from those with a view on the subject. This can mean that you get many extreme answers, indicating strong but divided opinions. In fact, opinion may be much more evenly spread within the population – but non-response by those who aren't particularly interested will hide this.

Questionnaires assume a certain level of literacy amongst respondents. This makes them inappropriate for surveying certain groups, for example, small children. Even when this is not expected to be a problem, misunderstandings can and do occur. Without an interviewer present there is no check that the questions have been understood. Respondents cannot ask for clarification and may guess an answer, or throw the questionnaire away. Either way the quality of the results will be reduced.

Another problem with questionnaires is that the researcher has no control over who actually completes them. They may be passed on to other members of the family. They may be filled in as a joke by a group of friends in the pub! Uncertainty over whose answers you actually receive can completely invalidate careful sampling work.

Sometimes researchers want to get people's spontaneous response to a question. Respondents may give accurate answers to personal questions if

You have no control over who completes a postal questionnaire.

they reply spontaneously; but if allowed time to think they can pick answers that support the image they wish to project. You cannot expect to receive spontaneous responses from questionnaires.

Another limitation of questionnaires is that respondents can see all the questions at once. By contrast, an interviewer can control the order in which questions are delivered, so that answers are not prejudiced by knowledge of questions still to come. For instance, in a postal questionnaire, it is no use asking 'Can you name the body set up by the government to promote good race relations?', if a question below asks, 'Do you think that the Commission for Racial Equality is effective in promoting good race relations?'. Another thing that interviewers can do is to observe people's reactions to the questions as they are asked. This potentially useful information is not available with questionnaires.

Task

Questionnaires are very useful in some circumstances. Think about areas you may be interested in researching. Make a list, and for each write the pros and cons of using questionnaires to research them.

Choose the area which seems most appropriate for using a questionnaire. What problems could occur here? How can you minimise these problems?

Questionnaires have their advantages, and their limitations. A lot of data can be gathered quickly, but the researcher has so little control that the quality of the information obtained may be poor. A data collection technique which allows the researcher much more control is the **structured interview**.

Structured interviews

Interviews involve the researcher meeting with individual subjects and collecting information directly from them. It is up to the researcher to decide whether to make the interview a more or less formal meeting. An interview can follow an inflexible schedule, or it can be conducted in a more relaxed, less structured way. Interviews which follow a well-defined and fairly rigid plan are known as structured interviews.

An important aim of structured interviews is to ensure that each interview is carried out in exactly the same way. This means that any factors that could bias a response are minimised or, at least, they are theoretically the same for all respondents. Uniformity in interviews is important if valid statistical comparisons are to be made between the responses of different subjects. Interviewers follow an *interview schedule* which dictates their input into the interview meeting. Interview schedules contain a list of questions, similar to a questionnaire. They also contain instructions for the interviewer to follow. Questions are read out to respondents and their answers recorded by the interviewer. To help maximise uniformity the schedule contains set comments to prompt a reply, or probe an area more deeply. Interviewers are *not* expected to deviate from the questions, or the prompts and probes provided in the interview schedule.

In practice, the degree of uniformity described above is often very difficult to achieve. Nevertheless the structured interview is a useful and widely used research technique which has several advantages.

It can be hard to pin down interviewees

The response rate obtained by structured interviewing is likely to be good. If the sample chosen is small enough to handle, and is easily accessible, the only difficulty is in pinning respondents down for an interview.

Misunderstandings over the meaning of questions can easily be dealt with in an interview. Interviewers can repeat the question and add prompts allowed by the schedule. Interviews can also follow up interesting lines of enquiry that a respondent's answers might suggest. The schedule can be structured so that certain responses result in an extra range of questions being asked.

The pace of questioning is up to the interviewer, which allows them to draw subjects into giving quick answers. The result can be spontaneous responses which the subject hasn't had time to consider.

Interviewers may also pick up good background data from observing a respondent's reactions to the questions. These observations can be recorded on the interview schedule if space is reserved for them. In addition, the responses can be guaranteed to come from the respondents themselves. There is no danger of collusion with others if the subject is 'trapped' in an interview!

One main advantage of the structured interview technique is that quantitative data collected can be analysed statistically, and conclusions made about the population as a whole. Many of the pitfalls of postal questionnaires are avoided because of the control an interviewer has over data collection. The uniformity of method attempts to offset any distortion that the presence of the interviewer creates. Structured interviewing attempts to be as 'scientific' as possible, so that the results can be convincingly applied to the whole population.

Well-presented results can look convincing, particularly if charts and graphs are used to demonstrate a point. But structured interviewing can produce distorted data, and thus distorted results. A major problem is that sample size is often small. Interviewing is very time consuming. Contacting a representative sample may mean travelling, or waiting for respondents to turn up. Interviews that are really useful are likely to last for at least several minutes, and you need to add time to complete your notes. The lone researcher cannot hope to complete a large number of structured interviews and must select a sample small enough to be interviewed in the time available. But a small sample is unlikely to be representative of the population as a whole.

One way to overcome this problem is to set less ambitious aims for your investigation, and select a research topic which has a smaller population. For instance, if you are interested in attitudes to smoking, choose to research attitudes amongst local students, rather than attitudes amongst all young adults. This makes it much easier to select and interview a representative sample. The results may not be as far reaching, but they are far more likely to be accurate.

The interaction between respondent and interviewer is a source of distortion that can never be completely eliminated. An interview is a type of conversation. Even when verbal messages are standardised by an interview schedule, the interviewer's appearance, accent and personal characteristics can affect what takes place. Non-verbal signals pass between the participants, and the respondent may be looking for cues that indicate what sort of answers the researcher wants. If they have negative perceptions of the interviewer, respondents may give deliberately provocative answers. If they wish to impress, they may give answers that project a positive image of themselves.

Distortions caused by interaction between interviewer and respondent are difficult, if not impossible, to assess. There is no doubt though that they do occur. Studies have repeatedly shown that different interviewers often get different answers to the same questions. Awareness of this issue has led to attempts by researchers to reduce its effect. For example, the government has a well established recruitment and training procedure for interviewers. Things like tone of voice, facial expression and posture are looked at and training aims to increase standardisation. Also the formal nature of the structured interview is itself an attempt to minimise interviewer influence.

Think it over

What problems are likely to occur if a small group of interviewers are working together? Can you think of methods which could be used to estimate the influence that different interviewers tend to have on respondents?

Of course, all these safeguards rely on the honesty and good intentions of interviewing staff. Honesty can be checked, particularly if the data collected by one interviewer differs wildly from the rest. Deliberate influence, by gesture, tone of voice or deviation from the schedule, is much more difficult to detect.

One final point to remember is that a structured interview is only as good as the questionnaire design and content allow. A poorly considered set of questions will not give useful data, however scrupulously the interviews are conducted and the results calculated.

Structured interviews and questionnaires are very useful for collecting quantitative data. Questions on situation, behaviour and attitudes can be answered using some type of scale so that number values can be applied and results analysed statistically. However, both data collection techniques have similar limitations. Many aspects of opinion are difficult to explore through a fixed set of questions. People's attitudes, beliefs and opinions are personal matters and formal, quantitative techniques may not be the best way to bring them out. Respondents often find it easier to make a safe, respectable response rather than think deeply about a sensitive issue on which their real views are not so clear cut. Authentic opinion is more likely to emerge in a relaxed, less formal meeting.

Because questions are fixed the respondents have no room for manoeuvre. They may be forced into making choices, possibly between a set of equally inappropriate alternatives. Respondents may have other, strongly held, views that the questions fail to bring out and which the interviewer never becomes aware of. The questionnaire and interview schedule define the territory to be explored, and define it in the researcher's terms. Answers may be obtained; but are they important or relevant to the lives and outlook of the respondents themselves?

In-depth interviewing

In-depth interviews are less fixed and formal than structured interviews. At the extreme the in-depth interview is more like a chat, with the interviewer supplying only the topic for conversation. The interviewer can provide guidance as things progress, to keep the topic in view. The aim of the in-depth interview is to encourage respondents to open up, and provide as much detail as possible.

In-depth interviews have big advantages when it comes to finding out what people really think. Subjects don't have to choose between alternative answers. They can introduce areas for discussion that are important to them, and they can give any information that they feel to be relevant. This means that the data is given according to the respondent's frame of reference and view of the world. Connections may be made that would never have occurred to the interviewer. Also there is likely to be a good deal of information collected since in-depth interviews can last for a fairly long time, sometimes for several hours.

This open and inflexible approach may be the best, if not the only, way to get information about poeple's real attitudes, values and opinions. In the informal atmosphere of the in-depth interview the respondents' inhibitions are reduced. They can be encouraged to talk about sensitive subjects and give

Task

Make a list of subjects that you are considering researching. For each subject, identify the pros and the cons of using structured interviews. Choose the subject which you think is best suited to structured interviewing. Can you justify your choice in terms of getting useful bias-free results?

In-depth interviews can last for a long time

views that they would not usually reveal to others. If interesting points arise, that merit further investigation, the interviewer has the freedom to steer the discussion towards them.

In-depth interviews provide rich information which is likely to represent respondents' views accurately. Of course, all the data collected is qualitative and the results cannot be analysed statistically. Comparing results between respondents is usually impossible since each will have given information in their own terms. Respondents may approach the same topic from a completely different viewpoint. Different people will provide different items of data. Apart from this, the sample size is likely to be very small because of the length of time needed to carry out and report on interviews. Even if comparisons between respondents can be made it is meaningless to try projecting the results onto the wider population. This is a characteristic of in-depth interviews, not a weakness of them. Researchers using the technique are aiming for depth and authenticity in difficult areas of enquiry, not for quantitative results.

The main issue that arises in in-depth interviewing is the level of skill required of the interviewer. Respondents must be put at ease and feel happy about talking openly to a stranger. Interviewers need to encourage their subject to speak, whilst subtly keeping the conversation focused on the topic they are interested in. As well as this, interviewers must try to avoid imposing their own bias on the discussion. Urging respondents on to make 'out of character' comments will not produce accurate results. All the problems of interviewer influence that can occur in structured interviews apply also in in-depth interviews. In fact, the freedom and depth of interaction that occurs in in-depth situations make the problem even more serious. To some extent the length of the interview can help, since subjects have time to get used to the interviewer and begin to behave naturally. Apart from this it is the skill and integrity of the interviewer that is relied upon to make the interview useful.

In-depth interviews also pose practical problems. It is important that a suitable place is chosen for the interview. Time and privacy are needed and this may

be difficult to arrange for some subjects. Recording the information is another problem. Taking notes is slow and may inhibit the subject, reminding them that they are in an inteview situation. Quickly jotted notes are likely to be at best a brief summary of the conversation, and later interpretation may lead to distortions. You cannot hope to remember all the information you receive, and things you have been too slow to write down are gone forever. One way to solve this is to record the interview on tape. Nothing verbal will be missed, but visual data about the subject's behaviour during the interview is not recorded. Some people are put off by the presence of a tape recorder and will not speak freely if you use one. Planting a hidden recorder is unethical practice, and you should resort to note-taking if a tape recorder puts subjects off.

Task

Think about subjects you are interested in researching. Write down any that could be researched using in-depth interviewing. Write down the pros and the cons of using in-depth interviews for each of these subjects.

Choose the area that seems most suited to using in-depth interview techniques. How could you justify your use of this method to research that particular subject?

Reliability and validity

There is a marked contrast between the rigid uniformity of the structured interview and the flexible openness of an in-depth interview. But the differences between the two methods go further than interview style.

Structured interviews stress *reliability*. This means that repeats of the research using different samples should reliably produce the same results. Every aspect, from question design to interviewer style, is planned so as to maximise reliability. If the results of structured research seem not to be reliable then the research has failed on its own terms. Reliability can only be assessed if results are expressed statistically.

In-depth interviews stress *validity*. This means that the information collected comes very close to the subject's real views. It gives a valid picture of what they truly believe. In-depth interview data is not expected to show reliability. Subjects' responses are individual, and are not intended to be compared directly. Certainly they cannot be compared statistically since the data is qualitative.

Research which emphasises reliability may lose validity in the process. Questions that reliably receive a similar range of responses have to be carefully designed in order to achieve this. Questions which produce conflicting or erratic responses are pruned out so that reliability is ensured. This can result in questions that ask only about trite, safe subjects. More seriously, it can result in real variations of opinion and attitude being ignored because they don't fit the researcher's notion of what is being researched. Questions may reliably receive invalid responses.

Research which emphasises validity may make no attempt to be reliable. In in-depth interviewing it is not expected that different respondents will give comparable data. Comparisons may be suggested but there is no list of allowed responses against which reliability can be assessed. The results don't help us to gauge the views of the wider population, and without wider applicability the research may be regarded as merely interesting.

So far we have looked at two extreme positions in research methodology. In practice many researchers pitch their work somewhere between them, or try to use both methods. In-depth interviews may provide information that suggests a pattern of opinion worth exploring further. Structured interviews may be used to check how far that pattern of opinion extends into the wider population. Different research aims and methodologies should be seen as complementary, not in opposition to each other.

Observation

Observation is another popular and useful research technique. There are two types: **direct observation**, where the researcher remains detached from the subjects; and **participant observation**, where the researcher joins in with the people being studied. Observation means 'studying by looking'. To be classed as research, rather than merely looking on, observations need to be structured. As with other research techniques, data collection has to be organised so that relevant and useful information is sought and recorded. Well-organised observation has several advantages as a research technique.

One key advantage of observation is that you can observe what people actually *do*, not what they tell researchers that they do. People are studied in their own environment and should be expected to behave as they do naturally. Observation can detect 'taken for granted' behaviour that subjects are not aware of, and so would not report if asked in an interview.

Another useful feature of observation is that groups can be studied, as can the interactions between their members. Other research methods look only at individuals, making group behaviour difficult to investigate. Also observations can be done over time, allowing changes in groups or situations to be revealed.

Direct observation

Direct observation can be regarded as similar to bird watching. Subjects are watched as they go about their normal lives and observations are recorded by the researcher. Both qualitative and quantitative data can be collected through direct observation. For example, quantitative data about playground usage is probably best collected by this method. Observers can count arrivals and can group them in terms of gender, age and other observable characteristics. Observers can also record qualitative data, such as how the children behave towards each other in the playground and which seem to be friends.

Direct observation may be the only way to observe some groups, for example, small children. It can be useful in any situation where a researcher's presence would be unobtrusive. However, direct observation also has problems associated with it.

One simple problem is that of recording the data. Making notes distracts the researcher from observation. It may be easy to miss something important, particularly when a fairly large group is being studied. Some methods of observation can raise ethical problems. Should researchers use secret techniques for collecting and recording data? This could be something fairly innocent, like fixing an electronic counter to a door to check how many people use it. However it could include bugging phones, or using two-way mirrors to observe private behaviour.

A more serious difficulty is interpreting what is observed. Direct observers are not 'inside', and they cannot see behaviour from the subject's point of view. For example, children may believe that they are playing a boisterous game, whilst the observer perceives a violent confrontation. Observers may project their own theories onto what they see, and fail to understand what is happening so far as the subjects are concerned.

It is because of the difficulties with interpretation that direct observation is a poor way to research opinions and values. Inferring beliefs from observed behaviour is likely to produce highly distorted results. Of course, observed behaviour may suggest

lines of enquiry that can be followed up with other methods. For example, you may observe that staff at a day centre seem to spend less time talking to black clients. Further research using interview techniques could probe staff attitudes to race and discrimination.

The group of subjects that is being observed is unlikely to be a representative sample of the population as a whole. Observers must study whoever is available; they cannot select representative sample groups to study. This means that quantitative data collected cannot be taken to represent a wider picture. However, the data can be very useful in giving a local picture.

Task

Think about subjects you are interested in researching and list those where you could use observation. For each subject list the data that you could collect. Will it be qualitative or quantitative? Choose the subject that you feel is most suitable for observational techniques. How can you justify your use of direct observation to study this subject?

Participant observation

Participant observation means that the researcher becomes part of the group being studied. There is probably no better way of really getting to understand the way groups work than to join them. Several classic social research projects have involved this method. Researchers have sometimes spent years living and working with their subjects, whilst at the same time recording data about them. This clearly requires dedicated professionalism and a good deal of time. The commitment required puts participant observation beyond the scope of most researchers. Nevertheless, there are several strengths to the technique.

The data provided by participant research is likely to be very valid. Researchers are living alongside the respondents and can see things from their point of view. There is little danger that serious misinterpretations will occur. Researchers can get to know their subjects so well that a valid picture of their values and opinions can be built up. Participant observation can produce excellent qualitative data.

Participant observation may also be the only way to study some groups. For example, people who are homeless and sleeping rough may only open up to someone who has become a familiar part of their world. Other groups, like street gangs, may be so hostile to outsiders that participant observation is the only way to get close to them. This sort of social science is not for the faint hearted!

Participant observation may not suit everyone

The main limitation of participant research is the time and commitment it demands. In addition, participant researchers need special skills if the study is to remain objective. It is all too easy to get sucked into the world you are now a part of. This can mean that things are only seen from the subject's viewpoint. Researchers have to remain detached whilst being fully involved. Involvement can mean that only unusual events are noticed and recorded. Valuable background data may be unnoticed because it is now such a familiar part of everyday life for the researcher.

Where researchers are so fully bound up in the life of their subjects it is certain that they are influenced

by them to some degree. The effects of this depend very much on the skills of the individual researcher, and how the research is being conducted. Some researchers reveal themselves to the group and seek acceptance as a harmless observer. This makes it much easier to take notes, and gives an excuse for the occasional probing interview. Others may try to pass themselves off as ordinary group members, and so must scribble their notes in secret whenever they get a chance. This sort of clandestine (secret) observation has ethical difficulties. Is it right to record people's private lives secretly in detail, particularly if you intend to publish the results?

Participant observation can lose quality because the researcher is not fully accepted by the group, but may be kept on the fringes of the group's activities and never really find out what is going on. Observers may not be aware that this is happening and may report what is observed as the whole picture.

Think it over

Think about groups that you belong to. How would it feel to conduct participant research with them? What problems would you expect to face whilst doing the research? How easy do you think it would be to remain objective?

· SAMPLING METHODS ·

Whatever research technique is used, social researchers must decide who to collect information from. Without vast resources, or a particularly small population, it is impossible to cover everybody. This means that a *sample* must be selected. Many researchers seek quantitative data, and want to apply their results to the whole population. To be able to do this they need a sample which is as representative of the population as possible. This means that the proportions of people with different characteristics in the sample should reflect the proportions in the population as a whole. The sample should be a 'representative cross-section' of the population being studied.

Careful sampling is crucial if quantitative results are to claim broader applicability. Even if research is qualitative subjects must be chosen. This is sampling of a sort, although being representative is seldom such an issue. All researchers should be able to explain how their sample was selected, and how representative it is likely to be.

How big should a sample be? To be representative it needs to contain a similar range of people to the population being studied. Very small samples run the risk of missing important groups. Social researchers want their sample to reflect the spread of things like age, gender, ethnic group and class background. The spread of such characteristics within a population is called **variance**. Some populations have much more variability than others. For instance, children in the same class at a primary school serving a local estate will have a lot in common. On the other hand, variance amongst people studying in an evening class at college is likely to be far greater. In practice, the

A sample should be a representative cross-section

size of samples usually depends on the researcher's resources. If you select as big a sample as you can manage then you have helped to make it representative and cover variance in the population.

Random sampling

Even if samples are of a reasonable size it is possible for distortions to occur. If sample selection is left entirely to the choices of researchers then their own personal bias will be a problem. Random sampling methods are designed to eliminate the chance of personal bias influencing sample selection. Random sampling does *not* mean haphazard sampling. Rules of sample selection are strictly applied so that sampling errors can be calculated and stated mathematically. Of course, other factors such as interviewer bias, or poorly designed questionnaires, can influence and distort results in ways which are difficult to estimate. But if random sampling methods are used then at least errors due to sample selection can be precisely estimated.

Basically, random sampling means that a group is selected randomly from the whole population. All members of the population must have a measurable chance of being selected. Where all members of the population have the same chance of selection the method is known as *simple random sampling*. To begin random sampling the researcher needs to have a list of all members of the population. This list is known as a 'sampling frame'. It is important that the sampling frame provides complete coverage of the population. If the sampling frame is incomplete then some members of the population can never be selected, and the principle of randomness breaks down. *So a sampling frame is the list that the sample will be drawn from.*

A sample can be selected from the sampling frame in different ways. One method is known as *systematic sampling*. Names are picked at regular intervals from the sampling frame until the required size of sample is obtained. All members of the population must have a chance of selection and it is important that the size of the interval allows this to happen. For example: if the sampling frame has 1000 names, and you want to select a sample of 100, then you need to select every tenth name. This will give you a sample of the required size. The number of the first name picked also needs to be randomised. In this case a pair of dice could be used to give a random number. In our example, if 11 or 12 came up then the last selection needed to complete the 100 names will end up being one of the first two names on the sampling frame list. This is because you will need to return to the beginning of the list to get all the people you need for your sample. For example: the dice numbers 1 to 10 cover the last ten names; 11 or 12 on the dice means that you have to return to the first names on the list.

There can be problems with the systematic sampling method. Sampling frames are usually acquired by researchers and seldom created by them from the start. Most lists are not at all random in order. Many will be alphabetical, and some are grouped in other ways. In our example above, a list which is grouped in sets of ten would give a very biased sample. You could try to randomise the sampling frame *before* systematic sampling. However this is a long process, and introduces the problem of how to make the list truly random.

A solution to the problems of systematic selection is to use *random number tables*. These consist of lists of randomly chosen numbers which are used to select a sample from the sampling frame. This is a better method than systematic sampling, although it takes a bit longer.

One problem with simple random sampling is that a biased sample may be chosen by chance. For example: suppose the population consists of 500 males and 500 females. It is quite possible for a random sample of 100 to be entirely composed of one sex; giving seriously biased results. A larger sample size does not guarantee balance, unless the whole population is selected. To overcome this stratified random sampling may be used.

Stratified sampling

Stratified random sampling is a way of making sure that important groups are represented in a sample. The sampling frame is split up into groups that need to be represented. Random methods are used to select a proportion of the sample from each group. In our example, the sampling frame is split into two lists: one containing 500 males, and one containing 500 females. To get our sample of 100 we randomly select 50 males and 50 females. Our sample is sure to reflect the gender balance in the population and has still been chosen randomly.

The method described above is an example of *proportionate stratified sampling*. The proportions of each group chosen for the sample were the same as their proportions in the population. If the population had consisted of 600 males and 400 females we would have chosen 60 males and 40 females to get our sample of 100.

Sometimes groups within the population may be small but still important to the research. For example: a day centre may cater mainly for able-bodied people, but have a few disabled clients. Proportionate stratified sampling may allow only one or two disabled clients to be selected. The sample will thus fail to represent fully the views and needs of an important group. *Disproportionate stratified sampling* can be used to get over this problem. The researcher deliberately weights the proportions of different groups in the sample to include greater numbers of small but important groups.

Stratified random sampling is an improvement on simple random sampling but has some drawbacks. To stratify a sampling frame you need some prior knowledge of the groups within it. Unless the list contains extra information you may have to guess which groups people belong to. If you only have a list of names to go on, even guessing who is male or female can lead to mistakes. Apart from this, going through a sampling frame and identifying groups and proportions is a long process.

Another problem is that you could choose to stratify by characteristics which are *not* useful to your study. For example, you may stratify according to gender but not according to age. Later you could find that important differences of opinion occur between age groups. It is difficult to know how to stratify a population, even if it is possible to do so.

Both simple and stratified random sampling need a sampling frame. The problem is getting hold of a suitable list. Records kept for many purposes may be useful as sampling frames, but most are also confidential. Even if you do obtain a suitable list there is no guarantee that it is accurate *and* complete. Also it may be ordered in ways you are unaware of, making systematic sampling liable to bias. There are populations for which it is impossible to find or create a sampling frame. Other sampling methods then have to be used.

Opportunity sampling

If, for example, you are interested in people's opinions about a new exhibition it is impossible to draw up a suitable sampling frame. The best way to find a sample is to hang around the exhibition exit. You simply stop and question some of the people who pass. This is known as *opportunity sampling*.

Opportunity sampling can be used for situations where it is impossible to use other techniques. For instance, if you want to talk to ex-smokers you are only likely to find them by stopping people and interviewing those who fit into your population. It has the advantage that the sample can always be ensured to be of the desired size. If there is a problem with non-response from one person, you

Interviewers may avoid people they don't like the look of

simply ask another. The major problem is that the selection of the sample members is entirely at the interviewer's discretion. It is *not* random sampling. Interviewers may pick people who they like the look of. They are likely to avoid those who they perceive as looking demanding or threatening.

Interviewer bias can jeopardise the results of opportunity sampling. It is bound to occur when interviewers have a free choice. However, one way of dealing with this is to introduce some controls on who the interviewer may pick.

Quota sampling

Quota sampling is a type of stratified sampling, but it is not a random sampling method. As in opportunity sampling, the final selection of the sample is left to the interviewer. In quota sampling, however, the interviewer must pick a specified number of people from certain defined groups. For example, an interviewer might have to pick 50 men and 50 women for their sample. Quota sampling is much used for market research and opinion polls. Street interviews are the usual method, and interviewers have a quota of people in different categories to stop and question. This is an improvement on opportunity sampling as there is some assurance that different types of people will be covered.

Quota sampling has several advantages. It is cheap and quick to do. There is no need to find a sampling frame and select a sample randomly from it. There is no problem with non-response. For example: if you need a particular quota of women with children you simply carry on until you have interviewed enough of them. Quota sampling gets quick results from a varied sample.

One problem with quota sampling is that it is *not* a random method. The final decision on who to talk to is left to the interviewer, and this introduces the problem of bias in selection. Even if interviewers must speak to a quota of people in a group, their selection may still be biased. It may be easier to stop and interview a woman with one child than one with four children to handle! Quotas of 'over-65's' are likely to under-represent older members of the age group, particularly if interviewing is done in the street.

Most quota samples use gender, age and social class as the basis for setting quotas. Interviewers generally have no trouble identifying gender, and only a little more estimating age. However, the identification of class by appearance is a risky business: it is likely to be heavily influenced by the interviewer's perceptions and ideas.

Another problem is in drawing up the quotas for interview. Decisions can only be made if researchers have some prior knowledge of the population they are researching. This does not mean that a sampling frame is needed, but statistics indicating proportions of different groups in the population must be found.

Another important issue is *where* and *when* the sampling and interviewing takes place. If you interview in an 'up-market' shopping street it is likely that you will get a different type of sample than you would in a less prosperous area. If you interview on a midweek afternoon you are likely to miss working people. Unless you interview door-to-door you will miss people who are housebound. In short, quota sampling misses people who are difficult to 'bump into'.

The sampling method you choose will depend on who you are studying, and the resources available to you. Whatever method you pick, try to think out your decision. Will your method give a biased result? Can you do anything to improve how representative and random your sample selection has been?

As a warning consider the case of the disastrous poll carried out in 1936 by the American periodical *The Literary Digest*. They intended to predict the result of the forthcoming presidential election between Landon and Roosevelt. A sample was chosen randomly from telephone directories and car registrations, and the result predicted an easy win for Landon. Roosevelt won. The problem was that the sample was *not* representative of voters. Only the well-off had telephones and cars at that time. Poorer people were not asked and Roosevelt's popularity was seriously under-estimated. *The Literary Digest*

claimed too much for their research. If you are aware of the problems that may have occurred due to your sampling method you can be more realistic about the accuracy of your own results.

Task

List subjects that you are considering researching. For each subject think about methods you could use for selecting a sample. Write down the method you think most appropriate for each subject.

Choose one subject from your list. Explain how you could make your sample as representative as possible, with the method of selection you have chosen.

· DOING RESEARCH ·

This section is concerned with carrying out a primary research project. In particular we will be looking at how research, using structured questionnaires and structured interview schedules, is conducted. These methods are especially useful for collecting quantitative data that may be analysed statistically and applied, with due caution, to the whole population.

Social research is often concerned with discovering opinions. Qualitative methods are good at this, but if statistical analysis is sought we need to collect quantitative data. This means that research must be planned and carried out extremely carefully. We should be aiming to produce results that are reliable and valid. Thorough planning maximises our chances of achieving this aim.

Defining a research problem

The first step in planning research is to decide exactly *what* you are researching. Broad areas of interest, such as 'single parents' or 'people with disabilities', are so vast in scope that no list of questions can cover them. A narrower focus is needed, and a clear statement of what your work aims to investigate. Clear aims make the research much easier to do. You know what you need to find out. A well-defined research problem also gives a frame of reference to your work. This can help you to identify links with other research, or with social theory.

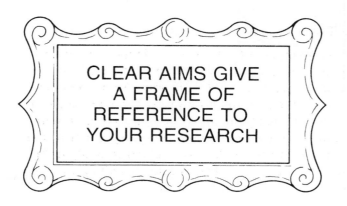

CLEAR AIMS GIVE
A FRAME OF
REFERENCE TO
YOUR RESEARCH

Defining a research problem may well begin with a broad area of interest like those above. It helps to choose an area you know something about. It is far easier to plan if you know a little about the issues involved. The next step is to choose an aspect of the area to concentrate on. For example: if you are interested in elders with disabilities you could decide to concentrate on their opinions about local day care provision. At this stage you should have decided on a problem or question that can be investigated. This may be a good time to begin secondary research. Your research problem ought to be specific enough now for relevant secondary sources to be identified. You may pick up useful ideas and background which will make your planning easier, and results more relevant.

Some research is designed to investigate problems stated in the way we have done so far. Other researchers want to stick closely to methods used in the natural sciences. They need a well defined statement which their results can confirm, or disprove. This statement is known as an *hypothesis*. Statements like, 'Most elders with disabilities are satisfied with local day care provision' or, 'Most married men believe that housework should be

shared equally' are hypotheses. Whether they are true or not can be gauged from statistical analysis of quantitative research results. The development of a clearly stated hypothesis will provide a very specific focus for your work.

Task

Choose an issue you are interested in researching and write a range of hypotheses that could apply to it. Make sure that they are specific and narrowly focused. Try to think how you could research each hypothesis. Identify which are likely to be difficult to prove or disprove. Against each hypothesis you have created, note what you think it could tell you about the issue you are interested in.

Choosing a research method

The research method you decide to use will depend mainly on two factors: the population you are interested in; and the sort of data you want to collect.

Population

Defining your population clearly is very important. It is a statement about who your results can be applied to, and who your sample must be selected from. Remember that it is likely to be easier to select a representative sample if the population is not too large. The hypothesis, 'Most students believe that smoking is harmful to health' implies that the population includes *all* students. Does this mean all students in Britain, or is the research world-wide? Suppose we alter the hypothesis to, 'Most local students . . .' How do we decide what 'local' means? Does 'students' include people studying at school, or older people attending evening classes? To define the population even more closely we could say, 'Most full-time students at this college (or school) believe that smoking is harmful to health'. Now it is much clearer who we are talking about, and we know exactly who to take a sample of.

When the population has been defined you can start to note down things you already know about them. Be particularly careful not to note down assumptions, however widely held or taken for granted they may be. Characteristics of the population will affect the research method that you can use. If they are geographically spread, and likely to be interested in the subject, a postal questionnaire may work well. If they are easy to get hold of, and likely to need encouragement to respond, interviews would probably be better.

Task

Choose a research problem or hypothesis that you have devised and intend to research. Try to define the population it refers to. Be as precise as you can. Think about this population and write a list of characteristics that you already know about. Look over your list and eliminate any items that you are not absolutely sure of. How can you confirm that the items you have left are true for your population?

If you hope to use random sampling methods you need a sampling frame. Is there a way of getting one for your population? Difficulties here often lead researchers to resort to quota sampling techniques, but this isn't always necessary. If you are studying your fellow students then the college or school will have a list. (Whether you can get access to it is another matter.) Another approach is to tailor your research to a sampling frame you can obtain. For instance, you could use a street directory to select a sample and treat people living in a particular area as the population. The danger with this is that you may end up researching a different group from the one you intended, and one that is not very interested in the subject.

Think it over

Think about a situation where a sampling frame for your population may exist. How accurate is it likely to be? Can you make up your own sampling frame? What difficulties might you have here?

Data

The other issue to think about is the type of data you want to collect. Will it be quantitative or qualitative, or a mixture of both? Sometimes data can be obtained in either form. There are ways of collecting quantitative data on views and opinions (explained in detail below). You may prefer to use quantitative methods if you intend to analyse the results statistically. This is also something to consider in the planning stage.

Task

Write a list of the range of data you could collect from your population that is relevant to the subject of your research. Which data is factual (age, gender), and which is about opinions?

With a clear hypothesis, a closely defined population and a good idea of the data you want to collect, you can decide which research method to use. Whichever you choose you will need a sample.

This is a good time to think about how you can make your sample representative. Can you obtain a sampling frame? Can you acquire enough prior knowledge of the population to assign proportions for quota sampling? How big a sample can you handle using the research method you have chosen?

The first two questions can be tackled with thought and some investigation. The last one can be estimated fairly well by conducting a *pilot survey*.

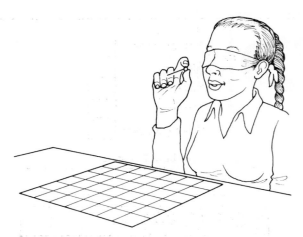

Random samples give better results

This means trying out your research on a few people to find out how well it works. Pilot studies give you the chance to time the research. They also let you test your questionnaire or interview schedule.

Theory into practice

Which research method will suit the population and data you are interested in? List the characteristics of the population you know about, and the data you want to obtain. Can you justify your choice of research method in terms of this information? Do the same exercise for your sampling method. Why is it the right choice for your research project?

The next step is to begin designing your questionnaire. You have decided what data you need; now you can decide what type of questions to use for collecting it.

· QUESTIONNAIRES ·

Questions and responses

Question style is an important feature of questionnaire design. There are two basic types of question, *open* and *closed*. Open (or open response) questions allow respondents to answer in their own words. They give qualitative data. Closed (or fixed response) questions ask respondents to choose from a set of alternative answers provided. They give quantitative data. Most surveys use both types of question.

Open questions can give very useful background data. Respondents don't have to choose between alternatives and can answer in their own terms. Open questions can be especially useful in pilot surveys. They can indicate the sorts of things which people think are important to an issue, and help in the design of more relevant fixed response questions.

One problem with open questions can be that the respondent's answers get rather lengthy. Interviewers have to record replies, and this usually means making notes in your own words. The need to sum up lengthy answers, or keep up with rapid ones, is a potential source of error. In postal questionnaires, answers can be limited by providing only a small space for them. The main limitation of open questions is that replies cannot be analysed statistically. Nevertheless they are very useful at the beginning of questionnaires as 'icebreakers': to get people thinking about a topic, and put them at ease before fixed response questions probe more specifically.

Fixed response questions restrict respondents to a choice between fixed alternatives. They may be used to collect quantitative data about fact or opinion.

Open questions can put respondents at their ease

Some data is factual, such as gender, age group, or religion. It includes any information where opinion is not involved. This data allows you to classify your respondents during the analysis stage and link, or correlate, their characteristics to their opinions. If quota sampling is used it is vital to check that the respondent falls into a group you need. Factual questions used to collect background information about respondents are called *demographic* questions. In structured interviews, responses to demographic questions can lead to a particular set of follow-up questions being asked. For instance, positive answers ('yes') to the factual question, 'Do you smoke cigarettes?' can lead to a set of questions specially directed at cigarette smokers.

Other fixed response questions seek data on opinions. There are different ways to design these questions, and the style of response required varies between them. The most basic opinion question asks, 'Do you agree with (X)?', and allows respondents to choose between 'yes' and 'no'. However, usually it is better to allow more options so that strength of opinion can be indicated. Most opinion questions use some form of scaling or ranking method, to allow differences between respondents to be measured more closely.

Scaling

Rating scales are a way of measuring the strength of a person's opinion on an issue. A number of options, often five or seven, are offered for selection in answer to an opinion question. Options can be presented in a number of ways. They may be expressed verbally, say from 'strongly in favour' to 'strongly against', with tick boxes. Alternatively, a graphical scale could be used with fixed points for respondents to indicate how strongly they are for or against. (See Figure 8.1.)

The number of scale points offered can be odd or even. If an odd number is used respondents can select a safe, middle of the road position. Research has shown that respondents often cluster round this 'safe' option if it is available. An even number of options prevents respondents remaining neutral and forces a choice.

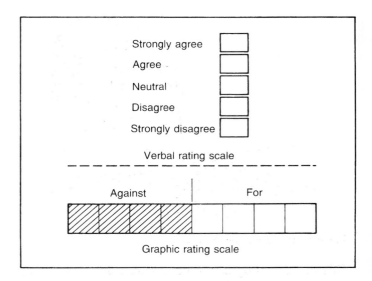

Figure 8.1 *Verbal and graphic rating scales*

This form of rating scale is the most basic. Professional social researchers often use more sophisticated scaling methods, where responses from a group of questions are linked to give an overall view of opinion. Responses are very sensitive to things like the order or wording of questions, and there is a vast number of different ways of asking questions about a subject. Scaling methods try to select a sample of these questions so that the overall result will be as representative as possible of the respondent's true opinion.

Sets of questions can seek opinion on a topic from different angles. This prevents one small aspect of an opinion from giving a distorted impression, which could happen if only one question was asked. For example, a respondent may say that she believes doctors to be very well qualified. This person may nevertheless not believe in the ability of doctors to cure her. A grouped set of questions using a scaling method would reveal more accurately this person's lack of faith in doctors. The technical aspects of these more sophisticated scaling methods are beyond the scope of this book. For more information see the recommended reading at the end of the chapter. However, you could try to design your questions so that different approaches are taken to the same subject. This allows a check on consistency of response, and helps to minimise the effects of badly constructed questions.

Think it over

Some of the data you need could be collected using sets of rating scales. Decide which data could be collected in this way. Can you devise questions which ask about a topic from different angles? What problems might occur if you try to group questions on a particular topic?

Decide whether any of the opinion data that you need could be collected using the semantic differential method. If possible devise a set of pairs of polar adjectives which could be used. Explain why each pair of polar adjectives should give you the information you require.

Another way of scaling opinions is the *semantic differential technique*. Respondents are asked to give their opinion on a scale between adjectives which are 'polar opposites'. Polar adjectives are opposites like: good and bad, hard and soft, fast and slow. Pairs of polar adjectives can be chosen that apply to the subject in question. Thus if students are being asked how they see smokers, possible polar adjectives might be: healthy or unhealthy, worldly wise or naive, sociable or antisocial. Respondents are asked a single question and give a number of responses by choosing their position between several pairs of polar adjectives. This contrasts with rating scales where several questions ask for one type of response, the respondent's level of agreement.

Ranking alternatives is another method of recording responses. Respondents are asked to rank a list in order of preference, quality, or some other factor. This method has the advantage of making direct comparisons between alternatives. Items must be familiar to respondents, and seen by them to be related. Things that don't seem to fit will lead to confusion.

Items to be ranked can take a variety of forms. They could be statements, such as the different qualities associated with nurses. Here respondents could be asked to rank which qualities they thought most important. Items could be posts within the caring services, such as doctor or care assistant. Respondents could be asked to rank these in terms of the level of help they offer, or how hard working they seem to be. Ranking allows opinion on a linked group of items to be scaled, and is very useful when comparisons need to be made.

Semantic differential

Respondents indicate their position between each pair of polar adjectives.

Good	–	–	–	–	–	Bad
Hard	–	–	–	–	–	Soft
Fast	–	–	–	–	–	Slow
Cheap	–	–	–	–	–	Expensive

The semantic differential technique can build up a useful picture of opinion. Well-chosen polar adjectives can give indications of a variety of views. For instance: you could add 'attractive or unattractive' and 'happy or unhappy' to our list on smokers, and probe more deeply into respondents' feelings. Polar adjectives must always be chosen with care. They must be understandable to the respondents and must fit their view of the subject. Again, open questions in a pilot survey can help you.

A ranking order question

What qualities are most important in nurses? (Please number the boxes 1 to 5 in order of importance)

Good qualifications ☐
Dedication ☐
Experience ☐
Caring attitude ☐
Physical fitness ☐

Writing questions

The quality of the questions is one of the most important aspects of survey design. All your careful planning is invalidated if the questions fail to collect the data intended. Sadly, there are no strict rules to follow which will always give good questions. However, there are points to guide you which, together with your judgement, should make the job easier. Knowledge of your population, commonsense, and a pilot survey will all help you to write better questions.

One thing to decide is how many questions to include. Too many will exhaust the respondent – and the interviewer! Postal questionnaires are likely to suffer from a particularly poor response if they are too long or complicated. On the other hand, too few questions will give very sketchy results. Try to strike a balance by thinking about your respondents. How long would they be prepared to spend on your questionnaire? How long will it take to carry out an interview? Guesswork can give you an idea of the answers, and a pilot survey will help refine them.

Think it over

Think about your population and the questions you want to ask. How long should a questionnaire (or interview) last, given their likely interest in the research subject?

Question length is also important. Long questions should be avoided as they are likely to bore, and confuse, respondents. If you seem to be producing long questions try to split them into a number of shorter ones. Long questions may occur because you want to set the scene for respondents. You could get around the problem by using a general introduction and then asking several shorter questions around this theme.

Question content is crucial to the survey process. Respondents must be able to give answers to the questions they are asked. Questions about things that respondents have no knowledge of, or no opinion on, will produce worthless results. It is also important that questions are about subjects that respondents are willing to discuss. Even answers to factual questions can be biased by choice of subject. For example, responses to the question, 'How often do you clean your teeth?' are likely to be biased in the direction of respectability. Opinion questions are even more likely to be affected by a respondent's willingness to answer on a particular subject.

Questions need to offer options which cover the full range of possible answers. Fact questions must have an option for every possible member of the population. For instance, if you ask, 'How do you travel to college?' your options need to cover all possible modes of transport. But you should always add an 'Other . . .' option. There can often be 'other' options that you failed to predict.

Another aspect of option choices is exclusivity. This means that respondents are not left confused about which box to tick. The question above may have a problem with exclusivity. Some people may use both bus and train to travel. The need to cover all possible options may lead to a long list being created. In interviews this can lead to respondents forgetting earlier items, and inaccurately picking one they can remember in order to save face. A solution to this is to have a card containing the options which is given to the respondent as the question is read out. This is known as a prompt card.

Prompt cards can help respondents to choose the right option

The wording of opinion questions needs to be looked at carefully to minimise the risk of bias. Questions must be specific. If you ask, 'How would you rate the service in this canteen?' some respondents may have difficulty in answering. They may think that some staff give good service whereas others do not. They may think service is good at lunch times, but poor during morning breaks. A more specific set of questions would get a more accurate, and fuller, response. Wording must be specific. Questions like, 'Do you use this canteen often?' leave the respondent to decide what 'often' means. The frame of reference of the question must be spelled out in specific terms.

Your questions must not make presumptions about the respondent. For example if you ask elders, 'Do you find it easy to live on a state pension?' you are presuming that they have no other source of income. Answers could often be a guess about how easy others may find it. Some respondents may be offended. You can insert factual questions to identify people who fit a particular category, if you need to ask particular questions of them.

Wording needs to be easy for respondents to understand. This means that language should be kept simple and non-technical. Try to avoid using an uncommon word when one or two simple ones would do. For example: use 'end' instead of 'terminate', 'worker' instead of 'practitioner', 'say' instead of 'state', 'need' instead of 'require'. There is nearly always a simpler way of expressing something. Clarity can also be obscured by confusing use of double negatives. The question, 'Do you think that not having enough money never affects people's quality of life?' is fairly difficult to understand. It is easy to reword it so that the double negative doesn't appear, i.e. 'Do you think that money may affect people's quality of life'.

Wording also needs to be unambiguous. All respondents must understand the question in the same way. For example the question, 'Is work important to you?' is very ambiguous. Does it mean important in financial terms, or is it asking about personal attachment to a job? Is it about paid work, or about work in a more general sense? The same word can mean different things to different people.

Questions must not lead respondents into giving a particular answer. If you ask, 'You don't think that the health service is improving, do you?' you are obviously leading the reply. The respondent is being led to say 'No'! Questions can also lead the respondent in more subtle ways. If you ask, 'Do you think that social workers should get involved in people's private lives?' it sounds as if you may be suggesting that they are 'nosey' rather than being caring and supportive. Leading questions can be difficult to spot. Try to examine question wording for signs of being leading. Ask others how neutral the question sounds.

An important issue in question wording is that respondents don't find questions embarrassing or threatening. This can apply to factual, as well as opinion, questions. For instance, questions on income may seem threatening and some respondents may find information on age or disability hard to give.

Theory into practice

Use this section to draw up a checklist of points to look for when writing questions. Your list should include things like ambiguity, making presumptions, etc. This checklist can be used to assess questions you have written.

Opinion questions may be perceived as threatening if they touch on sensitive subjects. One problem is predicting which areas respondents are likely to find sensitive. Once again, a pilot survey with open questions will help. Sometimes threat can be reduced by careful wording. For example, asking retired people, 'Do you feel less fulfilled now than when you were working?' is fairly threatening. You could change the question to, 'Some people find that they feel less fulfilled during retirement than when they were working. What do you think could cause this feeling amongst them?' A follow-up question can ask whether respondents feel themselves to be a part of that group, this approach is now less likely to offend.

Task

Draw up a list of questions that you might ask to get data from your population. Use your checklist to examine question wording, and improve the question set. Are your questions now likely to produce the data you want without bias? Why are these questions likely to give good results?

An important influence on how people respond to sensitive subjects is the way they are presented in the questionnaire or interview schedule. This leads to the issues of question order, layout and presentation.

Question order, layout, and presentation

The way you order and present your questions can influence the responses you receive. There are no rules on question order, but there are guidelines to help improve the quality of responses in different situations.

During interview situations respondents must be put at ease early on. This means that opening with a sensitive opinion question is usually a bad idea. Opening with a battery of demographic factual questions (needed to find out who you are talking to) can also put respondents in a less co-operative frame of mind. It is generally better to put these items lower down in the schedule. A good way to start is with an open question which introduces the survey topic in a broad, non-threatening way. This should stimulate respondents' interest in the questions that follow, and prepare them for the sort of answers that may be expected of them.

If quota sampling is being used it is important to collect some demographic data (individual data linked to details of the community or population) fairly early on. Everybody's time will be wasted if interviews are conducted with people who don't fit the quotas. Usually only a few details are needed to establish whether a person fits a category needed for

interview. These can often be discovered by a combination of observation and a couple of brief introductory questions. When you have established that you should proceed with the interview, you can relax and start with your first open question. It is always a good idea to explain to respondents why you need to ask demographic questions (or details about them) whenever they appear. This will make your enquiry seem less intrusive or threatening and may help to get more accurate answers.

The order of the bulk of the questions is very much up to the researcher. One common approach is to begin with general questions on a topic, then gradually narrow down the field of enquiry. This is intended to focus respondents down onto a topic, by taking them from the general to the specific. It is sometimes known as the *funnel method*. The idea is that respondents are prepared for the specific questions when they arrive because they have been gradually oriented or led towards them. They may therefore be more prepared to give sensitive information, or answer questions on threatening topics. Also, respondents' answers to later questions may be more accurate because they have had time to think out their opinions.

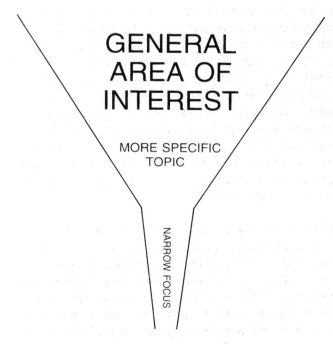

Narrowing your area of enquiry

There is another reason for putting general questions before more specific ones. Answers given to specific questions can bias answers to general questions which follow. People may have strong views on a narrow aspect of a subject. If reminded of these by a specific question they may distort or exaggerate their response to questions about the subject as a whole.

Another point concerning question order is that perfectly good questions can become leading questions if they are badly placed. For instance: suppose you asked a string of questions designed to measure people's views on violence against children. If you followed these with the question, 'Do you think that police and social workers should be given more powers to deal with violence against children?' it is likely that some respondents will bias their answer because of feelings aroused by the preceding questions. The way to eliminate sources of bias due to question order is by careful reading of your questionnaire or interview schedule. A solution tried by some researchers is to randomise the question order for different respondents. However, this is time consuming and complicated to do. Also it doesn't attempt to eliminate bias. A randomised question order ensures that bias occurs with some, unidentified, members of the sample.

Task

Take the list of questions you have devised and try to put them in an order which will give good results. How will your question order help to get accurate results? How does your question order attempt to eliminate bias?

Layout and presentation

Layout and presentation are particularly important with postal questionnaires. If they are cluttered or confused they will probably end up in the bin. Respondents must find questionnaires clear and easy to follow. They should also find them friendly. Introductions and directions that sound too scientific and formal can put people off.

You should always introduce your survey with an explanation of what the research is about and why you are asking people to respond by questionnaire. Failure to 'sell' your questionnaire at this stage may mean that a respondent never completes it. Keep the introduction short and simple, but try to convince respondents that the questionnaire is worth filling in and returning.

Questions should be clearly separated so that respondents have no difficulty making their way through them. Keep the layout neat and uncluttered to prevent any confusion. Respondents must decide where their response to a particular question should be recorded. A clear layout should make it obvious which responses link with which questions.

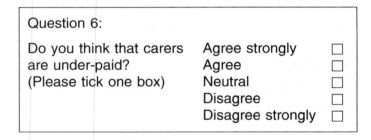

Figure 8.2 *Make sure your questionnaire is clearly laid out*

Make sure that it is also clear how responses to particular questions are to be recorded on the questionnaire. If you use rating scales, semantic differential or ranking techniques you will have to explain how you want respondents to indicate their answers. Keep these explanations simple and brief, but make sure that the instructions are clear and adequate. If you try to incorporate all three of the techniques in a questionnaire you run the risk of making it seem complicated. It may be better to use only one or two, so that respondents are not put off.

When planning the layout of questions and answers in your questionnaire you should remember that the respondent is not the only person you need to consider. If everything goes according to plan you will be receiving a large number of completed questionnaires, and will need to collate the data from them. If you lay the answers out clearly it can make this task much easier. *Collating* involves putting answers from different respondents together to build a picture of the overall response. This task is made very much easier by the use of computers (Chapter 12 on information technology shows you how this can be done). Whatever way you collate responses it is far easier and quicker if you *pre-code* the answers.

Pre-coding means assigning a number or letter to the possible responses for each question. For example you may code gender as simply M or F. Responses to a rating scale question could be coded 1 to 5, or however many are needed to cover all available answers. If pre-coding is not done the reply must be coded when the completed questionnaires are gone through, which is a much longer process.

Question 1:

| Please indicate your gender | Male | ☐ M |
| | Female | ☐ F |

Question 2:

Do you think that carers are overworked?	Agree strongly	☐ 1
	Agree	☐ 2
	Neutral	☐ 3
	Disagree	☐ 4
	Disagree strongly	☐ 5

Figure 8.3 *Examples of pre-coded questions*

The overall presentation of your questionnaire should be as professional as possible. People perceive professional-looking documents as more important than those which look amateurish. They are more likely to take your survey seriously if the questionnaire looks impressive. Your response rate is likely to be higher, which makes the research far more useful. The best way to produce a professional looking questionnaire is by using information technology. Again Chapter 12 gives advice on this.

One final point on postal questionnaire design is to remember to add a thank you at the end. Respondents need to feel motivated to return the completed form and a final word may help. You can use the opportunity to remind them why the research is important and further increase the likelihood of getting a return. For example: if the survey is about services for people with disabilities you could end with, 'Thank you for taking the time to fill out this questionnaire. Your answers will greatly help our research into services for people with disabilities'.

· STRUCTURED INTERVIEWS ·

Structured interview schedules don't need such care in presentation as questionnaires, but layout is important if things are to go smoothly. A professional approach can again improve the quality of responses. Professionalism is likely to be judged on how smoothly the interview is conducted, and a well-organised schedule can help with this. Interviewers must be able to keep track of the interview process.

This may be straightforward when the questions simply follow one after the other. But often interviews branch into different areas, depending on the responses given to certain questions. If you ask, 'Do you smoke cigarettes?' you may have prepared a separate set of supplementary questions to ask smokers and non-smokers. Interview schedules can turn into complicated documents. It may be best to put questions belonging to a particular branch together on a separate sheet of paper. This way you can quickly flip to them, and return to the main run of questions when you have finished. Remember to include guidance notes, even if they are to yourself! It is all too easy to forget where to return to when a branch of questions has been completed.

As with questionnaires, make sure that answers are clearly linked to questions and pre-coded. Try to make the schedule as easy to use as possible. Don't foget to allow sufficient space for recording answers to open questions. You could also leave space for your own comments, to collect qualitative background data. It is best to use information technology resources to design and create your interview schedule. A printed schedule is much easier to follow. You can use effects like *italic* and **bold** to separate clearly interviewer instructions from things to be read out to respondents. The document will then be much clearer, and easier to use.

Task

Design a layout for your questionnaire or interview schedule. Try to make the document as clear and well presented as possible. How does your layout satisfy the needs of your research method?

Probes and prompts

Structured interviewing stresses *uniformity*. It is essential that the effect of the interviewer on a respondent's answers is as small as possible. Even the way interviewers read words when asking a question can exert an influence. Try reading out loud a few times the question, 'Do you believe that the government is doing a good job?' putting the stress on different parts of the question. Stressing the word 'good' implies that there may be some doubt. Stressing the word 'government' implies that they are being compared with something else. Interviewers are instructed to read out questions in as neutral a way as possible, to reduce the possibility of biasing an answer.

With this in mind it is clear that the questions asked must not be varied by the interviewer. If this is allowed it is even more likely that bias will occur. This is fine provided an interview goes smoothly, but in practice interviewers don't always have such an easy time. Problems with responses can take a variety of forms. You may get only a partial response, where the respondent does not give enough information for the response to be recorded, or the response may be irrelevant to the question. Respondents could side-track the questioning process, perhaps by commenting on a previous question instead of answering the one just asked. Some responses are inaccurate, and obviously so. This may be an indication that the question has been misunderstood. Also you may get no response at all. Your question could be met with silence: perhaps

because respondents are thinking it over, or because they don't know what to say.

Interviewers have the problem of dealing with response problems without biasing the results. The solution is to have a prepared list of statements which can be used to tackle response problems. These are known as *probes*. Probes can be printed on the schedule to ensure they they are used similarly for each respondent. If interviewers vary the content and wording of probes it defeats the object of using them.

Sometimes a *non-verbal probe* will help. If the problem is non-response, it may be best to stay silent and allow a noticeable pause to develop. Respondents may pick up that it is their turn to speak and provide you with an answer. Another method is to use a nod, raised eybrows or similar non-verbal signal to indicate that you are waiting for a reply. Remember to standardise the non-verbal cues you intend to use; they are also probes and haphazard use can introduce bias. If these tactics don't work you could ask if they would like you to repeat the question.

Partial responses may be solved by using silence or non-verbal cues. If there is no improvement verbal follow-ups could begin with, 'I see', accompanied by a nod to indicate you want more. Or, more directly, 'Can you tell me more?'.

Responses which are irrelevant or inaccurate may be the result of a misunderstood question. This can be tricky, since you need to avoid insulting or belittling respondents by highlighting their mistake. You could try saying, 'I'm sorry, I may not have asked that question very clearly,' and then repeat the question. Respondents may take care to listen closely as you have indicated that a problem of some kind has occurred, and the error has been transferred onto you. You could try stating the subject clearly before repeating the question. A probe like, 'This question is about . . .' can cover questions on many subjects. To minimise bias, the subject of each question needs to be indicated on the schedule in case this probe has to be used.

Theory into practice

Make a list of the things you might want to say in different situations where there are response problems. Separate your list between probes designed to get extra information, and those designed to correct misunderstandings. Reduce the lists to a manageable number that should cover most problems. How will these probes help to improve the quality of your results?

A standardised welcome and explanation of the purpose of the survey is also needed, as are introductions to new parts of the interview. All of the interviewer's input needs to be written down. Keep introductions brief and friendly, and be sure to stick to them with each respondent. Things go much more smoothly if the interviewer's input is clearly highlighted on the interview schedule.

Prompts are used to make respondents aware of the possible answers to a question. For instance: the available answers to an opinion question may range from 'agree strongly' to 'disagree strongly', with three other less extreme options in between. The interviewer reads out the options, prompting a respondent to choose one. Sometimes it is useful to write prompts on a card which is handed to the respondent for them to pick an option. Prompt cards have been discussed in connection with questions having many options.

Prompts are also useful where information is sensitive or threatening. For example, questions on income may seem threatening – particularly if asked in a street interview. Respondents can be given a prompt card with income groups listed on it and coded. They only have to answer with a code number which the interviewer notes down. This can seem far less intimidating than saying an income level out loud. Prompt cards are also useful for ranking type questions. Here respondents need to consider comparisons, and having all the options in front of them will give far more accurate results.

Putting the research together

Carrying out your own social research project can be a lot of work. Meaningful results depend on the planning and thought that have gone into it. But if you follow rules of good practice at each stage your research can be useful and informative. The stages of planning can be summed up as a list:

- Define your problem or hypothesis precisely.
- Define the population you are studying, and the type of data you want to collect from them.
- Choose a research method that suits this population and data, and is feasible with the resources available to you.
- Decide on a method of sampling that is likely to give as representative a group as possible.
- Carry out a pilot survey to make sure that you are on the right track, and help with question design.
- In the light of the pilot results, design a questionnaire or interview schedule.
- Select your sample, and either carry out your interviews or distribute your questionnaires.

However, these steps are not the whole story. When the responses come in they have to be dealt with. This means collating and organising your data, and interpreting what it means. We now need to look at how data can be analysed and presented.

· DEALING WITH DATA ·

When your interviews are completed, or your questionnaires returned, it is time to process the data. Processing data simply means adding up answers and getting totals. If you have used a postal questionnaire, and received a good response, totalling answers manually can be fairly time consuming. It is also easy to make errors. If you want to make comparisons between answers given the job is even more laborious. There really is no reason to deal with your results by hand. Computers make the processing, and analysis, of data straightforward and fast. It is assumed that you will be using computer software to deal with your data.

Entering the data

The best software to use for handling your data is likely to be a database. Each respondent's set of answers is entered as a separate record. This means that an individual's results can be recalled and looked at if necessary. Pre-coded answers are easy to handle: you simply enter the code for the answer given by the respondent. If answers are not pre-coded, or if they are answers to open questions, they need to be coded before they can be entered.

Coding the results of open questions means drawing up a *coding frame* for the question. A coding frame is simply a list of all possible answers, with each one given a code. The difficulty is that each answer has to be read and judged to decide which code to apply. This process can introduce errors. Respondents will have expressed themselves in different ways, and it is up to your judgement whether one answer means the same as another. The range of answers in your coding frame may not cover all the responses that you get. You must either extend the range of the coding frame (i.e. add extra answers), or try to fit an answer into an existing slot. In practice it is unlikely that all answers can be neatly pigeon-holed, and there is a practical limit to the length a coding frame can be allowed. A certain amount of approximation is likely to occur. The important thing is not to claim scientific accuracy for data that has been

coded in this way. As long as you are honest about potential errors the procedure is perfectly valid.

Task

Draw up a coding frame for the open questions you have used. Have you listed all possible answers, including 'Don't know'? How will you deal with answers that fall outside your categories?

Looking at totals

When all the data has been entered you can start to examine it. A good starting point is to look at the total responses for questions which are demographic or factual. How many men and women responded? What are the proportions of respondents in different age groups? These figures give a profile of the people who responded. They allow you to check whether your respondents were a representative sample of the population. Remember that even if your sample *was* representative the group who responded from that sample may not be. Of course, if quota sampling was used you should already know the proportions of different people amongst your respondents.

The other set of totals you need are those for opinion questions. These will reveal how many people gave particular answers for each question. You can record numbers of people giving each answer and build up a picture of the way opinion differs within your sample. These totals, along with demographic totals, can be presented as tables. They can also be presented in graphical form as graphs or charts. (Chapter 10 on 'Application of Number' deals with presenting data in these ways.)

Although these totals are useful, the point of social research is usually to identify links between items of data. Your hypothesis may indicate a need to do this. For example, suppose your hypothesis is, 'Female students are more aware of the risks due to smoking than male students'. To test the hypothesis you will need to link answers indicating awareness of the risks of smoking with the gender of respondents. The term used for linking responses in this way is **correlation**. In this example we are looking for a possible correlation between gender and smoking awareness. Simple totals are rarely sufficient for analysing data in this way. More detailed statistical methods are required.

Theory into practice

What correlations are you expecting to make within your data? Can you explain how these correlations will help answer your research question, or prove your hypothesis?

Frequency distributions

A good starting point for a closer examination of data is to draw up a *frequency distribution diagram*. This is a graph which shows how often each answer has been reported. As an example, suppose we had asked the question, 'Do you think that the caring services do a good job?'. We have allowed respondents to select an answer from a nine-point scale ranging from 'Strongly agree' to 'Strongly disagree'. Our scale is coded from '1 = Strongly Agree' to '9 = Strongly Disagree'. We have received 50 answers from our sample and the results are as shown in the table below.

Response	Number of answers
1 Strongly agree	2
2	4
3	6
4	8
5 Neutral	10
6	9
7	6
8	4
9 Strongly Disagree	1
Total responses =	50

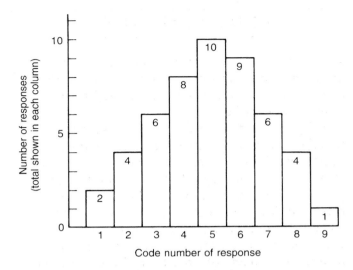

Figure 8.4 *A frequency distribution diagram*

A frequency distribution diagram for these responses would look like the one in Figure 8.4.

The data gives a roughly curved shape, with a peak near the middle value (a neutral opinion on the question). The number of answers tapers off towards each end of the diagram, indicating that extreme views are far less widely held. The shape of the diagram in our example is a familiar one in statistics. For many types of data, a frequency distribution diagram will resemble a bell-shaped curve. It is so common that the shape is referred to as a *normal distribution curve*. A typical normal distribution curve is shown in Figure 8.5 (page 334).

All kinds of data give approximations to a normal distribution when plotted as a frequency distribution. Things like shoe sizes, income or opinion, tend to follow the basic pattern. Most cases tend to cluster near the middle, and the numbers tail off towards the extremes. So common is the shape that researchers are alerted when a distribution *fails* to approximate to the normal curve.

If you plot a frequency distribution diagram for responses to each question you can quickly see whether opinion is distributed approximately normally. The normal distribution curve has some very useful characteristics which can make analysis easier. We will look at this in more detail below.

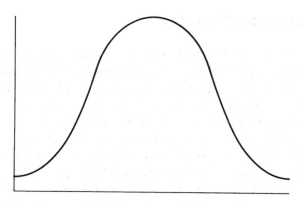

Figure 8.5 *A normal distribution curve*

Task

Plot frequency distribution tables for your data. Do they approximate to the normal distribution? Can you explain why some distributions have a slightly different shape from others?

Creating statistics

A useful statistic which can be used to compare results is the *mean value*. The mean simply is the average of a set of data (see Chapter 10 on Application of Number for methods of calculation). The mean gives the point around which the data is clustered and can be marked on your frequency distribution diagram.

However, the mean is not always useful. If you have asked people to state their religion then the responses are not a measure of quantity or degree. Here it is more useful to take the *mode*, the most frequently occurring response.

Another statistic which is sometimes used is the *median*. This is the value which divides respondents so that an equal number lie above and below it. The median takes no account of the strengths of individual responses.

Think it over

For which items of your data would it be unsuitable to calculate the mean? Can you explain why they are unsuitable, and suggest another possible measure to use?

A frequency diagram shows the *range* of a set of data graphically. Range is the distance between the highest and the lowest value. Range is a simple measure of variability, or spread, within the results. If data is normally distributed, or at least approximately so, variability can be shown more clearly by calculating the **standard deviation** of the data. Standard deviation is a way of showing how much the data varies from the mean. The size of the standard deviation indicates how spread out opinion on an issue really is.

To calculate standard deviation you need to measure the distance between each response and the mean value. Some data is higher than the mean and so gives a positive number. Other data is below the mean and so has a negative one. If you add all the deviations together the result should be zero, since this is how the mean is defined. To get positive numbers to work on, the deviations from the mean are squared before being added together. This total is known, logically, as the sum of the squares. You are trying to find the *average* deviation from the mean so you now need to divide the sum of the squares by the number of data items. This gives the mean of the squares, also known as the *variance*. The standard deviation is the square root of the variance.

The calculations are not particularly difficult and can be made even easier if a computer is used. The point of finding the standard deviation is that you can now exploit some of the useful properties of the normal distribution curve.

Fixed proportions of the curve fall within standard deviations from the mean. For example, 68.27 per cent of all responses fall within one standard deviation either side of the mean. Figure 8.6 shows

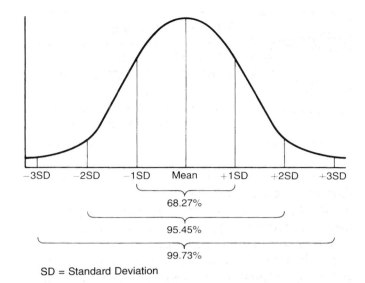

SD = Standard Deviation

Figure 8.6 *Percentage proportions of normal curve between standard deviations*

the proportions of the curve that lie within standard deviations from the mean.

Standard deviation is often used to express probabilities associated with the data. You could say that there is a 68.27 per cent chance that an answer will lie within one standard deviation of the mean. There is a better than 99 per cent chance that an answer will lie within three standard deviations of the mean. To put it another way, you can say that there is a 68 per cent probability that an answer lies within one standard deviation from the mean, and a 99 per cent probability that it lies within three. Expressing your results in this way gives a statistical probability that future results will have a particular value. You have quantified your predictions based on analysis of your data.

Making comparisons

The point of statistical analysis is usually to compare results from different questions and draw conclusions based on this. Comparison of means and standard deviations can show up differences in opinion between different sections of the population. For example: results of a question on income may indicate that females have lower values for mean and standard deviation than males. This implies that, on average, women's pay is lower than men's. It also implies that variability is higher amongst men, i.e. that women's income is more tightly clustered around the mean whereas men's is more spread out across different income levels.

Another way of analysing data is to look for relationships between two variables. Suppose you are interested in the relationship between age and opinions on the behaviour of young people. If you plot a graph of age against opinion you could get results like those in the scattergram shown in Figure 8.7.

Each dot represents the age and opinion of an individual respondent. (More details of scattergrams can be found in Chapter 10.) Here there seems to be a clear trend for opinions to become lower as age increases. A line of best fit would make the relationship more specific.

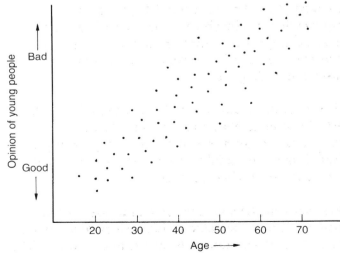

Figure 8.7 *Scattergram of age against opinion of young people's behaviour*

The relationship between the two variables is called **correlation**. If correlation was perfect all the points would lie on a straight line. There are mathematical techniques for finding the line of best fit exactly, and for expressing the degree of correlation shown by the data. These lie outside the scope of this book but more information can be found in the recommended reading at the end of the chapter. Generally, a correlation is fairly easy to spot. If your scattergram shows a random pattern of dots it implies that there is no relationship between the variables you have chosen to plot.

You may want to compare different combinations of statistics in this way to check how groups in the population differ. Ideally you should have predicted which comparisons are relevant to the subject of your research. If you are researching with a hypothesis in mind then comparisons need to be related to it.

Task

What meaningful correlations can you make with your data? Draw scattergrams of correlations between sets of data, and attempt to draw a line of best fit on each one. Do you think that the correlations are demonstrated, or are you still in doubt? How will these correlations affect the results of your work?

· PRESENTING THE DATA ·

When you have examined and analysed your data you need to think about how you are going to present it. One way is simply to use text. You can present your results in the form of a written report, which includes descriptions of your findings and your analysis of them. This is the only way in which qualitative data can be presented. Most surveys collect a certain amount of qualitative data, and it is a good idea to report this as carefully as quantitative results. Background information adds context and

interest to what may otherwise seem a cold, rather detached set of results. Social surveys are about people and text-based information often feels more personal, even if it is talking about general issues.

Quantitative data can also be presented in a text-based fashion. However, usually numbers have more meaning if they are displayed in a form that allows comparisons to be revealed. This means using tables or a graphical method to present results.

Most social surveys present their results in table form. This means that all the relevant figures can be read directly. But tables can look bland and they don't bring out relationships within results as effectively as graphical methods. Graphs and charts can add emphasis to your results and give a rapid visual confirmation of the conclusions you have made. You could use pie-charts, line graphs, histograms and scattergrams. (Chapter 10 has more details on each of these methods.) Presenting your results graphically can help you to convey your message more clearly. However, graphical methods can also obscure the facts.

Graphical representation usually prevents the exact magnitude of a result from being revealed. A graph illustrating a close correlation between two variables may not show that only a small proportion of the sample were involved in obtaining the result. Choice of scales for the axes of graphs can also present a distorted picture. The increase in a variable may be made to look spectacular if the scales are suitably shortened. For example the number of people attending a day-care centre may have risen from 200 to 210 between two particular weeks. This could be shown as in the bar chart in Figure 8.8.

Now compare the graph in Figure 8.8 with one where the scale has been adjusted so that it begins at a different point and is more spread out; see Figure 8.9.

Graphical methods are capable of distorting the data they display, even when it is accurately represented. You need to use methods of data presentation fairly, and be aware that different methods can affect the message that is conveyed.

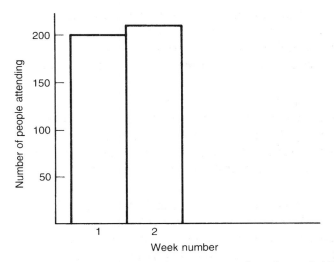

Figure 8.8 *Bar chart showing day centre attendance by week (1)*

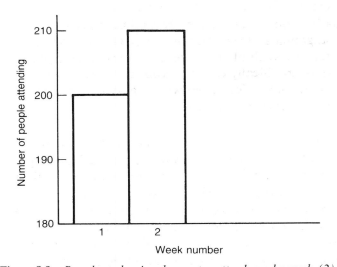

Figure 8.9 *Bar chart showing day centre attendance by week (2)*

Task

How will you present your data? Decide which data should be textual, and which graphically presented. What graphical presentation methods will you use? Explain why the methods you have chosen are appropriate for the data to be presented.

Sources of error

When you have collated and examined your results, and produced statistics and graphs from them, it is often easy to believe that they are true. But throughout this chapter we have seen that there are ways in which error and uncertainty can enter into the research. Making valid claims for your data means being realistic about sources of error that may have occurred.

Errors can occur in the collection method. Was the method right for the population you are concerned with? Could you use it to collect the data that you wanted? If you used a postal questionnaire, the number of responses you received is a good measure of the suitability of the method. A low response indicates a major source of error and should be mentioned in your report. If structured interviews were used, the most likely source of errors is interviewer–respondent interaction. These are very hard to estimate, but you should be able to remember how the interviews went. If respondents proved uncooperative, or you needed to use probes not written into the schedule, then it is likely that significant bias has occurred.

The collection tools themselves may have introduced errors. This may be shown by returned questionnaires that have obviously been misunderstood. Or your interviewing experiences may have revealed that certain questions simply didn't work, needing many probes to get the desired answer. Non-returned questionnaires can leave you guessing at the source of the problem. Did a questionnaire take the wrong approach? Or were some of the questions too intrusive or confusing? Whatever the reason, non-returns represent a source of error in the results. Problems with interview schedules will be only too familiar to you by the time you have finished the field work.

Errors can also occur through the sampling process. There are ways of estimating errors when random sampling methods are used, although it is probably not worth calculating them for your research. For small samples such estimates are meaningless; and small samples are always prone to errors because they are not fully representative of the population.

Representativeness can be checked by looking at the demographic balance amongst your respondents. Proportions of people within the sample should be available from your results, and can be compared with the profile a representative sample should have. Sometimes you have to use a particular sampling method because no other is available. You need to consider how errors might have occurred through the method you used.

Statistical analysis of your results can also lead to errors. It is always possible that you have carried out calculations incorrectly, but if you use a computer (correctly!) this risk is eliminated. A more likely source of error is the way the statistics have been used. One problem is misreading correlations between items of data. Correlations are often easy to identify, but difficult to explain or account for. You may find that a correlation seems to exist between two variables and wrongly assume that one is the cause of the other. However, there could be a third factor which is the cause of both effects. For example: there is a correlation between day length and the number of clothes people wear. This is not because long days themselves bring about the wearing of light clothing, but because long days occur when the weather is warmer.

Another source of error when using statistics is *extrapolation*. This means extending your results beyond the range of your data, and attempting to predict what values a variable would have in extreme circumstances. The dangers of this can be shown by the scattergram in Figure 8.10.

Here the relationship between age and income has been plotted for people between the ages of 25 and 55 years. If the line of best fit is extended beyond the range of the data it seems that most people are on a very high income indeed by the time they reach 80 years of age. In fact we know that this is not the case, and income usually drops off sharply after retirement. Extrapolation is a very hazardous process. You should check your ideas carefully against other data, and in the light of common sense.

Sources of error occur in every research project, however well designed and resourced. The main

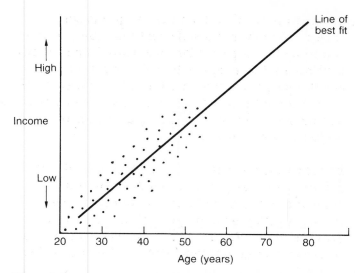

Figure 8.10 *Scattergram showing income against age*

point is to be honest in your estimation of errors. If you claim too great a level of accuracy for your work, it is actually less likely to be assumed to be valid and reliable. Research that is honestly evaluated shows that the researcher was trying to seek the truth, not trying to prove a theory.

Theory into practice

Can you identify possible sources of error in your research work? List the sources of error that could apply and write a short statement describing how each could have affected your results.

Writing your report

The final stage in the research process is the writing of a report and presentation of results. The report should contain: details of the hypothesis or question being investigated; methods used; results obtained; conclusions drawn from the results; and the possible errors that have occurred.

Always explain why you chose the hypothesis or question that you investigated. Why are you interested in it? You don't need to justify your choice at length, but a statement indicating what led you to look at a particular area helps. The methods used need a fuller explanation. Your conclusions about your population, and the data required from them, should be linked to the method chosen. Why was the method you used the right one for the subject of your research?

Sampling methods also need to be explained. Why did you pick that particular method for your population? Try to be honest if your sampling method was forced upon you by circumstances. Provided that you have done your best to obtain a representative sample your methods are acceptable.

Presenting the results may involve creating tables, graphs and charts. Good graphics here can make a report look very impressive, and may help to display your results clearly. Remember to add titles to all presentations of results, and an explanation of what they show. Reports are far better if they are easy to follow and clear graphical presentation will help in this.

The conclusions are important in stressing the usefulness of the research. It is not so important that the results appear to be conclusive. In fact, this can raise the suspicions of experienced social researchers. More important is that the results are an honest statement of what you have found. If your findings, and your levels of confidence in them, are fairly stated your research will be more valuable and scientific. Finally, remember to identify potential sources of errors in your research. This helps to establish the worth of your results, and shows that you are serious about your research.

Good social research often raises more questions than it answers. If your research has provoked you into wanting to find out more then it has been worthwhile.

Self-assessment test

1 The following are examples of data about an individual
   a height

b educational qualifications
c income level
d political opinion.
Which one of the list above is likely to be qualitative data?

2 Researchers use open and closed questions to seek opinion. The following two statements have been made.

Statement 1:
Closed questions are good for collecting qualitative data.

Statement 2:
Open questions are good for collecting quantitative data.

How are these two statements best described?
   a True, True   b True, False
   c False, True   d False, False

3 Social researchers often look at secondary sources. Which two of the following statements describe advantages of using secondary research methods?
   i   you can be certain that published results are accurate
   ii   you may find out about concepts that help with your primary research
   iii secondary sources are always easy to understand
   iv   you might get ideas for methods you could use in your research
   a i and iii   b ii and iii
   c ii and iv   d iii and iv

4 You are carrying out research to find out how students on your course feel about smoking and health. Which one of the following statements best describes your population
   a all GNVQ health and caring students
   b the people who live in Great Britain
   c the students on your course
   d smokers.

5–7 The following are methods of data collection used in social research
   a postal questionnaire
   b in-depth interview
   c participant observation
   d structured interview.

Which data collection method is being described in each of the following statements?

5 A quite formal meeting where a fixed set of questions is asked.

6 Involves the researcher joining in with the group being studied.

7 Allows respondents to answer questions in privacy.

8 Structured interviews are designed so that each interview is conducted in exactly the same way. The following two statements have been made about this.

Statement 1:
Structured interviews are conducted uniformly so that the data collected is as valid as possible.

Statement 2:
Structured interviews are conducted uniformly so that the data collected is as reliable as possible.

How are these two statements best described?
a True, True   **b** True, False
c False, True   **d** False, False

9–11 The following are examples of sampling methods
   a quota sampling
   b systematic sampling
   c stratified sampling
   d opportunity sampling.

Which sampling method is described in each of the following statements?

9 A random sampling method designed to ensure that important groups are represented in the sample.

10 A random sampling where names are picked at regular intervals from a sampling frame.

11 A non-random sampling method designed to ensure that important groups are represented in the sample.

12 A researcher included the question 'Don't you agree that the welfare state is underfunded?' in interviews. Which of the following is the most serious problem with the question?
   a it makes presumptions about the respondents

b it is a leading question
c it is ambiguous
d it is threatening.

13 When doing structured interviewing it is important to conduct each interview in the same way. This is because
   a it minimises bias created by the presence of an interviewer
   b all respondents have a right to be treated in the same way
   c it is easier than having a less formal type of interview
   d it prevents respondents from deviating from the questions.

14–16 The following is a list of different forms of response that questions may ask for
   a open response
   b ranking
   c rating scale
   d semantic differential.

Which form of response is being described in each of the following statements?

14 Allows respondents to indicate how strongly they feel about the question.

15 Unlikely to give quantitative data.

16 Allows respondents to judge their opinion between two extremes.

17 If you wanted to look for correlations between different sets of data you could use
   a the means of the data
   b the normal distribution curve
   c frequency counts
   d a scattergram.

18 It is often useful to find the standard deviation of a set of data. The following two statements have been made.

Statement 1:
The standard deviation can indicate how variable the data is.

Statement 2:
The standard deviation can indicate how valid the data is.

How are these two statements best described?

a True, True   b True, False
c False, True   d False, False

19 Which two of the following are sampling errors?
   i   a low response rate
   ii   respondents not representative of the
      population
   iii   a very small group chosen to be interviewed
   iv   respondents' answers are affected by the
       interviewer's behaviour.
   a i and iii   b ii and iii
   c ii and iv   d iii and iv

20 Interview schedules often contain probes. The
following two statements have been made about
probes.

Statement 1:
Probes are useful for dealing with response
problems.

Statement 2:
Probes are useful for getting extra information.

How are these two statements best described?
   a True, True   b True, False
   c False, True   d False, False

Fast Facts

Census A vast social survey, carried out by the government every ten years. The census attempts to collect information from every household in Britain.

Closed question A question which has a fixed set of possible answers predetermined by the researcher. Closed questions produce quantitative data.

Coding frame A list of the possible answers to open questions used by researchers to code responses.

Demographic A form of quantitative data. Demographic data describes factual characteristics such as age, gender or income level. This data is often used to distinguish between groups within a population, for example in quota sampling.

Frequency distribution A graphical method showing how often different answers to a question have been given. Frequency distributions often approximate to the normal distribution curve.

Funnel method A way of ordering questions in which general areas are covered first and more specific topics gradually introduced.

Hypothesis A statement which is able to be tested by research.

In-depth interviewing An interviewing method which has a fairly loose structure. Respondents are encouraged to open up and provide detail on their views.

Interview A meeting between a researcher and a respondent where data is collected.

Interview schedule A document used in structured interviewing to direct and control the process. A schedule contains the questions, and strict instructions for the interviewer to follow.

Mean The average value of a set of data.

Median The value that occurs in the middle of a ranked list of responses. The median is chosen so that half the responses lie above, and half below it.

Mode The mode is the most frequently recorded response in a set of data.

Normal distribution curve A bell shaped curve which often results when frequency distributions are plotted. The mathematical properties of the normal distribution allow percentage probability statements to be made.

Official statistics Data collected by national and local government. Official statistics cover a vast range of topics.

Open question A question which respondents answer in their own words. Open questions are often used to collect qualitative data.

Opinion poll A survey method intended to collect information on public opinion. Opinion polls often use street interviews and quota sampling techniques.

Opportunity sampling A method of choosing a sample which allows the interviewer to decide who to include. People are chosen partly because they are conveniently available to be questioned.

Participant observation   A method of social investigation in which the researcher joins in with subjects and observes from the inside.

Pilot survey   A test run of a survey which is carried out on a small sample. Pilot work is intended to help evaluate and refine the research method.

Polar adjectives   Pairs of adjectives which are direct opposites of each other, such as bad/good, hot/cold. Polar adjectives are used in the semantic differential scaling technique.

Population   The whole group that a survey or research project is concerned with. A population usually consists of people, though it can be other things such as households.

Postal questionnaire   A research method where questionnaires are sent to respondents by post.

Pre-coding   Giving a code to each available answer for a question. Pre-coding makes it easier to deal with the data during compilation of results.

Primary data   Data that you have collected yourself. Primary research involves carrying out your own investigation to collect primary data.

Probes   Comments designed to get further information from a respondent. Probes can help deal with response problems, and follow up lines of enquiry.

Prompts   Statements which are read out to respondents to make them aware of possible answers to a question.

Qualitative data   Data which cannot be expressed in numerical form. Qualitative data is descriptive, and is often about attitudes, opinions and values. Qualitative research methods seek to collect this type of data.

Quantitative data   Data which is expressed in numerical form. Quantitative research methods seek to collect this type of data.

Questionnaire   A list of questions designed to collect primary data. Questionnaires are filled in by the respondents themselves, without an interviewer being present.

Quota sampling   A method of sample selection where a population is stratified into types of people. Interviewers are given quotas of people to interview from each category.

Random sampling   A method of choosing a sample which uses random methods to eliminate bias in selection.

Ranking   A method of obtaining respondents' opinion of the differences between items in a group. Respondents rank the group in terms of the criteria set by the researcher.

Rating scale   A method recording answers to closed questions. Respondents indicate the strength of their opinion by choosing a scale point.

Reliability   A quality of research results. A result is reliable if it can be obtained again by repeating the research on another sample.

Research   The process of finding things out in an organised and thoughtful way.

Respondent   A person who provides data for a social investigation.

Response rate   The proportion of sample members who return information. Postal questionnaires often have a poor response rate.

Sample   A group chosen from the population on which research is conducted directly. Samples are intended to be representative of the population as a whole.

Sampling frame   A list containing all members of a population from which a sample can be chosen.

Scattergram   A graphical method of showing correlations between different sets of data.

Secondary data   Data that has been collected by other people. Secondary research involves looking at existing sources of information.

Semantic differential   A method of recording opinion on an issue. Respondents are shown pairs of polar adjectives and indicate their position between them.

Standard deviation   A way of indicating the variability in a set of data. Fixed proportions of the normal curve lie within standard deviations of the mean.

Stratified sampling   A method of making a sample more representative. The population is grouped and a proportion of the sample picked from each group.

Structured interviewing   A method of social research which uses tightly controlled interviews to collect data. Structured interviewing aims to minimise differences between each interview to help eliminate bias.

Survey   An enquiry designed to collect primary data. Social surveys usually involve asking people questions.

Systematic sampling   A method of choosing a random sample from a sampling frame. Names are picked at regular intervals from the list, for example every fifth name.

Validity   A quality of research results. A result is valid if it accurately represents the view of a respondent.

Variability   The degree of spread of a feature within a population.

References

Dooley, D. (1990) *Social Research Methods* Prentice-Hall

Hammersley, M. (1993) *Social Research. Philosophy, Politics and Practice* Sage publications

Langley, P. (1987) *Doing Social Research. A Guide to Coursework* Causeway Press

Moser, C.A., Kalton, G. (1971) *Survey Methods in Social Investigation* Heinemann

North, P.J. (1980) *People in society* Longman

Shipman, M. (1988) *The limitations of social research* Longman

Walker, R. (1985) *Applied Qualitative Research* Gower Publishing

chapter 9 COMMUNICATION

This chapter provides information on a range of communication skills. These include verbal and non-verbal communication, such as discussions and using the telephone, using images and communicating in writing.

Communication is an essential skill for anyone working in a care setting. Care work involves the ability to value others with appropriate communication. Supportive skills depend on communication.

Communication cannot be a separate part of health and social care work. It is something which you practise all the time and which connects with the other parts of your job (and your life). Communication includes talking, with familiar and unfamiliar people, and writing so that your meaning is clear. Being able to use diagrams and sketches, photographs and tables, where appropriate, will enhance your meaning. Being skilled in interpreting such information will help you to understand better the other units you are studying. It is essential that you are able to read and understand information in order to keep accurate records and to help clients who may need support with this area of life skills.

> Communication is essential
> in health and social care work

Above all, communication is about understanding other people and being able to make your meaning

Communication is a two-way process. (Winged Fellowship Trust Images of Caring Competition by Ian Ferrie.)

clear for them to understand. It is your job as a care-worker to be able to listen carefully to clients and to see and hear what they are trying to tell you (whether this is in words or through their body language).

Communication is the sending and receiving of information and messages, a two-way process. People often check their understanding by asking questions. For example, a student nurse, seeing a notice above a patient's bed which said 'Liquids only', may want to check if this includes such foods as soup.

. UNDERSTANDING AND CHECKING . INFORMATION

Read the following short story. On a separate piece of paper write the numbers 1 to 12. When you have read the story read the statements below. Then write 'True', 'False' or 'Don't know' in answer to the statements against the numbers.

At the entrance to the health centre, one morning, a young woman with a baby and a doctor were talking quietly. Suddenly the young woman fell to the floor. The baby screamed in its pram. The doctor stood over the woman then rolled her over. She said, 'This lady will be all right in a minute – don't crowd her. But she's suffering from anaemia.' The waiting patients, a receptionist and the nurse drew back as the young woman said weakly, 'What happened?'.

Statements

1 The doctor and the young woman were outside the surgery.
2 The young woman was shouting at the doctor.
3 The young woman was the baby's mother.
4 The doctor was a woman.
5 The baby was only a few weeks' old.
6 The doctor moved the young woman off the table where she had fallen.
7 The young woman had fainted from fear.
8 The doctor put the woman in the recovery position.
9 Everyone else crowded round to see what was happening.
10 The young woman never regained consciousness.
11 The incident took place after lunch.
12 It was pouring with rain so everyone got wet.

What happened . . . One morning at the health centre a young mother with her baby in a pram was saying goodbye to the doctor, who had come to open the door for her. The doctor, a woman, was concerned that the mother's haemoglobin level was so low several weeks after the birth of the baby. Suddenly the young woman fainted to the floor, so the doctor placed her in the recovery position. The baby cried because it was hungry. The other patients, plus a receptionist and the nurse, came rushing up but the doctor asked them to move away. The young woman regained consciousness almost immediately. We don't know what the weather was like outside!

Answers to the statements

1 *Don't know.* We know that they were at the entrance, and the rest of the story implies that they were inside, but we don't know for sure.
2 *False.* They were talking quietly.
3 *Don't know.* The implication is that the young woman is the baby's mother but it is not stated.
4 *True.* 'She' in the fifth sentence has to refer to the doctor.
5 *Don't know.* A baby in a pram could be a few weeks old or up to a year old.
6 *False.* The young woman fell to the floor.
7 *Don't know.* It seems unlikely that the young women fainted from fear – anaemia is a more likely explanation – but we are not told she wasn't afraid.
8 *True.* The doctor rolled her over – we understand this to be the recovery position.
9 *True.* We know this because the doctor asks them to move away.
10 *False.* The young woman asks what has happened.
11 *False.* We are told this happened one morning.
12 *Don't know.* There is nothing in the story to tell us what the weather was like!

Discussion

This exercise serves to illustrate how often we are confident we understand a situation when in fact we only understand it from our own interpretation. We make assumptions and jump to conclusions without knowing all the facts. As well as this, most people don't like to admit that they do not know the answer to a question. Many of the statements after the story could only be answered by 'Don't know' – but many of us are unwilling to admit this! Any sort of answer will do.

The point of all this, in relation to dealing with clients, is that we would be wrong to assume

There are some things we can't be expected to know – but other things can be found out quite easily!

Think it over

Have you ever been in a situation where people are speaking a language you don't understand but you have still been able to tell what the mood of their conversation was?

It is easy to tell what someone's meaning is by the pitch of their voice, the speed of their speech, whether they are speaking quietly or noisily. An argument is obviously an argument even in a foreign language. We know that it's often not the words that we use, but the way that we use them that is important. You would not use the same tone to say 'I love you' and to say 'I am angry with you', and you probably would not use the same tone to speak with an adult as with a child. Unfortunately, because some adults have a disability, such as a learning difficulty or a hearing impairment, people tend to speak to them in what is age-inappropriate language. This means they are treating them differently from the way they would treat someone of that age who did not have a disability. To do this is patronising. You may want to refer to Chapter one for more discussion of this.

Some people find it difficult to know how to respond to clients who are confused or have limited understanding. One way is to repeat what you have said using different words and gestures, to give another opportunity for the client to grasp the meaning. It makes sense to use simple uncomplicated sentences, but not to adopt a high-pitched voice as one might with a child; speak as you would to another adult.

everyone had had the same experiences and therefore developed the same expectations. Logically we know this. We are aware that clients in our care come from a variety of backgrounds and cultures, but it is still natural to 'read' situations from our own standpoint. It is necessary constantly to step out of your own shoes and into the shoes of others to understand how they might feel and respond.

As professionals we tend to need to have answers. People depend on us and expect us to 'know'. The story illustrated that there are often things we don't know. They are outside our sphere of information or experience and we should learn to be more comfortable with admitting that there are some things we can't be expected to know. (However, this is not a perfect excuse for being lazy and not taking the trouble to find information!)

USING AN APPROPRIATE TONE AND MANNER

As a care-worker you will be working with people of all ages, from all types of backgrounds and with a range of abilities, so it is important to use the appropriate tone of voice and manner in communication.

A time and a place

As we grow up we become more sophisticated in our communications. We realise that what is appropriate language and behaviour in one situation would be embarrassingly wrong in another.

Think it over

Can you remember a time when you have 'misread' a social situation and behaved inappropriately? You would have behaved differently if you had understood the situation properly.

Discussion

An example. A person went to a very large discount warehouse to buy some paint. They couldn't find the right area so they asked an assistant where the paint was kept. The assistant said 'Aisle C' and disappeared. This sounds like 'I'll see' so the person waited and waited, thinking the assistant had gone to check. Eventually the person went to find the assistant again and said, 'Well, where is the paint?'. The assistant replied, 'But I told you – Aisle C'. Communication failure can be embarrassing!

We adapt the formality or informality of our remarks and behaviour to the circumstances in which we find ourselves. The subtlety of this is something we learn as we grow up. We make judgments about when to speak and when to keep quiet. There is an old saying, 'least said, soonest mended'. This means it is easy to be hurtful by saying the wrong thing and we are well advised, sometimes, to keep quiet.

· USING THE TELEPHONE ·

The telephone plays a major part in our lives in helping us keep in touch with others, but using a telephone for work, official contacts, is something some people avoid. This could be because we are aware of having to use a more formal mode of communication for official calls than for talking with friends. People worry that they will forget what they wanted to say and feel silly, or that they will not be able to get through to the person they want.

Another barrier to using the telephone is that you are not able to see the person and so there are no non-verbal cues to help. You have to make

Some people worry about using the phone for official contacts

judgments about the other person's meaning, and know when to break into the conversation, based purely on what you are hearing. You do not have the benefit of eye contact or seeing if the person seems relaxed or tense. Using and understanding the appropriate tone of voice is therefore doubly important on the telephone.

If you are unused to making business calls you should make a list of what you are likely to need to say before you begin. Write down the number you want and the name of the person you need to speak with. Write down the information you want or what you want to say. Think of what message you may have to leave if the person is unavailable and make sure you know the number of the phone you are using in case they have to call you back.

When you make a business call you will have to tell the person at the other end who you are. They will not recognise your voice as a friend would. Give your name and the name of the organisation you are working for, if appropriate.

In an organisation the telephone is likely to be answered by a person working on a switchboard and so you may have to ask to speak with the person you are calling. Always have a pencil and paper with you when you make a call so you can remind yourself of your points and make a note of replies.

Task

Here is an exercise to practise making telephone calls. Make a list of the points you would need answers to.

Your group is visiting the city of Midborough to gather evidence for an assignment about homeless people and the agencies working with them. You would like to visit a shelter and speak with the workers and, if possible, the clients. You will need to know dates, times, addresses, transport references, client group etc.

Sample conversation

- Say who you are and where you are from.
- Ask to speak with someone regarding arranging a visit from a group of students.
- Ask if it might be possible for a group to visit the shelter/hostel.
- Say when you would ideally like the visit to be.
- Ask what time would be convenient to visit.
- Ask how many people would be the maximum size for the group.
- Ask for the address of the hostel.
- Ask what the nearest station would be.
- Ask for details of the client group.
- Don't forget to note the name of the worker to whom you are speaking.
- Thank the person and say you will confirm the arrangements by letter.
- If an appropriate person is not available ask when you can call back.

When you itemise the points for this call it is easy to see why it is necessary to write them down beforehand. Only with very simple or familiar calls is it possible to remember all the points you need to make or ask. You need to reflect in your mind the possible course of the conversation and plan as much as possible beforehand.

Answering the telephone

When you answer the telephone at work you are the first contact the caller has with your organisation. It is important, therefore, that you give the impression of being business-like and efficient. You should give the telephone number or the name of the establishment first and then say, 'x speaking' (giving your own name). The caller will then usually say who they are. But if they do not say who they are you should ask who is speaking to make accurate notes. It is very annoying to receive a message about a phone call only to be told that the person who took it doesn't know who it was from!

Below is a conversation between a clerk in the Special Services Division of the Education Department and a teacher from a local school.

Teacher 'Hello, could I speak with Ian Lovell, please?'
Clerk 'I'm sorry he's not in the office at the moment, could I take a message?'
Teacher 'Yes, it's Mr Holt from The Mount School, I'm ringing about Sudeb Kumar Mandal. He got all his 9 GCSE's at 'A' grade but he's partially sighted and he started his 'A' level Design and Technology course in September and he still has not had his equipment upgraded. It is February now and he can't produce his assignments until he has a computer and the necessary software to work with. The IT Support Service came to school to make an assessment in October and we are still waiting. Sudeb's parents are getting very irate and threatening to write to the Director of Education to say his statemented needs are not being met. I know it's difficult with the funding but this lad's going to miss out and he doesn't deserve it. His work is brilliant but it's full of mistakes he can't see when he's working on the PC. Will you ask Mr Lovell to ring me back on 0977 324750 tomorrow between 11 and 12. Thanks, goodbye.'

The message should read like this:

- Message for Ian Lovell from Mr Holt, The Mount School.

- Sudeb Kumar Mandal (partially sighted pupil) has still not had his IT equipment upgraded and he can't proceed with his 'A' level course work.
- Mr and Mrs Mandal are threatening to contact the Director of Education if the equipment does not arrive soon.
- Please telephone Mr Holt on 0977 324750 tomorrow (Wednesday) between 11 and 12.

Think it over

List the situations in which a person working in social care is likely to need to use written communication in the course of their work.

Task

Compose a sample message you would write before making each of the telephone calls outlined below.

1 You want a placement at a local Adult Training Centre. Say what your work pattern would be (days, dates, times) and what experience you have had on other placements. How would this placement relate to your course work: what would you need to do during the placement in order to collect evidence? What kind of report would your course require?

2 You are thinking of applying for university and want to know what types of courses specific establishments offer. You want to know what qualifications they will accept, if many people apply and where students can live while at university. You will need to speak with the Admissions Tutor.

· WRITING CORRECTLY ·

It is virtually inevitable that you will have to record your work experiences and those of your clients in writing. Being able to communicate in writing is an essential skill, both to record information accurately and to support clients. If a worker fails to record a situation accurately it could be life threatening for the client.

Discussion

You will have realised that virtually everything we do in life needs writing down at some point. The range would be from routine administration, to letters, to reports, to record cards and summarising complex documents. In addition, the people reading what you write will vary. Some will be those who know what you mean, such as colleagues, supervisors, tutors etc., so certain assumptions of knowledge can be made; but other people reading your reports, letters, notes etc. will be those who have no knowledge of the situation.

In order to make our written work clear, conventions such as grammar and punctuation are used. Punctuation marks are needed purely to make writing easier to understand. The theory is that if everyone sticks to the same rules it should make the writing unambiguous. Remember always that punctuation exists to make the meaning clear. It is not to decorate a piece of work, such as putting an apostrophe after an 's' because it looks lonely without one!

Below is a quick revision of basic grammar and punctuation to remind you where to use it.

- A **sentence** is a group of words which begins with a capital letter and ends with a full stop. It must tell you something about someone or something and to do this it needs a *subject* and a *verb*. For example: 'The old lady was ill'.
- A **verb** is a word which describes an action and so is sometimes known as a 'doing' word. For example: 'The old lady's neighbour *telephoned* the doctor'.
- The **subject** is the name given to the noun or pronoun (see below) about which the statement is being made. In the example above the old lady's

neighbour was the subject who telephoned the doctor.

- Some sentences will also have an **object**; in the sentence above the doctor is the object.
- **Noun**. This is the name of an object, person or place. For example, mug, Marcus, Manchester. You will notice that Marcus and Manchester begin with capital letters. This is because they are *proper nouns*, i.e. the name of a person, town or country. But mug is a *common noun* and, unless it is at the beginning of a sentence, does not need a capital letter.
- A **pronoun** can be used instead of a name. If we were to say a name every time we referred to a person, place or object it would get very monotonous so pronouns such as 'him', 'she', 'it' are used instead. For example, 'The doctor visited the old lady and agreed that she was very ill'.
- **Adjective**. This is a word which tells us something more about a noun we have used; e.g. 'The old lady was very ill', 'The new baby was ugly'.
- **Adverbs** are used in the same way to describe verbs; for example, 'The ambulance arrived very quickly'.

Once you have learned the basics of grammar you will begin to apply them automatically and your writing will be clear and understandable. Discipline yourself to write correctly all the time, so that eventually you will not have to think about it – it will be natural to write correctly. In the long run, therefore, it is worth the initial 'pain' of having to think all the time about writing correctly in order to acquire a lifetime's effortless skill!

Task

Read the passage below which is without punctuation. See if you can put in the capital letters, commas and full stops to make it understandable.

centres vary enormously in how much guidance and support they offer students to make realistic and considered progression plans it was found important that the regular planning and review sessions throughout the programme do not concentrate solely upon performance on the current programme some review of longer term goals should also take place checking that the process of narrowing down options is happening without support at this time hasty decisions may be made at the start of the second year on the basis of limited and inadequate information students need to be encouraged to make use of open days and other he taster opportunities taking place throughout the year ideally he visits should take place towards the end of the first year but if this does not occur early in the second year work experience outside speakers and feedback from former students could all be used to clarify students thinking about particular courses

Here is a corrected version which should be easier to understand!

Centres vary enormously in how much guidance and support they offer students to make realistic and considered progression plans.

It was found important that the regular planning and review sessions throughout the programme do not concentrate solely upon performance on the current programme. Some review of longer-term goals should also take place, checking that the process of narrowing down options is happening. Without support at this time, hasty decisions may be made at the start of the second year on the basis of limited and inadequate information.

Students need to be encouraged to make use of open days and other HE taster opportunities taking place throughout the year. Ideally, HE visits should take place towards the end of the first year but, if this does not occur, early in the second year. Work experience, outside speakers and feedback from former students could all be used to clarify students' thinking about particular courses.

In addition to capital letters, commas and full stops you will have had to use new paragraphs in the passage above. A new **paragraph** is used to introduce a new topic.

A **comma** is used to show a pause and to separate items in a list such as: 'I was carrying my bag, a file, some crisps and a drink when I fell down the stairs.' Notice that the last item in the list above, 'a drink' is preceded by 'and' and so does not have a comma after it. A comma is also used to separate different parts or descriptions within a sentence such as, 'I spilled the drink, which is hardly surprising, but everything else survived!'. The sentence would have made sense without 'which is hardly surprising' and putting it between commas made the sentence easier to understand.

A **question mark** is used *instead* of a full stop when a question has been asked. It comes at the end of a sentence, in place of a full stop, never in the middle. Is that clear?

The apostrophe

The apostrophe,', a much misused device, is used in two different ways. First, the apostrophe shows that a letter or letters have been *missed out* of a word. When we use the apostrophe in this way we put it where the missing letters would have been. For example, we sometimes shorten 'is not' to 'isn't'. In this case the apostrophe in 'isn't' goes where the 'o' would have been in 'is not' if the full words had been written. In the same way the apostrophe in 'I'm' goes where the 'a' in 'am' would be. Sometimes

people put the apostrophe in the wrong place because they have not learned the rule. Have you ever seen 'is'nt' or 'Im'?

The second use of the apostrophe is to show that something *belongs* to something. If the owner is one person or thing, i.e. a mum or the car, the apostrophe would be before the 's'. For example, 'It was mum's outing' or, 'The car's doors were damaged.' However, if the reference was to more than one mum or one car the apostrophe would be after the 's' to indicate this. For example, 'It was a mums' outing' or 'The cars' doors were damaged.'

The only exception to this possessive use of the apostrophe is with the word *it*. When you see 'it's' it always means 'it is' and the belonging use is written just as 'its' *without* the apostrophe. For example, 'It's a lovely tree but some of its branches are rotten'. It is a mistake that is commonly made so watch out for it!

Task

Write out the passage below putting in apostrophes. It is taken from Stan Barstow's A Kind of Loving and the speaker is Victor's mother discussing her sons.)

'No, we shant be going to Victors wedding yet awhile . . . Give him time; hes not twenty-one yet. An I dont even think hes courting. Course, I suppose Ill be the last to get to know when he is. Im not bothered about him, though. If they were all as steady an content as him wed do well enough. Its young Jim at worries me sometimes. Allus studying, yknow. Never seems to give his mind a rest. He fancies bein a doctor an I suppose hell have to work hard if hes going to pass for college; but I sometimes think he overdoes it a bit. I found him one night, Edna – and this is without a word of a lie – I found him sitting up in bed in the middle of the night, fast asleep with his books open all round him. Fast asleep he was. Ysee he cant even leave it alone when hes supposed to be resting. His mind never rests; its allus on the work. I dont like it. Hes growin fast and

he never did have Victors constitution. Like a young horse from the day he was born Victor was. Never a minutes worry over illness with him – except the usual kids ailments, o course, an that time he fell on the railings an cut his head open.'

· WRITING LETTERS AND MEMOS ·

You will often need to write letters as part of your work. If you take time to revise your grammar you will be well equipped to begin communicating in writing.

Earlier in the chapter you were asked to make notes about a telephone call to an agency providing shelter for homeless people, asking if it might be possible to arrange a group visit. It is often possible to get people to respond to requests if you speak with them personally, but it is then wise, and courteous, to confirm the conversation and the arrangements by letter. If arrangements are not confirmed in writing it is easy for one party to misinterpret or forget exactly what had been agreed, and this can lead to a lot of inconvenience.

A business letter needs to be laid out to contain certain necessary information. It needs to have the addresses of both the sender and recipient, the date and sometimes a heading and reference If the letter begins with 'Dear Sir or Madam' it should end with 'Yours faithfully', (note where the capital letters are!). If the letter begins with a person's name, for example, 'Dear Mr Singh', it ends with 'Yours sincerely'.

A letter will sometimes have a heading to give a clue what the letter will be about before the recipient has read it through. This allows the reader to 'key in' to the subject before reading the letter.

If the letter is going to a large organisation there will often be a reference code. This is because when the envelopes arrive at the organisation someone has to open and sort them first. The letters may then be sent on to the workforce who will deal with them. If a letter has no reference there is no clue as to who is

dealing with the matter. The only way to find out might be by the person opening it, reading the subject matter and trying to guess. In a large company letters with no name or reference can be circulated in a procedure known as 'the oddments' for days before anyone claims them as theirs. Obviously, having your letter circulating in this way will severely delay a response – so if there is a reference use it! If you do not have a name or a reference to use, there may be a department you could direct it to, in order to save the letter getting 'lost'.

Figure 9.1 shows a sample layout of a formal letter. The sample used is known as 'fully blocked', that is, everything begins at the left-hand margin. There are other styles of letter known as 'semi blocked' and

```
New College
Station Road
Bromfield BD1 2SB

30 March 19..

St Saviour's Refuge
Chapel Street
Midborough MB12 3KR

Ref: Kevin McNamara

Dear ........

Student Visit

(Main letter content)




Yours ......
(signature)


Nicola Philipson
```

Figure 9.1 *A typical layout of a formal letter*

'indented', where items are spaced in to the right. Organisations will usually have a preferred style.

Task

If you write a letter to an agency making arrangements for a group visit, as outlined in your telephone notes, you may be able to use it as evidence of written communication for your portfolio. Additionally, if you use the word processor to produce it you may be able to use it as IT evidence.

Memos

When written messages are sent by people within the same company it is not necessary to set them out with addresses, so a shortened form of communication is used. This is called a memorandum or memo. In many ways a memo serves the same function as a letter. It is a means of each party having a note of what arrangements are, or need to be, and is very useful to refer to when someone denies/forgets about having been asked to do something!

If the group which has been arranging to visit a provision for homeless people needed to book the college minibus for the visit, a memo would probably need to be sent confirming this arrangement.

Task

Figure 9.2 shows an example of a typical layout of a memo. When you have read it you could draft a reply memo from Ben James, confirming the booking. If you do this well you will be able to use it as evidence for communication and IT.

MEMORANDUM

To: Ben James

From: Nicola Philipson

Date: ......

Subject: Minibus Booking

I should like to book the college minibus for (insert date). The group using it will be GNVQ Advanced Social Care who will be visiting Midborough. We will depart at 08.30 and return at approximately 19.00. Please advise me if the bus will be filled up with petrol prior to departure and where I should arrange to leave it on return.

(Optional signature)

Figure 9.2 *Example of a memo*

· FILLING IN FORMS ·

As soon as we come into existence forms are generated to record details about us. Even before a baby is born records are kept at the hospital and doctor's surgery about its growth and development. It is almost impossible to exist without having our progress through life recorded. As a care-worker you will not only have to complete forms relating to yourself, but to clients as well.

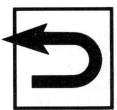

Think it over

What types of forms exist about you in your life to date?

Forms are designed to collect information in a structured way, to make sure all the details necessary are given and nothing is missed out.

As we have said, details are recorded before we are even born; but the first form in a person's own name will be the birth certificate. There will follow various medical records, allowance records, school records, passport records and maybe immigration, social service or criminal records, as well as housing, bank and building society, tax and National Insurance records!

Whether you decide to look for work after this course, or to go on to higher education, you will need to complete various forms to give prospective employers or institutions information about yourself. When you were reading through Chapter 2 in this book you will have come across exercises which were designed for you to evaluate your strengths and weaknesses. This type of exercise is a good preliminary to completing an application form because it enables you to be clear about what you feel you have to offer to an employer/institution. When you are applying for a course or a job in social care, personal qualities are often as important as formal qualifications and should not be overlooked in the interests of modesty. You will need to be able to work in goups, to take responsibility and co-operate with others.

Opposite is an exercise for you to evaluate your level in certain skills. There are no right or wrong answers; it is designed to help you make a personal evaluation before beginning to draft a statement for an application form.

If you have scored over 90, it would suggest that you have good communication skills but whatever you have scored it is worth exploring any areas of weakness.

Completing an application form

Forms are used to give structure to a range of information and to make comparisons easy. If the same facts appear in the same places on several forms it is easier than if they occur at random

---

Self-evaluation

How good are you at communication in health and social care work?
Scoring – circle 1 if you are *never* good at it
circle 2 if you are *seldom* good at it
circle 3 if you are *sometimes* good at it
circle 4 if you are *often* good at it
circle 5 if you are *always* good at it

1 Starting a conversation
2 Carrying on a conversation
3 Ending a conversation
4 Listening
5 Expressing a compliment
6 Expressing appreciation
7 Expressing encouragement
8 Asking for help
9 Giving instructions
10 Expressing affection
11 Expressing a complaint
12 Persuading others
13 Expressing anger
14 Responding to praise
15 Responding to the feelings of others
16 Apologising
17 Following instructions
18 Setting a goal
19 Gathering information
20 Concentrating on a task
21 Evaluating your abilities
22 Setting priorities
23 Self control
24 Negotiation
25 Assertiveness

---

throughout several sheets of writing. The first part of most forms, therefore, will ask for a range of personal details. Figure 9.3 (page 355) shows the course details and Figure 9.4 (page 356–359) is an example of a form designed for people wanting to apply for a higher education course at a college. It has been completed on behalf of an applicant to show what details will go where.

Higher national certificate in caring services
(care management)

Attendance
1 day per week over 2 years

Course aims
To meet the needs of students working in a range of care settings, for example, social services, private and voluntary care, social security, police, housing welfare. These staff will acquire and demonstrate skills to allow them to develop the new management roles required by the changes taking place in the care sector.

Course content
The first year provides a broad based education in social policy, applied social sciences, methods of social research, developing human resources, the legal environment. Students will also gain experience in the use of information systems and technology. In the second year, students concentrate on care management and work, or a consultancy project as a group.

Entry requirements
The minimum age of entry is eighteen. Students should hold either an appropriate BTEC National qualification or GNVQ Advanced or A-level equivalent. Entry will also depend on the student's relevant experience. Applicants with other entry qualifications will be considered if they can provide evidence of relevant experience and ability to study at an advanced level.

Assessment
Assessment is continuous throughout the course. Academic study and practical experience in the workplace are linked to produce an integrated programme of learning. Students will work on assignments individually and in groups. Links with the line manager and tutor will develop a work based assessment of the student.

Additional information
This is a new course running for the first time in September 19–. The college is currently negotiating with a number of universities to develop links with their Diploma in Social Work programmes.

Figure 9.3 *Course details*

Personal statement

Probably the most important part of any application form is the *personal statement*. This is your opportunity to 'sell yourself', to influence the reader into wanting to interview you or offer you a place on a course. Remember that the only information the reader has is what you put on the form. If it is not there the reader will not know about it – so make sure you put in all you can.

Your personal statement should contain details of your work experience, interests and achievements, what you believe your personal qualities to be and why you think you are suitable for the job/course. It is likely you will have listed your qualifications earlier on the form and the names of any employers, so concentrate on skills which you have acquired which can be transferred from one situation to a new one. For example, if you have been involved in fund raising at college this probably means you have experience of taking responsibility for organising/co-operating in events and working with others. This is a useful transferable skill which an employer or tutor will be interested in.

Figure 9.5 on page 360 gives an example of the type of personal statement someone on a social care course might write. It deals with the person's experience, personal qualities and interests. Claims are backed up with evidence. There is no point in writing things of the 'aren't I wonderful' mode without giving reasons why others might think so!

Task

It is always a good idea to draft your personal statement on a separate piece of paper and show it to a colleague or your tutor for advice before writing it on the actual form. Draft out your own personal statement now.

If you complete this activity well you will be able to use it as evidence for your Communication portfolio and use it as the basis for higher education or job

College Application
Form for Higher Education

Application No.

Personal details

Surname/Family Name
(BLOCK CAPITALS)
HADJICHARITOU

First names[s] ELIAS

Previous surname, if changed

Correspondence address 31 THE GROVE,
MANCHESTER

Post Code M40 2HJ

Telephone No [including STD code]   Daytime 061 243267   Evening [if different]

Fax No.

Home address if different
SAME

Post Code

Telephone No. [including STD code]   Daytime   Evening [if different]

Fax No.

Sex: Male ✓   Female ☐

Date of Birth

Day	Month	Year
0 4	0 9	7 5

Year age on 31 December in year of entry

Years 1 9   Months 0 3

Special needs or medical condition
Please tick this box if you have a physical, sensory and/or other learning disability which might in some way affect your studies at the college or may require special facilities or treatment.

✓

Country of birth   GREECE

Nationality   GREEK

Country of domicile or area of permanent residence
ENGLAND

Applicants not born in the European Community please state:

Date of first entry to the EC

Day	Month	Year
0 1	0 9	7 6

Payment of fees
Who is expected to pay your fees? [eg Research Council, LEA, yourself, family member, employer, other]

If an LEA, which one?   MANCHESTER

Details of course[s] to which you wish to apply

Month and year in which you wish to start

Course Title	Preliminary choice of main subjects/options [if appropriate]	Mode of study: full-time/sandwich/ part-time/other. Please specify
HIGHER NATIONAL CERTIFICATE IN CARING SERVICES (CARE MANAGEMENT)		P. T.
Please indicate how you heard of these courses		

Last two educational establishments attached
Name and address of the two most recent educational establishment attended

	From		To		FT or PT
	Month	Year	Month	Year	
ROUNDWOOD HIGH SCHOOL, UPPER LANE, MANCH.	9	1985	7	1992	FT
CITY COLLEGE, PARK STREET, MANCHESTER M40 8QT	9	1992	7	1994	FT

Figure 9.4   *Completed college application form*

Record of Achievement
Do you have an up-to-date (post 16) Record of Achievement?

Yes ✓   No ☐

Academic Qualifications
Applicants should, if applicable, list all subjects taken, whatever the result, in chronological order. If you are awaiting the result of any examination recently taken, write PENDING in the result column.

Level eg GCSE, A Level, RSA, Access, Degree, Professional	Subject	Date Month	Date Year	Place of Study	Result [grades or bands]	CATS points
GCSE	ENGLISH LANGUAGE	7	1992	ROUNDWOOD HIGH SCH.	B	
	ENGLISH LITERATURE	"	"		B	
	MATHMATICS	"	"		C	
	HISTORY	"	"		C	
	CHEMISTRY	"	"		D	
	BIOLOGY	"	"		C	
	DRAMA	"	"		A	

Qualifications awarded by BTEC, SCOTVEC, NCVQ.

	Unit, module or component title				
Title of award held	ENVIRONMENTAL HEALTH & SAFETY	94	✓	UNIT	PASS
	DEVELOPMENT OF SOCIAL POLICY	94	"	"	"
Title of current qualification GNVQ HEALTH & SOCIAL CARE (ADVANCED)	COMMUNICATION LEVEL 3 (ADVANCED)	"	3	"	"
	I.T	"	3	"	"
BTEC registration number for current qualification	APPLICATION OF NUMBER	"	3	"	"
	IMPROVING OWN LEARNING & PERFORMANCE	"	3	"	"
Name and brief address of college CITY COLLEGE, PARK ST. MANCHESTER M40 8QT	WORKING WITH OTHERS	"	3	"	"
	PROBLEM SOLVING	"	3	"	"

Unit, module or component title						AWARD OF GNVQ EXPECTED				
ACCESS, EQUAL OPPS. & CLIENT RIGHTS	94	✓	UNIT	PASS		AT MERIT LEVEL.				
INTERPERSONAL INTERACTION	"	"	"	"						
PHYSICAL ASPECTS OF HEALTH	"	"	"	"						
PSYCHOLOGICAL & SOCIAL ASPECTS OF HEALTH & SOCIAL CARE	"	"	"	"						
HEALTH PROMOTION	"	"	"	"						
STRUCTURE & PRACTICES IN HEALTH & SOCIAL CARE	"	"	"	"						
CARE PLANS	"	"	"	"						
RESEARCH IN HEALTH & SOCIAL CARE	"	"	"	"						
WELFARE SERVICES & SOCIAL CHANGE	"	"	"	"						
HUMAN BEHAVIOUR IN THE CONTEXT OF HEALTH & SOCIAL CARE	"	"	"	"						
SPECIAL NEEDS	"	"	"	"						

Figure 9.4 *(continued)*

Work Experience
Beginning with most recent.

[Give details of work experience, training and employment]

Job Title Nature of work/training	Name of organisation	Full-time or Part-time	From Month	From Year	From Month	From Year
CLASS ROOM ASSISTANT	ST. PETERS SCHOOL	P.T.	03	1993	04	1993
CARE ASSISTANT	THE GROVE	P.T.	05	1993	06	1993
CARE ASSISTANT	PENNINE HOUSE	P.T.	01	1994	02	1994
SUPERMARKET ASSISTANT	SUPERDRUG	P.T.	09	1992	TO DATE	

Further information
Please use this section to provide any additional information in support of your application. For example skills; relevant work experience [including voluntary work or time spent at home with your family]; reasons for choice of course; career aspirations etc.

DURING MY GNVQ PROGRAMME I HAVE WORKED WITH CHILDREN, ELDERS AND PEOPLE WITH PHYSICAL AND LEARNING DISABILITIES. MY EXPERIENCE OF WORKING WITH PEOPLE WITH PROFOUND LEARNING DISABILITY HAS PARTICULARLY HELPED ME TO UNDERSTAND AND INTERPRET NON-VERBAL COMMUNICATION. PLACEMENT WORK HAS HELPED ME TO DEVELOP SUPPORTIVE SKILLS AND TO FEEL CONFIDENT WHEN WORKING WITH INDIVIDUALS AND GROUPS.

THE COLLEGE PART OF MY GNVQ PROGRAMME HAS ENABLED ME TO DEVELOP SKILLS IN PLANNING, INFORMATION HANDLING AND EVALUATION. I HAVE CLAIMED A MERIT GRADE FOR THE PORTFOLIO OF EVIDENCE THAT I HAVE COMPLETED FOR GNVQ. I AM FAIRLY CONFIDENT THAT I WILL BE AWARDED A MERIT GRADE AT THE FINAL ASSESSMENT BOARD.

DURING MY TIME AT COLLEGE I HAVE HELPED WITH STUDENT UNION EVENTS AND WITH FUND RAISING FOR CHARITY. IN MY OWN TIME I TAKE PART IN THE LOCAL DUKE OF EDINBURGH SCHEME. THIS INVOLVES PHYSICAL AND SPORTING ACTIVITIES SUCH AS WALKING AND SAILING. I HAVE ALSO TAKEN PART IN A RANGE OF COMMUNITY PROJECTS SUCH AS WORKING WITH THE LOCAL HOSPITAL RADIO TEAM. I HAVE GAINED PART-TIME EXPERIENCE IN CARE WORK AND BY WORKING AS A SUPERMARKET ASSISTANT. THESE ACTIVITIES AND EXPERIENCES HAVE ENABLED ME TO FEEL CONFIDENT IN MY ABILITIES TO WORK WITH OTHERS AND ENABLED ME TO DECIDE ON A CAREER IN CARING.

I AM APPLYING FOR A PLACE ON THE PART-TIME HNC COURSE SO THAT I CAN GAIN PRACTICAL EXPERIENCE IN CARING BY WORKING AS A CARE ASSISTANT, WHILST ACHIEVING FURTHER ACADEMIC QUALIFICATIONS. MY LONG TERM AMBITION IS TO WORK IN CARE MANAGEMENT AFTER GAINING PRACTICAL EXPERIENCE.

Figure 9.4 *(continued)*

Special Needs
Please give details of any physical, other disability, or medical condition, including any which might necessitate special arrangements or facilities.

Creche
Do you wish to request a place in the college creche.

Yes ☐   No ☒

References
Please give the names and addresses of two referees

1 Name *J. MARLEY*	2 Name *M. McMANUS*
Address *BEDE HOUSE, COLLEGE GROVE*	Address *17 THE GROVE*
MANCHESTER M12 4E2	*ALWOODLEY, LEEDS LS17 8QT*
Telephone No. *061 247 839*	Telephone No. *0532 610 543*
Post/Occupation/Relationship *TUTOR*	Post/Occupation/Relationship *FAMILY FRIEND*

Declaration
I confirm that, to the best of my knowledge, the information given in this form is current and complete.

Applicants Signature   Date

Elias Hadjicharitou   *17 MAY 1994*

Please return this form to the Enrolments Officer.

Figure 9.4 *(continued)*

Personal statement

During my present course I have worked with children, elders and people with physical and learning difficulties. I have particularly enjoyed my present placement with children with profound learning difficulties. This has developed my ability to communicate with people in different ways, according to their needs. Through my placements I have gained confidence to approach new people and situations with a positive attitude. (Please see enclosed open reference.)

The course has developed my skills in information seeking, planning activities and evaluating the results. I have had experience in assessing people's needs, listening to and then carrying out instructions. I have gained additional care skills in the GNVQ units 'Working with others' and 'Improving own learning'.

Throughout my recent studies I have been actively involved in fund-raising activities. This has helped me work as part of a team, take responsibility and to be innovative. I help with organising student union events and this has developed my organisational skills and required commitment. During my spare time I take part in the Duke of Edinburgh scheme which involves me in outdoor activities, such as walking and sailing, and working in the community. One of my projects has been working with the local hospital radio team to broadcast programmes to the wards. This has been a creative challenge and helped me develop confidence. I also have a part-time job in a supermarket which has given me experience of relating to a range of customers and responsibilities for personal time management and presentation.

I would like to take the Higher National Certificate course to enhance my academic qualifications and give me further experience of the work opportunities in the field of social care.

Figure 9.5 *A sample personal statement*

applications. However, remember that when you are applying for a course or a job you will need to adjust your statement to show why you think your qualities and experience match those needed.

If you want to have more practice you can search out some advertisements from one of the social work journals or university prospectuses and 'match' yourself against their criteria. Remember this is you selling yourself and it is a complex process to cram all your experience and qualities into a page or so of writing. It will take practice and patience to get it right!

Forms in the workplace

As mentioned earlier, there is a huge range of forms in existence (a form for nearly every situation you can think of) and you will have to complete them for your employer and for clients.

Figure 9.6 shows an example of an accident report form. Employers are legally required to complete accident reports for people who have accidents on their premises. This is so that they have a record of exactly what happened in case they become liable for payment of damages.

Task

The following case-study sets out the details of an accident which took place on an employer's premises. See if you can complete the accident report from the details given. If you can you may be able to use it as evidence for your Communication portfolio.

ACCIDENT REPORT FORM

PART A   TO BE COMPLETED BY FIRST AIDER

DETAILS OF INJURED PERSON

SURNAME	FORENAME	SEX	D.O.B.	STATUS (tick)	
		M/F		EMPLOYEE	SELF-EMPLOYED
				YTS TRAINEE	OTHER

ADDRESS

DEPARTMENT

OCCUPATION

NATURE OF INJURY OF CONDITION

PART AFFECTED (LEFT OR RIGHT)

DETAILS OF ACCIDENT

DATE			19		TIME		AM/PM
	DAY	MONTH	YEAR				

IF NOT ON THESE PREMISES STATE WHERE ▶

WHERE ON THE PREMISES ▶

WAS THE INJURED PERSON SENT TO HOSPITAL	YES	NO	DATE/TIME CEASED WORK	
			DATE/TIME RETURNED	

PART B   TO BE COMPLETED BY SUPERVISOR

WHAT WAS INJURED PERSON DOING?

KIND OF ACCIDENT

Indicate what kind of accident led to the injury or condition (tick one box)

Contact with moving machinery or material being machined ☐	Injured whilst handling, lifting or carrying ☐	Trapped by something collapsing or overturning ☐	Exposure to an explosion ☐
Struck by moving including flying or falling object ☐	Slip, trip or fall on same level ☐	Drowning or asphyxiation ☐	Contact with electricity or an electrical discharge ☐
Struck by moving vehicle ☐	Fall from a height ☐	Exposure to or contact with a harmful substance ☐	Injured by an animal ☐
Struck against something fixed or stationary ☐	Distance through which person fell metres ☐	Exposure to fire ☐	Other kind of accident (give details) ☐

Figure 9.6   *An accident report form*

Case-study

Lavinia White, a cleaner employed by Easy Clean, a contracting cleaning company, arrived for duty at Sowell Grange at 7.45 am on Tuesday 30 March, 1994. Lavinia White's home address is 12 The Close, Notton, WF2 8JP. Her date of birth is 26 February, 1946.

As she walked down the steps in the hall toward the staff room Mrs White lost her balance, tripped on the corner of a carpet and fell down four steps. She was carrying her bag, a packet of crisps, a cup of hot coffee and a file.

Fortunately the coffee did not burn her but she sustained injury to her left knee. She was examined by the officer-in-charge, Christine Burnley, and an ambulance was called to take her to hospital. She left the premises at 8 am. She is presently off work and likely to remain so for at least two weeks.

Think it over

Make a list of as many different ways of communicating as you can think of.

You have probably thought of hand-signing, body language, sketches, diagrams, still photographs, graphs and perhaps more ways of communicating. It would be a good exercise to spend some time in a group of people not speaking and see if you can make yourself understood.

We often see diagrams, such as the ones in Figure 9.7, in public places. They are designed to convey information quickly and reinforce the written or spoken word.

Before written language as we know it now was invented, people used to leave messages for each other by drawing what they had to say. Some of these are still in existence today. This is a very useful way of extending meaning where there is a difficulty in understanding or where people speak different languages. Diagrams are also often used nowadays

· USING IMAGES ·

A care-worker often has to help people who have difficulty in understanding spoken or written communications. They may not hear well; they may not understand the meaning of some words, perhaps because English is not their first language, or because of learning difficulties; or perhaps there has been damage to the part of their brain which deals with language following an accident, stroke or illness.

If someone has a problem understanding spoken or written language you can use your face, body or diagrams to help them understand. When you consider how much we can 'say' without speaking you will realise we do this often anyway, but you can make further deliberate efforts to get meanings across. To use all the available forms of communication is called *total communication*.

Figure 9.7 *Images are used to convey information quickly*

to keep people's attention, for example, during a presentation where charts to illustrate what the speaker is saying are often used.

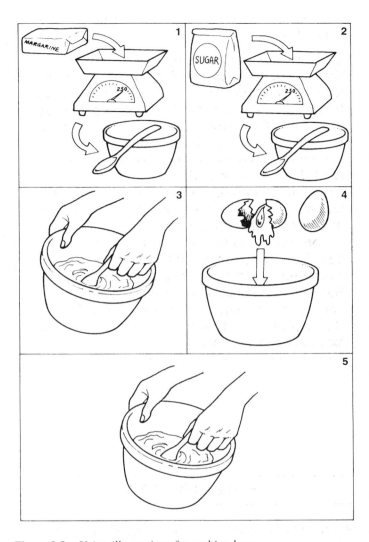

Figure 9.8 *Using illustrations for making buns*

Task

If you had to teach a skill to someone with little English, or who had a hearing impairment, you could do so by illustrations. Figure 9.8 shows an example of beginning to teach someone how to make buns using illustrations. If you choose a task, and produce a series of illustrations to teach it, you may be able to use it as evidence for your portfolio (using images to illustrate points). You will find you need to break the task down into very small steps. This is called task analysis.

Task

Read the information below and decide on a suitable means of illustrating it. If you use your IT skills you can use the results as evidence for both your Communication and IT portfolio.

Whilst they were visiting the hostel the students had the opportunity to talk with some of the residents and staff. The staff try to adopt a non-judgemental attitude to the people they help. It is important that the clients are able to trust the staff to respect their right to confidentiality; when the clients feel secure about this the staff are more able to help.

You may have seen the text which follows on using diagrams in the *Health and Social Care: Intermediate* book in this series. However, the information is so valuable as an example of how images can be used, that it is included again here.

Task

Below is an explanation, written for teenagers with learning difficulties, to let them know what a key worker is and how they can be helped by their key worker. The first two examples have a small drawing beside them to help the person understand and remember what the written part said. Read through the information and draw symbols to show how you would illustrate the six sentences which are shown without a drawing.

While you are at school your key worker will help you:
in your learning both in class and in the group

to make friends and learn to be a member of a group

. . . to keep in contact with your family and friends at home
. . . by listening to what you say and knowing how you feel
. . . by helping you to decide what you need for your life
. . . to arrange special times in your life like birthdays, holidays, Christmas and your free time
. . . to look after yourself and your clothes
. . . to look after your money and possessions.

These are the sort of diagrams you might have produced:

–to keep in contact with your family and friends at home. (The telephone and envelope show the person that these are means of 'talking' with family and friends when they are living far away from them.)

– by listening to what you say and knowing how you feel. (The picture of an ear tells the client that the key worker is always – within reason – ready to listen to them and try to understand their feelings.)

– by helping you to decide what you need for your life. (The picture of someone apparently 'balancing' with their hands is meant to indicate choices, decisions which the key worker would help the client to talk through.)

– arranging special times in your life like birthdays, holidays, Christmas, and free time. (This diagram reminds the client that on special occasions we don't always

follow the same routine and the key worker will help them plan for different times in their life.)

– to look after yourself and your clothes. (A picture of neat clothes reminds the client they will need to take responsibility for some aspects of looking after themselves and their key worker will help them with the necessary skills.)

– to look after your money and possessions. (A picture of money and a person keeping something to the body reminds the client not to leave valuables around.)

· USING PHOTOGRAPHS ·

Another way of communicating with images is to use photographs. Photographs can record images with almost total accuracy. When used over a lifetime they can become a personal pictorial history.

A photograph is a valuable visual reminder of people, events and places

It is very important to particular client groups to have photographs of themselves to help them form a clearer picture of where they came from, what their experiences have been and who they are now.

Photographs are a valuable means of recalling people and events. Elders who may have difficulty remembering recent events can often be helped to remember their past lives and relationships by looking at photographs. This is called reminiscence therapy and is invaluable in helping people to discuss and value their past experience. People who are mourning the loss of a loved one, either through separation or death, may find comfort in having photographs around. Photographs can help people with learning difficulties to remember what they did and where they have been. If a child is no longer living with its birth parents, having a photograph is also very valuable. A photograph is a permanent visual reminder of people, events and places.

Task

Below is a railway timetable from Bromfield to Midborough. You will see that, reading from left to right, the train leaving Bromfield at 05.41 will arrive in Midborough at 08.33. The appointment at the hostel is at 2 pm and the group need at least one hour to take the tram and find it.

- *What train will they have to catch from Bromfield to get them there in time for the appointment?*
- *What services/restrictions will be available on this train?*
- *Will they have to change trains?*

Task

If you are on work placement you may notice clients' pictures around, and they may like to talk to you about them.

Keep a record of your conversations to provide evidence of using images.

· USING MAPS AND TIMETABLES ·

Earlier in the chapter some of the exercises related to a group planning to visit a hostel for homeless people in Midborough. The hostel has agreed to the visit and the group must now decide on the best method of getting to the premises. They discuss whether to take the train and tram or to travel in the college minibus.

Bromfield and Wakeham → Midborough

Mondays to Fridays				Saturdays		
	Bromfield depart	Wakeham Westgate depart	Midborough Central arrive	Bromfield depart	Wakeham Westgate depart	Midborough Central arrive
✕	—	0512	0726	—	0517	0731
✕	0541f	0627	0833	—	0622	0836
	0636f	0712	0906	0636f	0634e	0916
	—	0732	0919	—	0717	0921
⊠	—	0752	0945	—	0739e	0951
✕	0705c	0807	1025	0735f	0816	1031
✕	0834f	0917	1125	—	0842e	1115
	—	0935e	1219	0834f	0916	1129
✕	0926c	1017	1230	—	0935e	1202
✕	1041f	1117	1333	0941f	1017	1231
	1126c	1217	1430	—	1035e	1312
✕	1241f	1317	1532	1041f	1117	1331
✕	1326c	1417	1630	—	1135e	1414
✕	1441f	1517	1704	1141f	1217	1432
	—	1535e	1808	1241f	1317	1530
	1526c	1617	1825	1341f	1417	1631
	1541b	1635e	1918	—	1435e	1716
	1641f	1717	1930	1441f	1517	1730
	—	1734e	2015	—	1535e	1828
✕	1723c	1817	2040	1549c	1647	1901
	1841b	1932e	2159	1650c	1747	2001
	1918c	2017	2248	1801c	1852	2106
	1941b	2035e	0023	1849g	1941e	2234
				1941f	2033	2251

Sundays		
—	0802e	1150
—	0832	1210
0806g	1014e	1350
—	1032	1410
1054g	1214e	1550
—	1232	1610
1254g	1414e	1725
—	1432	1735
1406c	1532	1800
1454c	1632	1910
1621c	1732	2004
1722c	1832	2110
1851g	2005e	2323
2021c	2112	2350

Notes
b   Change trains at Wakeham Westgate
c   Change trains at Newton
e   Change trains at Southford
f   Change trains at Wakeham Westgate
g   Change trains at Newton and Southford
⊠   Restaurant (First Class only).
✕   Restaurant.
•   No catering available.
Times in **bold** type indicate a direct service.
Times in light type indicate a connecting service.
All services shown in this timetable offer
– First Class and Standard accommodation.
– Light food, hot and cold drinks for most of the journey.
– Reservable seats available.

When the group arrives at Midborough Central station they will take the tram to Chapel Street. Below is a map of the tram network showing the different routes. A circle, O, indicates that it is possible to transfer to another tram.

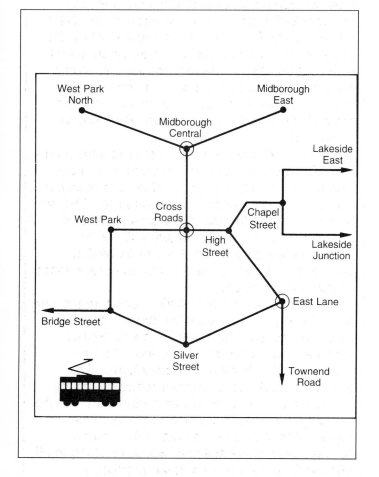

These are the possibilities if the journey is made by rail. However, some of the group would prefer to use the college minibus. Below is a map which they would have to use to work out their journey once they get to Midborough.

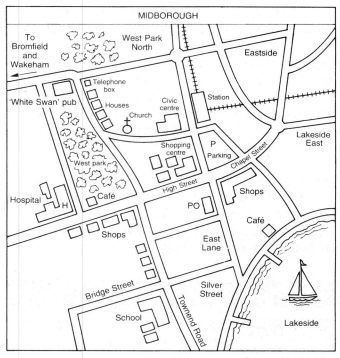

Task

- *Using the tram route map say how the group will travel from Midborough Central station to Chapel Street. How many stops is the journey? Where will they change trams?*

- *If there is time after the visit, the group would like to window shop in the Silver Street area. How would they get there? Would they need to change trams again?*

Task

The driver knows the way to Midborough as far as West Park North but then needs written instructions to get to the hostel. Prepare written instructions from West Park North to Chapel Street. If you produce clear information you may be able to use it as evidence for your portfolio.

· DEVELOPING WRITTEN SKILLS ·

Summarising

Every day, in both our working and personal lives, we take in a great deal of information. We cannot possibly remember word for word all of what is said to us or all we read. What happens is we listen to what is said or read and select *important points*. This is a kind of mental shorthand to remember the parts we need and we do it automatically. If you were to recount an event, or a film you had watched, to a friend you would select the bits which formed the plot. This is sometimes called *summarising* or *précising* and it is an essential skill. When you read textbooks you will be mentally summarising what you read and picking out the important points to make notes or to remember.

When the group mentioned earlier visited the hostel for homeless people they were given the Development Report (below) which discusses how the project had moved forward during the previous year and its subsequent plans.

Task

Read the report below and see if you can reduce it to approximately one-third of its original length. Each paragraph makes a specific point so it is worth looking for the main idea in each paragraph when making notes.

If you do this well you can use it as evidence of summarising a complex document for your portfolio.

Development report

This year two major developments have come to fruition, both of which demonstrate our commitment to developing and providing quality accommodation.

Our 'Nightshelter' has at last moved to its new home. This project has been in development for the last eight years. So we have now said goodbye to Dickensian dormitory facilities. The new hostel has single bedrooms with a separate area for women, affording residents a much greater degree of privacy and allowing people to retain their self esteem, often threatened by the experience of homelessness. Equally important is the substantial increase in communal areas; living rooms and dining area. The improved standards also allow residents greater acess to the building and the term 'nightshelter' is now outmoded.

Our second major development provides short-term emergency accommodation for homeless women in two different types of accommodation: two five-bedroom hostels and 24 flatlets. The aim of this design is to cater for a broad range of housing need and levels of support and to produce a building which through its design contributes to our aim of meeting the preferences of individual women.

Quality is also a theme which runs through our plans for the future. Following the nightshelter's move to new premises, the Women's Hostel which is situated in the upper floor of an old building is also in need of a new home. The Women's Hostel is a valuable resource which caters for women over 25. In conjunction with the Housing Association we hope to develop a replacement scheme. As part of the design process we will consult with women staying in all our provision to ensure that we produce a building which meets the needs of homeless women as they themselves perceive them.

This consultation is part of the quality assurance philosophy we are developing within the organisation.

We also hope to develop quality accommodation for those groups of homeless people who are currently inadequately catered for. One such group is street homeless people with alcohol problems. This group of people are particularly vulnerable living on the streets because they drink. Their drinking also means they are more likely to develop health problems, yet they tend to be excluded from much of the residential provision for homeless people because of their drinking and the structure and self control necessary to take advantage of detoxification services often excludes them. Therefore, we hope to develop a 'Wet House' where such people will be provided with quality housing which is not dependent on their ability to control their drinking. One of the aims of this scheme will be to provide a secure and pleasant housing environment in order to break the vicious circle of drinking in order to make living on the street bearable.

The report above also contained information in written form of various statistics (not given). There are other ways this information could have been given. What ways can you think of?

Below is an account from a client living at one of the hostels who has suffered sexual abuse. She has finally gained enough self confidence to want to contact her mother again. She is, however, anxious that the contact is on her terms and is not yet prepared to say where she is living. She does not want her mother to feel she blames her, but is worried her step-father may try to contact her. 'Paula' asks the worker to help her write to her mother. Before you begin the Task you may want to refer back to Chapter 2 on how to convey warmth, understanding and sincerity.

Task

Read 'Paula's' story and draft a letter to her mother, in order to try and arrange a meeting between Paula and her mother. The letter would not discuss the abuse, but it would need to be very carefully worded and skilfully designed in order to result in a successful meeting. You will need to discuss how Paula might introduce the idea of a meeting and where the meeting might be arranged.

When you have drafted the letter, evaluate how you would have gone about the task with Paula and why you have designed the letter the way you did.

You may want to work with a colleague and discuss how to write the letter.

If you complete this task well you may be able to use it as evidence for your portfolio of writing a letter on a sensitive issue.

Paula's Story

'I and the other girls in my family (three) were abused sexually by our step-father for a number of years. He was eventually sent to prison but left behind a lot of messed up girls. I have had several nervous breakdowns and been in a number of psychiatric institutions. Finding a place of safety has been my only aim and only now do I feel safe.

Before coming here I thought my life was totally worthless. This was not helped by the fact that some of the places I had found myself in prior to here actually made me believe this. Now I have gathered enough self confidence to recognise there is good to be gained from talking more to the people who know what it is like to be abused.'

Fast Facts

Adjective   A word which says something about a noun.

Adverb   A word which says something about a verb.

Agenda   A list of items for discussion at a meeting.

Apostrophe   A punctuation mark used either (i) to show something belongs, or (ii) that something has been omitted. If the person or thing to which the object belongs is plural, the apostrophe goes after the 's'. When a letter or letters are missing the apostrophe is put where they would have been.

Assumption   You make an assumption when you think you know something without checking it first.

Capital letter   This is used at the beginning of a sentence, and for names of people or places.

Comma   This is used to separate items in a list, or different parts within a sentence.

Communication   An activity that can be verbal or non-verbal (or both). It can involve using sketches, diagrams, photographs, tables or graphs to make meanings clearer.

Key worker   A care-worker who has special responsibility for certain clients. A key worker helps the client with all aspects of their daily life, gets to know them well and helps them plan their lives. Key workers will help plan leisure activities, holidays, birthdays and help the client keep in touch with friends and family.

Memorandum (memo)   A message between workers of the same organisation. It will not have an address in the heading.

Non-verbal communication   Using our face, body or voice tone to convey meaning.

Noun   The name of a person, place or object.

Object   The name given to someone (or something) in a statement to whom the verb applies (e.g. 'He saw *the baby*').

Précis   Picking out the important points from information in order to make a shorter version. Also known as summary.

Pronoun   A word used instead of a noun (e.g. him, her, it).

Sentence   A group of words put together to make complete sense. It must have a subject and a verb.

Subject   The name given to the noun or pronoun about which a statement is being made.

Total communication   Using words, body language and signs, often together, to help get meaning across.

Verb   A word describing an action (e.g. 'I *walked* to college').

chapter *10* APPLICATION OF NUMBER

This chapter is designed to help you achieve your core skills in the Application of Number. It explains the concepts and procedures involved and provides you with the opportunity to use those skills. This chapter will also show you how often number skills are used in everyday life and in the field of health and social care to work things out. For example, working out how much it costs to equip a care establishment, how to increase a recipe that serves four to serve 20, or to work out how many staff are needed to provide effective care for clients.

Number skills are also used to collect data, compile it into a suitable form for *analysis* and then to draw *conclusions* from the results shown. This can help to show patterns that might, for example, be used for forward planning of services or budgets. Some of this is explained in more detail in Chapter 8, Research, which draws on many skills for collecting information, such as questionnaires, observations and interviews. Therefore, Chapter 8 should be used alongside this chapter to develop your core skills.

Throughout this book, evidence tasks have included the use of number skills, e.g. in surveys and questionnaires. This chapter supports those tasks and provides further opportunities to achieve your core skills in the Application of Number.

Four rules of number, fractions, percentages and ratios

This chapter assumes that Advanced level students are competent in using whole numbers, fractions,

percentages and ratios. If you need further practice with these, it is worth looking at the beginning of the Application of Number chapter in the *Health and Social Care: Intermediate* book in this series.

· ESTIMATION ·

This means an **approximate judgement**. You certainly want to get your number applications correct, so it is very useful to have a rough idea of what your answer should be so that you know when you have made a mistake. Many people don't use estimation and common sense in their arithmetic, and then they complain about the number of sums they get wrong.

For instance, many people don't realise that when two fractions are multiplied together the answer is *smaller*. Take two simple fractions you are familiar with, $\frac{1}{2}$ and $\frac{1}{2}$. Multiply them together and you get $\frac{1}{4}$. This may seem puzzling because you are used to thinking that $\frac{1}{2} + \frac{1}{2} = 1$, and indeed it does. But when multiplying these fractions together you are in fact saying a half of a half – and when you reflect on that, the answer *is* a quarter.

Another estimating tip, useful with both fractions and decimals, is to look at the whole number parts. For example, if adding together 16.956 and 2.305 look at the whole numbers 16 and 2 (added together = 18). Next look at the decimals – the first shows 9 in the tenths position and the second shows 3, so when added together these are going to make at least another whole one. Hence your answer is going to be 19 point 'something not very big'.

Also try to get into the habit of 'rounding' in your estimates. Take for example 3.75 × 5.02. This sum is 'nearly 4' multiplied by 'just over 5', so your answer must be in the region of 4 × 5, which is 20.

Think it over

Do you remember how to multiply the sum above using the 'pen and paper' method? How many figures will there be after the decimal point in the answer? Do the sum now to check that the answer is in the region of 20.

Remember:
Practise estimation in your work – it only takes a few seconds, but pays off in accuracy.

Another useful tip is to get used to the mental images of lengths, areas, volumes, weights etc. so you have a better understanding of them. For instance:

- The average weight of an adult man is 70 kg, but it is not unknown for a care-worker to write someone's weight as 7000 kg! Clearly the unit has no clear meaning for such a person.
- A litre is approximately $1\frac{3}{4}$ pints – we are all familiar with a pint milk bottle, so a pint is roughly $\frac{1}{2}$ a litre (just over in fact).
- Most people know the feel and size of a 2 pound bag of sugar, but many have not noticed that sugar comes now in 1 kilogram bags (= 2.2 pounds). They did not notice that it had changed because the weight is so similar. So, try to remember that a pound is roughly $\frac{1}{2}$ a kilogram, or 500 grams (just under in fact).
- Fabric used to be measured by the yard, and a popular way of 'measuring' in the UK was to hold the length of fabric between your nose and the fingers of an outstretched arm – this was approximately a yard. Now, a metre is only about 3 inches longer than a yard, and this is about the length of a nose – so if the head is turned away from the outstretched fingers, one can still use the old-fashioned way to measure a metre!

- An excellent way of estimating some lengths or heights is to use your own body. Get to know your own height in metres and in centimetres (or millimetres). The average height for a woman is 1.60 metres, and her fully stretched handspan (from little finger tip to thumb tip) is about 20 centimetres. Measure yours to check.
- Measure your biggest stride and you will always be able to pace out a distance.

When you get a feel for measurements, estimating will be that much easier for you.

Calculators

When we want to be precise in our calculations, we usually use calculators. They are important tools in today's society. Calculators shorten the tedious business of long and complicated calculations and of repeating the same type of sum over and over again. Yes, of course, you should use a calculator in your GNVQ work, but a word of warning: *they cannot get the sum correct for you if you do not enter the correct data or use the right method.* It is therefore sensible to make sure you know what you are doing with the figures first.

People sometimes use a calculator to perform a long division sum and quote their answer to 6 or 7 decimal figures. They may be surprised or upset if tutors cross out all but the first decimal place or two! The fact is that those last figures are nonsense, because the data entered into the calculator may only have been gathered to an accuracy of one decimal place!

If you take a ruler and measure the page width of this book, you will have good eyesight to be accurate in measuring to half of a millimetre; but you certainly could not be accurate to a 1000th of a millimetre. So it is usually nonsense to quote an answer to that degree of accuracy in health and care situations. A calculator has not got common sense and will go on dividing as long as it has spaces to do so.

· CONVERSION TABLES ·

It is useful to have conversion tables or formulas to help you transfer measurements from one system (scale) to another. It is often necessary where different sets of scales are regularly used (e.g. metric and imperial in weights and heights, miles and kilometres for distance.) To use the tables, find the figure on the reading you have taken and read directly across to the adjacent figure. That is the equivalent in the other scale. An example of using a scale is given below.

You can also convert by doing simple calculations. To convert **to** metric you *multiply* by the figure shown. To convert **from** metric you *divide* by the figure shown.

miles/kilometres	1.60
feet/metres	0.30
inches/centimetres	2.54
pints/litres	0.56
pounds/kilograms	0.45
ounces/grams	28.34
stones/kilograms	6.35

Imperial to metric conversion table for volumes (approximate)			
imperial (fl oz)	metric (ml)	imperial (fl oz)	metric (ml)
1	30	8	230
2	60	9	260
3	85	10 ($\frac{1}{2}$ pint)	280
4	110	15 ($\frac{3}{4}$ pint)	425
5 ($\frac{1}{4}$ pint)	140	20 (1 pint)	570
6	170	40 (1 quart)	1140
7	200	160 (1 gallon)	4500

Imperial to metric conversion table for weight (approximate)			
metric (g)	imperial (oz)	metric (g)	imperial (oz)
10	$\frac{1}{3}$	100	3
20	$\frac{2}{3}$	120	4
30	1	150	5
40	$1\frac{1}{2}$	200	7
50	$1\frac{3}{4}$	250	9
60	2	300	$10\frac{1}{2}$
70	$2\frac{1}{2}$	400	14
80	3	450	16
90	3	500	$17\frac{1}{2}$

Cooking Temperatures					
Gas Regulo→Centigrade→Fahrenheit			Gas Regulo→Centigrade→Fahrenheit		
	°C	°F		°C	°F
	70	150	4	180	350 (normal hot frying)
	80	175	5	190	375 (upper limit for frying)
	100	212 (boiling point of water)	6	200	400
$\frac{1}{4}$	120	225	7	220	425 ('hot' oven)
$\frac{1}{2}$	130	250	8	230	450
1	140	275	9	240	475 ('very hot' oven)

For example:

– to convert 12 stone to kilograms
$12 \times 6.35 = 76.2$ kg
– to convert 400 grams to ounces
$400 \div 28.34 = 14.1$ oz

For convenience, these figures are sometimes rounded to the nearest whole number – so 400 g would be 14 ounces. You can use these conversion figures to make *estimates* of the approximate answer before you complete the calculation. This can help you to judge if your final answer is likely to be correct.

For example, if converting 4 inches into centimetres, a rough estimate of the result would be $4 \times 2.5 = 10$ cm. (2.5 is used as it's close to the actual figure and easy to multiply.)

The actual calculation is $4 \times 2.54 = 10.16$ cm. If your answer had been 16 cm, your estimate would alert you that a mistake had been made somewhere, and you would re-calculate.

Remember: you can *check* your results for validity by converting the answer back to the original figure e.g. 10.16 cm $\div 2.54 = 4$ inches. You can use estimates and checks like this for many kinds of calculations.

Task

A student who is work-shadowing a social worker has to travel the following distances in a morning to visit clients/establishments:

- *Home to office = 4 miles*
- *Office to Client 1 = 3 miles*
- *Client 1 to Establishment 1 = 6 miles*
- *Establishment 1 to Client 2 = 8 miles*
- *Client 2 to office = 7 miles*

1. *If the social worker followed this pattern each day for a six-day rota, how many miles would be covered?*
2. *On the mileage record, the social worker has to record the distance in kilometres. What is the figure:*

a per day?
b per week?
c Present the cumulation of miles over the week on a line graph

· COLLECTING DATA ·

Application of number requires you to use a number of processes to collect and record data. These include questionnaires, interviews and observation.

Chapter 8 (Research) looks at developing a **questionnaire** in a lot of detail, including question types and sampling methods. It also covers the importance of trialling a questionnaire before distributing it to a large sample. Refer to this chapter for further details.

Further ways to collect primary information include **interviews** (covered in more detail in Chapter 8) and **observation**. Refer to Chapter 8 for more details on this, including participant and non-participant observation.

Surveys

A survey is another way to collect data which is discussed in Chapter 8. When carrying out a **survey**, you may talk to people to gain their opinion or you may just record what you see. A survey may be shorter than a questionnaire and may involve less detail than an observation. It can be a quick way to gain information.

Before you carry out a survey, you need to be clear about:

- what you wish to survey
- where you are going to carry out the survey
- if you need to sample the participants in any way (e.g. talk to every fifth person).

You also need to construct your recording sheet *before* going. This ensures you are adequately prepared and do not waste time. The recording sheet needs to reflect possible answers/results you may get

Age range	Own home	Rest home	Nursing home	Sheltered accommodation	Relatives' home	Other
<60						
61–65 yrs						
66–70 yrs						
71–75 yrs						
76–80 yrs						
81–85 yrs						
>86						

A simple survey recording sheet

and it should allow the results to be recorded easily. For example, if you were going to survey the age and housing situation of people using a social services day centre, the survey sheet might look like the one above.

This record sheet would give you a view of both the age and the type of accommodation that the people being surveyed live in. A variety of conclusions could then be drawn from the data, such as: is there a trend in the type of living accommodation of those who use a day centre? Does there appear to be a trend in the type of accommodation and is this related to age in any way?

Alternatively, you may design a survey which collects the data without categorising it in any way until the survey is complete. For example, you may collect the ages of the people who use the day centre. This information would then be grouped before it could be used to produce tables, graphs, pie charts etc.

Tables

A table is a way of presenting a range of information in a neat format. It is particularly useful if you want to compare data. For example, the following table shows the formal qualifications of staff in a day centre for adults with learning difficulties at different points since the centre opened.

Qualification	1985	%	1989	%	1993	%
NNEB	2	20	1	10	0	0
BTEC Nur. Nur.	0	0	0	0	1	10
Teaching	1	10	1	10	1	10
CSS	3	30	3	30	2	20
BTEC Soc. Car.	0	0	0	0	4	40
GNVQ Intermediate Health and Social Care	0	0	0	0	1	10
None	4	40	5	50	1	10
Total	10		10		10	

Qualification changes of staff

You could use this information to draw a number of conclusions. Setting the information out in such a way makes it easier to see any pattern which may be emerging.

When collecting data, however you choose to do it, always be well prepared. Make sure your notes are clear and legible so, when you come back to use them at a later date, you can understand them. Whatever method you choose to present your data, you should always label the diagram clearly. The work should be neatly presented and coloured if appropriate.

If using figures to work out an answer, *always* show your workings as core skills accredit the methods used and the process followed as well as getting the right answer! The evidence tasks that follow later

Now – where did I put last week's survey?

will allow you to obtain credit for some of these core skills.

· CALCULATING DATA ·

Calculating the **mean**, **median**, **mode** and **range** of data can also help you to draw conclusions from information collected. The following data will be used to illustrate how to calculate each.

> The haemoglobin levels of a group of nine pregnant women at the same stage of pregnancy (28 weeks) were recorded:
>
> 12.5 10.2 12.0 11.0 9.5 12.0 11.5 10.1 10.5

Mean

The mean is the average of the group of data collected. To calculate the mean you add all the figures together then divide by the number in the sample. For example:

$12.5 + 10.2 + 12.0 + 11.0 + 9.5 + 12.0 + 11.5 + 10.1 + 10.5 = 99.3$

$99.3 \div 9 = 11.03$ The mean value is 11.03.

Mode

The mode is the most frequent or popular figure in a series of numbers. So:

9.5–1
10.1–1
10.2–1
10.5–1
11.0–1
11.5–1
12.0–2
12.5–1

Therefore the mode is 12.0, the number that occurs twice. Other numbers only occur once in this list.

Median

The median of a group of data is the middle value. To find the median, you need to order the data from its lowest figure to its highest and then locate the middle value. So:

9.5 10.1 10.2 10.5 11.0* 11.5 12.0 12.0 12.5

The median value is 11.0.

* = median value. The fifth value is 11.0, there are four values on either side of this number, 11.0 is in the 'middle'.

Range

The range shows the scope between the lowest and highest figures in a group of data. To find the range simply subtract the lowest figure from the highest. For example, the range of the haemoglobin levels is:

$12.5 - 9.5 = 3.0$

Grouped frequency tables

One way to organise data into groups is to create a grouped frequency table from the set of data. It is important to choose a suitable *class interval* when doing this. Therefore, you first need to find the range of data and then decide how many intervals you want.

For example, returning to the day centre data, if the ages of those attending the day centre were as follows:

56 57 60 61 66 64 58 82 87 77 76 59
67 68 83 79 77 74 72 90 88 77 87 78 64

The age range is from 56–90. Using a class interval of 5 years will give you 7 intervals starting at 55 and ending at 90. See table below.

Class interval	Tally	Cumulative frequency
56–60	JHT	5
61–65	III	8
66–70	III	11
71–75	II	13
76–80	JHT I	19
81–85	II	21
86–90	IIII	25

Grouping like this shows how the ages are distributed. Using larger age gaps (for example of 10 years) would not show the spread of ages so readily and class intervals of less than 5 years would do little to simplify the information into anything meaningful. This table also includes a column for frequency, which shows how many of the clients are a certain age or under. For example, 19 clients are aged 80 years or under.

· GROUPED DATA ·

If you are working with grouped data, you cannot find the exact mean, median, mode and range because you do not know the exact values of the data – only the group it is in. To overcome this, you use the class mid-value to represent the class. Therefore, using the day centre data, each would be calculated as given below.

Mean for grouped data

This is calculated by finding the mid-value of each class. This is then multiplied by the frequency of the class. Each figure is then added together and finally divided by the overall number in the sample. For example:

mid-value		frequency	
56–60 = 58	×	5 =	290
61–65 = 63	×	3 =	189
66–70 = 68	×	3 =	204
71–75 = 73	×	2 =	146
76–80 = 78	×	6 =	468
81–85 = 83	×	2 =	166
86–90 = 88	×	4 =	352
Totals		25 =	1815

$$1815 \div 25 = 72.6$$
Therefore the mean is 72.6 years.

Median for grouped data

The median is the class which contains the middle value: in this case the thirteenth age when placed in order from the youngest to the eldest. This is 71–75 years. The mid-point of the median class gives an approximate value for the median, i.e. 73 years.

Mode for grouped data

The mode is the class with the highest frequency: in this case 76–80 years. The mid-point of this class gives an approximate figure for the mode.

Range

The range is the difference between the upper boundary of the highest class (maximum value) and the lower boundary of the lowest class (minimum value). In this case:

$$90 - 56 = 34$$

Therefore the range is 34 years.

Theory into practice

Compile a survey to find out information on an aspect of development for a sample of 10 people from a chosen age group.

For example, shoe size of children in a nursery or height of clients at a day centre.

- *Tabulate the information.*
- *Calculate the mean, median, mode and range of the data.*
- *What conclusions can you draw?*

Collect information on a further 15 subjects. Collate with the information above and compile a suitable grouped frequency chart. Calculate the mean, median, mode and range for this.

· PRESENTATION OF DATA ·

Besides using tables to present data, you can show the information in a more pictorial form such as graphs, histograms, scatter graphs and pie charts.

Graphs

There is a range of different graphs you can use to present data you have collected. Graphs are often used to show changes in data over a certain period of time. Graphs can be used to illustrate text, and doing this will help you gain core skills in Communication.

The most common type of graph is a **bar chart**.

Bar charts have the following features:

- All the bars are the same width.
- The height or length of the bar indicates the frequency.
- Only the axis has a scale. The other may be colours, numbers of children etc.

An example is shown in Figure 10.1.

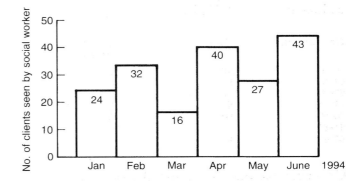

Figure 10.1 *Bar chart*

Another form of graph is a **line graph**. It can be used to show clearly how values have changed over a period. It can also show cumulative information. An example of each is shown in Figure 10.2.

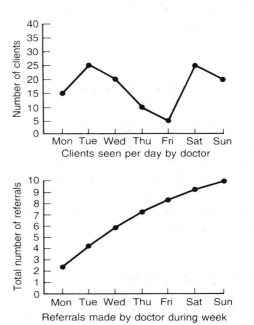

Figure 10.2 *Line graphs*

Histograms

Histograms are usually used with grouped data. A histogram looks very similar to a bar chart but there are a number of significant differences:

1 The width of the columns is always in proportion to the size of the class or group it represents. Therefore the columns may have different widths.
2 There are no gaps between the columns.
3 The frequency for a class is indicated by the area of the column.
4 The horizontal axis must have a scale. The scale is the same as any other on a graph where the same distance always represents the same number of units.

Using the data on the ages of clients at a day centre as given below, a histogram would be calculated as follows.

Class interval	Frequency
56–60	5
61–65	3
66–70	3
71–75	2
76–80	6
81–85	2
86–90	4

First you need to calculate the height and width of each column. The width will be the class interval. To calculate the height, or frequency density, of a column, you divide the frequency by the width. So:

$$\text{height (frequency density)} = \frac{\text{frequency}}{\text{class interval}}$$
$$\text{i.e. } 0.08 = \frac{5}{60}$$

Class interval	Frequency	Frequency density
56–60	5	0.08
61–65	3	0.04
66–70	3	0.04
71–75	2	0.02
76–80	6	0.07
81–85	2	0.02
86–90	4	0.04

Figure 10.3 shows what a histogram of this data would look like:

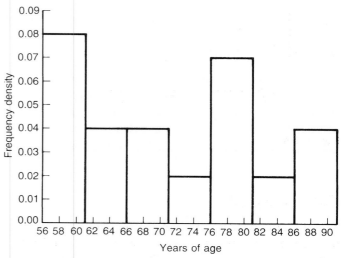

Figure 10.3 *Histogram*

Interpreting histograms

If the columns on a histogram are all the same width, then comparison between the frequencies of the classes can be made by comparing the height of the columns. If all the widths are different, then comparison can only be made by calculating the area of each column.

Scatter graphs

Another way to present data is to use a scatter graph. This is often used when analysing the data involved in investigating the relationship between two variables, e.g. blood pressure and age. You might want to answer a question such as, 'Does blood pressure (diastolic) increase with age?'. Using a scatter graph to present this information would easily show a correlation if it existed.

For example, look at this data:

Age 44 56 34 65 71 42 50 34 38 60
B.P. 70 80 75 80 85 60 65 70 75 85

This information could be presented as seen in Figure 10.4.

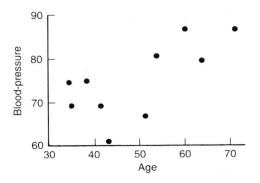

Figure 10.4 *Scatter graph*

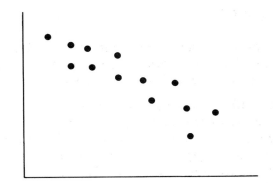

Figure 10.6 *Graph showing negative correlation*

Correlation

When changes in one variable have an effect on the other, there is said to be a **correlation**. Correlation can be positive, negative or show little/no correlation. No correlation is shown when the points are spread all over the graph and there appears to be no pattern. The scatter graph shown in Figure 10.4 shows that there is some correlation between age and blood-pressure. A strong correlation would look something like the graph shown in Figure 10.5. This shows that one variable is clearly linked to the other.

by which to link the two variables. From this you could predict the value of one variable, given the value of another.

Pie charts

A pie chart presents the total picture of the data collected, according to its components. To compile a pie chart you first have to convert your results into percentages. To do this, you divide the component number by the total number then multiply by 100.

Figure 10.5 *Graph showing positive correlation*

A strong negative correlation would look something like the graph shown in Figure 10.6. This would indicate that the opposite would be true: that the younger you are, the higher the B.P.

You can draw a *line of best fit* to make the points look as if they are clustered around a single line. You could then use this line to generate a formula

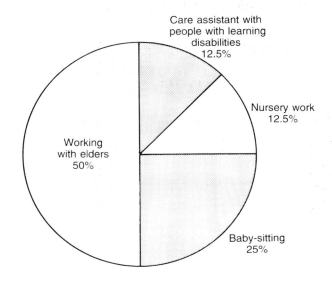

Figure 10.7 *Pie chart*

For example, imagine you were looking at how students on a care course travelled to their work placements. Your results were as follows:

No. of people
(component numbers)

Public transport (bus)	15
Public transport (train)	5
On foot	10
By car	5
Bicycle	3
Motor cycle	2

Total = 40 people

To work out the percentage of those who travel on foot, you would do the following:

On foot $\dfrac{10}{40} = 0.25$

$0.25 \times 100 = 25\%$

Task

Work out the rest of the percentages from the example above and present them in a pie chart.

Shape/Solid	Area (x^2)	Volume (x^3)	Perimeter (x)
triangle H = height	½ base × height – A	—	sum of the 3 sides
circle	πr^2 r = radius	—	$2\pi r$ or πd d = diameter known as circumference
cylinder		$\pi r^2 H$	—
square	length × width L = length W = width	—	2 × length + 2 × width
rectangle	as above	—	as above
cuboid or bar	—	length × width × height	—
parallelogram	as for square and rectangle	—	as for square and rectangle
trapezium	half the sum of the parallel sides × the perpendicular distance between – d	—	as for square and rectangle
prism	—	area × length	—

· AREA, VOLUME AND PERIMETER ·

The following table shows methods for calculating the area, volume and perimeter dimensions of some common shapes.

Points to remember:

i Units of area are always 'squared' and this is shown symbolically by the small letter 2, to the upper right of the unit symbol; e.g. area in metres – m^2

ii Units of volume are always 'cubed' and this is shown symbolically by the small letter 3, to the upper right of the unit symbol; e.g. volume in metres – m^3

iii Always check that your measurements are all in the same units. Never multiply a length in centimetres by a length in millimetres. Unless a question specifies particular units, it usually does not matter whether you use higher or lower measures; but it is better not to work in either too small numbers with many decimal places, or too large numbers with a lot of zeros.

iv Remember the value of π (pie) is 3.14 or, as a fraction $\frac{22}{7}$.

v Irregular shapes can be divided up to form squares, rectangles and triangles for area calculation, and then added together. (See the following example.)

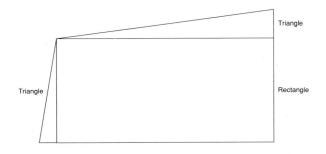

vi Very irregular shapes which do not make squares and triangles can be calculated on squared paper. Do not forget to count and then multiply by the number of surfaces. If the shape has depth you must also estimate for that. If the object is very large you might need to make your own squared paper.

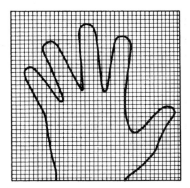

Task

A GNVQ classroom measuring 10 m by 6 m by 3 m is used for 23 learners. If Health and Safety regulations say there should be 4.75 m of airspace per person, is the room complying with the regulations?

· SYMBOLIC NOTATION ·

Sequences

Figures sometimes appear in **sequences** e.g. 0, 3, 6, 9, 12, 15 and so on. The rule for this sequence is +3,

starting with 0. This can only allow you to calculate a *term* or figure if you know what term or figure comes before it.

If you wanted to calculate the 100th term in this sequence you could work it out manually. Alternatively, you could use a type of algebra known as symbolic notation. This means you can work out a figure (or term) by the number of the term without having to work out all the figures or terms which went before. To do this you need to number the terms. The first term is referred to as u1, the second u2 and so on. Everything you need to know about the sequence is given by the general term or *nth* term (un).

For example, the symbolic notation for the sequence above is

$$un = 3n - 3$$

Therefore the first five terms in the above sequence would be shown as follows:

$$u1 = 3(1) - 3 = 0$$
$$u2 = 3(2) - 3 = 3$$
$$u3 = 3(3) - 3 = 6$$
$$u4 = 3(4) - 3 = 9$$
$$u5 = 3(5) - 3 = 12$$

The 100th term would therefore be calculated

$$u100 = 3(100) - 3 = 297$$

Task

Calculate the following terms:
a 15th
b 9th
c 25th
d 66th

Check your answers:
a 42   b 24   c 72   d 195

Symbolic notation could be used in a range of health and social care situations where it is necessary to do calculations of quantities which are standard. For example, if a residential home knew they would need three new sheets per bed each year to cover wear and tear, and ordering them in bulk would prove cheaper, they could calculate the number needed using this method. Imagine they had 45 beds. The calculation would be:

$$u45 = 3(45) - 3 = 132 \text{ new sheets}$$

Sequences which are generated by adding or subtracting the same number each time are called **arithmetic sequences**. If you study this sequence, you can see that the sequence increases by 4 each time:

Term number	1	2	3	4	5
Term	3	7	11	15	19

The 'gap' between the terms is always 4. However, multiplying the term number by 4 gives the sequence:

4, 8, 12, 16, 20.

The figure is always one more than the required term each time. To correct this you subtract 1, giving the sequence:

3, 7, 11, 15, 19

So the symbolic notation for this sequence is:

$$un = 4n - 1$$

Task

After leaving college with a GNVQ qualification in health and social care, Ahmed works as a care assistant in a residential home for elders. His salary is £6,500 per year. Each year, his salary is increased by £600.

1 *What is the symbolic notation for working this out? (Work out the nth year first.)*
2 *What would Ahmed's salary therefore be after 5 years?*
3 *What would his salary be after 12 years?*
4 *What would his salary be if he worked for the same home for 30 years?*

Geometric sequences are sequences generated by multiplying or dividing by the same number each time. For example:

Term number	1	2	3	4	5
Term	1	3	9	27	81
		(x3)	(x3)	(x3)	(x3)

Equations or simple inequalities

Symbolic notation can also be used to help solve equations (or simple inequalities). An equation is a statement including the equals sign (=) which shows that two things are equal to each other. For example:

$$x + 3 = 7$$

A **linear equation** does not have squares or higher powers. To solve an equation you have to find the value (or values) of the unknown which makes the statement true. In doing this you *satisfy* the equation.

That has satisfied the equation!

To solve a linear equation, you need to get the unknown value on one side. Then the other side will give the answer to the equation. For example:

$$x - 4 = 9$$

Add 4 to both sides of the equation to remove the −4.

$$x - 4 + 4 = 9 + 4$$
$$x = 13$$

The result is that the x is left equalling the answer. This process is called the **balancing act**. The balance will be maintained as long as you always add or subtract the same value from both sides of an equation, or multiply or divide by the same amount.

To help find the unknown quantity, look at what has been done to an equation and do the opposite. For example, if 5 has been added then take 5 away; if multiplied by 5 then divide by 5.

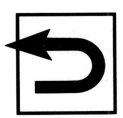

Think it over

Calculate the following equations:
a $x + 8 = 16$
b $b - 4 = 12$
c $3x = 15$

*Check your answers: **a** x = 8; **b** b = 16; **c** x = 5.*

When equations get more difficult, you need to break them down into smaller stages. You always add and subtract first, then multiply and divide. (Remembering you do the opposite to what is stated to find the unknown figure.) For example:

To solve $4a - 8 = 8$

$$4a - 8 + 8 = 8 + 8$$
$$4a = 16$$
$$4a \div 4 = 16 \div 4$$
$$a = 4$$

You can always substitute your answer back to check it.

If brackets are used in the equation, you should deal with what's *outside* the brackets first. For example:

$$2(x + 3) - 6 = 4$$
$$2(x + 3) - 6 + 6 = 4 + 6 \qquad \textit{Add 6 to remove −6}$$
$$2(x + 3) = 10$$

$$\frac{2(x + 3)}{2} = \frac{10}{2} \qquad \textit{Divide by 2 to remove × 2}$$

Then deal with what's inside the brackets.

$$(x + 3) = 5$$
$$x + 3 - 3 = 5 - 3 \qquad \textit{Subtract 3 to remove + 3}$$
$$x = 2$$

Think it over

Solve the following:
a $6a - 6 = 6$
b $4x + 4 = 16$

*Check your answers: **a** a = 2;*
b x = 3.

It is possible that the unknown can appear on both sides of the equation. For example, $2x + 4 = 19 - x$.

To be able to solve this, you first need to get all the unknown or letter terms on one side of the equation.

For the equation above, first add x to both sides of the equation – which has the effect of removing the x from the right side.

$$2x + x + 4 = 19 - x + x$$
$$3x + 4 = 19$$

Now you can solve the equation as before, i.e.

$$3x + 4 - 4 = 19 - 4$$
$$3x = 15$$
$$\frac{3x}{3} = \frac{15}{3}$$
$$x = 5$$

To check, refer back to the original equation and work through:

Left $2x + 4 = 19$
$\qquad\quad 2 \times 5 = 10 + 4 = 14$
Right $19 - x$
$\qquad\quad 19 - 5 = 14$

Think it over

Zubadia, Jane and Ravi have been assigned a task of raising money for a charity of their choice as part of their GNVQ programme. Zubadia collected three times as much as Jane and Ravi collected £5 more than Jane. Altogether, they collected £55. How much did each collect? To calculate this, you need to work through the following equation:

$$x + 3x + (x + 5) = 55$$

· PROBABILITY ·

If a coin is tossed it has an equal chance of coming down heads or tails. We often say there is a 50/50 chance (or 1 in 2) that it will show either head or tail – because there are only two possibilities. Mathematically, we write this as $\frac{1}{2}$. If two coins are tossed the possible outcomes are:

HH, HT, TH, TT

All are equally likely. If we are looking for one of each, a head and a tail, then there are only two possible outcomes from four, thus it is written $\frac{2}{4}$ or $\frac{1}{2}$. The other two outcomes, two heads or two tails will each be $\frac{1}{4}$ as there is only one possibility or probability. When added together these probabilities total 1:

$$\frac{2}{4} + \frac{1}{4} + \frac{1}{4} = 1$$

You will find that the outcome of all certain probabilities is always one. For example, if you toss a genuine coin, it must come to lie either heads or tails; the outcome is certain to be one or another. Incidentally an event certain *not* to happen has an outcome of 0.

$$\text{Probability of an event} = \frac{\text{number of wanted outcomes}}{\text{number of possible outcomes.}}$$

Probability tree diagrams

Sometimes it is easier to show probabilities by a tree diagram. This shows all the possible events and their probabilities.

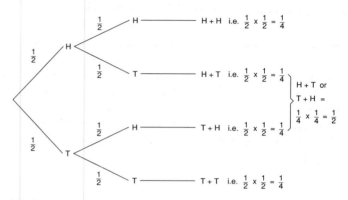

N.B. All probabilities add up to 1

Figure 10.8 *Tree diagram*

Look again at the example of tossing a coin. The tree diagram would look like the one shown in Figure 10.8. Try using this for another task – you may prefer this method of working.

Task

Mrs Watkins was moving rooms in her sheltered housing complex. She had hurriedly placed all her stockings in a large plastic sack. Unfortunately she was in a hurry to catch the coach for a day trip to the seaside and pulled odd coloured stockings out. There were 5 black stockings, 4 brown and 3 navy.

If she puts her hand in the bag for two stockings what is the probability of drawing two black coloured stockings out at the first attempt?

Number of wanted outcomes   = 1 (two black)

Number of possible colour combinations = 9 (Bl/Br, Bl/N, Bl/Bl, Br/Br, Br/Bl, Br/N, N/N, N/Bl, N/Br)

Think it over

Work out the probability of a) pulling out two stockings, one brown and one black, and b) two odd coloured stockings.
Answer: a) $\frac{2}{9}$ b) $\frac{6}{9}$

The first fraction in the answer above cannot be simplified anymore, but you could convert it to a decimal 0.22, or a percentage 22% chance of happening. The second fraction can be simplified to $\frac{1}{3}$, 0.33 or 33% and this is how it should be presented.

Think it over

A survey of college students revealed that 23 per cent used the gymnasium for fitness activities at some point in their programme. What is the probability that a vice-principal picks at random a student walking down the corridor who has never been to the gymnasium? Note You may need to use the following equation.

Probability that an event does not happen equals 1 minus the probability that it happens.

When probability is 1 it is a certainty, when impossible it is 0; so probability must by definition be between these two values. A very small figure, nearer to 0 is unlikely to happen, whereas figures nearer to 1 are more likely to happen.

Think it over

In Namibia, the probability that a child will develop a form of malnutrition caused by protein deficiency is 0.69, whereas in the UK the probability is 0.001. What do these figures mean?

Experiments on probability

At some time you may wish to work out the probability during an experiment to calculate a *prediction* of the likelihood of something occurring or happening. This can only be an estimate of probability based on the results from your experiment.

There are certain days at a drop-in centre allocated for disabled people who are unemployed. The days are Mondays and Thursdays; the system works well, but the caterer complains that he never knows how many people will be attending so has difficulty in providing lunchtime snacks. An experiment is set up to log attendance for set periods of 6 weeks at intervals throughout the year. The results are as follows:

Mondays

Total possible	Numbers attending	Probability
Trial 1 103	56	$\frac{56}{103} = 0.54$
Trial 2 99	24	$\frac{24}{99} = 0.24$
Trial 3 121	37	$\frac{37}{121} = 0.3$
Trial 4 121	36	$\frac{36}{121} = 0.3$
Trial 5 85	25	$\frac{25}{85} = 0.29$
Trial 6 95	33	$\frac{33}{95} = 0.34$

This can be shown graphically, as below.

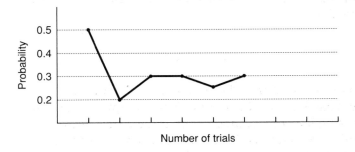

The graph shows that although the first few trials are not producing any steady results, further and later trials produce a 'hovering' about 0.3. *Caution*: this was an *estimate of the probability* used to predict the likelihood of the number of people turning up on any one day. Use this information now to tell the caterer how many lunches he should prepare each day for the drop-in centre to be cost-effective.

Mutually exclusive events and combined events

This term is used if one event prevents another event from happening. For instance, at the drop-in centre, a person could not both be there (one event) and *not* be there (another event); so these are said to be *mutually exclusive*. When calculating the probability of one event *or* another, the probabilities are added.

For example, in a college of 10,000 students, 25 are on a BTEC National Diploma in Health Studies, 45 are on an NNEB course and 30 have just started GNVQ in Health and Social Care. What is the probability of a student picked at random being on a caring course in that college?

(*Note P = probability of*)
P (Caring course) = P(BTEC) + P(NNEB)
   + P(GNVQ)

P(Caring course) = $\frac{25}{10,000} + \frac{45}{10,000} + \frac{30}{10,000}$ = 0.01
   (i.e. 1 in a 100)

However, two events could be, for example: predicting the number of wheelchair users in the drop-in centre and those who require assistance with toileting. Clearly, these two events are not mutually exclusive as a wheelchair user may require help with toileting. Such events are called *combined events*.

So, what is the probability of an individual being wheelchair bound and needing toileting assistance in a drop-in centre of 100 callers? There has been a recent survey which showed 32 wheelchair users and 15 people who needed assistance with toileting:

Probability of being a wheelchair user is $\frac{32}{100}$ and the probability of needing assistance to toilet is $\frac{15}{100}$.

Therefore the probability of both events is:

$$\frac{32}{100} \times \frac{15}{100} = 0.048 \text{ or } 0.05 \text{ (2 decimal places)}$$

In other words, 5 people in wheelchairs in each day are likely to be needing assistance. One member of staff could cope with this aspect of the drop-in centre. Notice that for combined events, the probabilities were multiplied together. Sometimes it is easier to look at a diagram, but with large numbers, like the 100 people at the drop-in centre above this would not be sensible.

If three severely disabled people visit a drop-in centre open Mondays, Wednesdays and Thursdays, what is the probability that they will visit on a Wednesday, when the centre is staffed only by volunteer help? Each person visits twice a week.

	Person A	Person B	Person C
Monday	X	X	X
Wednesday	X	X	X
Thursday	X	X	X

There are 9 possible outcomes and 2 occurrences of Wednesday visits, therefore the probability of one of these three attending on a Wednesday is $\frac{2}{9}$. Having this information will now enable the centre management to decide whether to 'ban' Wednesdays for severely disabled people, spend money training the volunteers or buy in trained help. In other words, they will be able to make a more *informed* decision.

There is more information on probability in Chapter 8.

Task

1 Choose a client group that you can access in a group setting.
2 Choose two aspects of their lifestyle or development which can be measured/recorded accurately and between which you feel there may be some correlation, e.g. age and weight.
3 Collect the appropriate data from the clients.
4 Collate the data using a pictorial form for each aspect chosen.

5 Calculate the **a** mean, **b** median, **c** mode, **d** range, from your sample (show your workings).

6 Plot the data on a scatter graph and draw a line of best fit.

7 What conclusions do you draw from your findings?

8 Justify why you have drawn those conclusions.

Task

Study the chart below and answer the questions, showing your workings.

1 What trend can you identify from the data?

2 What reasons can you give for this trend?

3 What was the increase in places between 1985 and 1990?

4 The ratio of care staff to clients has to be 1:6. How many staff were needed in 1985, 1987 and 1991?

5 If a care assistant is paid £150 for a 40-hour week in 1989, what would the salary bill be for one week in 1989?

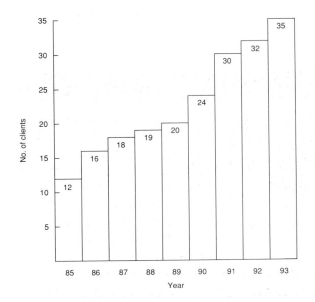

No. of older people being cared for in a residential home in 'Restwood' from 1985–1993.

6 There is also one qualified nurse sister who works in the home (over and above the care assistants) who is paid £13,000 per annum. What ratio is this to the care staff's pay?

7 A pay rise of £7.50 per week is awarded for 1990 for the care staff, what percentage of the salary is this?

8 The nurse was given the same percentage rise. How much increase in salary per week will she receive?

9 How much extra pay per week would the home need to find in total following the pay rise?

10 In 1991, the income from social services to support payment by clients was £45 per person per week. What was the total income from this source per week? What percentage of the staffing budget did this cover?

Task

Design a questionnaire to give to your peer group to find out which services the members of their immediate families (including themselves) have used at their local GP surgery or health centre. Any individuals not able to consult family could choose up to six people from work, placement, school or college in order to find the same information. You may wish to define particular services to limit your options and this may involve investigating these first. (Alternatively you may have such a survey already completed in one of your units.)

List the options from the services and choose two at random. Find the probability of one of your survey participants using two of your options in one year.

Task

A group with learning disabilities have a small garden and like to sell plants to raise money for seeds and tools. A local carpet firm has offered them wasted strong inner tubes from carpet rolls for cutting up to produce small plant pots for their plants.

The tubes are quite wide and the group leader is worried about the quantity of compost needed to fill each pot. You have the following information:

- *Carpet tube is 3 metres long and the diameter is 30 centimetres.*
- *They need pots 22.5 cms tall to give sufficient strength.*
- *Their usual plastic pots were 6 inches tall, diameter 7 inches and cost 32p each.*
- *Compost is £3.50 per 50 litre bag.*

No-one at the centre can work out whether the free tube offer is helpful to the hard-up group or not. Can you help them?

Fast Facts

Conversion Changing one unit to another, e.g. pounds to ounces or ounces to grammes.

Correlation Looking for a relationship or link between two or more variables.

Equation A mathematical statement which expresses that two sides are equal.

Generalisations Picking out the pattern or trend shown by a set of figures and making comments or judgements about what they show.

Justification Reasons why you have made generalisations or predictions or providing proof to back them up.

Mean The average of a set of values calculated by adding together all the values and then dividing by the number of values. For example: $1 + 2 + 3 + 4 + 5 = 15 \div 5 = 5$.

Median The half-way value of a series of values when lined up in order. For example: 1 2 3 4 5. Median = 3

Mode The most common value in a set of values or the figure which appears the most times. For example: 1 2 3 4 5 3 4 3 2 3. Mode would be 3.

Observation A way to collect data where you watch your subject for a certain period of time and note down what you see.

Precision Being accurate to make sure you get the correct answer.

Predictions Using data or figures to guess what might happen in the future.

Probability The likelihood of an event happening.

Questionnaire A written set of questions which are given to a set number of people to gain information on a topic. Questions can be *open*, where the person asked can answer as freely as they like, or *closed*, where there is only a yes or no answer.

Range The difference between the lowest value in a sequence of numbers and the highest value.

Sample The name given to the group of people you ask.

Sequence The order in which a calculation must be carried out in order to get the correct answer.

Survey A way to collect information on an area and examine it carefully – perhaps to draw conclusions.

Three dimensional Gives the effect of depth (and is more life like); will have area and volume.

Trialling Testing out a questionnaire or survey on a small number of people before giving it to the whole sample, so major mistakes are ironed out.

Two dimensional A drawing which is flat on the page and therefore has area but not volume.

chapter *11* INFORMATION TECHNOLOGY

This chapter aims to help you to get the most out of the information technology (IT) resources that are available to you during your health and social care studies. The chapter focuses on:

- background information concerning the use of computer technology
- planning the use of IT resources
- how three popular computer programmes can help you with your coursework

The aim is to help you to become accustomed to the uses of IT and to show how computer technology can be applied to your work in health and social care.

· INFORMATION TECHNOLOGY · – A CORE SKILL

No doubt IT has already become a part of your daily life, perhaps as a computer-generated bill or bank statement, or a mass-mail letter with your name and address neatly printed on it.

When shopping at the supermarket purchases are recorded by a computerised till, and the daily newspaper is produced with the help of the new technology. IT has become inherent in our modern society and it is not hard to see why. IT is a very powerful tool that can help us to store, work on and present many different types of information. The uses of IT are so myriad that organisations, businesses and individuals in many different areas now see IT as essential to their work.

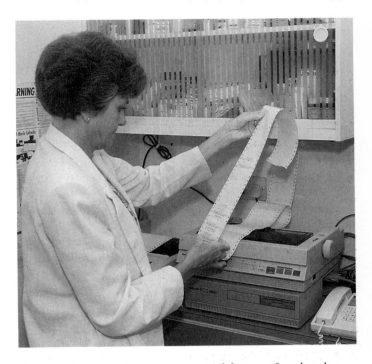

Figure 11.1 *Computers are an essential feature of work today*

As a student of health and social care you will discover how IT can be invaluable in your work. You will find out how to store, organise, work on and present the different types of information that you will be dealing with. In so doing you will have gained skills that can be applied in your further studies, in your career and in your own areas of interest.

Information Technology is a compulsory GNVQ core skill, along with Communication and Application of Number. This is because IT is so useful and so widely used.

A certain level of skill and knowledge in the use of IT is expected of everyone who is awarded an advanced GNVQ qualification, whatever subject it is in. This chapter will help you to use IT effectively by showing you how it can be applied to work that you will be doing. The chapter will also help you to identify work which may count as evidence towards the IT unit.

The computer screen icon appears occasionally to emphasise important points.

You may already be reasonably competent in using IT, or you may be a complete beginner, but this chapter should be of use to you whatever your level of experience. If you have not used IT before please read it all carefully, and be sure to do all the tasks that are set. The chapter has been written assuming no prior knowledge and you should find that it all begins to make sense when you begin to use the computer. If you have used IT before, in whatever context, you will still be able to benefit from this chapter as it shows you how to apply IT; it may contain some techniques and ideas that you haven't come across before.

The single most important thing to do is actually to use the equipment that is available – to get 'hands-on' experience. You need to become familiar with the machines that you will be using, and with the tutors who can help you to use it. This book can indicate what you are able to do: then you have to put it into action for yourself.

· WHAT IS INFORMATION TECHNOLOGY? ·

What is meant by Information Technology? Obviously it refers to the use of new technologies to deal with information, but a number of terms are used where the meaning is not so obvious. Some basic explanations are therefore given now.

Hardware

Hardware can be defined simply as the physical equipment used in IT. This includes the computer itself, the monitor screen, the mouse, the keyboard and the printer.

Figure 11.2 *Computer hardware*

There are also other useful devices available that fall under the description of hardware and you may have access to some of them; but the important point is that the term means the physical equipment that is used in IT.

Software

By **software** we mean the term used for the set of instructions which the computer follows when performing a task. This may also be referred to as a **program** or as an **application**. This may seem confusing but these are more or less just different words for the same thing.

Software is the name given to the set of instructions that the computer carries out

Different types of software are designed to perform different types of task. One important type are programs known as **operating systems**. These are used to start the computer running and to control its activities. Operating systems manage the entry, flow and display of information and software between different parts of the computer. The operating system must be running before other types of software can be used.

Software is also available which is designed to do particular jobs, such as writing letters, doing calculations or playing games. The software applications that you will be using have been produced commercially and are intended to be easy to use ('user-friendly'). It is not necessary to be knowledgeable about the intricacies of computer programming in order to use IT effectively, any more than you have to understand fully the principles of the internal combustion engine in order to drive a car.

You are likely to be working with some of the most widely used, popular and useful types of application available. One of the most common uses of IT is **word-processing**. The word-processor may be thought of as a very sophisticated typewriter, and it allows the non-typist to produce well-presented documents very easily. However, word-processors can be used for many more functions than an ordinary typewriter. They make it easy to create, edit and print professional-looking documents.

We will also focus on the uses of the **database**. Databases are a means of storing information in the form of lists; so an address book could be considered as a basic sort of database. They resemble a file card record system such as may be found in libraries or offices, but they are more straightforward to use and can do more useful things than simply record data. Databases are an ideal way of storing any repetitive form of information, such as names and addresses, or types and prices of equipment.

The third application we will look at is the **spreadsheet**. This is designed to deal with numerical information. It can help to arrange numbers in columns and rows, perform calculations on them, and present the results as a chart or graph. Spreadsheets are used for scientific work, in finance and in any activity where calculation of numbers occurs. Spreadsheets can help you to deal with the numerical information you will come across during research activities.

The three applications mentioned above are powerful tools for handling information. Each has a wide range of uses, some of which fall beyond the scope of this chapter. This potential is considerably increased when applications are used in conjunction with each other. A word-processor, used together with a database of names and addresses, can produce a mass 'mail-shot'. The graph or chart from a spreadsheet can be sent to the word-processor and incorporated into your report. The ability of software applications to share information like this creates many opportunities to make your work easier, better presented and more effective.

Memory

The computer's memory is known as **RAM**, which stands for Random Access Memory. The RAM holds the information and instructions that are being used by the computer during your work sessions. However, RAM cannot be seen as a permanent storage place for work because everything is deleted from it when the computer is turned off. The chapter looks at how you can save work later. You may also come across the term **ROM**, which stands for Read Only Memory. CD-ROMs use compact disks to store the contents of books, encyclopaedias etc. A CD-ROM cannot be used to store your work but it is a useful term to remember.

Computer memory is measured in **bytes**. A byte is a single piece of information and any single keypress such as a letter, a number or a space is one byte of information. Memory size is usually described in terms of **kilobytes** and **megabytes**. One kilobyte(K) equals 1024 bytes and one megabyte (Mb) equals 1024 kilobytes (or 1,048,546 bytes).

The computer's memory is measured in bytes. One keypress is one byte of information

Compatibility

A term used in connection with both hardware and software is **compatibility**. It can be understood as the ability of computers and applications to work with other computers and applications. This is an important issue as can be seen from a brief review of the recent history of IT.

Over the last twenty years the rapid development of the IT industry has led to the growth and success of many computer hardware companies. Several different types of computer have been produced during this time; many of these were designed to work in their own particular way and run their own type of software. The result of this was that work begun on one machine could not be taken away and completed on another. (It would be like trying to play a CD on a cassette player.)

Eventually a small number of operating systems became widely used, which led new manufacturers to produce hardware that was compatible with these popular types of computer. One of the most popular is a type of computer known as the 'IBM compatible' or Personal Computer (PC). PCs are made by many different companies but all are compatible with each other, so software applications that will run on one PC should generally also run on another, provided it is powerful enough. The computers that you will be using may be PCs, or of

another popular type, or there may be a mixture of both available.

Compatibility between software applications is another issue. Here, compatibility refers to the ability of applications to share information with each other. A number of versions of the popular applications (word processors, spreadsheets and databases) are available for use on the PC. Some of these are compatible with each other; others are not. The applications that you will be using will need to be compatible so that information can be shared and transferred between them.

The task below is the first of a series that will appear in this chapter. You may like to attempt each one when you come to it. This first task might seem an obvious one, but some later tasks might appear less necessary or harder to fulfil. You may like to get advice from a tutor if you are unsure about a particular task. You may need to complete the tasks in order to get the most from this chapter and from the IT resources that are available.

Task

You need to find out:

- *what equipment you will be working with*
- *which machines are compatible with each other*
- *which machines are running compatible software applications of the type you need*
- *what access you can get to the machines you wish to use*
- *what tutor support is available to assist with using the software applications.*

The first step is to talk to your tutor or an IT specialist. Find out about the equipment and its compatibility. It may be important that you have identified times when you have access and times when someone is there to help you. Remember that if you plan to work on more than one computer you must ensure that you use machines which are compatible with each other, and which are running compatible software applications.

· SAFETY ·

You will be using IT equipment that has been designed to be as safe to use as possible. The computer itself, and peripheral equipment like printers, are powered from the mains electricity supply, like other domestic electrical applicances. They are insulated and earthed to protect users from electrical hazard but they must be treated with care to prevent accidents.

Cables connecting items of equipment to the electrical supply, or to each other, must be arranged so that they don't endanger health and safety. Cables must be protected from damage; they must not be allowed to 'snake' or loop around work areas so that they form a hazard in themselves.

If you are the person to connect items of equipment like printers be sure to arrange the cables safely. Always check to make sure that the cables are safe.

Figure 11.3 *This should not happen*

The arrangement of the work surface is also important. The computer keyboard is light and mobile, which means that you can arrange its position to suit your own preferred way of working. However, it also means that you can clutter up your work surface with books, papers, pens and other equipment. Try to avoid doing this – a crowded work surface increases the chance of accidents. It is unlikely to make your work any more efficient!

It is important never to eat or drink around IT or other electrical equipment. Liquids are particularly dangerous and a spilled drink can cause a serious electrical hazard, as well as causing considerable damage to equipment. Try to make sure that this rule is enforced, both for your own safety and for that of others.

Computer equipment is designed to be adjustable so that it can be set to the individual requirements of the user and the environment. The keyboard has small pull-out feet at the back edge, to increase its angle of incline, which some people prefer; it is easily moved into the most comfortable position for typing. The monitor may be swivelled left and right, and tilted up and down. This allows the screen to be orientated to a position where it is facing you directly, so that you are not having to sit in an awkward or uncomfortable position to see it clearly.

The screen is also adjustable for brightness and contrast and you need to set these so that you can see your work clearly. It is important, however, not to work with the screen turned up too brightly. Prolonged use of a bright screen at close quarters can strain eyes and should be avoided. The lighting conditions in the room can be very influential in the visibility of monitor screens. The screen will need to be turned up much more brightly to be seen in a well-lit room, particularly if lights are reflected directly onto it. Sunlight creates the same problem and a screen facing a sunny window is very difficult to see. Try to ensure that you adjust the lighting conditions so that you do not need to have your screen excessively bright to be able to work.

Another important feature of the environment is the seating used with the computer equipment. Most institutions provide adjustable typist's chairs for IT users, which are designed to be adjusted to a variety of positions to suit the height and build of the user. It is important to set it to your own requirements. Set the height of the seat so that your feet are comfortably on the floor, and the back rest so that your back is adequately supported. Working at a keyboard in a badly adjusted chair can lead to backache and discomfort in quite a short time; so always take the trouble to adjust the chair to your needs.

As well as protecting yourself and the computer hardware from damage, it is also important to take care of stored data. So-called floppy disks are actually quite hard, and are durable enough when used and stored correctly, but they must be protected from physical damage. Keep them in a dry secure place as you would a CD or cassette tape. Remember also that information is stored electrically on floppy disks and that this can be damaged or erased if the disk is exposed to strong magnetic or electrical fields. Many domestic appliances produce electrical fields so the best rule is to keep disks away from electrical apparatus.

· SAVING WORK ·

As described above, the work that is done on the computer is temporarily stored in the memory and when the computer is switched off the work is lost unless it is saved first. Work is saved on disks. There are two types of disks that you are likely to encounter – hard disks and floppy disks.

Hard disks

Most computers have a 'hard disk' installed. The hard disk is permanently fixed inside the computer's case and cannot be removed from it.

The hard disk can be used to store large amounts of information and can be heard clicking away when the computer is switched on (known as 'booting up') and when some software applications are used. The

The hard disk cannot be removed from the computer

reason for this is because some of the information the computer needs to set itself up for use is permanently stored on the hard disk inside it, and because some applications are themselves stored on the hard disk. It is possible to save your work on the hard disk but it is extremely unwise (and it will probably be against the local IT users' rules). The practice is unwise because any work saved on the hard disk can be recalled later by any other user, which could result in tampering or even accidental but complete erasure of your work! However, this can be avoided easily by saving work on a floppy disk.

Floppy disks

Floppy disks are a compact, cheap and secure way to save work. A flopy disk can be purchased for less than a pound and most will store the equivalent of over 200 pages of text. Physically they come in two sizes: $3\frac{1}{2}$ inch and $5\frac{1}{4}$ inch. The computer that you use may take either or both.

Despite its smaller size, the $3\frac{1}{2}$-inch disks can store more information than the $5\frac{1}{4}$ inch disks; they are the type you are more likely to be using.

Floppy disks are the best way of keeping work secure. You can insert your own personal disk into the computer and save your work onto it. When you correctly shut down the application the only copy of your work that remains is on your floppy disk. Once the disk is removed all the work is safely in your possession, which is the safest way to keep it.

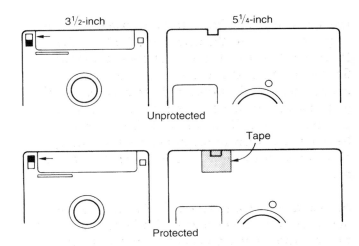

Figure 11.5 *Use tape to protect work on floppy disks*

Figure 11.4 *Floppy disks*

Formatting a floppy disk

Floppy disks are not unlike a cassette tape in one respect, as it is possible to 'record' and 'play back' information on them. However, the way in which they store work may seem more like a CD, or LP record, as the surface of the floppy disk is divided into tracks and sectors. These are invisible storage blocks, created by the computer in a process known as **formatting**. It is necessary to format a new floppy disk before work can be saved on it. It is very easy to format a disk: simply insert the disk into the slot and tell the computer to format it. However, it is important to understand when reformatting a used disk, that formatting permanently removes any work that was previously stored on the disk. You could lose work that you meant to keep! This can be avoided by closing the read/write 'gate' on the floppy disk if it is necessary to prevent the contents being erased. When the tab is closed, the information on the disk can still be read but not altered or deleted. This is very secure but, of course, prevents any new files being saved on the disk.

Disk capacity

The storage capacity of a floppy disk is measured in **bytes**, in the same way that a computer's memory is. This is important when buying and formatting a $3\frac{1}{2}$-inch floppy disk because they come in two memory sizes: 720K and 1.4Mb. The difference between them is that a 1.4Mb disk can hold twice as much information. Either type can be used to store work, but it is necessary to format the disk according to its storage capacity.

Task

- *Buy a floppy disk which is suitable for use on the hardware you will be using. Check with your IT adviser for a local supplier.*

- *Find out how to format disks correctly using the local equipment. Format your own floppy disk.*

When this task is completed you should have your own floppy disk, formatted and ready for work.

· FILES AND DIRECTORIES ·

Every piece of work that is created and saved on the computer is known as a **file**. Files are linked to the applications in which they were created; so that a word-processed letter is saved as a word-processor file and a database listing books you have read is saved as a database file.

The computer needs you to give your files a name as you save them, and it will add its own bit of code at the end as a reminder of what application the file belongs to. However, you are restricted to a maximum name length of only eight characters when you save. So as you add files to the floppy disk it can soon contain a confusing list of meaningless initials, unless it is *organised* properly.

Directories

A straightforward way to avoid dealing with a bewildering list of file names is to organise files into *groups*. The computer can set up the floppy disk so that files to be kept together are stored in the same place, in a **directory**.

It may be helpful to think of the files saved as if they were paper files to be stored in a filing cabinet. You would probably want to put all the work you were doing for a particular assignment together in the same drawer; but you may want to divide that up further so that you can easily find work intended for a particular part of the assignment. The drawer could be labelled as ASSIGN1, and the sections inside SURVEY, LETTER, LIST, RESULTS, and so on as required.

The computer can create a similar arrangement for the files saved on a floppy disk. Imagine that you are beginning work on a new assignment on care, the third assignment you have done in this area. You plan to use IT to help you with parts of the work and to write the final report. You can tell the computer to create a directory on your floppy disk called ASS3CARE, and then save all the files you create for the assignment in the ASS3CARE directory.

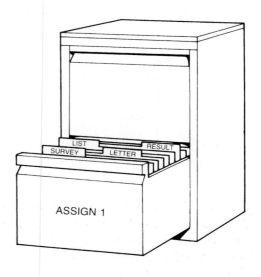

ASSIGN 1

The directory can be used to save any type of file, so it is possible to save a word-processed letter together with a spreadsheet in the same place. If it is a large assignment, and you expect to be using IT for different parts of it, then you can create further divisions within the directory, known as sub-directories. This arrangement could be thought of as a branching tree, with one route to the tip of a particular branch (see below).

Suppose your care assignment involved you in looking at care and communication, care and the law, and care in a residential establishment. You may decide to save the IT work that you do for the assignment in three separate sub-directories called, say, COMMUNIC, LAW and RESESTAB.

When you want to save a piece of work in a particular sub-directory you need to tell the computer the path to follow to that sub-directory.

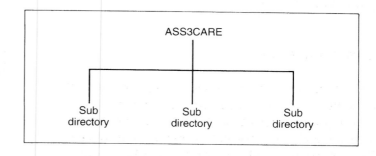

Figure 11.6 *One directory can be split into several sub-directories*

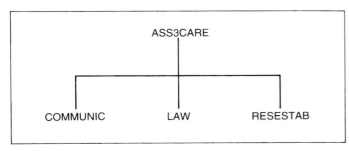

Figure 11.7 *Names can be given to the sub-directories*

Suppose you have devised a survey form to help assess students' awareness of communication in care and you wish to save it with the name SURVEY, in the COMMUNIC sub-directory of the ASS3CARE directory. Then you specify the path, ASS3CARE\COMMUNIC\SURVEY, and your file is saved where you want it.

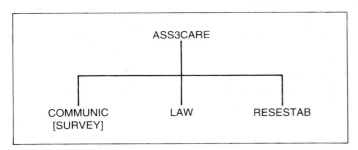

Figure 11.8 *A unique address for a file in a sub-directory*

This path provides a unique *address* for the file which you use to reload it for editing or printing.

It is possible to keep track of work quite easily by careful use of directories and sub-directories. The computer can quickly show the layout and contents of a floppy disk so there is no need to remember the paths to all your files.

System options

The operating system defines the way in which the computer operates. It controls features of the working environment, such as the colours of the screen display and the behaviour of input devices like the mouse. It also controls the selection of output devices, like printers. You can choose from different system options that are available in these areas, and make adjustments to suit your needs.

Sometimes you need to double-click a button to start an application or give a command. The mouse buttons can be adjusted in terms of how fast a rate of double-click is needed. You can adjust the time interval between presses required for the computer to recognise a double-click. Some people prefer more time to double-click in, others are happy with a faster rate. The speed of the pointer as it moves across the screen can also be adjusted. On a fast setting the pointer may seem to flash across the screen, whereas on slow settings it might seem sluggish. Set the pointer speed to suit your preferences.

Another feature of the environment is concerned with the colours of the screen display. Here again there are different options available. You can try changing the colours of different parts of the screen and come up with a combination that you find easy to work with.

Printers, and other peripheral devices, are connected to the computer through sockets in the back of the

Figure 11.9 *The movement of the mouse pointer can be adjusted*

case. These are known as **ports**. The system needs to know what is connected to a port so that data can be sent to it. For instance, if a printer has been newly connected to a port the system needs to be set to recognise this. Setting up a port involves selecting an option on the screen to tell the operating system what has been connected. Your tutor will show you how this is done.

A piece of software called a **printer driver** is used to help the system software to work with the printer. Printer drivers interpret data from the system so that the printer can understand it. You must have the right driver loaded and selected before printing can be done. Ask your IT tutor how to show you how this is done.

Changes to the system options are stored in the system software and will remain when the machine is switched off. This means that other users will find the settings as you left them. If you alter system options you should return them to the original settings when you have finished working.

· USING INFORMATION TECHNOLOGY ·

It is always both necessary and advisable to plan work carefully. When starting a new assignment you will first need to decide on a plan of action to carry out the work, and this is the time to consider how IT can be used. We will follow the progress of a fictitious group of three Advanced GNVQ Health and Social Care students as they use IT in their work for an assignment, from the early planning stages to the completion of a finished report.

Action planning

Lucy, Ravi and Chris are studying Advanced GNVQ Health and Social Care. They are working as a group to research health and lifestyles. They are particularly concerned with cigarette smoking as a hazard to health and decide to examine attitudes to smoking amongst the public and in the business community.

They begin by having a meeting to decide the details of what they need to do and to formulate an action plan to help them organise the work. The discussion results in the decision to carry out a *questionnaire* of smoking habits and attitudes amongst their fellow students, and also to carry out a postal *survey* to discover what the policies are on smoking in local cinemas and restaurants. The group hope to be able to compare the results of their research and to find out how aware of the health risks of smoking local businesses and the public are.

Lucy, Ravi and Chris have been using the local IT facilities and plan to use them to help with this assignment. They have designed and created their own action planning forms using the computer and printed out the result. It will be possible to alter the form if they wish to, and print out copies whenever they are needed. Below is a copy of their first action plan for the smoking research project. Further action plans will be written later to help them to deal with the results of their research.

Lucy's action planning form shows the steps that the group intended to take in their research, and the deadlines they have set themselves. Ravi, Lucy and Chris have planned their use of IT resources and have predicted where there will be opportunities to collect evidence. They know that their work will provide evidence towards the mandatory units, but they also know that their planned use of IT will allow them to collect evidence towards the information technology core skill unit at the same time. Lucy has identified on the action plan some possible evidence collection opportunities towards the IT core skill unit. She prefers to identify evidence collection opportunities towards other units on separate copies of her action plan. To this end she has filled in another action plan to indicate evidence collection opportunities towards the mandatory units. As we are concerned here with collecting evidence towards IT units it is not necessary to see the other action plans.

GNVQ Action Plan			Date: 10/11/1994			Lucy		
Aim	Activity	Knowledge needs	Sources of information	Dates for completion	Reflection opportunities	Evidence opportunities	Elements
To conduct a survey of students views on smoking.	Write questionnaire form with Ravi and Chris. Ravi to design and print out form on word processor. All to carry out questionnaire in canteen at lunch time.	How to write questionnaire questions. Word processor techniques to help with layout. Issues involved in carrying out a questionnaire.	Speak to tutors about questions. See IT tutor for WP layout tips. Check library for books on questionnaires.	Questionnaire form to be produced by 17/11/94. Questionnaire to be completed by 21/11/94	Meet with Ravi and Chris to discuss survey wording and layout. Meet with Ravi and Chris to decide how we do questionnaire.	Towards IT Core Skill Unit: Creation of form, saving, editing and printing.	
To conduct a survey of smoking rules in local cinemas and restaurants.	All to write letter to cinema and restaurant managers. Type into WP for mail merge. Create a database of names and addresses. Send letters.	How to create a letter for merging with a database of names and addresses. How to set up a database. Where to find addresses.	Talk to IT tutor for help on mail merge. Talk to IT tutor for help on databases. Check library for addresses.	Letter to be produced by 17/11/94 Database to be completed by 17/11/94 Letters to be sent by 19/11/94		Towards IT Core Skill Unit: Creation of database, creation of form letter, transfer of information between applications.	

Figure 11.10 *The action plan*

Task

You can plan the headings and layout of your own action planning form, ready to create it on the computer.

Study the action plans in this book and others you have seen during your studies. You may have had a format suggested to you by your tutor, and probably already have ideas of your own.

Think about the way you approach planning your work and design a form that fits your style. Discuss your ideas with your tutors; they will be helping you to use the action plan forms.

Your action plan form can be created later using the computer. The design you have done can provide evidence of planning in the use of IT.

An important aspect of the action plan is the identification of *knowledge needs*. Lucy realises that she needs to find out more about word-processing to carry out the work in her action plan, and so the use of word-processors will be considered in more detail.

· WORD-PROCESSING ·

Initially, using a word-processor can seem very similar to using a typewriter. The computer keyboard on which text is typed is arranged in the same layout as a typewriter keyboard; and the word-processor can certainly produce the sort of high-quality documents that professional typists produce. However, the advantage of a word-processor is that it enables you to produce these documents without needing the skills of a professional typist.

With a word-processor it is possible to:

- enter text as required
- make corrections, revisions and major changes easily and without substantial retyping

Word-processing enables the creation of professional looking documents

- create special styles for headings and important points
- alter the layout to suit requirements
- add headers and page numbers
- import information from other applications, such as a spreadsheet or database, and incorporate it into the document
- print work when you are satisfied with it
- save a file on a floppy disk in order to reload it later and make further changes, and copies, if required.

The word-processor is thus a powerful tool for dealing with text-based information.

Task

Consider your current course work and select a piece of text that could be word-processed. This could be a letter, a short report or even a questionnaire form. The important thing is to choose something that will be presented as part of your portfolio or assignment work, and which can be used to show evidence of planning the use of IT in your work.

Document creation

The first thing to do, of course, is to switch on the computer and start up the word-processor. In this, as with other functions of IT described here, your local equipment will have particular ways of doing things and you need to find out the details from your IT tutor. The next step in document creation is

to start a new word-processor file and you will then see the screen in which you will be working.

Towards the top left of the screen you will probably see a flashing cursor which indicates where your typing will appear (the insertion point), and above this there is usually a ruler. There are marks on the ruler to show the margins set for your text. The **cursor** shold be below the left-hand margin mark, ready for you to begin keying-in text.

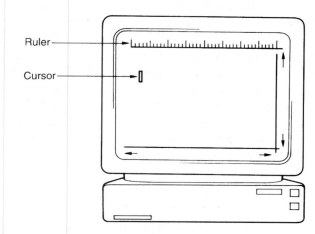

Figure 11.11 *The computer screen*

The rate at which the cursor flashes or blinks can be changed if required. You can set the rate of blink so that it is not so fast that it distracts you nor so slow that the cursor becomes hard to spot.

Entering text

As you type, the cursor moves to the right – ahead of the text. As the right-hand margin is approached there is no need to press the return/enter key, as is necessary on a typewriter, because the word-processor automatically starts a new line without

New lines are started automatically. Don't press return unless a new line is needed

breaking up a word – you simply keep on typing. This is known as *word-wrap*.

It is not necessary to use the return key unless you want to start a new line. This is because the word-processor remembers every key push as a character, including return and space, and unnecessary 'returns' can produce some odd results if the layout of the document is changed later.

Text is entered in the same way as you would use a typewriter, pressing return *twice* to create a blank line between paragraphs. If there is a mistake you can press the *backspace* key and the cursor moves to the left, deleting the incorrect text. It is also possible to delete spaces and returns in the same way. When the amount of text is increased so that the whole document cannot be displayed at once, the document slips up the screen so that the insertion point is always visible. This is called **scrolling**.

Figure 11.12 *Imagine scrolling like this*

If it is necessary to look at the earlier part of a document that has scrolled partly out of view you can do this by moving the cursor with the *direction arrow* keys on your keyboard. These keys move the cursor left and right, and up and down, and as you move the cursor up your document the earlier parts scroll back into view (however, remember that you cannot move the cursor down below the end of a document).

The arrow keys mean that the cursor can be positioned anywhere in the document, which is an extremely useful facility. It is possible to move the cursor to a particular point and type in new text, and also to delete using the backspace key. When new text is typed within a document, all the text below moves along to make room for it. This is called **insert mode**. It can be changed if required so that the new typing overwrites the original text.

Task

You can now use the word-processor to create the document you chose earlier, and save it as a file on a floppy disk. You need to:

- *boot up the computer and run the word-processor*
- *start a new file*
- *type in your text, making minor alterations as you go*
- *save your work on the floppy disk, using an appropriate file name*
- *print out a copy of the document*

It may be helpful to talk to your IT tutor about starting new files on the word-processor, and saving your work on a floppy disk.

The printed copy of your document can be used as evidence towards the IT core skill unit.

Our group of students has also been using the word-processor. Lucy, Ravi and Chris began their work by agreeing a list of questions to be asked. They will be conducting their questionnaire in a crowded canteen so they want to keep each interview short. It was decided that they should use a small number of brief 'closed' questions, which need only a yes or no answer. Lucy has entered their questions into the word processor and saved the file as SURVEY1 in a directory called SMOKE on a floppy disk.

She has printed a copy of her file, which is shown on the next page.

```
Smoking Awareness Research Project: Survey

1. Do you think smoking can harm other people's
   health?
2. Would you let someone smoke in your home or
   room?
3. Do you smoke cigarettes?
4. If so, why do you smoke cigarettes?
5. Do you think that smoking is bad for your
   health?
6. Do you think that smoking should be allowed in
   enclosed public places like cinemas and
   restaurants?
```

Lucy, Ravi and Chris meet to check the questionnaire form and decide that they need to make some changes. They feel that question 4 should be left out, as it is an open question which could lead to long answers that are difficult to assess numerically. They also think that the question order could be improved and decide to begin with question 5, followed by question 1, then question 6, with question 3 next and question 2 at the end.

They want to allow room for the other answers and so decide to put more space between the questions and to provide multiple-choice answers to be filled in. They want to add a question to find out whether the respondent is male or female, and decide to put this near the bottom. Finally they feel that the look of the form would be improved with better headings and with the question numbers hanging out to the left of the question text.

This sounds like a lot of work but in fact it can all be done in a few minutes.

Task

Study the printout of the document created for the last task or another document created using the word-processor. You need to:

- *decide on improvements to the content, including: moving, adding, deleting and copying text*
- *decide on improvements to the layout including headings and spacing.*

Indicate the changes you decide to make on your copy using pencil. This can be used as evidence towards the IT core skill unit.

Editing text

Editing text has already been considered – in the form of the use of the backspace key to delete text just typed. Knowing how to move the cursor to any part of the document means it is possible to delete and insert text wherever you wish. But suppose that you want to move a large piece of text to another part of the document. The method above would necessitate the slow deletion of the existing text (character by character) and the even slower process of typing it back in another location. And what if you then changed your mind?

An easier way to manipulate text, whether you want to move, copy or delete it, is made possible by the ability of the word-processor to **select** text. It is possible to select a character, a word, a line, a sentence, a paragraph or even an entire document. Once the text is selected, it is easy to move, copy or delete it. The backspace key can be used to delete selected text and this is a much quicker method than working backwards, character by character, if you need to delete more than a few words.

Select text that you want to delete, copy or move.

This process of selecting and moving or copying text is also known as *cut and paste*. It describes what happens quite well. First, you select the text you want to move or copy. Then you instruct the word processor to 'cut' if you want to move the text, or 'copy' if you want to leave the original text unaltered.

Then you move the cursor to the place where you want to insert the text and tell the word processor to 'paste'. Your text will appear and, of course, the text below moves down to make room for it.

Formatting characters

Changing the appearance of a document is called **formatting**. Formatting characters refers to the effects that can be added to the text to alter the way it looks. You can use **bold**, or *italic*, or <u>underline</u>, or CAPITAL LETTERS, or even ***<u>ALL FOUR</u>***, to make parts of your text stand out. The method of selecting text and then changing it can be used to format headings in this way.

It is also possible to make changes to the size and shape of the text. The text that is printed out by the computer has a consistent shape and style, whether it includes letters or numbers. The term used for a full set of characters in a particular style is a 'character set' or *font*. Most typewriters use a font called Courier which looks like this, and this book is set in a font called Times. Text size is measured in *points*. Normal text is usually formatted at 10 point or 12 point; 6 point is getting too small to read and 24 point is too large for most uses.

The font and size of selected text can be changed which will greatly alter its appearance. Careful selection of fonts and sizes can much improve the look of the whole document, as any available fonts

can be applied to any part of the text. Even greater emphasis can be added to headings, and good-looking title pages can be created, but beware! It is all very easy to ruin a perfectly good-looking document by getting carried away with a battery of fonts and effects. The golden rule is to keep character formatting simple and neat for the best presentation. It is likely that you will be limited, anyway, in the range of fonts and sizes available to you by the equipment you are using; but some word-processors and printers can produce a large number to choose from.

All the different character formats mentioned above can either be applied to text already entered by selecting it, or chosen before beginning so that everything typed comes out in the style required.

Formatting paragraphs

Formatting can also be applied to paragraph layout, so it is possible to control the alignment of the paragraph and the line spacing.

Printed text is aligned between the margins of the page in one of four ways, as can be seen in Figure 11.14 on the next page.

Line spacing can also be adjusted if required. The standard spacing is one line but this can be increased in half space steps. A format and spacing can be chosen before typing or it is possible to select and change, as with other editing features described above.

Alignment of paragraphs takes place between the margins, as mentioned above. It is possible to change the position of these margins for particular paragraphs or for the whole document.

This is 6 point

This is 10 point

This is 12 point

This is 24 point

Figure 11.13 *Text size is measured in points*

Left aligned text is arranged so that lines are even on the left-hand side but the right-hand side is ragged.

Right aligned text is similar to the above except that it is lined up on the right.

Justified text is adjusted by the computer so that the lines are of an even length, although it can lead to a lot of extra spaces being added. Newspapers are printed with justified text.

Centred text is centred.

Figure 11.14 *Variations on text alignment*

One change that Lucy, Ravi and Chris want to make is to have the question numbers hanging out to the left of the text. This can be achieved by selecting the question paragraphs and then setting the left margin in a short way, but setting the first line of each paragraph back over to the left. This produces what is called a *hanging indent* (see below) and although it may sound complicated it is a common procedure. The word-processor has been designed to make it easy to do.

This is an example of
a hanging indent
where the first line
protrudes on the left.

Figure 11.15 *The word-processor can do hanging indents*

Lucy, Ravi and Chris have been using some of these methods on their questionnaire form. They began by selecting and deleting question 4, then rearranged the text and order of the remaining questions by selecting and moving the text, and lastly renumbered them.

Next they inserted a blank line between each question by moving the cursor to the question numbers and pressing return. Using the tab key they

moved the cursor a short way over to the right along the blank line below each question and inserted a multiple-choice answer ranged right.

They then selected the question paragraphs and set a left margin with a hanging indent, so that the numbers stand out to the left. It had been decided to ask the sex of respondents and the students want to put this in a little below the other questions. They can't move the cursor directly to the spot because their document ends at the last question; so they add blank lines at the bottom by pressing return. They use the tab key again to space the check boxes along the line. They decide to add a 'thank-you' line in the same way. Finally they tackle the headings. Both headings are centred and made bold, with 'survey' changed to 'questionnaire' and put in capital letters. They decide to leave the size and font as they are for this document.

When they have completed these changes they save and print the file. The survey document now looks like Figure 11.16.

This is much clearer to read than the original draft. The students' survey form now looks like a well-presented document.

Smoking Awareness Research Project

QUESTIONNAIRE

1. Do you think that there is a risk that smoking could damage your health?
                                    Yes/No/Don't know
2. Do you think that passive smoking can harm other people's health?
                                    Yes/No/Don't know
3. Do you think that smoking should be allowed in enclosed public places like cinemas and restaurants?
                                    Yes/No/Don't know
4. Do you smoke?
                                    Never/Sometimes/Often
5. Would you let someone smoke in your home or room?
                                    No/Sometimes/Yes

Please tick the correct answer
Male 	Female ....

Thank you for your help with our survey on smoking

Figure 11.16 *The students' final questionnaire*

Task

You may have made some decisions about the changes you would like to make to your own document and now you can carry them out. You need to find out how to:

- *select text on your word processor, and how to use the cut and paste method to move and copy selected text*
- *add effects to characters including bold, italic, capitals and underline*
- *align paragraphs to the left, to the right, justified or centred*
- *change margin markers to alter the width of paragraphs and create a hanging indent on the first line*
- *change the font and size of characters in your document*

You could see your IT tutor for help with using your local word-processor to carry out these editing operations, and practise them on your document. Obtain a printout of one or two versions to get an idea of how the changes you are making will affect the final appearance.

Try out all the editing features that have been described even if you don't intend using them for the final version of your document. You will get practice in using the equipment, and will be well prepared to use the techniques later with other documents.

Remember that you can make changes to your document, and print copies of your changed versions, without altering the original file saved on your floppy disk – provided that you don't save a changed version using the same name as the original. If you like an altered version but want to keep the original as well, you can save the new version with its own name, thus keeping both files stored on your disk.

A printout showing editing changes to your document can be used as evidence towards the IT core skills unit.

· USING A DATABASE ·

For the next stage of their research Lucy, Ravi and Christ need to contact a range of cinemas and restaurants. They decide to send out twenty letters and to use the local directories in the library to build a list of contact addresses. The plan is to create a database on the computer to store the contact list so that the information can be used in a variety of ways later.

What is a database?

A database is a list of information, such as address books and library catalogue systems.

Computers are very good at handling lists and the software application that is used for this is called a *database manager*. It is usually referred to simply as a database.

A computerised database can be used to do a variety of things, such as:

- locate particular information instantly
- add extra information
- update and alter information
- rearrange the order of the list
- make smaller sub-lists from the information
- share information with other software applications

Setting up a database

In order to begin setting up a database it is first necessary to decide what information is to be recorded. Perhaps you want to keep track of the books that you have read or referred to during an assignment. For each book you would want to note the title, author (first name and surname), publisher and date of publication. Each of these categories of information is known as a field, and you can enter data into these **fields** for each of the books to be listed. The information held for a particular book is called a **record**; in our example each record will contain the title, author, publisher and date fields.

In order to set up a new database you must tell the computer what fields you need. The information you are storing will be of different types: some will be numbers and some will be words (or perhaps words and numbers together). Data consisting of numbers, such as a price or a quantity, is known as *numeric data*. Data which is text, or a combination of text and numbers, is called *alphanumeric data*. Names, titles of books and telephone numbers are all alphanumeric data. Telephone numbers are not used to do calculations with so it is easier to treat them as alphanumeric data. It is necessary to decide what type of fields you need to create for your data and in our example we would need only alphanumeric fields as no numbers are being stored.

Numeric fields store numbers fields, alphanumeric fields store text and text mixed with numbers

It is also necessary to decide on the *length* of the fields, which is specified by a number of characters. We will allow 80 characters for the title, 20 characters for the author's surname, 20 characters for the author's first name and 25 characters for the publisher.

When the fields are set up there will be a blank record looking something like this:

Title:
Author's surname:
Author's first name:
Publisher:
Publication date:

It is only necessary now to enter the details of the first book into the fields. When this is finished, go on to the next record and fill in the data for the next book, and then you carry on creating new records until all the data is stored. When this process is finished you have created a database.

Lucy, Ravi and Chris have created a database of their local cinemas and restaurants. They have included the following fields for each record:

Name:
Type:
Title:
Manager's _surname:
Manager's_first name:
Address_1:
Address_2:
Address_3:
Postcode:

The group is now able to look at the entries made in a variety of ways. Looking at records is known as *browsing* and you have a lot of control over how you arrange them. When you browse records they are displayed in rows with the field names written as *column* titles at the top, like this:

Name	Type	Title	Manager's_surname
Beefhouse	Restaurant	Mr	Phillips
Blue Bay	Restaurant	Ms	Williams
Calcutta	Restaurant	Mrs	Shah
Chez Nous	Restaurant	Mr	Distel
Clarion	Cinema	Mr	Collins
Decathlon	Restaurant	Mr	Platos

Not all the field columns are displayed on the screen at once because there is simply not room. The screen could be thought of as a window that can only show part of the scene at once. The window can be moved around to view other areas using the cursor keys. In the same way that you can scroll down a document with the word-processor, so you can move across the database to view the contents of the other fields.

In this case the records have been displayed alphabetically, using the name field as the index. The records could also be displayed sorted by the manager's name, or by the address, or by using any of the fields.

The group has discovered that the Beefhouse Restaurant has recently been taken over by a new owner. It is now called the Vegibyte Restaurant,

Records can be sorted by using any field as the index.

although the students don't know the new manager's name. They decide to edit the record, all the same.

The computer can search for a particular record, or group of records, in a database and edit the data they contain. The text or numbers that you are looking for must be specified and all the records that contain it will be displayed. In this case the students search for the word 'Beefhouse' in the Name field and the following record is displayed:

Name: Beefhouse
Type: Restaurant
Title: Mr.
Manager's_surname: Phillips
Manager's_first name: John
Address_1: High Street
Address_2: Upton
Address_3: Noneton
Postcode: NO1 2BE

The students amend the record by moving the cursor to the data they want to change and entering the new information. The record now looks like this:

Name: Vegibyte
Type: Restaurant
Title: Sir
Manager's_surname:
Manager's_first name:
Address_1: High Street
Address_2: Upton
Address_3: Noneton
Postcode: NO1 2BE

They have left the manager's name fields *blank* but have included the word 'Sir' in the title field. The reason why they have done this will become clearer later when we look at merging database information with a word-processed standard letter.

Ravi has been told that the cinema in Station Road has been closed down but none of the group can

remember its name. This time all they know is that they are looking for a cinema in Station Road so they decide to *search the database*. To make the search it is necessary to specify which fields you are interested in and the data that you are looking for in these fields. Ravi specifies the data entry 'Cinema' in the type field, and the data entry 'Station Road' in the Address_1 field. As there is only one cinema in Station Road the following record is displayed:

Name: Palace
Type: Cinema
Title: Mrs
Manager's_surname: Rank
Manager's_first name: Annie
Address_1: Station Road
Address_2: Downton
Address_3: Noneton
Postcode: NO2 8IT

Ravi then deletes the entire record from the database.

Searching the database for a particular record is very useful but what if you want to look at a group of records with something in common? Lucy, Ravi and Chris want to check how many cinemas they have included so they decide to *query the database*. A query is made by specifying the fields to be queried, and the information to be searched for. The records which fit the requirements are displayed as a list which you can work on using all the database management tools that we have described.

Query the database to list records with similar contents in certain fields

The students' query displays the list of records shown on the next page.

These records have not been taken away from the main database, of course, but have simply been chosen for display, leaving the records on restaurants hidden. The students are satisfied that they have

Name	Type	Title	Manager's_surname
Albion	Cinema	Mr	Grimes
Clarion	Cinema	Mr	Collins
Commodore	Cinema	Mrs	Plowright
Empire	Cinema	Mr	Attenbrough
Realto	Cinema	Ms	Taylor
Regal	Cinema	Mr	Hardy

included enough cinemas and save their complete database file on floppy disk.

Task

You can now set up your own database containing information that you need to organise. First you need to decide what information to store in your database. Remember that you can store any information that is in the form of a list. You then need to decide on the field titles and lengths required. When you have decided on your data you need to find out how to:

- *set up a new database with the fields that you want on your local equipment*
- *search the database for particular records*
- *add, delete and edit records*
- *query the database for a list of records containing certain information in common*

If necessary, talk to your IT tutor to find out how to perform these tasks on your equipment. Practise using the database management tools that have been described. When you are satisfied you can save your file on a floppy disk.

The work that you do can be used as evidence towards the IT core skill unit.

. SHARING INFORMATION BETWEEN . APPLICATIONS

The next stage of the students' action plan involves sending letters to all the addresses on their database. They intend to use the word-processor to create a letter and to link it with their database of cinemas and restaurants.

Creating a form letter

The document created on the word-processor for a mail-merge is known as a **form letter**. Form letters are typed in like an ordinary letter except that you indicate the places where information from the database is to appear. The students want to ask the same questions on smoking to each of the managers, but will need to have a different name and address on each copy of their letter.

Lucy, Ravi and Chris meet to decide on the wording of their letter. Chris has agreed to use his home as the sender's address so that he will be sent all the responses. The group plan the letter, leaving spaces where information from the database will be included. The text of their letter is shown below, with boxes to indicate where they want to put database information:

```
                                    29 Forest Road
                                    Middleton
                                    Noneton
                                    NO9 8HE

                          Current date goes here.

The manager's name,
and the name and
address of the cinema
or restaurant go here

Dear      Manager's title and surname go here

We are Advanced GNVQ Health and Social Care
students at Noneton College. As part of our
studies we are carrying out some research into
smoking habits.
  This research requires us to find out more about
the policy on smoking in local restaurants and
cinemas. We would be grateful if you could answer
the following questions in the spaces provided
and return this letter to the above address.

Is there a smoking policy in your establishment?

If smoking is allowed do you provide a designated
non-smoking area?

Thank you for your help with our research.

Yours sincerely
```

Figure 11.17 *The first draft of the students' letter*

Now that they are happy with the *content* Lucy, Ravi and Chris go to the word-processor to create their form letter. They intend to number their questions and use hanging indents to make the numbers stand out; they need to use the tab key to create accurately positioned answer spaces.

The students also need to indicate where database information is to be included so that the right things appear in the right places. This is done by typing the name of a database field into the letter, positioned where you want the data contained in that field to appear. It has to be made clear to the computer that you have typed a field name and not just another word, and the word processor you are using will have a way of indicating this. These specially marked field names are called *merge fields* and act as an instruction to the computer to bring information from a database file into a word-processor file when it is printed.

Merge fields in a form letter show which data fields the informatiom will be imported from

It is important to realise that merging only takes place *when the document is printed*. The details of particular records cannot be seen displayed on the screen in the letter, only the field names of the database which the records are stored in.

Lucy, Ravi and Chris have created a form letter on the word processor, and have included merge fields where they want database information to appear. They have also included a special field for the *current date* to be inserted when the letters are printed. They have been careful to type the field names exactly as they are written in their database file so that the computer can recognise them, and have enclosed them in angled brackets – which is what their particular word-processor uses to define a merge field.

Figure 11.18 shows their letter as it appears on the computer monitor screen.

```
                                    29 Forest Road
                                       Middleton
                                        Noneton
                                        NO9 8HE
                                        <date>

<Manager's_First name> <Manager's_Surname>
<Name> <Type>
<Address_1>
<Address_2>
<Address_3>
<Postcode>

Dear <Title> <Manager's_Surname>,
We are Advanced GNVQ Health and Social Care
students at Noneton College. As part of our
studies we are carrying out some research into
smoking habits.
This research requires us to find out more about
the policy on smoking in local restaurants and
cinemas. We would be grateful if you could answer
the following questions in the spaces provided and
return this letter to the above address.

1. Is there a smoking policy in your
   establishment?                        ........

2. If smoking is allowed do you provide a
   designated non-smoking area?          ........

Thank you for your help with our research.


Yours sincerely
```

Figure 11.18 *The students' letter including field names*

The merge fields have been placed carefully so that the printed letters will have database information in the right places. The manager's surname and first name appear in the right order, and the address is laid out neatly beneath.

You may remember the Vegibyte Restaurant where the manager's name was unknown. For this record the students left the manager's name fields empty and typed Sir in the Title field. This means that the letter to the Vegibyte Restaurant will begin 'Dear Sir', as they require.

Task

Now you can use the word-processor to create a form letter and link the merge fields to a database file that you have created.

First you need to decide on the content and layout of your merge document, and where you want the information from the database to appear. When you have planned your merge document you need to find out how to indicate merge fields on your local word-processor.

Now create your document. Take care to enter the field names accurately and in the correct positions, and be sure to indicate the merge fields so that your computer will recognise them. Finally, save your document on a floppy disk when you are satisfied with it.

The planning that you do for your merge document may be used as evidence towards the IT core skill unit.

Carrying out a print merge

Lucy, Ravi and Chris are now ready to print their letters. To begin with they run the word-processor and *load* the file containing their merge letter. They then instruct the computer to perform a *print merge*, which is one of the print options available. The students take care to specify the path to their database file, and its name, so that the computer can find it. Finally, they tell it to print and the computer produces a personalised letter for each record on the database.

The students now need to print *labels* for the envelopes which they will do from the database. They run the database programme and load their mailing list file. The database has address labels included in its printing options. They simply specify the fields to print and the position they are to appear on the label. When they instruct the

computer to print it produces a label for each record in the database.

Address labels can be printed from the database

There may be occasions when it is only necessary to print a letter for a few records on the database. This can be done when printing the merge document with the word-processor. As well as specifying the name of the database you can identify particular records that you want to use by using a method similar to querying the database.

Lucy, Ravi and Chris could have used this method to print letters to all the cinemas on their list. With their merge letter loaded into the word-processor they would need to select print merge and then specify not only the database name and path, but the particular field contents to look for. In this case they would specify the entry Cinema in the Type field. The computer would then produce letters to all the cinema managers on the database.

Task

You might now wish to print a merged document. Run the word-processor and load the merge document you created earlier.

You probably don't want to produce a document for every record on your database so you will need to decide what records you do want to include, and how to specify them by the contents of particular fields. When you have done this you need to find out how to:

- *select the print merge option on your word processor*
- *specify the records you want to merge with your document.*

Finally tell the computer to print out your merged document.

The work that you do in performing a print merge can be used as evidence towards the IT core skill unit.

Recording results with a database

A database is a good way of keeping track of responses received from a survey questionnaire. Each question is allocated its own field in the database. Answers are entered into these fields using a suitable coding system, and each respondent's set of answers is stored as a separate record. When results need to be examined, a query will quickly reveal how many people gave a particular answer or combination of answers.

The responses to the students' smoking questionnaire have been entered in a database in this way. They intend to do statistical analysis on their data with a spreadsheet. To do this they will need to find out how many people gave answers indicating awareness of the dangers of smoking. They have coded an aware answer as 'A', and an unaware answer as 'U'. Gender has been coded 'M' and 'F'. They have also added a field which gives the number of aware responses given by each respondent. This field is coded 0 to 5, since respondents can have a maximum of five aware answers and a minimum of none.

The students' database has thirty records, as they received thirty completed questionnaires. Now that they have entered their data it is possible to find out the totals they need. A query will show how many people gave a particular number of aware answers. The students are interested in differences in awareness between males and females, so they query the database separately for each group. From this they are able to see how many males gave five aware anwers, how many females gave four aware answers, and so on. The totals that this analysis gives can be looked at in more detail using the spreadsheet.

· USING A SPREADSHEET ·

Lucy, Ravi and Chris have now sent out their letters and carried out their student survey. Whilst they wait for the postal responses to arrive they decide to begin work on the results they have so far.

They have asked 30 students to fill in questionnaire forms and now intend to use the **spreadsheet** to record and work on the results. We will now look at the sorts of things a spreadsheet can do.

What is a spreadsheet?

A spreadsheet is designed for working on numerical information. This information is organised into columns and rows, and you can see this arrangement on the screen when running the spreadsheet. Figure 11.19 shows part of a typical spreadsheet screen.

	A	B	C	D	E	F
1						
2						
3						
4						
5						
6						
7						
8						
9						
10						
11						
12						
13						
14						

Figure 11.19 *Part of a spreadsheet display*

The spreadsheet is composed of cells which make up the columns and rows. Each row and column is labelled, and in this spreadsheet example letters are used to label the columns and numbers are used to label the rows. This is the system to be found on most spreadsheets.

This labelling system means that each cell has a *unique address*, known as the **cell reference**, which is written using the column letter and the row number. The cell in the top left corner has the cell reference A1, as it is in the column labelled A and in the row labelled 1. You can move the cursor arrow keys from cell to cell and highlight any cell in the spreadsheet. The highlighted cell is called the *active cell*. Information that you type in is entered into the active cell, and to enter information in a particular cell you need to highlight it as the active cell first.

Information is entered into the active cell of a spreadsheet

The computer screen can only display a part of the spreadsheet at any one time, as happens with the other software applications that we have looked at. There is actually a large number of rows and columns available. As you move the active cell highlight across, or up and down, your spreadsheet other parts will come into view.

Text or numbers can be entered into the cells of a spreadsheet. Text is used to label columns and rows, and to create spreadsheet titles. However, the function of a spreadsheet is to work with numbers. There is a range of facilities with which to do this.

What can a spreadsheet do?

Calculations can easily be performed with a spreadsheet. In order to illustrate this, Figure 11.20 shows a spreadsheet that has been set up to record

the monthly expenditure of a GNVQ Health and Social Care student.

The student has entered the months as text in cells B1 to F1 to provide column headings, and has entered spending categories as row headings in cells A2 to A6. The amounts spent per month have then been entered into the appropriate cells. The computer recognises which cell entries are text and aligns them over to the left, whereas numbers are aligned to the right.

Each entry has been made by positioning the active cell highlight to the required position and typing. The entry appears in the active cell, and also in a special part of the screen outside the main spreadsheet area. It is possible to edit the entry until it is correct and then press the enter key to confirm it.

The look of a spreadsheet can be improved by changing the size of rows and columns, and by formatting the text and number entries to suit requirements. For example: the word 'Entertainment' will not fit in the space provided, but this can be solved by increasing the width of the A column to provide enough room. Also, the numbers entered are amounts of money so a £ sign would help. These adjustments will leave the spreadsheet looking like Figure 11.21.

	A	B	C	D	E	F
1		Jan	Feb	March	April	May
2	Food	80	74	82	76	85
3	Clothes	20	35	12	18	20
4	Entertain	70	75	50	67	54
5	Books	50	12	35	50	22
6	Savings	29	30	41	24	32
7						
8						
9						
10						
11						
12						
13						
14						

Figure 11.20 *A student's expenditure record (first draft)*

	A	B	C	D	E	F
1		Jan	Feb	March	April	May
2	Food	£80	£74	£82	£76	£85
3	Clothes	£20	£35	£12	£18	£20
4	Entertainment	£70	£75	£50	£67	£54
5	Books	£50	£12	£35	£50	£22
6	Savings	£29	£30	£41	£24	£32
7						
8						
9						
10						
11						
12						
13						
14						

Figure 11.21 *A student's expenditure record – corrected*

You may now create your own spreadsheet. First you must decide on the information you want to store and what column and row labels you will need. Then you will need to find out:

- *how to set up a new spreadsheet and enter text and numbers in the cells you wish to use*

- *how to change the appearance of your spreadsheet by varying column width and altering the format in which text and numbers are displayed.*

The planning and creation of your spreadsheet can be used as evidence towards the IT core skill unit.

The spreadsheet is obviously a very neat way to display numbers. But its real power lies in its ability to use formulae to perform calculations on the numerical contents of cells.

Formulae

Formulae use mathematical and other symbols to operate on the contents of different cells in the spreadsheet. A formula is entered into the active cell and operates on the contents of other cells in the spreadsheet. The result is calculated and displayed in the active cell.

The symbols used on a computer for basic arithmetic calculations are: + for add, − for subtract, * for multiply, / for divide. These are all available on the keyboard. Maths symbols like these which are used in formulae are called mathematical operators.

Formulae can include a range of mathematical, statistical and scientific symbols; your equipment will have a set of such symbols that it will recognise and use. You can also use parentheses, or brackets, in formulae as you would in mathematical calculations.

Writing formulae

Imagine, as an example, that you want to add the contents of cell A1 to the contents of cell B1 and display the result in cell C1. First, you use the arrow keys to make C1 the active cell. You must then instruct the computer that you are entering a formula. Your machine will recognise a particular symbol as indicating a formula. It is *essential* that you enter it correctly otherwise your formula will be treated as a text cell entry. Now type the first cell reference, followed by an operator, then the final cell reference. The formula in cell C1 would look like this:

$$= A1 + B1$$

(Note that in this example we have used the equals sign (=) to signify a formula.)

As with other cell entries the formula appears *both* in the active cell and outside the spreadsheet area *until* you press Enter to confirm your entry. When Enter is pressed the formula is no longer displayed in the cell but the result of the calculation appears there instead. The formula remains visible in the other part of the screen so that you can recognise that the spreadsheet is displaying the result of a calculation.

The top part of Figure 11.22 shows how a spreadsheet might look before our formula is confirmed as the contents of cell C1.

=A1+B1

	A	B	C	D	E	F
1	8	12	=A1+B1			
2						
3						
4						

Figure 11.22 *Entering a formula*

When Enter is pressed the computer will add the number 8 in cell A1 to the number 12 in cell B1 and the result (20, of course) is displayed in cell C1. (See Figure 11.23.)

Using formulae means that results are automatically recalculated when changes are made to the contents of a cell that has been referred to in a formula. For instance, if we change the contents of cell A1 from 8

=A1+B1

	A	B	C	D	E	F
1	8	12	20			
2						
3						
4						

Figure 11.23 *The calculation is done*

to 12 the result displayed in cell C1 automatically changes to 24.

In the GNVQ Health and Social Care student's expenditure spreadsheet (Figure 11.21) it would be useful to find out what the total spending was in each month. This can be done by entering formulae into the cells where you want the results to appear. So to display the total spending for January at the bottom of the Jan column we need to enter a formula in cell B7 that adds together the contents of cells B2, B3, B4, B5, and B6.

It would be possible simply to enter B2 + B3 + B4 + B5 + B6 as this would do the job. But spreadsheets will accept certain short-cut commands which make formulae easier to write. It is possible to use the command SUM to add together the contents of a number of cells along a row or down a column. First highlight cell B7 as the active cell, then enter the formula SUM(B2:B6), remembering to indicate that this is a formula and not ordinary text. The symbol ':' has been used here to instruct the computer to include all the cells from B2 to B6 in the calculation (your machine may use a different symbol). When Enter is pressed, the result is calculated and displayed in cell B7 as shown in Figure 11.24.

It is necessary now to enter formulae in other cells of Row 7 to calculate the total spending for the other months. This could be done column by column, changing the cell references in each formula, so that it adds the contents of the cells above. However, there is a much better way to repeat similar formulas along a row or down a column.

Copying formulae

It is possible to copy cell contents to other cells in a spreadsheet, whether the cell contains text, numbers or a formula. There may well be other occasions

=SUM(B2:B6)

	A	B	C	D	E	F
1		Jan	Feb	March	April	May
2	Food	£80	£74	£82	£76	£85
3	Clothes	£20	£35	£12	£18	£20
4	Entertainment	£70	£75	£50	£67	£54
5	Books	£50	£12	£35	£50	£22
6	Savings	£29	£30	£41	£24	£32
7		£249				
8						
9						
10						
11						
12						
13						
14						

Figure 11.24 *Using a formula to obtain a column total*

when it is useful to copy text or numbers, but the ability to copy formulae to other cells is especially helpful. This is because the cell references in the formula adjust to the new location, so that the formula now refers to a different range of cells.

For example, if the contents of cell B7, which is the formula SUM(B2:B6), is copied to cell C7 it changes to the formula SUM(C2:C6). Now the result displayed in cell C7 is the total of the contents of cells C2 to C6. Cell references in formulae which are able to change in this way are known as **relative cell references**. The formulae we have seen so far have contained only relative cell references as we have not indicated otherwise to the computer.

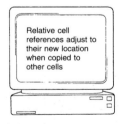

Relative cell references adjust to their new location when copied to other cells

If it was necessary to *fix* a cell in a formula, so that it would not change when the formula is copied to a different cell, this can be indicated using a symbol that the computer recognises. Cell references in formulae which have been fixed in this way are called **absolute cell references** (see below).

Copying the formula in cell B7 to cells C7, D7 and so on can be made even easier by using the ability of the spreadsheet to copy the contents of one cell to a number of other cells. First, select a group of cells along a row or down a column, beginning with the one containing the formula you wish to copy. Then fill the formula into the selected cells, either across or down as appropriate. All the relative cell references in the formula will adjust to suit their new location and the results of their calculations will be displayed.

So in order to copy the formula into all the cells from cell B7 to cell F7, it is first necessary to select cells B7 to F7 as shown in Figure 11.25.

=SUM(B2:B6)

	A	B	C	D	E	F
1		Jan	Feb	March	April	May
2	Food	£80	£74	£82	£76	£85
3	Clothes	£20	£35	£12	£18	£20
4	Entertainment	£70	£75	£50	£67	£54
5	Books	£50	£12	£35	£50	£22
6	Savings	£29	£30	£41	£24	£32
7		£249				
8						
9						
10						
11						
12						
13						
14						

Figure 11.25 *Copying a formula across cells*

The computer is then instructed to fill the selected cells with the formula. When Enter is pressed the formula is copied and the results are displayed as shown in Figure 11.26.

=SUM(B2:B6)

	A	B	C	D	E	F
1		Jan	Feb	March	April	May
2	Food	£80	£74	£82	£76	£85
3	Clothes	£20	£35	£12	£18	£20
4	Entertainment	£70	£75	£50	£67	£54
5	Books	£50	£12	£35	£50	£22
6	Savings	£29	£30	£41	£24	£32
7		£249	£226	£220	£235	£213
8						
9						
10						
11						
12						
13						
14						

Figure 11.26 *The completed expenditure totals*

The students' results

We will now see how Lucy, Ravi and Chris have used a spreadsheet to analyse their results. Their questionnaire form contained five questions:

1 Do you think that there is a risk that smoking could damage your health?
2 Do you think that passive smoking can harm other people's health?
3 Do you think that smoking should be allowed in enclosed public places?
4 Do you smoke?
5 Would you let someone smoke in your home or room?

For questions 1 and 2 the answer 'yes' shows that the respondent is aware of the dangers of smoking, and for questions 3, 4, and 5 the answer 'no' would indicate this. The students intend to analyse these 'aware of the dangers' answers on a spreadsheet, separating the responses between males and females so that any difference of attitude between the sexes can be picked up.

Figure 11.27 shows the spreadsheet that they have created to display their results before any formulae are put in.

The students have used row 1 to provide a title for their spreadsheet and have entered the question numbers as column headings in cells B2 to F2. Cells A3, A4 and A5 contain the row labels Male, Female and Total. The results have been recorded in the appropriate cells so that the number of males and females giving 'aware' answers to each question is

	A	B	C	D	E	F
1		Smoking Awareness Survey – Results				
2		Q. 1	Q. 2	Q. 3	Q. 4	Q. 5
3	Male	12	10	11	9	5
4	Female	11	9	10	8	3
5	Total					
6						
7						
8						
9						
10						
11	People asked					
12	Males	16				
13	Females	14				
14	Total	30				

Figure 11.27 *The students' spreadsheet*

displayed. Cells A11 to A14 and B11 to B14 have been used to display the total number of the people asked.

The students now need to calculate the totals in cells B5 to F5 and they are going to use a formula for this. They make B5 the active cell and enter the formula B3 + B4, which will calculate the total 'aware' responses for question 1 and display the result in cell B5 as they require. In order to total the remaining columns they copy the formula across as far as cell F5, using the methods described earlier. As the formula uses relative cell references their copies adapt to their new location and calculate the correct totals in B5 to F5.

The students also want to show their results as a *percentage* of people asked so that they can more easily compare attitudes between male and female respondents. They enter row labels in cells A7, A8 and A9 so that the spreadsheet now looks like Figure 11.28.

	A	B	C	D	E	F
1		Smoking Awareness Survey – Results				
2		Q. 1	Q. 2	Q. 3	Q. 4	Q. 5
3	Male	12	10	11	9	5
4	Female	11	9	10	8	3
5	Total					
6						
7	% Males					
8	% Females					
9	% Total					
10						
11	People asked					
12	Males	16				
13	Females	14				
14	Total	30				

Figure 11.28 *Preparing to calculate percentages*

In order to calculate the percentage responses Lucy, Ravi and Chris need to use a formula like this:

$$\frac{\text{number of 'aware' responses}}{\text{number of people asked}} \times 100$$

They will apply the formula in the cells where they want the result to appear. For example, to calculate the percentage of males giving an 'aware' response to question 1 they need to divide the number of aware responses in cell B3 by the total number of males asked, which is in cell B12, and multiply the result

by 100. They have marked cell B7 as the place to display the result, so they make B7 the active cell and enter the formula B3/B12*100.

As you know, when the formula is copied to other cells in row 7 the relative cell references will adjust to their new locations. However, the students want the reference to cell B12 to remain fixed since the total number of males asked doesn't change. The answer is to include a special symbol in the formula so that cell B12 is given an *absolute* cell reference which will remain exactly the same when the formula is copied to other cells. We will use this symbol '$' to indicate an absolute cell reference; your equipment will have its own way of recognising this.

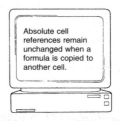

Absolute cell references remain unchanged when a formula is copied to another cell.

Therefore Lucy, Ravi and Chris enter their formula in cell B7, as shown in Figure 11.29.

B3/$B12*100

	A	B	C	D	E	F
1		Smoking Awareness Survey – Results				
2		Q. 1	Q. 2	Q. 3	Q. 4	Q. 5
3	Male	12	10	11	9	5
4	Female	11	9	10	8	3
5	Total					
6						
7	% Males	75				
8	% Females					
9	% Total					
10						
11	People asked					
12	Males	16				
13	Females	14				
14	Total	30				

Figure 11.29 *Completing the first calculation*

They can copy the formula into cells C7, D7, E7 and F7 and the absolute cell reference will remain unchanged. For instance, the formula copied into cell E7 will be adjusted to E3/$B12*100.

The students then enter formulae into cells B8 and B9 to calculate the percentage of 'aware' answers from female respondents, and the percentage of 'aware' responses from all respondents. They copy these formulae, including the appropriate absolute cell references, to the necessary cells in rows 8 and 9. All the results are calculated by the computer and their spreadsheet looks like Figure 11.30.

B3/$B12*100

	A	B	C	D	E	F
1		Smoking Awareness Survey – Results				
2		Q. 1	Q. 2	Q. 3	Q. 4	Q. 5
3	Male	12	10	11	9	5
4	Female	11	9	10	8	3
5	Total	23	19	21	17	8
6						
7	% Males	75	62.5	68.7	56.2	31.2
8	% Females	78.1	63.9	71	56.8	21.3
9	% Total	76.7	63.3	70	56.7	26.7
10						
11	People asked					
12	Males	16				
13	Females	14				
14	Total	30				

Figure 11.30 *The final table of results*

Task

You may now wish to enter formulae into your spreadsheet. Decide what calculations are necessary and try writing them down using spreadsheet cell references in your formulae. Decide whether you need to use any absolute cell references in your formulae.

To enter formulae into your spreadsheet you will need to find out:

- *what symbol to use on your equipment to indicate that a formula is being entered*
- *what symbol your equipment recognises as indicating an absolute cell reference*
- *what range of mathematical and statistical and other operators your spreadsheet is able to use in formulae.*

To copy formulae along rows and down columns you need to find out how to:

- *select a range of cells along rows and down columns*
- *copy a formula along a row and down a column*

Your equipment may have sophisticated presentation features to make your spreadsheet look better when printed. Experiment with these and when you have completed your spreadsheet obtain a printout. Remember to save your spreadsheet file in an appropriate directory on a floppy disk.

The work that you do creating, editing, saving and printing your spreadsheet can be used as evidence towards the IT core skill unit.

Analysing data with a spreadsheet

Spreadsheets can be used to do sophisticated statistical analysis. It is easy to find the *mean* and *standard deviation* of a set of data. The results of the students' survey show how many 'aware' answers each respondent gave. This is a different way of dealing with the data than we have seen so far. Now we need to look at the *frequency* with which each possible number of aware answers occurred. The respondents' database has been queried to give the total 'aware' answers per respondent, together with the respondents' gender. These results have been entered into rows of cells in a spreadsheet (Figure 11.31).

	A	B	C	D	E	F
1						
2		Number of aware answers (Coded)				
3	1	2	3	4	5	6
4						
5	Males					
6	1	2	3	6	3	1
7						
8	Females					
9	0	1	4	5	3	1
10						
11						
12						
13						
14						

Figure 11.31 *Total 'aware' answers per respondent*

Notice that the number of aware answers has been coded so that a zero doesn't appear for 'no aware answers'. This is so that people with no 'aware' answers do not disappear when the mean is calculated.

This shows the **frequency distribution** of 'aware' answers for each gender group. The students are interested in the *mean awareness* results. This is easily calculated by asking the spreadsheet to give the average of a range of cell contents. The mean is, of course, the same as the average value. They begin with the results for males. The mean value is intended to appear in cell A11 so they need to enter a formula in that cell.

Their software uses AVG to indicate that an average is needed. They enter the formula =AVG(A6:F6) in cell A11. The mean awareness for male respondents is now calculated and displayed in A11. A similar formula is entered into cell A13 to find the average awareness of female respondents.

The students now wish to find the standard deviations of their two sets of data. The software they are using uses the command STD to indicate that a standard deviation is required. The cell C11 is chosen to display the standard deviation amongst males. The formula =STD(A6:F6) is entered in this cell and the result appears there. A similar formula is entered in cell C13, but this time to calculate the standard deviation of the data on females in cells A9 to F9.

These results show that males and females have a similar average awareness of the risks of smoking, but that awareness is more widely spread amongst males.

Spreadsheets can do other, more sophisticated statistical calculations, but it is unlikely that you will need to use them during your GNVQ studies.

· CREATING A CHART OR GRAPH ·

The spreadsheet does an excellent job of recording and performing calculations on numerical data, but often it is useful to display the results in a form that emphasises a particular point. A good way to do this is by the creation of a chart or graph from part of a spreadsheet. These can be made in a variety of forms such as the pie chart or the bar chart. Lucy, Ravi and Chris want to create a chart from the results of

their smoking awareness research. First they need to decide which cell contents they want to display in the chart. The percentage results are chosen.

Next they decide what type of chart will display the results best and they agree that a bar chart will show up the *differences* in responses that they wish to highlight in the final report. Figure 11.32 shows the results produced by the spreadsheet. The chart file can be saved in a suitable directory on a floppy disk, ready to incorporate into their report. It will need a suitable title.

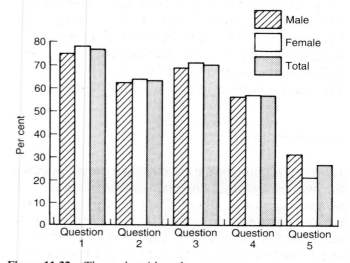

Figure 11.32 *The students' bar chart*

Task

You may be able to create a chart or graph with your equipment, either using data from a spreadsheet or by importing data with the keyboard. You need to:

- *decide what data you want to make a graph or chart from, and what type of presentation your data needs*

- *find out how to create a chart or graph on your equipment*

- *experiment with the range of chart and graph styles available to you*

When you are satisfied with your work save your file on a floppy disk and obtain a printout of the finished chart. The work that you do in creating and printing a chart from your spreadsheet results can be used as evidence towards the IT core skill unit.

· COMPILING A REPORT ·

When a research project is completed, like the one Lucy, Ravi and Chris have been working on, the best tool to help in the compilation of the final report is the word-processor. Some of the word-processor's impressive capabilities have already been looked at and the creation of a longer and more detailed document introduces other features.

Importing data

Lucy, Ravi and Chris have created a word-processor file and are keying in the text of their smoking awareness research report. They decided to put the charts that they have created into the report and, as an appendix, to attach a sample questionnaire form and letter and a list of the cinemas and restaurants contacted.

The software applications they are using can share data between them and the students use this facility to **import** their charts into the report file. They run the word-processor and load their report file. The cursor is moved to the part of the document where the first chart is to appear and the import procedure is begun. The computer must be given the path and file name of the chart file and the disk containing it put into the computer's floppy disk drive. The chart is copied into the word-processor file at the insertion point and the original chart file on the floppy disk is unaffected.

Lucy, Ravi and Chris decide to import copies of their letter and questionnaire form into the report file, rather than print separate copies from the original files. This is because they intend to use the computer to insert page numbers on the report and they want the appendix to be included in the

numbering. The procedure is similar to that used for the charts, except that this time they are importing another word processor file and, of course, the path and filenames are different.

The next thing is that data from the database is imported in the form of a list of cinema and restaurant names. They only require a list of the contents of the Name and Type fields and need to specify this when importing the data.

When importing data you must specify the file name and path correctly.

Formatting

The only thing left to do now is to arrange the document for printing. The pages of a word-processed document can be formatted in several ways before printing. The word processor prints text between four margins on each page: the left, right, top and bottom (Figure 11.33).

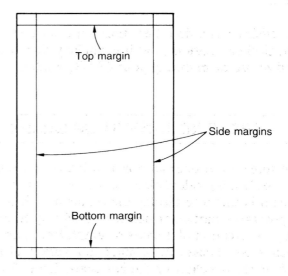

Figure 11.33 *There are four margins to set during formatting*

The text wraps onto the next line automatically when the right margin is reached and in a similar way a new page is begun when the bottom margin is reached. The page margins can be altered so that text gets closer to, or further from, the page edges. This can be used to alter the look of a document and to vary the number of pages by fitting more or less text on each sheet.

There may be an occasion when it is helpful to keep part of the text on its own page, without the possibility of it being spread into a second page if text is added later to an earlier part of the document. This can be done by inserting *hard page breaks*. A hard page break is an instruction to the computer to begin a new page, regardless of how far down the current page you have got. Insert a page break before the section you are concerned with and it will begin on a new page, insert one after and it will be printed on a page of its own.

Another option in page design is which way round the paper is printed on. It is possible to choose either portrait layout or landscape layout (see Figure 11.34). Work is still confined within the margins whichever layout is used.

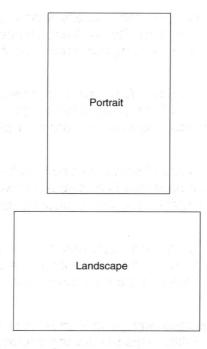

Figure 11.34 *Portrait and landscape options*

It is also possible to add page numbers automatically throughout the document. The page number can be omitted from the first page so that it can be used as a *title page*, and numbering will then begin on the second sheet.

These are just a few of the ways a word-processor can be useful in dealing with longer documents. The equipment that you use will have its own range of additional facilities.

Task

Use the word-processor to create the final report for an assignment you are completing as part of your studies. Try importing relevant data from other files such as spreadsheets, databases and other word-processed documents. Adjust the format of your document before printing to reduce paper usage, and add a cover page and page numbers. Save and print your file. You need to find out how to:

- *import into the word-processor data from files created in other applications*

- *format your document by adjusting margins and including page breaks*

- *add page numbers to your document.*

You can use these techniques together with those we have looked at earlier to create a well-organised and smartly presented report. Remember to plan your use of IT when beginning an assignment in order to carry out each part more effectively and to bring your results together easily in a neat final report.

Evidence of your planning can be used towards the IT core skill unit, and quality of planning is one of the factors taken into account in the awarding of Merit and Distinction grades.

Finally . . .

These are by no means the only IT applications that are available, and you may well have access to other useful software that you can use to good effect during your studies. For example, there could be a *graphics* application on your equipment which you can use to create plans and illustrations. As you use the computer you will find out what is available – if you make good use of the IT staff who are there to help you.

Fast Facts

Absolute cell reference   In a *spreadsheet* formula an absolute cell reference remains unaltered when the formula is copied to other cells. See also **relative cell reference**.

Application   A word used for the set of instructions that the computer carries out. The word 'application' refers to **software** that has been designed to be applied to a particular task such as word processing or spreadsheeting. See also **software** and **program**.

Byte   A single piece of information; one keypress is one byte. Bytes are used as a measure of computer memory size. See also **kilobyte** and **megabyte**.

Cell   In a **spreadsheet** a cell is the area where an item of data or a formula is stored.

Cell reference   The unique address of a cell in a spreadsheet. The cell reference is given by the row and column headings which apply to the cell.

Compatibility   The ability of **hardware** and **software** to work together.

Cursor   A blinking line or dash on the screen which indicates where your typing will appear, or your editing take place.

Cut and paste   A term used for the process of selecting and moving text.

Database   A database manager (usually referred to simply as a database) is a **software** application used to deal with information in the form of lists. Strictly speaking a database is any listed information, and so a telephone directory or your address book are databases.

Directories   Electronically-created compartments on a disk that are used to group **files** that you wish to keep together.

Field   A category of information contained in a **database**. Records contain data entered into fields.

File   A piece of work that has been created and saved on the computer.

Floppy disk   A portable piece of hardware used to store data. Floppy disks are small, lightweight and durable.

Form letter   A word-processed letter that contains **merge fields** linked to a **database**. Form letters are used to create mass 'mail-shots'.

Formatting floppy disks   The process of electronically dividing a floppy disk into tracks and sectors. Disks must be formatted before files can be saved on them.

Formatting text   This refers to alterations made to the way text looks, either by changing character size and type, or by varying the arrangement of paragraphs.

Graphics application   A software application designed to deal with graphical information. Graphics applications are used to produce artwork and plans.

Hard disk   A piece of hardware used to store information. The hard disk is permanently fixed inside the computer's case and cannot be removed from it.

Hardware   The physical equipment used in IT. This includes the computer, the monitor, the mouse, the keyboard, cables and other devices such as printers.

Information technology   The term is used to refer to modern, scientific ways of handling information. It is applied to the fields of computing, video and telecommunications and the rapidly developing links between them.

Landscape layout   Work printed with the long edge of the paper horizontal.

Margins   The boundaries within which your work is printed. There are margins at the top and bottom of the page, as well as on either side.

Megabyte   A measure of amount of information. One megabyte (Mb) = 1024 **kilobytes** = 1,048,546 **bytes**.

Kilobyte   A measure of amount of information. One kilobyte (K) = 1024 **bytes**.

Merge fields   Specially marked parts of a form letter which contain the titles of fields in a database.

Operating system   Software which starts the computer running and controls its activities. The operating system must be running before you can run other types of software.

Portrait layout   Work printed with the long edge of the paper vertical.

Program   A word used for the set of instructions that the computer carries out. See also **software** and **application**.

RAM   Stands for Random Access Memory. The RAM holds the information and instructions that are being used by the computer during your work sessions. It is completely cleared when you switch the computer off.

Record   The information held in a database on a particular item. Each record consists of data entered into fields.

Relative cell reference   In a spreadsheet formula a relative cell reference adjusts to its new location when the formula is copied to other cells.

Scrolling   Bringing other parts of a document into view on the screen.

Selecting   Identifying certain parts of a file with a highlight so that the selected section can be deleted, moved or copied.

Spreadsheet   A **software application** designed to deal with numerical information.

Software   A word used for the set of instructions that the computer carries out. See also **program** and **application**.

Word-processor   A **software application** that is designed to deal with text-based information.

ANSWERS

Introduction

1 Standards are definitions of what has to be demonstrated and assessed in order to get GNVQ awards and qualifications. Standards don't explain what has to be studied – only what gets assessed. Standards provide an alternative to exam-based qualifications. Exam-based qualifications are like a competition: only the people who come in top do well. With standards, it only matters if people can demonstrate what's needed.

2 Standards often contain technical words and descriptions. People will need to know a great deal about an area before standards for that area can be easily understood. At the beginning of a programme, people often don't have the knowledge to understand what is meant by particular element and performance criteria statements. Understanding standards are part of the learning goals for GNVQ.

3 Assessment to standards requires evidence. The standards define what is needed for an award; evidence is the information that shows that a person has done what was needed. They have reached 'the standard'. When all the appropriate standards have been reached, the person is qualified.

4 Action plans enable individuals to work out how they will collect evidence to meet 'evidence indicators'. Action plans can also be used to plan assignments, practical demonstrations and placement and project work. Action plans might be useful in helping candidates to meet standards requirements. Action plans are necessary for Merit and Distinction grades, as candidates have to show skills in planning and in monitoring courses of action. Records of planning will be needed to provide evidence of planning and monitoring skills.

5 Yes! A candidate can work out what is needed and, provided they do the work and submit the necessary evidence, they should be able to guarantee the grade they want. GNVQs are not a competition – grades don't depend on some final assessment of group results. Candidates can get advice and guidance as they go through the programme, to ensure that they have the necessary evidence for Merits or Distinctions.

6 Evidence of: independent action planning, monitoring, use of sources, checking validity, evaluation and justification.

7 A portfolio is a portable collection of evidence, including assignment work, which aims to demonstrate that national standards have been met. The portfolio will, therefore, include an index of assignment evidence, core skills and grading evidence. This will be used by assessors and verifiers who will check the quality of a candidate's work.

The portfolio will be complicated and work on it should start early in the programme. Leaving the design of the portfolio to the end of the programme may make it difficult to achieve Merit or Distinction grades. If the collection of evidence is regularly 'self-assessed' or checked, then candidates can change their work to ensure that it meets the requirements for these grades.

If the records are not kept, or not checked, then it may become too late to do the right kind of work at the end of the programme.

8 They should revise their own portfolio of evidence and assignments for the unit, discuss unit content with other people and make notes of their work! Discussion might help memory. Use the Fast Facts sections of this book as an aid to recognising concepts and ideas.

9 Good grades on GNVQ depend on reflection and self-assessment. Candidates have to provide enough evidence to meet the grading criteria. A good way to make sense of all this work is to self-assess the evidence before presenting it. The development of self-assessment skills would cover much of what is needed to meet the grading criteria.

10 Reflection is a skill which enables people to experiment with their ideas until the ideas work in a useful way. Reflection is a skill that will enable self-assessment and evidence collection.

Reflection will also enable a carer to help others to clarify their thoughts and feelings.

Chapter 1: Access, Equal Opportunities and Client Rights

1 b The family is usually the focus for a child to learn acceptable behaviour, including the cultural norms and values.

2 d The family is the primary agent, whereas all the others are secondary agents.

3 a By recognising cultural need, staff are working to sustain the client's self-esteem. Culture is part of self-concept.

4 c as it is essential for the development of the whole person. Remember the importance of PICES?

5 a as staff are in a powerful position to ensure all clients' rights are upheld in the care setting.

6 d This is about overt or open discrimination being displayed in language and/or behaviour.

7 c The Community Health Council offer advice and support in matters dealing with community health services.

8 a deals with any concerns about employment in terms of gender. The Council offers help and support, and will take the case to an industrial tribunal if they consider that there is a case to answer.

9 c The Sex Discrimination Act 1975 deals with discrimination faced by either sex in employment.

10 b because it is less obvious discrimination in that you are avoiding possible embarrassment – as you see it. You are still discriminating against your friend who happens to be black by leaving him/her out.

11 a = **iv** because an assumption is made that there is no point in asking as the person will not understand!
b = **i** because the emphasis is on only implying that girls are inferior!
c = **iii** because the facial expression and laughter is making fun of someone who is in difficulty.
d = **ii** because the use of the word 'black' here is in a negative sense. The phrase is applied to people who are seen as deviant, i.e. they do not conform to others' expectations, rather they have somehow let the side down!

12 d as both are true. An appeal may be made to the Civil Court and on to the House of Lords. Any decision reached must comply with EEC Equal Treatment Directive (76/207/EEC).

13 c as both are true.

14 d This Act deals with employment of people with disability. **a** is not specifically to do with disability and the other two deal with provision rather than employment of people with disability.

15 a The officer in charge should be your first contact when addressing a complaint in a residential setting. **d** may be contacted if there is no satisfactory outcome.

16 d should be your first point of contact. Later **b**, possibly **c**, depending on the actual situation.

17 c as the social role is the 'part' one 'acts' to meet the expectation of others in a given situation. We learn these roles by observation and role-modelling during the process of socialisation.

18 d as **i** is the expected behaviour of someone in the social role of carer being patient and understanding; therefore it is true.
ii is false because a teacher is not supposed to swear or get impatient with a child in the classroom. By doing so they fail to match the prevailing expectations of someone holding that social role.

19 b as institutional racism is concerned with the way organisational culture and systems discriminate against one group, to support the superiority and therefore power of another. For example: tolerating racist/sexist jokes; failing to encourage all staff to participate in staff development initiatives; only promoting men rather than women as well.

20 c as the emphasis is to ensure that all members of society have the same rights in law and society. To treat everyone the same (**a**) devalues the individual as all are different in terms of biology and socialisation. To ignore individual differences (**b**) is to behave oppressively as there is a failure to respect the person's identity. **d** is to patronise people because they are different, which in itself is a form of discrimination! It denies the right of the individual to be themselves.

Chapter 2: Interpersonal Interaction

1 Communication can be divided into verbal (what we say and how we say it) and non-verbal (body language) communication.

2 Body language includes our facial expressions, the positions and positioning of our bodies, and the use of signs.

3 d Gaze tells someone how you feel about them. It can indicate attraction, anger or be used to reject someone.

4 c To be distracted by reorganising a file does not indicate attention. Assuming an open body posture, tolerating silences, smiling and nodding do indicate attention.

5 Maslow identified the basic physiological needs as being the satisfying of thirst, hunger, sexual appetite and the need to eliminate. People also need rest, activity, temperature regulation and oxygen.

6 b Be assertive and confident enough to listen to the problem and then decide whether the criticism is valid.

7 c You have the right to have different needs and wishes from other people. This does not mean you are entitled to do what you want, or should expect others always to agree with you, or that you should always say what you want to.

8 b A child with a parent constantly in Critical Parent mode is likely to feel inadequate, often judged to be wrong. This would make them feel guilty or stupid and promote the need to abide strictly by the parent's rules.

9 There are many advantages to working in groups such as: wider range of knowledge or skills, being motivated by others, sharing responsibility, feeling secure and confident, having more power, dividing tasks, doing the parts you are good at, improving the parts you are less good at, getting feedback, questioning assumptions, achieving more together than individuals would – synergy, having fun.

10 c Having a place to meet, someone to record the process of the meeting and having some finance are all useful resources for a group. However, the essential component is that everyone is working to a common aim.

11 b A chairperson experiencing difficulties with one member of the group would be well advised to seek the help of the group by jointly agreeing to support one another. Reinforcing acceptable behaviours may influence the person to realise their own behaviour is unacceptable, but if this does not work it may be necessary to speak with them outside the group. It is unlikely that saying the chairperson is 'boss' will be effective.

12 c Groups may fail if they are too rushed or there is no time scale so nothing ever gets finalised. If members are suspicious of each other or lazy they are unlikely to form a successful group.

13 d Being non-judgemental means recognising that someone is entitled to their own views and to make their own decisions even when these are different to your own. It means not judging people even if you need to confront their behaviour.

14 c Being independent means we should have the opportunity to make choices. It is not realistic to believe anyone should do everything without help from others, or that anyone can do anything or go anywhere. Everyone has some limitations and people are interdependent. Degrees of risk must be carefully calculated.

15 d It is possible to have privacy without an en-suite bathroom, but the other criteria are necessary.

16 It is important to build on the positive features of a person. Carers should find out about the client's previous experience and knowledge and see if that can be used to enhance the quality of life rather than merely 'managing' issues such as confusion or incapacity.

17 d A self-fulfilling prophecy occurs when someone's behaviour is so influenced by another's expectations that they actually behave as predicted. It may be that someone could fail a driving test because they believed someone who had said they would.

18 Areas to be considered would include: a place to live, daily occupation, income, leisure/training/education, social contacts and social and emotional needs met, support for individual physical needs, support for cultural needs.

19 It is important to be allowed to make mistakes in order to have the experience of learning from them. Of course, this does not mean people should be not warned of serious or life-threatening consequences, but to deny opportunities to learn from our own decisions is frustrating and demeaning.

20 All information relating to a client is confidential and must not be shared without the client's permission. Exceptions to this are when the worker must seek advice from a line manager because not doing so may endanger the client or others and could leave the worker liable for disciplinary action or prosecution.

Chapter 3: Physical Aspects of Health

1 c **2** b **3** a **4** b **5** b **6** d **7** c **8** c **9** a **10** d **11** c
12 b **13** a **14** c **15** d **16** a **17** a **18** b **19** c **20** a

Chapter 4: Psychological and Social Aspects of Health and Social Care

1 c Primary socialisation will have a major effect on the early development of identity. Illness will probably be soon forgotten. Reinforcement influences behaviour, but will probably only have indirect effects on a person's understanding of themselves.

2 d To cope with modern life in Western society. Authors such as Breakwell and Kitzinger suggest that not every society has encouraged individuality and personal identities.

3 1 'You only care about yourself' – might be a threat to continuity (**b**).
2 'Oh but everyone cares about people' – might be a threat to distinctiveness (**c**).
3 'Caring people are useless' – might be a threat to self-esteem (**a**).

4 c Self-efficacy involves the belief that you can accurately predict your own ability in a given area. It may also involve a sense of control arising from the ability to predict.

5 a Clients must not be stereotyped because it will prevent the carer from understanding their identity needs. **b** and **c** are true, but are not reasons for avoiding stereotyping. **d** is not true, stereotypes are often involved in discrimination but this does not mean that they *always* result in discrimination – that would be a stereotype!

6 b Social context is a context or setting for social influences and learning. It doesn't create identity, nor is the fact that it is influenced by culture of any great significance here.

7 b Unemployment. If **a** or **d** are life-event threats for you, then you need help urgently!

8 a Temperament refers to behaviour styles based on biological influences. This is much more specific than the broad term 'personality'.

9 b By causing lower self-esteem. Abuse could do all the other things as well – but these can only indirectly threaten identity. Self-esteem is the most direct area of threat.

10 Concepts enable us to classify, interpret and predict both physical and social reality. Concepts have to fit with our experience of reality (perceived world structure), simplify experience (cognitive economy) and be usable socially (shareability). Concepts which are readily available get used to make sense of our social experience. When we try to understand ourselves (self-concept) we are likely to use culturally available ideas to explain what we do. There is a danger of self-stereotyping and labelling linked to the way we think in concepts.

11 Norms are the rules of behaviour that exist within a group. Norms are first learned during primary socialisation. People may evaluate themselves in terms of norms they have learned earlier. People may also evaluate other people from different groups using their own norms. This might lead to in-group/out-group conflict.

12 a Shareability. The others are all classic 'Freudian' defences.

13 d This is Barrie Hopson's model for explaining the crisis of moving from one view of self to another. All the other combinations are nonsense.

14 b Osteoporosis – brittle bones, more associated with later life.

15 a An automatic physical reaction which follows threat and adapts the body for 'fight or flight'.

16 a Counselling and **b** reflective listening within a supportive relationship – two correct answers!

17 Supportive relationships may help people to lower tension levels and reduce the effects of prolonged activation of the stress response. Relationships may also provide an opportunity for supportive conversation work. This may help an individual to work through grief or transitions. Conversation may help individuals to make sense of their identity when threatened. Argyle (1987) believes supportive relationships may boost the body's immune system by producing positive emotions.

18 The obvious answer is that poverty prevents the purchase of good food, heating, stress-free housing, etc. But it may also be that poverty reduces the significance of health and increases the threat to personal identity for some individuals. Poorer individuals may tend to ignore their health. In the past they may have made less use of services, such as immunisation, and been less concerned with hygiene and health maintenance activities.

19 c A learned pattern of behaviour which may be associated with heart disease.

20 This chapter suggests three central issues. First, the need for an effective and developed personal identity. Secondly, the need for friendship networks, partners and membership of groups which provide social meaning and support. Thirdly, avoid being poor – at least in later life. There may be many other issues which are associated with these three main ideas. The key problem is to achieve all three objectives: secure and positive identity; enough money; and enough friendships and love. Most people spend their life desperately trying to balance these areas, trading health for identity, love for money, friendships for social status and identity gains. Perhaps life *is* a game of snakes and ladders – at least for some people.

Chapter 5: Health Promotion

1 a – COSHH sets out the guidelines under which employers must assess substances as potential hazards. The Health and Safety at Work Act 1974 provides the framework for health and safety regulation. The other two options are fictitious.

2 a Excess alcohol causes liver damage – the cells of the liver are killed.

3 c – The only health risk listed that is connected to sexual practice is HIV.

4 b – Emphysema is a lung disease where the capacity of the lungs to absorb oxygen is reduced. This is often due to heavy smoking over a number of years.

5 b – solvents.

6 a – Drug misuse is the use of socially accepted drugs in an unacceptable way, e.g. tranquillisers, as opposed to *drug abuse* which is the use of socially unacceptable drugs such as heroin.

7 d – Cocaine belongs to the stimulant group; LSD is an hallucinogen; Valium is a tranquilliser; and Ecstasy is similar to amphetamine although is often grouped on its own.

8 c – Women should consume a maximum of 14 units per week, men a maximum of 21 units. This should be spread evenly throughout the week – it does not follow that you should consume the whole recommended amount in one day!

9 b – Anything the mother consumes will pass through the placenta to the foetus and will have effects on the development of the foetus.

10 c – Sharing needles is the only one which could lead to passing the virus from one person to another. The virus does not live long enough outside the body to be passed through sharing cups or swimming in the same water. Not enough bodily fluid is passed from one person to another whilst kissing to allow the virus to be passed.

11 b – The combined pill is considered to offer very high protection.

12 a – The only way to help to prevent contracting an STD is to use a barrier method, i.e. the condom.

13 c – The IUD is the best form of contraception for the woman. It is suitable because she has had children and is therefore easier to fit. Because she has a regular partner she will not be concerned about STDs and therefore a barrier method such as a condom is not essential. The spermicide gel is not an effective form of contraception alone. (Although the woman could also use a diaphragm or cap with spermicide gel as a barrier method.)

14 d – Evaluation allows the audience to comment on the programme and give feedback as to its appropriateness for them.

15 a – A good introduction should set out the content to be covered in a programme.

16 c – A conclusion involves a presenter summing up the main points delivered, or those they most hope the audience will remember and take away with them.

17 b – Audio visual means use of eyes *and* ears; the video and monitor calls for this. The others require one or the other.

18 The advantages of a leaflet are that:
a the audience can use it at their own pace
b it can allow the audience to recap on what was said at a presentation at a later date
c it reduces the need for note taking
d it can be cheap
The disadvantages are that it:
a might not be understood
b might not be read
c can be biased, especially if produced by a company
d is not durable and is easily lost

19 Aims refer to the goals of the programme; what the planner hopes to achieve at the end of it. Objectives are more specific and are often measurable. They often state how the aims will be achieved.

20 b – A question/discussion session is the time when the audience leads the programme and therefore offers most opportunity for clarification of points. An evaluation can only measure the appropriateness of a programme at the end and there may not be feedback from it to the audience. Summing up the main points and having a display do not allow clarification to be sought.

Chapter 6: Structure and Practices in Health and Social Care

1 Primary services; secondary care; community services.

2 Family Health Services Authorities; District Health Authorities; GP fund holders.

3 Taxation and National Insurance contributions.

4 GPs; dentists; practice nurses; opthalmologists; pharmacists.

5 District nursing; health visitors; domiciliary midwives; physiotherapists; occupational and speech therapists; chiropodists.

6 False. The purchaser/provider system was set in place with the implementation of the NHS and Community Care Act.

7 Budgets; resources; local policies.

8 Trusts can: determine their own management structures; employ their own staff; acquire, own and sell their assets; and retain surpluses and borrow money.

9 Health Boards.

10 Coronary heart disease and stroke; cancers; mental illness; sexual health and HIV/AIDS; accidents.

11 The National Assistance Act 1948 gave the local authorities the powers to provide services designed to improve the quality of life for people with disabilities. It also allowed them to provide homes and hostels for older people as well as for people with disabilities and to charge residents, according to their means. Additionally it empowered authorities to promote the welfare of people with disabilities, such as learning difficulties.

12 (1) The Health Services Public Health Act 1968 gave local authorities the general power to promote the welfare of older people. **(2)** The Chronically Sick and Disabled Persons Act 1970; although primarily aimed to promote the welfare of people with disabilities, because 60 per cent of all people with disabilities are aged over 60 years, it has great significance for older people.

13 The aim of the NHS and Community Care Act 1990, is to allow vulnerable people to remain within their own homes for as long as possible. The objectives include developing services to meet that aim; giving consideration to the needs of the carer; making assessment of the individual's needs; encouraging the development of services in the independent sector; clarifying the responsibilities of the health and local authorities and securing better value for money.

14 The Mental Health Act 1983 defines the term 'mental disorder' as: mental illness; arrested or incomplete development of mind; psychopathic disorder; and 'any other disorder or disability of the mind'.

15 Bath seats and bath boards; chairs with high seats; adapted cutlery; commodes; walking sticks and frames; hand rails; hoists.

16 The role of the continence adviser is to assist and advise people on the management of incontinence and to provide information about equipment that is available.

17 Certificate in Social Work (CQSW); Diploma in Social Work (DipSW); Certificate in Social Services (CSS); Preliminary Certificate in Social Care (PCSC); In-service Course in Social Care (ICSC); NVQs in Care.

10 Family-aide – who is a person who will offer practical help in the home. Family caseworker – usually a social worker, who works with the family as a whole, trying to improve the quality of family life for the children.

19 Both the provision for day centres and residential accommodation is moving away from large institutional establishments, to smaller units situated within the community. Along with much other service provision, more services are being commissioned from the independent sector.

20 'Home from Hospital' teams; teams working with people with dementia; bathing services; night-sitting schemes; peripatetic night-care schemes.

Chapter 7: Care Plans

1 A Care Plan is a written document which outlines how the needs of an individual are to be met.

2 A Care Plan is part of the Assessment and Care Management Process. (See diagram on page 276.)

3 i   Publishing information
  ii   Determining the level of assessment
  iii Assessing need
  iv   Care planning
  v   Implementing care plans
  vi   Monitoring
  vii Reviewing

4 a   Share and agree information – and inter-agency assessment of need

b   Define clients'/carers'/needs
c   Agree and plan options for packages of care

5 i   Determining the type of plan
  ii   Setting priorities
  iii   Definition of service requirements
  iv   Exploring resources of clients and carers
  v   Review existing services
  vi   Consider alternatives
  vii   Discuss options
  viii Establish preferences
  ix   Cost Care Plan
  x   Assess financial means
  xi   Reconcile preference and resources
  xii   Agree service objectives
  xiii Co-ordinate Care Plan
  xiv   Fix Review date
  xv   Identify unmet need
  xvi   Record Care Plan

6 To ensure that the client and carer, together with the purchaser and providers of services, have a written plan to work to. Also to ensure that monitoring of the care plan can take place.

7 True.

8 i   Environment and housing
  ii   Communication
  iii   Personal care
  iv   Housework
  v   Physical and emotional health
  vi   Abilities, aptitudes and social life
  vii   Employment, educational needs/wishes
  viii Financial information
  ix   Other agencies
  x   Carers and care networks

9 Care management stresses the importance of monitoring to ensure that objectives are being met and ensuring that the care plan is adapted to the changing needs of the client.

10 i   Home visits
   ii   Telephone calls
   iii Letters
   iv   Questionnaires
   v   Observation

11 a   To see if objectives have been achieved
   b   Evaluate reasons for failure or success
   c   Evaluate quality and cost of care provided
   d   Reassess current needs
   e   Revise objectives of the care plan
   f   Revise services that are required
   g   Reassess cost
   h   Note any unmet need
   i   Record results of Review
   j   Set date of next Review

12 i Scope
ii Venue
iii Review Worker

13 a Freedom from discrimination
c Confidentiality
d Independence
f Dignity

14 Confidentiality promotes trust in the worker, allowing the client to talk to them freely about their needs, thus ensuring a more accurate assessment.

15 True.

16 The Key Worker is the person who has most contact with the client. Their function is to ensure that the Care Plan is being appropriately carried out. They also alert the Care Manager to any changes in the client's circumstances that may require an alteration to the services provided.

17 True.

18 A purchaser is an organisation (e.g. Health Authority or Social Services Department) that holds the budget in order to buy in necessary services.

19 A macro care plan is a comprehensive identification of need and indicates all the service providers who will contribute in meeting those needs.

20 A micro care plan is a plan which the individual service provider will use to describe the action plan within their own care setting.

Chapter 8: Research in Health and Social Care

1 d **2** d **3** c **4** c **5** d **6** c **7** a **8** c **9** c **10** b **11** a
12 b **13** a **14** c **15** a **16** d **17** d **18** b **19** b **20** a

ICONS FOR PHOTOCOPYING

Photocopy any of the range of icons below and paste onto your GNVQ assignments. This will enable you and your tutor to see at a glance those areas which have been covered in your evidence collection.

 Communication

 Application of number

 Information technology

 I did this independently without help

 I did this with guidance

 GENERAL NVQ

 Access, Equal Opportunities and client rights

 Interpersonal Interaction

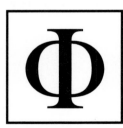 Physical Aspects of Health

 Psychological and Social Aspects of Health and Social Care

 Health Promotion

 Structure and Practices in Health and Social Care

 Care Plans

 Research in Health and Social Care

 Action planning

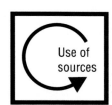 Use of sources

 Evaluation

 Monitoring

 Validity

 Justification

INDEX

The page numbers in brackets refer to Fast Facts

Absolute cell reference 414–416
Abuse 192–195, (209)
Academic 2
Acceptance strategies 190, 191
Action planning 11, 13, 15–19, 22–24, 29, 30, (31)
Active cell 412, 413
Activities 94
Adapted child 90
Adjective 350, (368)
Adrenaline 120, 129
Adverb 350, (368)
Advocacy 299, (300)
Age 174
Ageism 192
Agencies 215
Aggression 87
AIDS 214, 219–221, (241)
Aims 235, (241)
Alcohol 222, (241)
Alphanumeric 406
Alveoli 123
Amphetamines 227
Anaerobic respiration 126
Angina pectoris 127
Antigens 139
Anxiety 199, 200
Aortic valve 119
APL (Accreditation of Prior Learning) 29
Apostrophe 351, (368)
Application 390, 392, (421)
Appropriate tone 346, 347
Area 380
Arteries 122
Arteriosclerosis 129
Assertiveness 88, 89, (114)
Assessment 6, 7, 11, 280
Assessors 11, 13, (31), 277, (301)
Assignments 11, 12, 15, 21, 23, 30, (31)
Assumptions 169, 188
Asthma 130
Atheroma 127
Atherosclerosis 127
Atrio-vernricular node 119
Atrium 118
Attachment 188
Attitude 47, (71)
Attributing 95
Auditory 78, (114)
Autism 77
Autonomic nervous system 120
Awarding body 11, (31)

Bacteria 132
Balanced diets 147

Balancing act 383
Bar chart 377
BEAB 229
Behaviourist perspective 36
Belief 47, (71)
Bereavement 188, 191, 200, (209)
Beveridge report 59
Bibliography 22
Bicuspid valve 119
Biology 181, 182
Black 52, 53, (71)
Bleeding 230–231
Blood vessels 122
Body language 54, 344
Booting up 394, 401
Bronchitis 130, 224, (241)
Browsing 406
Buffering 201
Bundle of His 119
Byte 392, 395, (421)

Calculators 371
Candidates 3, 11, 13, 15, 18, 19, 21–23, (31)
Cannabis 227
Cap 218
Capillaries 122
Carbohydrate 143
Carbon monoxide 224, (241)
Cardiac cycle 120
Cardiac muscle 119
Care management 276
Care package (301)
Care planning 284
Care plans 194, 275
Careers guidance 3
CD ROM 391
Cell reference 411, 414, (421)
Census 304–305, 307, (341)
Change 184, 188, 190, 192
Children Act 66, 257, (271)
Choice 83, 106–113, 291, 299, (301)
Chronically Sick and Disabled Persons Act 255, (272)
Circulation 122
Citizens' Charter 68
Claudication 127
Clients' rights 106, 290, (301)
Closed question 322–323, (341)
Cocaine 227
Coding frame 332, (341)
Cognitive ability 180, 182
Cognitive economy 178
Collating data 328–329, 331, 333, 336
Combined events 386

Comma 351, (368)
Commission for Racial Equality (CRE) 63
Communication 8, 9, 278, 344, 347, (368)
Community care 272
Community Health Councils (272)
Community life 68
Community services 246
Compatibility 392, (421)
Composition of Air 125
Concepts 14, 15, 19, 21, 22, (32), 177–181, 183, (209)
Conclusion 238, (241)
Condom 218
Confidentiality 12, 85, 106–113, 291, 298, (301)
Constellation (constellatory) 180
Construction 176, 181, 186, 194, (209)
Constructive criticism 89, (114)
Constructs (209)
Contents list 22
Continuity 166, 167, 169, 187, 190, 192, 194, (209)
Contraception 216–218, 241
Contracts 245, (272)
Conversion 372
Coping strategies (209)
Core skills 4, 23, 24, (32)
Correlation 379
COSHH 232, (241)
Counselling 195
Criteria (see grading criteria) (32)
Critical parent 90
Cultural diets 159
Cultural needs 37
Culture 37, 38, 66, (71), 76–79, (114), 169, 171, 176, 179–181, 194, (209)
Cursor 400, 401, (421)
Cut and paste 402, (421)

Data 303, 305, 308, 314, 321–322, 331, 332, 337, 339
Data collection 373
Database 332, 391, 392, 396, 405–408, 410, 411, (421)
Defences 189–191, (209)
Deflection strategies 190, 191
Degenerative disease 131
Demographic 323, (341)
Denial 189–191
Department of Health 249, (272)
Department of Social Security 252, (272)
Dependency 193, 194, 226, (241)
Depersonalisation 190
Depression 191, 192, 200
Deprivation 40

Diabetic diet 155
Diaphragm 124, 218
Diastole 120
Diet 203, 205
Dignity 106–113, 292, 299, (301)
Direct observation 313–314
Directory 396, 401, (421)
Disability 179, 180
Disabled Persons (Consultation and
    Representation) Act 256, (272)
Disabled Persons' Act 64
Discrimination 49, 50, 55, 57, 58, (71),
    106–113, 174, 176, 182, 187, 188,
    192, 193, (209), 291, 297, (301)
Discrimination
    direct 50, 60, 62,
    indirect 51, 60, 62, (71)
Disease 217, (242)
Displacement 189
Display 237
Distinctiveness 166, 167, 169, 187, 190,
    192, 194, (209)
District Health Authorities 249, (272)
Drug abuse 225, (242)
Drug misuse 225, (242)

Ecstasy 227
Editing text 402–403
Education Act 52
Ego identity 169
    integrity 185
Elder 180, 194
Electric shock 229
Electrical safety 228
Elements 5, 8, 10, 11, (32)
Emotional needs 39
Empathy 41, 179, (71)
Emphysema 130, 224, (242)
Empowerment 194
Environment 215
Equal
    opportunity 59, (72)
    Opportunities Commission (EOC) 61
    Pay Act 60
Equations 382
Equipment 236, (242)
Erythrocytes 125
Estimation 370
Ethnic
    group 63, (72)
    minority 63, (72)
Eurocentric 49, (72)
Evaluation 19, 21–23, (32), 167, 182,
    183, 238–240, (242)
Evidence 8, 9, 11–15, 18, 22–24, 26, 27,
    30, 31, (32)
Evidence indicators 5, 8, 9, 12, (32)
Exams 7
Exercise 204, 205
Expectations 278
Expenditure 202
Expiration 124
Extrapolation 338

Extrovert 181

Facial expressions 76
Family 236
Family Health Service Authorities 249,
    (272)
Fantasy 190, 191
Fat 142
Feedback 238, (242)
Female reproductive system 217
Fields 405, (421)
File 396, 400, 401, 410, (421)
Floppy disk 394–397, 401, 408, (421)
Font 403
Food choice 156
Food hygiene 137
Food Poisoning 136
Form filling 353–359, 361, 362
Form letter 408–409, (421)
Formatting floppy disks 395, (421)
Formatting pages 419
Formatting text 403, (421)
Forming 99
Formulae (in spreadsheets) 413–415
Free response 239, (242)
Frequency distribution 333–334, (341),
    418
Functionalist perspective 36
Fungi 132
Funnel method 327, (341)
Fuse 228, (242)

Games 93, 237
Gaseous exchange 124
Gaze 77, (114)
Gender 174, 201
Generalisations 387, (388)
Genital herpes 219
    warts 219
Gestures 78, (114)
Goal 6, 7
Gonorrhoea 134, 219
GP fundholders 250
Grading 13, 16, 18, 22–24, 26, 28, 30,
    (32)
Grading criteria 2, 18, 20, 23, 28, 29, (32)
Graphics (421)
Graphs 336, 339, 377
Grief 188–190, 206
Group polarisation 101
Group values 104
Group work 13
Grouped data 376
Grouped frequency tables 375
Groups 96–106
GU's 217 (242)

Haemoglobin 125
Hallucinogens 227
Handouts 237
Hanging indent 404
Hard disk 394, (421)
Hardware 390, (421)

Hazards 232, (242)
Health 200–206, (209), 213, 214, (242)
Health and care workers 260
Health and safety at work 232, (242)
Health promoters 215
    promotion 215, 233, (242)
Healthy eating 158
Heart 117
Heart disease 148
Hepatitis B 219
Heroin 227
Higher education 3
Hinduism 159
Histogram 378
HIV 219–221, (242)
Holmes-Rahe scale 185, 186, 188, 191,
    (209)
Home life: A Code of Practice 68
Hyperlipidaemia 127
Hypertension 128
Hypothesis 39, (72), 320, 331, 332, 336,
    338, (341)

Icons 26
Identity 106–113, 164–177, 181–195,
    197, 200, (209)
    crisis 171
Immobilisation 191, 192
Impression management 47
In-depth interviewing 311–313, (341)
In-groups 175, 176, (210)
Income 202, 203, (209)
Independence 106–113, 291, 298, (301)
Indirect aggression 87, 89, (114)
Individual factors 215
Individual planning meeting 111, (114)
Individuality 167–169
Industrial tribunals 63
Infections 130
Influenza 138
Information Technology 389, (421)
Inherited disease 131
Injectable contraception 218
Insert mode 401
Inspection 293, (301)
Inspiration 124
Intellectual needs 36
Interaction 75, 80
Internalisation 191, 192
Interview 373
Interview schedule 309, 319, 322, 328,
    329, 331, (341)
Interview techniques 173
Intimacy 93
Introduction 237, 238, (242)
Introvert 181
Intuitive child 90
Ischaemia 127
Islam 159

IUD 218
Judaism 159
Justification 19, 22, 23, (32), 387, (388)

Key points 237, 238, (242)
    worker 285, (301)
Keyboard 343, 390, 399
Kilobyte 392, (422)
Kitemark 229
Knowledge 4, 5, 7, 8, 10, 11, 17, 21, 27, (32)
Kolb learning cycle 14, 21, 170, (210)

Labelling 176, 178, 180, 181, 185
Lactic acid 126
Landscape layout 420, (422)
Leaflets 237
Learning 1, 2, 14, 18, 27, 30, 31
    processes 170
Letters 352
Letting go 191, 192
Levels 2, (32)
Library 17–20
Life event threats 185, 188, 193, 199, 200, 202, (210)
Life strain 199, (210)
Line graph 377
Linear equation 382
Local Authority Social Services 257, (272)
Local Authority Social Services Act 254, (272)
Log books 12, 23–26
Loss 184, 185
Low salt diet 154
LSD 227
Lung cancer 129

Macro care plan 275, (301)
Macro society 39
Macro-nutrients 140
Magic mushrooms 227
Male reproductive system 217
Mandatory unit 4, 5, 14, 23, (32)
Maps and timetables 365, 366
Marginalise 42, (72)
Mathematical operators 413
Mean 334, 335, (341), 375, 417
Median 334, (341), 375
Megabyte 392, (422)
Memorandum 352, (369)
Memory 391–392
Mental health 213, (242)
Mental Health Act 255
Mental illness 131
Merge fields 409, (422)
Methodology (method) 19, (32)
Micro care plan 275, (301)
Micro society 39
Micro-nutrients 144
Minerals 146
Minimisation 191, 192
Mission statement (114)
Mode 334, (341), 375
Modelling 94
Monitor 390, 393, 397

Monitoring 13, 15, 18, 19, 23, (33), 292, (301)
Mutually exclusive events 386
Myogenic 119

National Assistance Act 254, (272)
National Health and Community Care Act 244, (272)
National Health Service 244, (272)
NCVQ (33)
Needs 234, 277, (301)
NHS and Community Care Act 58, 66, 277
Nicotine 223
Non-judgemental 82, 83, 111
Non-verbal 9
Non-verbal signals 75, (114)
Normal distribution curve 333–335, (341)
Norming 99
Norms 38, 44, (72), 169, 171, 173, 176, 182, (210)
Noun 350, (369)
NRA (National Record of Achievement) 4, 24, 29, (33)
Nurturing parent 90
NVQ - Care value base 164, 194, (210)
NVQ 3 (33)
NVQ value base 81, (114)

Objectives 235, (242), 282
Observation 373, (388)
Official statistics 304–305, (341)
OHP 237
Olfactory 78, 79, (114)
Open questions 322, 327, 329, (341)
Operating system 390, (422)
Opinion polls 305, (341)
Opportunity sampling 318, (341)
Optional unit 4, 23, (33)
Orientation 78, (114)
Outcomes 6
Oxygen debt 126

Pacemaker 119
Page break 420
Papillary muscles 119
Paragraph 351
Paramountcy 66
Parasympathetic nervous system 120
Parents' Charter 68
Participant observation 313–315, (342)
Participation 281
Passive smoking 224, (242)
Pastimes 94
Pathogens 131
Pathways 2
Patients' Charter 68
Pattern notes 16, 17
PC's 392
Peer group 44, (72)
Perceived world structure 178
Performance criteria 5, 8, 9, (33)
Performing 99

Pericardium 117
Perimeter 380
Permission 12
Personal identity 164, 171, 173, 174, 179, 181, 186, 188
Personal statement 355
Personality traits (114)
Pheremones 79, (114)
Photographs 364, 365
Physical appearance 182
    health 213, (242)
    needs 35
Physical illness 131
Pie chart 379
Pill 218
Pilot survey 321–322, 331, (342)
Planning 234, (242)
Pleura 124
Plugs 228
Polar adjectives 324, (342)
Population 307, 308, 310, 314, 320–321, 331, 335, 339, (342)
Portfolio 4, 12, 23, -26 (33)
Portrait layout 420, (422)
Ports 398
Positive action 63, (72)
Postal questionnaire 307, (341)
Posters 237
Posture 78, (114)
Poverty 204–206
Power 193, 203
Pre-coding 329, 332, (342)
Pre-emptive 179
Precision 371, (388)
Preconceived ideas (114)
Prejudice 49, 56, 58, (72)
Primary data 303, 306, (342)
Primary groups 173
    health promotion 216, (242)
    socialisation 43, 57, (72), 172
Primary health care team 244, (272)
Primary research 303, 306
Printer 390, 397
Printer driver 398
Priorities 235, (242), 282
Priorities and strategies 269
Privacy 106–113
Privation 36
Probability 384
Probability tree 384
Probes 309, 330–331, (342)
Problem solving 4, 17, 18, 24
Programme (33), 389, 390, (422)
Projection 189
Prompt cards 325, 331
Prompts 309, 331, (342)
Pronoun 350, (369)
Propositional 180, 181
Protein 141
Protozoa 132
Provider 293, (301)
Provision 252, 265, (272)
Provision and use of work equipment 231

Proximity 78
Psychodynamic 189
Pubic lice 219
Pulmonary artery 118
Pulmonary valve 119
Purchaser 248, (272), 293, (301)
Purkinje fibres 119

Qualification 2, 5–7, (33)
Qualitative data 303, 306, 312, 315, 316, 319, 321, 322, 329, 336, (342)
Quantitative data 303, 306–307, 309, 312, 316, 319, 321, 322, 336, (342)
Queries 407, 410
Question mark 351
Question/discussion time 238
Questionnaire 307–309, 311, 322–329, 331, 332, 337, (342), 373
Questions:design 322–323
   order 327–328
   writing 325–327
Quota sampling 318– 319, 321, 327, 332, (342)

Race 63, 66, (72), 174
Race Relations Act 61–63
Racial discrimination 62, (72)
Racial prejudice 62, (72)
Racism 62, (72), 187, 192
RAM 391, (422)
Random sampling 316–317, 321, 337, (342)
Range 5, 8, 9, (33), 334, 375
Ranking 239, 324, 328, (342)
Rating 239
Rating scales 323, 328, (342)
RCD 229, (242)
Re-evaluation strategies 190, 191
Records 405–407, 411, (422)
Records of achievement 12
Recovery position 230, (242)
References 20, 22
Reflection 13, 15, 18, (33), 170
Reflective listening 22, 27, 83
Regional Health Authorities 250
Reinforcement 36, 171
Relationships 75
Relative cell reference 414–416
Reliability 312–313, (342)
Religion 169, 174
Religious diets 159
Repression 189
Resources 236
Respiration 126
Respiratory system 123
Review 294, (301)
Review section 22
Reviewing 294, (301)
Rhythm method 218
Rickettsiae 132
Risk 232, (242)
Risk assessment 232
Rituals 93

Role confusion 171
Role play 237
Roles 169, 172, 173
ROM 391
Ruler 400

Salmonella 136
Sample 307–308, 310, 312, 314–319, 331, 337–339, (342)
Sampling frame 316, 321, (342)
Scaling methods 323–324
Scatter graph 378
Scattergram 335–336, 338, (342)
Scope 280
Script 95, 96, (115)
Scrolling 401, (422)
Searches 407
Searching for meaning 191, 192
Secondary data 303–306, (342)
Secondary groups 173
   health promotion 216, (242)
   socialisation 43, 46, (72), 172
Self advocacy 299, (301)
   assessment 11, 15, 21, 26, 27, 31, (33)
   concept 166, 178, (210)
   efficacy 184, 194, (210)
   esteem 166, 167, 169, 182, 187, 190, 192, 194, (210)
   image 166
Self-actualisation 86, (115)
Self-esteem 86, (115)
Self-fulfilling prophecy 110, (115)
Self-image (115)
Semantic differential 324, 328, (342)
Sentence 349, (369)
Sequence 381
Service specifications 293, (301)
Setting 280
Sex Discrimination Act 60
Sexism 45, 60, 61, (72), 192
Sexual intercourse 217
   orientation 181
   partnerships 169, 188
Sexuality 181
Shareability 178
Shock 230, (243)
Sign language 78
Simple inequalities 382
Sincerity 82–85, 111, (115)
Sino-atrial node 119
Skills 2, 4, 5, 8, 10, 11, 21, 28, 29, (33)
Slides 237
Smoking 204, 205
Smoking 129
Social care workers 264
Social class 168, 174, 203–205, (210)
   comparisons 182
   context 48, 58, (72), 165, 166, 171, 172, 179, 180, 187, 194, (210)
   factors 173
   health 213, (243)
   identity 174, 175, 182
   learning perspective 171

needs 42
role 44, (72), (210)
solidarity 167
station 168
status 44, (73)
stratification (210)
support networks 201, (210)
Social role (115)
Socialisation 43, 171–173, 183, 186, 201, (210)
Socio-economic factors 133
Software 390, 391, 412, (422)
Solvents 226–228
Soul 168
Sources 16, 17, 19, 20, 23, (33)
Special Health Authorities 250
Spermicide 218
Spread of disease 133
Spreadsheet 391, 392, 396, 411–418, (422)
Standard deviation 334–335, (343), 417
Standards 5–8, 10, 11, 27, (33)
Statutory organisations (272)
STDs 217, 219, (243)
Stereotype (stereotyping) 49, 56, (73), 175, 176, 178, 180,
Stereotyping 110
Sterilisation 218
Storming 99
Stratified sampling 317–318, (343)
Stress 191, 193–201, 205, 206, (210)
Stress 128
Stress related illness 198, (211)
Stress response 196, 197
Stroking 93, (115)
Structured interviewing 307, 309–312, 329–332, 337, (343)
Subject 349, (369)
Sublimation 189
Submissiveness 88, 89, (115)
Substantive content 22, 34
Summary, précis 366–368, (369)
Supportive relationships 179
   skills 9, 10, 21
Supportive skills 80, (115)
Survey 303, 336, (343), 373, (388)
Swann Report 51
Symbolic notation 381
Sympathetic nervous system 120
System options 397
Systematic sampling 316, (343)
Systole 120

Tables 374
Tackle 78, 79, (115)
Tar 224, (243)
Target audience 234, (243)
Telephone 347–349
Temperament 181, 182, (211)
Tendinous cords 119
Tension levels 199, 200
Tertiary health promotion 216, (243)
Testing 191, 192

Tests 2, 4, 27, 28, 30, (34)
Theory 1, 14, 15, 19, 21, 27, (34), 170
Thorax 123
Threat 167, 184–193, 194, 195, 199
Three dimensional 380, (388)
Thrush 219
Tissue respiration 125
Trachea 123
Transactional analysis 90–103, (115)
Transitions 191, 192, (211)
Tricuspid valve 119
Trust 282
Tutorials 17, (34)
Two dimensional 380, (388)
Type A behaviour 200, (211)

UN Convention of the Rights of the Child 67
Understanding (34), 82–85, 111, (115)
Units 3, 4, 5, 7, 8, (34), 222, (243)
Using images 362–364

Vaccination 204
Validity 19, 20, 23, (34), 312–313, (343)
Value base 5, (34)
Values 4, 5, 7, 8, 10, (34), 39, 47, (73), 81, 104, (115), 172, 173, 176, 182, (211)
Valuing others 81, (115)
Variance 316, 334
Vegan 148
Vegetarian 175
Vegetarian 148
Veins 122
Vena cava 118
Ventilation 124
Ventricle 118
Verb 349, (369)
Verbal 9
Verifier 11, (34)
Videos 237
Virulence 132
Viruses 132

Visual communication 75
Vitamins 145
Vocational 2
Volume 380
Voluntary organisations (272)

Wagner Report 68
Warmth 82–85, 111, (115)
Warnock Report 52
Wealth 201–203, (211)
Weight controlling diet 155
Western culture 169
   society 167, 168
Wholeness 167
Withdrawal 93
Withdrawal method 218
Word processing 391, 392, 396, 399–404, 408, 410, (422)
Wordwrap 401